[Author's attacks on Einstein show's he is not without biases.]

SIR ISAAC NEWTON

Painted by Sir James Thornhill. Now in the library of the Countess of Portsmouth.

Isaac Newton

A BIOGRAPHY

By

Louis Trenchard More

DOVER PUBLICATIONS, INC.
NEW YORK

Published in the United Kingdom by Constable and Company Limited, 10 Orange Street, London W. C. 2.

This new Dover edition, first published in 1962, is an unabridged republication of the work first published by Charles Scribner's Sons in 1934.

Library of Congress Catalog Card Number: 63-421

Manufactured in the United States of America

Dover Publications, Inc.
180 Varick Street
New York 14, N. Y.

This edition is dedicated to the memory of

LOUIS TRENCHARD MORE

1870–1944

PREFACE

The bicentenary of Isaac Newton's death (20 March, 1927) called attention to the fact that we are without any satisfactory critical biography of the man who is still regarded as the greatest of scientific geniuses. His very greatness, his achievements in so many fields of thought, and his studied aloofness from friends and society, have combined to make the task of writing his life more than ordinarily difficult.

Dr. Johnson twice expressed the opinion that only those who lived with a man could write his life with any genuine exactness and discrimination; and then he added that biography is rarely well done because few people who have lived with a man know what to select. But it is doubtful if an exact and discriminating account of Newton's life and work could have been written by any one of those who knew him personally. Even before his death he had been exalted into a superman, a national monument to the glory of England, and such an attitude of ecstatic adoration does not lend itself to dispassionate judgement. At all events, none of his contemporaries is known to have contemplated his biography except his nephew, John Conduitt; he merely collected memorabilia from his friends and wrote a short outline sketch. Judging from what he left, it was fortunate that he abandoned the project and preserved his material for others to use.

While the fact, that Newton's character and genius were regarded almost down to the present day as not to be profaned by the breath of criticism, greatly increases the perplexities of a biographer, the varied and complex activity of his life is an even greater deterrent. It restricts to a very small number those whose knowledge is sufficiently broad to undertake the work. In the first place, the biographer must be thoroughly conversant with mathematics, physics, and chemistry, and with the history and philosophy of those sciences during the Renaissance. But Newton's interest was by no means confined to science; indeed if we accept his own statements he found it to be an irksome taskmaster even during his period of greatest invention. During the latter half of his life, his thoughts were absorbed in theological and historical questions, and his activities in finance and politics. An adequate life of Newton thus requires the biographer to be equipped with a critical knowledge, in their broader aspects, of both science and human affairs.

If the historian, trained in the humanities, is debarred by his lack of knowledge of science, the difficulty is enhanced if we turn to the scientist. It is rare enough for the scientific specialist of today to have more than a rudimentary knowledge of the early history and philosophy of his own field; and one would have to make diligent search to find any who are capable of discussing the other subjects in which Newton was interested. In spite of this lack of interest and training, historical works on science, such as we have, are almost invariably written by scientists. As a result, the biographies of those scientists, whose lives were not absorbed in a narrow field of investigation, are lamentably lacking in philosophical and critical background, and in human interest; they are belated and shadowy survivals of the mediæval monkish chronicles.

Lastly, in this day of the utilitarian omnipotence of science, it is extraordinarily difficult for a biographer to sympathise with, or even to appreciate, the conviction of Newton and his contemporaries that their purpose in the cultivation of science was to demonstrate the action of the divine will in the natural world, and not to contribute to our comfort, safety, and power.

Whatever may have been the true cause of the neglect, we have only one biography of Newton which can, in any sense, be deemed worthy of its subject. In 1855, Sir David Brewster, a physicist distinguished chiefly for his investigations in optics, published *The Memoirs of Sir Isaac Newton*. We owe to him a debt of gratitude for his diligence in collecting materials; but in spite of many admirable qualities his work, by and large, is inadequate and untrustworthy.

Brewster adopted throughout his book the rôle of advocate to "The High Priest of Science" as he calls Newton. His hero is to be portrayed without blemish intellectually and morally, and it is his duty to explain away whatever may mar the ideal he would create. He says of himself that, where he found evidence which confirmed facts known to reflect adversely on Newton's character, he published it; but if the facts were not previously known, he felt bound in honour to respect the privacy of his discovery. The irritation and suspicion which such a policy inevitably arouses in the mind of the reader defeated his purpose. In contrast to the blameless character traditionally ascribed to Newton, there have been persistent rumours about his religious heterodoxy, and about certain weaknesses of temperament, which would have been quieted if all the facts of his life had been freely given. There is absolutely nothing in his life so serious that it should have been suppressed.

There is in Brewster's *Memoirs* almost no attempt to present Newton as a living man or to give a critical analysis of his character. And, if we can judge from his treatment, the author was not competent to discuss the science or the philosophy of the seventeenth and eighteenth centuries. It is also unfortunate that the importance of Newton's political and religious work is neglected, since it is easy to prove that he played an important rôle in the Revolution of 1687, and John Locke considered him to be one of the most profound theologians of his day. As this biography is the only one which even pretends to be authoritative, there is no need of apology for offering a new life of Newton.

A reference should be made to the principal sources of material for the present biography. With the efficient aid of Messrs. Henry Sotheran and Co., a practically complete collection of published works relative to my subject was obtained and also a number of rare pamphlets and private notes of Newtonian scholars. References to these works are carefully noted in the text. Wherever possible I also secured copies of each of the editions of important works and, in several instances, this practice proved to be important in settling vexed questions.

In only a few cases, I failed to find copies of needed works and these deficiencies were supplied by photostatic reprints. I wish to express my sincere thanks to the Director of the British Museum for the copy of a variation in the text of one of the two editions of Raphson's *History of Fluxions* which I could not find; to Dr. Brasch of the Library of Congress for a copy of those parts of Mrs. de la Rivière Manley's *Eginardus* which refer to the Earl of Halifax and to Mrs. Catherine Barton; to the Directors of the Pierpont Morgan Library for a copy of Newton's *Memorandum Book* which is one of the treasures of that collection.

While there are a few unpublished Newtonian documents in various places, the one great and indispensable collection is that belonging to the Portsmouth family. All of Newton's papers, manuscripts, and documents, at his death, passed into the possession of his niece Catherine Barton, the wife of John Conduitt. Her only child, Catherine Conduitt, married John Wallop, Viscount Lymington, and their son was the second Earl of Portsmouth. These papers, which have remained in the possession of that family ever since, are known as the *Portsmouth Collection*.

Shortly after Newton's death, Conduitt's manuscripts and memoranda were added to the *Portsmouth Collection* and they are the principal source of material for his personal life and character.

It is quite evident that a satisfactory biography of Newton cannot be written unless the author has the privilege of using freely the *Portsmouth Collection*. By the interest and courtesy of The Master of Trinity College, to whom I am under other obligations for many instructive and happy days when in Cambridge, I was permitted to inspect and use all the Newton manuscripts in the University. I am even more grateful to Blanche, Lady Portsmouth, and to her nephew, Viscount Lymington, who, although I was then a stranger to them, sent their priceless collection in Hurstbourne Park to the British Museum in order that I might examine and use it at my leisure. I have also to thank them for allowing me to have reproductions made of portraits of Newton at Hurstbourne Park. It is a pleasure also to express my thanks to the Custodian of Manuscripts of the Museum who gave me every convenience and help during those weeks of work, in which I read and copied the manuscripts written in the beautifully clear handwriting of Newton.

So far as I can learn, the *Portsmouth Collection* has been examined for use by the following persons:[1]

1. Dr. Thomas Pellett, F. R. S., was appointed by Newton's executor in 1727 to examine and select such manuscripts as he thought to be fit for publication. A rough catalogue of the papers was appended to the bond given by Conduitt and was published in Hutton's *Mathematical Dictionary*. As a result of this examination, the *Abstract of the Chronology* and the *Chronology of Ancient Kingdoms Amended* were issued in one volume by Conduitt in 1728.

2. The whole collection was inspected by Bishop Horsley, F. R. S., while preparing his *Opera Omnia Newtoni*, 1779–1785, in five quarto volumes. He made a few unimportant notes on some of the papers but he made no use of them. It was rumoured that he opposed the

[1] Much of this information is taken from the *Catalogue of the Portsmouth Collection*. Cambridge University Press, 1888.

publication of Newton's theological writings because of their heterodoxy.

3. In 1806, Edmond Turnor, whose family had purchased and still own Newton's Manor, inserted in his book on the *Town and Soke of Grantham* some of the material collected by Conduitt.

4. Brewster, while preparing for his *Memoirs of Newton,* 1855, was given the rare privilege of inspecting the collection at his leisure. He made a very considerable use of Conduitt's manuscripts and of abstracts from Newton's correspondence, and some use of the mathematical notes and papers. He, however, used his discretion in extracting and in omitting many important documents which seemed to him not advantageous to Newton's reputation.

5. About 1872, the Earl of Portsmouth, after a fire at Hurstbourne, decided to present to the University of Cambridge all that portion of the papers which related to science with the provision that those concerning Theology, Chronology, History, and Alchemy should be returned to Hurstbourne Park, where they would be carefully preserved.

The papers of personal, private, and family interest were also returned to Lord Portsmouth, but copies of the more important letters were made and deposited in the University Library. During his last illness, Newton burned a great mass of personal papers; and he must have wished to preserve the same jealous aloofness after death which he had maintained during life for no family nor intimate letters were saved.[2] There is little probability that any important collection of his letters to his relatives will be discovered; if such had existed, Conduitt surely would have sought for them when he was collecting materials for his biography. Nor can we hope that any unknown significant collection of his correspondence with acquaintances and friends has been preserved. Newton was singularly averse to writing letters, and he rarely mentioned any personal matters in the few he wrote. We might almost accuse his contemporaries of having entered into a conspiracy to destroy all the evidences of his humanity in order that he should be thought of as a pure ideal of intellectual genius.

When the *Portsmouth Collection* was received by the University, a syndicate was appointed consisting of H. R. Luard, G. G. Stokes,

[2] In the Preface of the *Catalogue of the Portsmouth Collection,* a short note of Newton's mother written to him at College is mentioned. I could not find it although I made special search for it. I did, however, find a note to Sir John Newton, in Soho Square, from his mother.

J. C. Adams, and G. D. Liveing, of which the Astronomer Adams was the most active member. The papers were found to be in great confusion and a large portion had been grievously damaged by fire and damp. The syndicate carried through their work in a most thorough manner. The papers were sorted and classified in sections with a short descriptive note for each item. This very laborious and excellent work of the syndicate was finally published, in 1888, by the Cambridge University Press with the title, *A Catalogue of the Portsmouth Collection.*

The letters and other quotations used in this Life were transcribed by me from the originals or from printed copies. One or two of Newton's shorter letters have been printed literally in order that exact specimens of his orthography may be exhibited. Modern English usage has been adopted in the other quotations, since it would merely annoy the reader and serve no good purpose to have retained the original spelling and abbreviations. While I am personally responsible for the translation into English of all the documents quoted, I did in a few cases submit my rendition for approval to classical scholars more proficient than myself. Without trying to adapt my style to that of the eighteenth century, it was found to be advisable to limit my vocabulary as far as possible to words which were then in ordinary usage, so that there would be a less abrupt break in style between quotations and the rest of the text.

L. T. M.

Graduate School,
University of Cincinnati,
January, 1934.

CONTENTS

ISAAC NEWTON

CHAPTER I

EARLY YEARS

1642–1661

SITUATED some seven miles south of Grantham, in Lincolnshire, is the little hamlet of Woolsthorpe. It comprised, in the seventeenth century, a modest manor-house, two or three small farms, and a few thatched cottages; the nearest church to the hamlet was in the village of Colsterworth, about a half mile to the east. The settlement lies in the beautiful valley of the Witham, and it would have remained in peaceful obscurity if it had not chanced to be the birth-place of Isaac Newton.

Grantham, in the period of the Stuarts, was a town of three or four hundred families, and had been sufficiently important to have been the seat of a suffragan bishop; and two noblemen, at least, had taken their titles from it. This whole region was the seat of the wars of the Commonwealth; Charles I raised his standard at Nottingham, thirty miles to the west, and the battles of Marston Moor and of Naseby were fought in these eastern counties. Cromwell recruited most of his famous Ironsides from the yeomen of Huntingdonshire, and established his headquarters in Cambridge. Grantham lay in a direct line between these two regions, and its inhabitants must have suffered continually from foraging parties and from the general disorder of civil war.

In this environment, in the Manor House of Woolsthorpe-by-Colsterworth, Isaac Newton was born on Christmas Day, 1642, and in the same year that Galileo died. A week later, he was carried to Colsterworth, and the visitor may still read in the parish record: "Isaac sonne of Isaac and Hanna Newton Baptized Jan. 1, 1642/3."

The Manor House is a moderate sized building of gray stone, facing west and near the orchard which contains a scion of the apple tree famous as the inspiration for the discovery of the law of gravitation. Above the front door, which is narrow and low, is a tablet commemorating the birth of Newton. On the first floor, the rooms are fairly large with low ceilings and stone floors. A steep and narrow stair-case leads to the bed-rooms in the second story. The room in which Newton was born is on the left; a drawing of the apple tree hangs on the wall, and over the fire-place is a stone tablet inscribed with Pope's couplet:

> "Nature and Nature's Laws lay hid in night;
> God said, Let Newton be!—And all was light."

The room, to the right, was probably his bed-room; and a space partitioned off in the southeast corner was used as his study. Several windows were blocked in order to reduce the window tax, and some of them have since been reopened.

The manor of Woolsthorpe[1] is first mentioned in 1450 as belonging to a gentleman named Pigot. It passed into the possession of several families till it was purchased, in 1614, by Robert Underwood, who demised it nine years later to Robert Newton, the grandfather of Isaac Newton. While the manor was a small and poor estate, rated at £30 a year, its owners were true lords of the manor, with court leet and court baron, and perhaps pit and gallows. Isaac possessed these rights all his life, after attaining to his majority.

Of Newton's ancestry, it has been impossible to go back with certainty further than his grandfather, Robert. In 1705, after Isaac Newton had been knighted and was at the height of his fame, he was granted, on the strength of his personal affidavit made to the College of Arms, a pedigree dating back to John Newton of Westby, in Lincolnshire.[2] The affidavit was accompanied by a certificate from Sir John Newton of Thorpe, who, as head of the family, stated his father had said that Isaac Newton was his relation and kinsman; that John Newton of Westby was their common ancestor; and that he believed the said Sir Isaac Newton to be descended from the oldest son of the said John Newton: "but knoweth not in what particular manner, but that the said Sir Isaac hath always been reckoned by him of the said name and blood with his family." The arms of

[1] Much of our information about Newton's life and home was collected by Edmund Turnor, Esq., of Stoke Rochford, and published in his *Collections for the History of the Town and Soke of Grantham,* London, 1806. In 1732, the manor and estate of Woolsthorpe passed to the Turnors by purchase from John Newton, heir-at-law of Sir Isaac, and is still in their possession. The manor has been restored, and generous permission is given to visitors to inspect it. Edmund Turnor was an antiquary, much interested in local history; he also had access to the *Portsmouth Collection.* He was thus the first to make public many of the facts and stories of Newton's life.

[2] Turnor (p. 158) found this bit of corroboratory evidence: "The oldest property of the Newtons at Woolsthorpe was a messuage and lands purchased by John Newton of Westby, in 1561."

Newton are: "Sable, two shin bones saltire-wise, the sinister surmounted of the dexter, argent." And above the entrance of the manor of Woolsthorpe some one had carved two shin bones, the emblem of his family. There is undoubtedly a serious break in this pedigree and we cannot be at all certain that it is authentic.[3] The Newtons of Thorpe were, probably, only too proud to claim an Isaac Newton for their family and he himself, during his official life in London, apparently valued kinship with a county family of gentle birth. This concern over his pedigree at any rate shows his desire to be thought of as a gentleman. But the actual facts are that the Newtons of Woolsthorpe were yeoman farmers, that the oldest property of the family was a messuage and lands purchased by John Newton of Westby in 1561, and that Isaac Newton could not with certainty trace his ancestry further than to his grandfather.[4]

Of Newton's immediate family, we know very little except that his grandfather, Robert, was buried in Colsterworth churchyard, September 20, 1641. Robert's oldest son, Isaac, was proprietor of the manor for only a year and a month when he died at the age of thirty-seven and was buried in Colsterworth on October 6, 1642. He had been married only a few months and so never saw his illustrious son.

If we look for traits of character in Newton's family which might predict his genius, we certainly cannot find them in his paternal ancestry. The Newtons were not distinguished by any unusual ability and the only reference we have of his father is that he "was a wild, extravagant, and weak man."[5]

Turning to Newton's maternal side, we have evidence that his

[3] Stukeley (*Portsmouth Collection*) states that the Parish Registers were miserably kept. Although there were found numerous Newtons in the Parish yet, because of the defective Register, a correct genealogy could not be drawn up. Stukeley thought that Newton did not have his genealogy drawn up, but in this he was mistaken; while Newton lived in Germyn Street he had one prepared by the College of Heralds.

[4] The pedigree which is given in this volume was preserved in the *Portsmouth Collection* and copied by me. Dr. William Stukeley (1687–1765), who first copied it and sent it to Dr. Meade, physician to Newton, was an antiquary, and practised as a physician in Boston, London, and Grantham; after 1729 he was successively vicar in Stamford, Somerby, and Queen's Square, London. He was an intimate acquaintance of Newton's and at the time of Newton's death, he was living in Grantham. On the request of Conduitt, Newton's nephew-in-law, who was preparing to write a life of his uncle, Stukeley collected all the information he could find in Grantham and Colsterworth and sent it in a letter, with his personal reminiscences, addressed to Dr. Meade. Although Conduitt never wrote the intended life, his MSS. and notes which he collected from Stukeley are preserved in the *Portsmouth Collection* and are the principal source of our knowledge of Newton's personal life. I have checked all these MSS. and have now given much that has never before been published.

[5] This information was published by Maude in his *Wensleydale*. It was given to him by his neighbour, the Rev. Barnabas Smith, stepfather of Newton. *Cf.* de Villamil, *Newton: the Man*, London, 1932, p. 29.

mother was a woman of high character and fine intellect. She greatly favoured her son Isaac, and their relationship was extraordinarily affectionate and tender. Conduitt[6] left this charming sketch of her character: "His mother was Hannah, the daughter of James Ayscough of Market Overton in the county of Rutland, a family formerly of great consideration in those parts—one of them built great Paunton Steeple, a curious fabric between Grantham and Colsterworth.—Her mother of the Bliths of Stranson in Lincolnshire, now extinct . . . then on both sides of a fair and honourable extraction, but what was of much more consequence to her son, she was a woman of so extraordinary an understanding, virtue, and goodness, that those who think that a soul like Sir Isaac Newton's could be formed by anything less than the immediate operation of a Divine Creator might be apt to ascribe it to her. . . . She remained a widow several years, and employed her time educating her son and doing good works." However, she transmitted to her three children by her second marriage no traits of distinction; and of the next generation, with the exception of Catherine Barton, four at least were anything but a credit. Those who are eager to trace the seeds of genius by heredity can find but little satisfaction, for Isaac Newton appeared in a family in no wise distinguished by any other event.

Newton not only had no apparent advantages of racial stock, but he also had a most unpromising start in life; he was not only a posthumous child, but he was also prematurely born and so frail that two women who were sent to a Lady Packenham at the nearby village of North Witham to procure something for him, did not expect to find him alive on their return. And for some time he wore a bolster round his neck to support his head as he was too weak to hold it upright. In his later years, he was fond of repeating that his mother often told him that he might have been put into a quart mug. But in spite of his untoward birth, he must quickly have acquired vigour. This may be inferred from the fact that his mother married again within two years and went to live with her husband, the Rev. Barna-

[6] John Conduitt married Catherine Barton, Newton's niece, in 1717, and lived with his uncle for the last ten years of his life. He wrote a letter (published by Turnor) to Fontenelle to correct mistakes made in his Eloge for the French Academy, and collected much information from friends for an intended life of Newton, for which only a sketch was written. All of his MSS. are preserved in the *Portsmouth Collection,* excepting one which was unfortunately destroyed in a fire at Hurstbourne.

Conduitt was educated at Westminster School and Trinity College, Cambridge. He travelled much in Portugal on public business; was a Member of Parliament, and Newton's successor at the Mint. His only daughter married John Wallop, Viscount Lymington; and their son became the second Earl of Portsmouth.

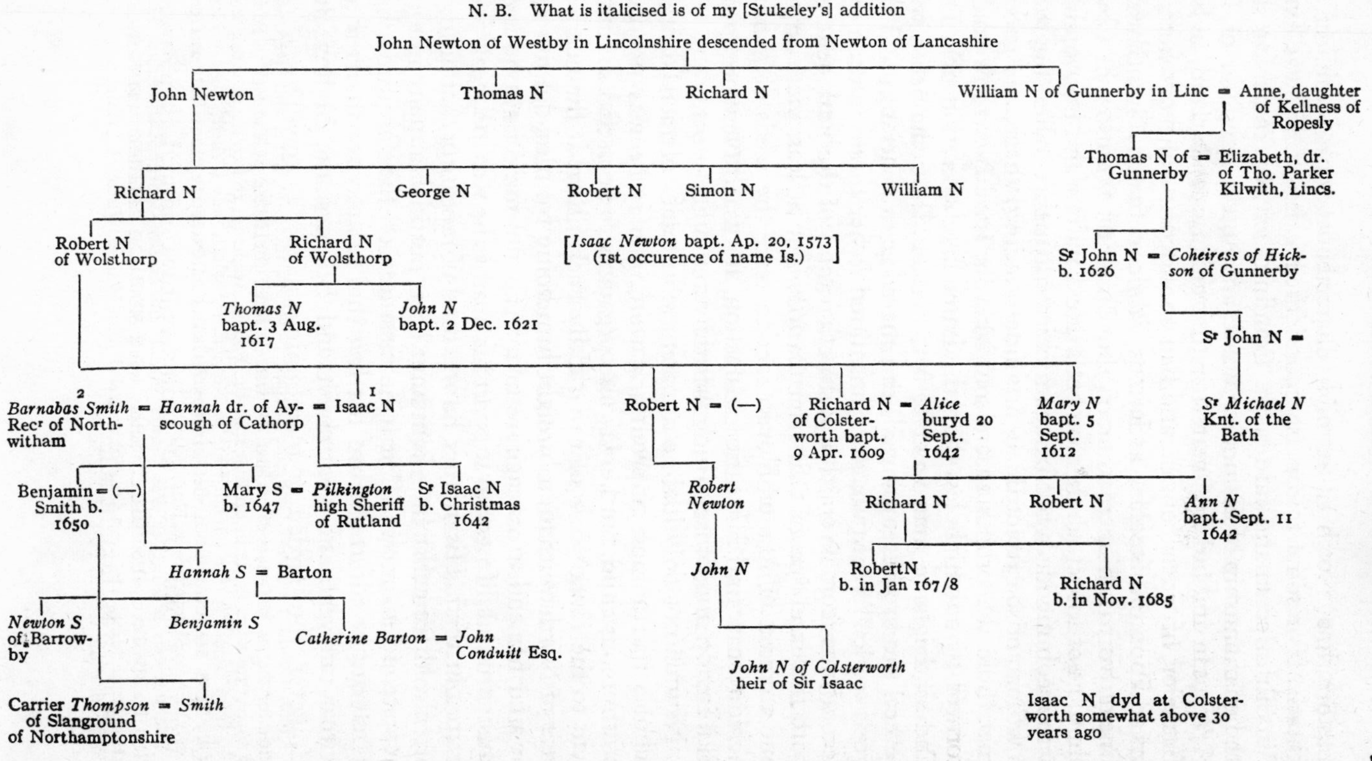
PEDIGREE OF Sr I. N. COPIED FROM HIS OWN HANDWRITING AT COLSTERWORTH 15 JUNE, 1727
N. B. What is italicised is of my [Stukeley's] addition
John Newton of Westby in Lincolnshire descended from Newton of Lancashire
John Newton
Thomas N
Richard N
William N of Gunnerby in Linc = Anne, daughter of Kellness of Ropesly
Thomas N of Gunnerby = Elizabeth, dr. of Tho. Parker Kilwith, Lincs.
Richard N
George N
Robert N
Simon N
William N
Robert N of Wolsthorp
Richard N of Wolsthorp
[Isaac Newton bapt. Ap. 20, 1573 (1st occurence of name Is.)]
Sr John N b. 1626 = Coheiress of Hickson of Gunnerby
Thomas N bapt. 3 Aug. 1617
John N bapt. 2 Dec. 1621
Sr John N =
2
Barnabas Smith Recr of North-witham = Hannah dr. of Ayscough of Cathorp = Isaac N
1
Robert N = (—)
Richard N of Colsterworth bapt. 9 Apr. 1609 = Alice buryd 20 Sept. 1642
Mary N bapt. 5 Sept. 1612
Sr Michael N Knt. of the Bath
Benjamin Smith b. 1650 = (—)
Mary S b. 1647 = Pilkington high Sheriff of Rutland
Sr Isaac N b. Christmas 1642
Robert Newton
Richard N
Robert N
Ann N bapt. Sept. 11 1642
Hannah S = Barton
John N
RobertN b. in Jan 167/8
Richard N b. in Nov. 1685
Newton S of Barrowby
Benjamin S
Catherine Barton = John Conduitt Esq.
John N of Colsterworth heir of Sir Isaac
Carrier Thompson of Slanground of Northamptonshire = Smith
Isaac N dyd at Colsterworth somewhat above 30 years ago

bas Smith, at North Witham, a village about a mile south of Woolsthorpe. For some reason, she considered it better to leave Isaac at Woolsthorpe in the care of his grandmother Ayscough and under the guardianship of his uncle, James Ayscough.

We can impute her marriage to prudence as Mr. Smith was a bachelor, fifty years of age, and had an independent income of £500 in addition to his salary as Rector. It seems that he was advised by one of his parishioners to marry, but he objected on the ground that he did not know where to meet a good wife. The widow Newton was recommended; but he again objected that he would not wish to ask her and be rejected. It was finally agreed that the parishioner should do the proposing and receive a fee for his day's work. Her answer was that she would be advised by her brother Ayscough, and so the same man went to Mr. Ayscough on the same errand. When the brother approved, the marriage was arranged. But the widow Newton stipulated that her son Isaac should have not only the income from Woolsthorpe, but that Mr. Smith should give him a parcel of land lying in Sewstern worth £50 a year and also repair and enlarge the Manor House.

Newton received his first education at two little day-schools in Skillington and Stoke which were near enough to his home to permit him to walk thither and back by himself. He stayed at these schools till the age of twelve, learning the reading, writing, and arithmetic of the time. Having outgrown their usefulness he was sent to the King's School in Grantham. He stayed there only four years as his mother then brought him home from school to learn to be a farmer and to manage his estate. The immediate reason for this change in his life was due to the death of his stepfather, which occurred in 1656. His mother returned to Woolsthorpe, bringing with her the three children,—Benjamin, Mary, and Hannah Smith,—of her second marriage. The circumstances of the family had been much improved, as she had her husband's estate, worth some £500 a year, and he had also rebuilt and enlarged the Manor House. However, the burden of maintaining a family, now large, and of managing a farm were doubly hard at this time because of the Civil Wars. In this emergency she turned to her son for assistance. The boy, now sixteen years old, had evidently not impressed his family as having any ability out of the ordinary; it was natural, then, to expect him to succeed his father, and for a yeoman farmer a rudimentary education was thought sufficient.

The plan was a complete failure, although it was persisted in for more than a year. The failure was due neither to willfulness nor to waywardness on the part of the boy, as he was docile and gentle by nature, but to a total lack of interest in the work of the farm. His years at school in Grantham had developed him from a child to a youth, and his intellectual tastes had begun to show themselves. Although he had become fond of books, his absorbing interest lay in the design and construction of mechanical toys and models. His return to the farm was utterly distasteful to him, and he could not be induced to show any interest in its management. If set to watch the cattle or sheep, he would pass the time reading, or making models of what struck his fancy with his knife; and while he was thus engrossed in his fancies, the animals strayed at their pleasure. The following anecdote may not tell the whole story, but it does bring to one a mental picture of a lonely and misplaced boy beginning to feel the powers of his genius. It recalls the story told of the youthful Giotto who passed the long and monotonous hours in the fields absorbed in the delight of drawing likenesses of his sheep, rather than in herding them.

A principal part of his duties consisted in going to market at Grantham on Saturday under the care of a trusted old servant in order to learn the intricacies of barter and trade. But they no sooner reached the town, and had put up their horses at the Saracen's Head Inn in Westgate, than he left the business to the servant and went to a Mr. Clark's house where he had formerly lodged. He stole into the garret and immersed himself in the delight of reading a parcel of old books which had been stored there; or he would ensconce himself under a favourite hedge at the foot of Spittlegate Hill, just before one enters Grantham, and pass the day reading and studying until the servant picked him up on the way home. He also fitted up for himself a study room, and here he made shelves to hold his few books, his mechanical toys, and his other boyish treasures; the walls he decorated with pictures, many of them drawn by himself and mounted in frames of his own handicraft. His mother finally gave up the experiment when she found that he was quite unfit to be a farmer, and agreed to send him back to school at Grantham to be tutored for college.

It would be difficult to estimate what the world owes to this decision of Newton's mother to send him to the University, nor did she imagine the honour which was in store for her and for him. And we can place the decision to the perspicacity of Mr. Stokes, the Master of Grantham School, for it seems, according to Stukeley,[7] that: "In the meantime Mr. Stokes, who had a great value for him, often strongly solicited his mother to return him to his learning, the proper channel of his inclinations. He told her it was a great loss to the world as well as a vain attempt to bury so promising a genius in rustic employment, which was notoriously opposite to his temper; that the only way whereby he could either preserve or raise his fortune must be by fitting him for the University. That if she sent him to school again he would remit his salary, which is forty shillings a year for those boys not born in the town or a mile distant which would alleviate the charge. In short, he prevailed upon her, and he remained at school till he went to the University. Thus in the main, the world is indebted to Mr. Stokes for the incredible advance in philosophy which this age has reaped from the studies of Sir Isaac Newton." This advice was supported by his uncle, the Rev. William Ayscough, rector of Burton Coggles. It is related that he found the boy under a hedge busied with a mathematical problem, when he should have been engaged in other business, and recommended that he be sent to Trinity College, Cambridge, where he, himself, had been educated.

There has been a considerable variation in the statements of the length of time Newton attended school. After a careful comparison of all the facts obtainable I feel sure that the following calendar is the most probable. After leaving the day schools at the age of twelve, he spent four school years at Grantham, beginning in the autumn of 1654; he then passed two years and a summer at home and returned to Grantham in the autumn of 1660; he was admitted as Subsizar at Trinity College, June 5, 1661. If these dates are accepted, his formal education at Grantham lasted in all five school years.[8] It is important to establish the dates of those critical years. His preparation at Grantham would be sufficient for entrance to college, for boys went up to Cambridge younger in those days than now and the standard of admission was especially low because of the demoralisation of the times. But, while he may have shown ability at school, his aloofness

[7] *Cf. Portsmouth Collection.*

[8] For example; Edleston, in his *Synoptical View of Newton's Life,* prefixed to his edition of *Newton's Correspondence with Cotes* (London, 1850), gives the following table:

"1655, Sent to Grantham School.—1656, Taken away from School.—1660, Sent back to school to prepare for college.—1661, June 5, Admitted Subsizar at Trin. Coll.; July 8, Matriculated Sizar." Thus Edleston gives four years and three months to his life on the farm, and only two school years at Grantham. His errors are due to the fact that he did not have

and the independent power of his imagination are what most impress us. Nor is this supposition unwarranted, as it was characteristic of him to accomplish his best work so secretly, and so unexpectedly, that no one knew when, or how, it had been prepared.

We can make a fairly certain conjecture as to the studies in which Newton would be tutored. The groundwork of his preparation was undoubtedly in the classics as it was for all University matriculates. Latin especially was important, as it was used generally as the medium for scholarly books, for correspondence, and in conversation. He would need to know less Greek, but it was a necessary and important subject. Modern languages were not required, and he learned little French and no German. Hebrew in fact was considered more important, and one of his memorandum books of this period shows that he had an acquaintance with the Hebrew characters. He would be thoroughly drilled in ancient or classical history, which was thought to be a much more important subject than contemporaneous history; and it was also a subject which he cultivated all his life. He would have lessons in Christian exegesis, Biblical history, and in grammar,—the latter sufficiently to study Sanderson's *Logic* as one of the first books to be read at college. In mathematics, his preparation was slight and must have been limited to arithmetic and a little geometry. The problems which are said to have engrossed his boyish years were probably merely simple calculations incident to his mechanical contrivances. It is at least certain that he had not studied Euclid with any thoroughness till he went to Cambridge. The above studies seem fairly certain; what else he may have learned must be left to conjecture.

Almost all our knowledge of Newton's early years is derived from the recollections of those who knew him while at school at Grantham. As the incidents are not dated it is impossible to give them chronologically, or even to assign them properly to the earlier or

access to the *Portsmouth Collection,* and also he seems to have confused school years, which omit the summer months, with calendar years.

My own table of dates is compiled from manuscript statements made by Conduitt and Stukeley, as follows:

Left day schools and went to Grantham School when he was twelve.—As he was twelve Christmas, 1654, I assume he went to Grantham in the autumn of that year.

Remained at Grantham four years.—He would thus stop school in the spring of 1658.

Returned to Grantham for three-quarters of a year.—That is, one school year and, as he was admitted to College in June, 1661, he went to Grantham in the autumn of 1660.

He thus passed five school years at Grantham, and two years and a summer at home between his two periods in school.

Brewster (*Memoirs of Sir Isaac Newton,* Edinburgh, 1855, vol. I, pp. 7, 13, and 14) so contradicts himself that he cannot be relied upon.

later of his two school periods; in fact, because of the confusion as to the time when he was at Grantham, some of the stories told of him may be placed as happening at Woolsthorpe.

The Old King's School at Grantham,[9] to which Newton was sent and where he was prepared for Cambridge, was established in 1528 during the reign of Henry VIII by Richard Fox, Bishop of Winchester and favourite minister of Henry VII. The building is now abandoned as a school, but it is still standing and is used regularly for an assembly hall; carved on its walls, amongst many other boys' names, may still be seen that of I. Newton, mute witness of his boyish days. The foundation also included a house and offices for the master; and the churchyard, directly on to which the school opened, did service for a playground. The then Headmaster, Henry Stokes, was esteemed to be an excellent scholar and a good teacher. He, if we can believe the story, became so proud and fond of Newton that, when the day came for the boy to leave school, he "with the pride of a father, placed his favourite pupil in the most conspicuous part of the school, and having, with tears in his eyes, made a speech in praise of his character and talents, held him up to the scholars as a proper object of their love and admiration."[10]

While at Grantham, during term time, Newton lodged with an apothecary, named Clark, whose house "was next to the George Inn northward in High Street, which was rebuilt about sixteen years ago [1711]." The reason for selecting this lodging was due to the intimate friendship of Mrs. Clark and Newton's mother, and it proved to be a happy choice, for the Clark family exercised a wholesome influence over the boy. They gave him the liberty to indulge his passion for making mechanical toys and models, they provided him with a study and books, and seem to have directed wisely his studies and life. Mr. Clark was certainly the cause of the boy's early interest in chemistry; and his later absorption in his chemical laboratory at Cambridge may have had its first incentive in the compounding of drugs and chemicals in the apothecary shop. Dr. Clark, M. D., a brother of the apothecary, was the mathematical usher at the school, and had the supervision of his most important subject. This

[9] This school has an honourable record. It carries on its rolls the names of several very distinguished men, such as Sir William Cecil, the statesman, Dr. Henry More, the philosopher, Dr. Newcome, Master of St. Johns, Sir Isaac Newton, Colley Cibber, the actor and poet-laureate, etc.

[10] *Isaac Newton: 1642–1727.* Ed. by W. J. Greenstreet, London, 1927, p. 142. This is a collection of essays, on Newton and his work, published to commemorate the bicentenary of his death.

Dr. Clark was a pupil of the famous Henry More of Christ College, who was himself a Granthamite, having been born in Mr. Bellamy's house over against the house of Dr. Stukeley to whose recollections we owe most of our knowledge of Newton's youth. A monument in the church of Grantham to Gabriel More describes him as "Nephew of Henry More, D. D. of Xts Col. in Cambridge by his learned writings in divinity and philosophy one of the greatest glories of our church and nation." Later, at Cambridge, Newton became an intimate associate of Henry More, who exerted on him a profound influence in both philosophy and religion. And, lastly, a stepdaughter of Clark was his most intimate friend and playmate. We can thus give to this family the honour of contributing much to the education and character of Newton.

Conduitt relates a story of Newton's school days which is important as it illustrates one of his most characteristic traits. All during his life, he required an external stimulus to arouse his latent power, and to exert himself to complete his work or to make public the fruits of his meditation. When he first went to the school at Grantham, he was placed in the lowest form and continued to be negligent in his studies: "When he was the last in the lowermost class but one, the boy next above him, as they were going to school, gave him a kick in his belly which put him to a great deal of pain. When school was over Newton challenged him to fight, and they went into the churchyard. While they were fighting the Master's son came out, and encouraged them by clapping one on the back, and winking at the other. Isaac Newton had the more spirit and resolution, and beat him till he would fight no more. Young Stokes told Isaac Newton to treat him like a coward and rub his nose against the wall, and accordingly Isaac Newton pulled him along by the ears and thrust his face against the side of the church. Determined to beat him also at his books, by hard work he finally succeeded, and then gradually rose to be the first in the school."[11]

We fortunately have preserved for us a contemporary account of Newton's boyhood interests and occupations which Dr. Stukeley gathered shortly after Newton's death from some of his schoolmates who were still alive and from unquestionable tradition. It is so interesting and so quaintly expressed that it is well worth quoting in full:[12]

11 *Portsmouth Collection.*
12 *Portsmouth Collection.* Also published in Turnor, pp. 176–178.

"Every one that knew Sir Isaac, or have [sic] heard of him, recount the pregnancy of his parts when a boy, his strange inventions, and extraordinary inclination for mechanics. That instead of playing among the other boys, when from school, he always busied himself in making knick-knacks and models of wood in many kinds. For which purpose he had got little saws, hatchets, hammers, and all sorts of tools, which he would use with great dexterity. In particular they speak of his making a wooden clock. About this time, a new windmill was set up near Grantham, in the way to Gunnerby, which is now demolished, this country chiefly using water mills. Our lad's imitating spirit was soon excited and by frequently prying into the fabric of it, as they were making it, he became master enough to make a very perfect model thereof, and it was said to be as clean and curious a piece of workmanship, as the original. This sometimes he would set upon the house-top, where he lodged, and clothing it with sail-cloth, the wind would readily turn it; but what was most extraordinary in its composition was, that he put a mouse into it, which he called the miller, and that the mouse made the mill turn round when he pleased; and he would joke too upon the miller eating the corn that was put in. Some say that he tied a string to the mouse's tail, which was put into a wheel, like that of turn-spit dogs, so that pulling the string, made the mouse go forward by way of resistance, and this turned the mill. Others suppose there was some corn placed above the wheel, this the mouse endeavouring to get to, made it turn. Moreover Sir Isaac's water clock is much talked of. This he made out of a box he begged of Mr. Clark's [his landlord's] wife's brother. As described to me, it resembled pretty much our common clocks and clock-cases, but less; for it was not above four feet in height, and of a proportionable breadth. There was a dial plate at top with figures of the hours. The index was turned by a piece of wood, which either fell or rose by water dropping. This stood in the room where he lay, and he took care every morning to supply it with its proper quantity of water; and the family upon occasion would go to see what was the hour by it. It was left in the house long after he went away to the University.

"I remember once, when I was deputy to Dr. Halley, Secretary at the Royal Society, Sir Isaac talked of these kind of instruments,—that he observed the chief inconvenience in them was, that the hole through which the water is transmitted, being necessarily very small, was subject to be furred up by impurities in the water, as those made with sand will wear bigger, which at length causes an inequality in time.

"These fancies sometimes engrossed so much of his thoughts, that he was apt to neglect his book, and dull boys were now and then put over him in form. But this made him redouble his pains to overtake them, and such was his capacity, that he could soon do it, and outstrip them when he pleased; and it was taken notice of by his master. Still nothing could induce him to lay by his mechanical experiments: but all holidays, and what time the boys had allowed to play, he spent entirely in knocking and hammering in his lodging room, pursuing that strong bent of his inclination not only in things serious, but ludicrous too, and what would please his school-fellows, as well as himself; yet it was in order to bring them off from trifling sports, and teach them, as we may call it, to play philosophically, and in which he might willingly bear a part, and he was particularly ingenious at inventing diversions for them, above the vulgar kind. As for instance in making paper kites, which he first introduced here. He took pains, they say, in finding out their proportions and figures, and whereabouts the string should be fastened to the greatest advantage, and in how many places. Likewise he first made lanterns of paper crimpled, which he used to go to school by, in winter mornings, with a candle, and tied them to the tails of the kites in a dark night, which at first affrighted the country people exceedingly, thinking they were comets. It is thought that he first invented this method; I can't tell how true. They tell us too how diligent he was in observing the motion of the sun, especially in the yard of the house where he lived, against the walls and roofs, wherein he would drive pegs, to mark the hours and half hours made by the shade, which by degrees from some years observations he had made very exact, and any body knew what o'clock it was by Isaac's dial,[13] as they ordinarily called it; thus in his youngest years did that immense genius discover his sublime imagination, that since has filled, or rather comprehended the world."

It is natural that these reminiscences should dwell on Newton's handicraft and give us so little of his mental life. The outward habits

[13] Several of these dials are still to be seen on the wall of the Manor House.—According to Conduitt: "To the time of his death he retained this custom of making constant observations in the rooms he chiefly used where the shade of the sun fell; and I have often known him both at Kensington and in St. Martin's Street, when anyone asked what o'clock it was, tell immediately by looking where the shadow of the sun touched as exactly as he could have by his watch."

and occupations of a boy are easy to observe and to remember, but to appreciate his inner life is, at best, a difficult matter; of one like Newton, who so jealously and persistently guarded the sanctuary of his mind, it would be next to impossible to form a judgement. It is probable that he never met a boy or a girl with whom he shared the confidences of his thoughts. We do know, however, that he early acquired the habit of reading and of recording his thoughts in notebooks, a habit which continued to grow with the years to such an extent that towards the end of his life his nephew, Mr. Conduitt, tells us that he was hardly ever without a book or pen in his hand. His first source of reading lay in that parcel of old books stored in Mr. Clark's attic, but unfortunately no one was interested enough to record their titles. Newton should not be characterised as absent-minded, but he was subject to fits of deep abstraction when profoundly engaged on a problem, and this habit of prolonged and intense meditation began in his boyhood. We have the stories of his days on the farm when he became absorbed in his books and forgetful of the duties assigned to him. In particular, it is told of him that once, when he was riding home from Grantham, he dismounted to let his horse walk up Spittlegate Hill, just beyond the town, and at the top, he turned to mount again, only to find that his horse had slipped away, leaving the bridle in his hand. On another occasion, his friend, Dr. Stukeley, called on him. Newton was out, but the table was laid for dinner. Dr. Stukeley lifted the cover, ate the dinner, and then replaced it on the dish. When Newton appeared later he greeted his friend and sitting down he, too, lifted the cover—"Dear me," said he, "I thought I had not dined, but I see I have."[14]

Newton was not only expert with tools but he had a talent for drawing which he apparently cultivated by himself, as his writing master at Grantham, Old Barley as he was called, seems not to have had any ability in that art. Mr. Clark told Dr. Stukeley, many years later, that the whole wall of his lodging room was still full of the drawings he had made upon it with charcoal: "There were birds, beasts, men, ships, and mathematical schemes, and very well designed." Dr. Stukeley also states that he furnished his room, at Woolsthorpe, with portraits, some copied from prints and others drawn from life which were placed in frames of his own making.

[14] Greenstreet, p. 142.—This trick played upon him is usually laid in Cambridge; but, as Stukeley was only ten years old when Newton left Cambridge, it must be referred, if true, to his later days in London.

As Newton is represented as singularly indifferent to, and even contemptuous of, all forms of art, we are left in doubt whether his habit of drawing resulted from his fondness for handicraft, or from an appreciation of the pictorial arts. If we can judge from his library, he had no interest in belles-lettres, and Conduitt states that, in his latter days, he often expressed a contempt for poetry; yet Newton once astonished him by remarking that he had, when young, excelled particularly in making verses. Surprising as this statement may be, we have a specimen of his skill. Under a picture of King Charles I hanging in his room, he wrote, Stukeley tells us, these verses which Mrs. Vincent[15] repeated from memory:

> "A secret art my soul requires to try,
> If prayers can give me, what the wars deny.
> Three crowns distinguish'd here in order do
> Present their objects to my knowing view.
> Earth's crown, thus at my feet, I can disdain,
> Which heavy is, and, at the best, but vain.
> But now a crown of thorns I gladly greet,
> Sharp is this crown, but not so sharp as sweet.
> The crown of glory that I yonder see
> Is full of bliss and of eternity."

These are very good verses in the fashion of the day to be written by a boy of his age, and I accept his statement of his skill, as I believe he could excel in any undertaking to which he applied his mind or hands. In addition to their skill, these verses are a convincing evidence that the boy was brought up in a family devoted to the Church of England and the Royalist cause. The piety attributed to the Martyr King is typical of the time, and we may be certain that he was opposed to the prevalent sympathy of the countryside to Cromwell. This is the more significant because, in later life, he became a convinced Whig and anti-Jacobite; and, while he remained a communicant of the Church of England, he adopted a rational protestantism very similar to that of Milton.

Newton was characterised by his chroniclers as a normal and wholesome boy and this is undoubtedly true if it be understood as referring to a moral and disciplined mind and temperament. But he was certainly anything but the usual type of country boy. No better

[15] Her maiden name was Storey; she was a stepdaughter to Clark and Newton's intimate friend while he lived with the Clarks.

sketch of his character as a youth has been given than that of Miss Storey, who knew him more intimately than anyone else and who apparently was a keen judge. She told Stukeley that: "Sir Isaac was always a sober, silent, thinking lad, and was never known scarce to play with the boys abroad, at their silly amusements; but would rather choose to be at home, even among the girls, and would frequently make little tables, cupboards, and other utensils for her and her playfellows, to set their babies and trinkets on." These traits were undoubtedly innate; but they were strengthened by two influences which have escaped the notice of his biographers, as none of them considers the effect on his character of the circumstances of his birth and of the times.

During his early years, Newton must have been physically weak because of his premature birth. He would be unable to compete in the active games and contests of his rough companions in the little country schools he first attended, and the only recourse of such a boy to escape the humiliation of being taunted as a weakling, and to avoid the physical torments inflicted by childish bullies, was to isolate himself. It is hard to realise the mental suffering such a child may undergo and how likely it is to fix upon him the habits of detached meditation and self-absorption, which may become so strong as to create an inability for ingenuous friendships. And, at home, he grew up in a lonely farmhouse situated in a countryside only slowly recovering from the terrors of a protracted and bitter civil war, and with no protection from the frights of his imagination except that of his grandmother and such unreliable labourers as could be hired.

He must have been familiar with the incursions of rough raiding parties after provisions and plunder, and he and his grandmother, suspected of sympathy to the royal forces, must have been frequently forced to evade embarrassing questions of the Commonwealth soldiers and of the local magistrates. In addition to these inducements to cultivate silence and reserve he would have for companions at home, also, only the children of his few neighbours, their rough play made still rougher by imitation of the lawless deeds of the soldiers. Such a child could not be in sympathy with them and would turn from outward companionship to the solace of lonely meditation.

Timidity and diffidence, added to a character of high purpose and essential nobility, will account for his hatred of cruelty, his sympathy and generous aid to those who might be in trouble. He preserved a steadfast and deep affection for members of his family with whom he felt unconstrained and at ease, but in general society he was cold and formal, and was singularly unable to form intimate friendships. But he had to contend with an even more serious defect of temperament. Though his biographers have earnestly tried to make of him a national monument not only of genius, but also of virtue, the fact is that he had a morbidly suspicious and secretive mind which must have had its source in a form of vanity, or in an exaggerated sensitiveness of personal honour. In spite of a strong will and the exercise of self-discipline, he was subject to peevish outbreaks of ill-temper, and of suspicious injustice even towards those who were his best friends. On such occasions he stooped to regrettable acts which involved him in a succession of painful controversies that plagued his life, robbed him of the just fruits of his work, and disheartened his sincere admirers.

His early love of solitude, his delight in the fancies of his imagination, his manual dexterity, and his habit of concentrated thought increased steadily with his years. They were the early evidence of his future power; and they give the clue to the apparently sudden, and otherwise mysterious, efflorescence of his enormous mental ability.

While Newton was at home helping his mother manage the farm, he began to keep note-books; Conduitt mentioned that two of these records of his youthful activities had been preserved all his long life and were desposited with the family papers. Brewster, who examined the *Portsmouth Collection* almost a century ago, found only the second, and later, note-book. When, or how, the other was lost is unknown, but by one of the strange tricks of fate, the first little volume, after dropping out of sight for more than a century, has recently been found amongst the manuscripts of the Pierpont Morgan Library in New York. Selected portions have now been published by Professor David Eugene Smith.[16] As he kindly gave me a photostatic copy with the permission of the Trustees to use what portions I desired, I can include some of the interesting items of this relic of Newton's early days.

The book is about 2¾ by 4⅞ inches and has a title-page: "Isaacus Newton hunc librum possidet. teste Edvardo Secker. pret: 2^d ob. 1659." The contents are a curious collection of odds and ends brought

16 Greenstreet, p. 16.

together by a boy of an unusually acquisitive mind who is planning to do large things but without any settled purpose. Thus, his love of orderly detail is shown by a catalogue running to forty-two pages, divided under sixteen heads, of such lists as "Arts, Trades, and Sciences," "Birds," "Household stuffe," "Minerals," etc. There are also samples of perpetual calendars, astronomical tables, and solutions of geometrical problems. Like many boys, he dabbled in languages and invented a scheme of phonetic writing. On one page he sets down his key of phonetic spelling and on the next page he gives a sample letter spelled in both ways. The note is as follows:

"Loving Friend.

"It is commonly reported that you are sick. Truly I am sorry for that. But I am much more sorry that you got your sickness (for that they say too) by drinking too much. I earnestly desire you first to repent of your having been drunk and you to seek to recover your health. And if it please God that you ever be well again, you have a care to live healthfully and soberly for time to come. This will be very well pleasing to all your friends and especially to

Your very loving friend

I. N."

Whether or not Newton had a bibulous friend, the note probably is expressive of his own character and is thus worth preserving.

The most interesting, perhaps, of the items in this book, are those referring to drawing and the making of pigments, as they show the great interest he took in the art, and to the chemical and medicinal recipes which he jotted down. A sample of each will be sufficient.

"A sea colour. Take privet berries when ye sun entreth into Libra, about ye 13th of September, dry y^{m} in ye sunn; then bruise them & steepe y^{m} in allum water, & straine y^{m} into an earthen poringer y^{t} is glazed."

"To make his powder to purge the head. Take vinger of the best, Orris powder of each halfe a dram; Pellitory of Spaine, & white hellebore, of each halfe a dram; All these into a fine powder & searce them well & add to them two dropps of oyle of Anniseeds. And when you will use it take the quantitie of a barley corne & snuff it upp into yor nose & it will cause a snezing, whereby it purgeth the head from all superfluous humo^{s} strengtheneth the memory causeth a cleare sight & is good for the thikness of hearing taken as abovesaid every other morning."

The second and third parts of the book were written at college and are much more mature. He drew up a scheme to reform spelling,—a matter of great importance in the seventeenth century,—that shows incidentally that he had some familiarity with the Hebrew alphabet. His interest in making sundials was still keen and he had passed from the cut-and-try stage to that of calculation. There are included in the mathematical section five pages of solutions of problems, two pages of notes on the Copernican system, and two more pages devoted to the working out of an elaborate ecclesiastic calendar. These casual notes on the Copernican system should be regarded as a most precious document for they are the germ from which developed his discovery of the law of universal gravitation.

The second of Newton's early memorandum books is still to be seen in the *Portsmouth Collection*. On the first page is the inscription: "Quisquis in hunc librum Teneros conjecit ocellos. Nomen subscriptum perlegat ipse nomen. Isaac Newton. Martii 19, 1659." And on the next page there is the heading: "Utilissimum Prosodiae Supplementum." The body of the notes contains rules of grammar. The remainder of the book is a running expense account. Most of these items refer to his college days and, as they shed some light on that period of his life, a selection from them will be given in the next chapter.

While Newton was preparing for college, he again lived with the Clarks, and his affection for Miss Storey deepened into love and an engagement to be married. On the authority of Dr. Stukeley, who had a long conversation with her in her old age: "Sir Isaac and she being thus brought up together, 'tis said that he entertained a love for her; nor does she deny it: but her portion being not considerable, and he being a fellow of a college, it was incompatible with his fortunes to marry; perhaps his studies too. 'Tis certain he always had a kindness for her, visited her whenever in the country, in both her husbands' days, and gave her forty shillings, upon a time, whenever it was of service to her. She is a little woman, but we may with ease discern that she has been very handsome."[17]

When his tutoring was completed, he left home as a shy and diffident country boy and entered the busy and populous life of Cambridge without acquaintances and without influence. His preparation

[17] *Portsmouth Collection.*

seems to have been somewhat defective; and his first years were passed without distinction, and in such loneliness that he seized every opportunity to return home where he would be free to indulge in his private meditations.

CHAPTER II

CAMBRIDGE UNIVERSITY. STUDENT LIFE. EARLY DISCOVERIES

1661–1669

CAMBRIDGE UNIVERSITY, which now became the home of the young Newton, had like the nation suffered terribly from the two decades of strife and turmoil of the Civil War. Exhausted in funds and deprived of many of its leading Fellows, the University during the period of his undergraduate life was badly disorganised; the number of students had been greatly reduced, their discipline had been relaxed and their instruction interrupted.

Cambridge had been steadfast in its devotion and loyalty to Charles I. Even while he was Prince of Wales, there had been an attempt made to elect him Chancellor of the University at the preposterous age of twelve years. Although the plan was finally defeated and every effort was made to consign it to oblivion in order to save the royal feeling of humiliation, yet the episode had its bearing on the future of the University as it focused the attention of the nation on the academic subserviency to the Crown. The more acute and observant minds in the University may have feared the ominous aspect of the times and the effects of the taciturnity and obstinacy of Charles's disposition, but hope and loyalty prevailed and the University was enthusiastic at his accession in 1625. His father, in his pedantic way, had been eager to be recognised as a scholar and to engage in learned discussions. So long as the University respected his obstinate belief in the divine right of kings and regarded him as its undisputed master, he was more than willing to be known as its patron and benefactor. Charles, in the early years of his reign, pursued the same policy and so encouraged Cambridge to hope for a further period of prosperity. As a reward for royal favours both father and son were permitted, and even urged, to meddle in matters of academic policy. In particular, they indulged more and more frequently in the exercise of arbitrary power in appointing heads and fellows of the colleges by Royal Mandate; though such appointments were contrary to custom and, in many cases, to the statutes, they were ratified with servile complacency in the hope of arousing generosity. This grave infringement on academic rights introduced not only the evils of court favouritism but gave rise to parliamentary hostility and intervention. The first interference in University affairs by the Commons was directed against this exercise of Royal Mandate. An Act "to prevent corruption in the presentations and collations to benefices and in elections to headships, fellowships, and scholars places, in Colleges and Halls" was read a second time in the House and referred to a Committee on February 23, 1629; and it would doubtless have become law if Parliament had not been dissolved in the following month.[1]

The increasing disposal of the church patronage of the University by the Crown was perhaps an even more dangerous interference in academic privilege. Both Oxford and Cambridge still preserved the traditional education preparatory to the learned professions of divinity, law, and physic. And, of these, divinity was undoubtedly of the greatest importance. Most of the Fellows of the colleges were in orders, and it was largely by supplementing the small stipends of their fellowships by the income from ecclesiastical livings that they met their expenses. Thus, if church patronage fell into the hands of the Crown so also the Fellows would be compelled to look to it rather than to the University authorities for appointments and preferment. Archbishop Laud, who was determined at all hazards to strengthen the hierarchy of the Church of England, eagerly seized on the power of Church patronage as a means to maintain the established Church in the Universities and to counteract the spread of Puritanism. Thus the Fellows were held in subjection and those who were recalcitrant, however able they might be in scholarship, were forced to submit or resign.

The stirring of the new knowledge on the continent which resulted from the scientific ideas of Galileo and Descartes had not seriously affected Oxford and Cambridge. Not even the influence of Francis Bacon, who had eagerly adopted the new inductive philosophy and become its foremost expounder and advocate and who had no peer in his loyalty to his Alma Mater, Trinity College, could shake the grip of the traditional Aristotelian philosophy which had fastened itself in the schools of divinity.

This was not so in Italy where the scientific renaissance was in full

[1] Mullinger, *History of Cambridge University,* vol. III, p. 99.

flower and had spread to France and Holland. There, the revival of humanism and the growth of experimental science had broken the power of mediæval philosophy and had become clearly indicated by a new interest in Platonism. Italy was the centre of culture and learning and eager students from all the other countries flocked to its universities. The relatively few Englishmen who made the pilgrimage were unable on their return to shake the conservative attitude of their own universities and they found little sympathy with their new ideas and few facilities for their work. The libraries were wretchedly deficient and inadequately housed; while astrology and superstition were almost as prevalent as they were in the Dark Ages. As an example of the credulity which existed even in Cambridge, this story may be cited. In 1629, "both town and university were alike disquieted by the occurrence of a singular natural phenomenon. On Midsummer eve, a volume containing three pietistic treatises was found in the belly of a codfish exposed for sale in Cambridge market. One of the bedells thought the incident sufficiently remarkable to be brought under the notice of the vice-chancellor, by whom it was looked upon as of the greatest gravity, and an incident, which a century later would have been regarded with no other feeling than that of amusement, appeared to both the learned and the vulgar of Cambridge an event fraught with dismal portent. The appearance of some gigantic comet in the heavens could hardly, in fact, have been the occasion of greater dismay."[2] Thomas Fuller, at this time a bachelor at Queens, relates the circumstances in a manner which shows that his keen sense of the ludicrous enabled him to rise superior to the superstition of his time. The book, he tells us, "was wrapped about with canvas, and probably that voracious fish plundered both out of the pocket of some shipwrecked seaman. The wits of the university made themselves merry thereat, one making a long copy of verses thereon, whereof this distich I remember:

> 'If fishes thus do bring us books, then we
> May hope to equal Bodlyes library.'

But whilst the youngsters disported themselves herewith, the graver sort beheld it as a sad presage." Among those of the 'graver sort' was the exemplary master of Sidney, Dr. Samuel Ward, who thought the prodigy worthy of being reported in all its details to his friend, Archbishop Ussher.[3]

[2] Mullinger, Vol. III, p. 71.

[3] *Ibid.*, Vol. III, p. 71.

The scholarly work which issued from the University was mostly confined to controversial treatises on theological or philosophical subjects, of large bulk but of small value. So the scholar, if he would win recognition and advancement, was pretty much restricted to exhaust his energies in making new commentaries on the classical authors or tortuous interpretations of the Scriptures. In mathematics, natural philosophy, and modern history there was hardly any interest. The first direct influence of Bacon's plea for a more liberal curriculum was shown by the establishment of a lectureship on modern history by Fulke Greville, first Lord Brooke. The significant feature of the ordinance was that: "A foreigner was to be considered eligible, but no one 'in holy orders' was to be considered so, as well 'because this realm affordeth many preferments for divines, few or none for professors of profane learning, the use and application whereof to the practice of life is the main end and scope of this foundation; and also because this Lecture must needs hinder a divine from the studies and offices of his calling due to the Church.' "[4] It seems incredible to us that contemporaneous history should have been absolutely neglected in a great university; but it was a fixed tenet of scholars that all the examples of human wisdom and human folly had been perfectly illustrated by classic writers and profit could be obtained only by study of their works. As late as the eighteenth century, a long and heated controversy was waged between Bentley and the foremost scholars of England as to whether any modern man had been the peer of the great heroes of Greece; and the consensus of opinion was that there had been no one equal to them in either intellect or character. Cambridge could not provide a person qualified for the chair of history, and it was necessary to secure a young scholar from Leyden.

The best type of the Cambridge scholar of the age can be illustrated by Joseph Mede (1586–1638), Fellow of Christ's College. He was skilled both in the technical knowledge and in the philosophy of the schools; he was conversant with the meagre mathematics current in the University; he was an excellent modern linguist, and his knowledge of history and chronology was considered remarkable; he was a profound theologian and an eminent classical scholar; and he was an anatomist and a botanist. In addition to these varied accomplishments he was the ablest and most effective teacher in all the University, and he maintained a voluminous correspondence with all sorts

[4] Mullinger, Vol. III, p. 84.

of people who sought his advice on state and political affairs. Yet this paragon of scholars used his valuable time and energy in compiling a large quarto volume in which a vast number of Greek, Latin, and English words were traced back to their supposed Hebrew roots. There was a sort of magnificent simplicity and directness in the philology of those days which puts to shame the confused efforts of our modern searchers for verbal roots. All the races of mankind were assumed to have descended from Adam and Eve, so, since they spoke with the Hebrew tongue, all words in all languages could be traced back ultimately to that prototype if one had only sufficient ingenuity and diligence. Those naïve philologists remind us of the modern biologists who assume an ancestral protozoon and trace all the species of life to that mythical ancestor. Both assumptions are equally futile, for both sources lie buried in the oblivion of time.

But it was not so much as a scholar and teacher of profane subjects that Mede impressed his influence on his contemporaries. His monumental work was his *Clavis Apocalyptica,* originally written in Latin in 1627 and translated into English in 1642 by Richard More. The author's purpose was to form a connected and chronological sequence of actual and prophetic events from the mystical rhapsody of the Book of Revelations; on this dream he lavished all his profound erudition and critical acumen. "The *Clavis* won for its author the regard of Hartlib and the praise of nearly all learned Holland; it modified the religious belief of John Milton; and taking rank, for more than a century, as a classic, it exerted an influence on theological thought which no English writer on the period appears adequately to have recognised."[5] But what is significant to us is that the book had a direct influence on Newton, who was profoundly interested in such exegesis and referred to Mede in his own religious writings as his guide in prophetic interpretation.

Another book, the *Life of Jacob Boehme* by Durand Hotham, is known to have received the careful attention of Newton. The mystical doctrines of Boehme had a great influence in England; his aversion to theological disputes and to formal services seemed a haven of rest to those wearied by the controversies between the ritualistic Roman Catholic and English Churches, and bleak Puritanism,—a refuge where one could worship in seclusion, directed by the dictates of the inner light.

[5] Mullinger, Vol. III, p. 24.

Space will not permit a detailed discussion of the tangled and disastrous history of the University while it was almost ground to dust between the dissensions of the Royal and Commonwealth parties. The eleven years, which followed the dissolution of Charles's third Parliament in 1629, have been described as the darkest hour of Protestantism, whether in England or in the world at large. In Cambridge a feeling of profound moral and intellectual depression set in, caused by the suspension of freedom of discussion and enhanced by the horrors of the plague of 1630 which drove great numbers of the students out of town, practically stopped classes and study, and even silenced temporarily the ardour of theological controversy.

That the University survived the spoliation by both the royalists and the anti-royalists and not only regained, but soon surpassed, its former prestige and wealth, is a witness to the stability of academic institutions. Of all the causes which can threaten the existence of a university, there is none so dangerous and so bitter as the combination of political and religious opposition. Of the two, political hostility is much less serious than the attacks of those who regard the teachers of youth as the perverters of their personal faith. Yet, so far as I can recall, there is scarcely an instance of a university, once well established, which has not been able to weather all the vicissitudes of political and religious upheavals.

It is a surprising commentary on the kaleidoscopic swiftness of the events which convulsed the nation and its seats of learning to remember that they were compressed almost exactly into the nineteen years between the birth and matriculation of Newton. By the latter time the long ordeal was over and on Thursday, the 10th of May, 1660, the Restoration was celebrated by the vice-chancellor and the doctors in scarlet gowns, the regents, non-regents and bachelors with their hoods turned, and the scholars in caps. Perhaps, there was no more significant sign that the University had returned to its traditional life and established customs than the general re-appearance of the student *mortar-board* cap in place of the round *pileus* which had been required during the Commonwealth.

However important an understanding of the state of the University, as a whole, may be in obtaining a correct background for Newton's life, it is even more necessary that an account should be given of Trinity College, where he lived so long and which he so adorned. Henry VIII had founded in 1546 one spacious college, for the maintenance of a Master and sixty Fellows and Scholars, dedicated to the

Holy and Undivided Trinity. Queen Mary afterwards added twenty Scholarships. During the reign of Elizabeth the foundation was completed and the statutes of its government were formulated in the most liberal spirit. Almost from its start Trinity College took a commanding position, and during the reigns of Elizabeth and James I, when unusual care was paid to merit in ecclesiastical appointments, Trinity could claim as her sons the Archbishops of Canterbury and of York, and seven others of the principal Bishops. So great was the reputation of her resident Fellows for theological learning that no less than six of them were among the translators of the Authorised Version of the Bible. In public life she counted Francis Bacon and Sir Edward Coke. In *belles lettres* many of the Elizabethan poets, and later Cowley and Dryden were among her students. Finally, her scholarship was held in such high esteem that her Fellows were chosen to fill the Headships of the majority of the other Colleges of the University.

The civil troubles, and the bigotry of the Puritans, fell more heavily on Trinity than on any of the other Colleges. The revenues were dissipated, many of the ablest Fellows were ejected and those who remained were either inferior in ability or were depressed in spirit. During the last half of the seventeenth century the College declined in numbers and in reputation and the body of Fellows comprised fewer able scholars than at any preceding or subsequent period. When Richard Bentley became Master in 1700, he repeatedly accused the Fellows and students of both sloth and drunkenness.

When Newton went to Cambridge Henry Ferne was Master, but his tenure of office continued only two years. He was succeeded by John Pearson in 1662 and by Isaac Barrow in 1673; Bishop Monk, in his life of Bentley, characterises them as "two of the brightest characters which grace the period of Charles the Second." During their short administrations the finances were improved, building was carried on, and stricter discipline exacted. Unfortunately, before the better conditions had been established, Dr. Barrow was succeeded by the Hon. John North (1677–1683) and he by the Hon. John Montague (1683–1700). Both of them were weak men and their rule lasted the remainder of the period of residence of Newton at Cambridge. Bishop Monk lays the decline of Trinity during the most fruitful years of Newton's life to the following causes: "First, the acknowledged relaxation of discipline under the last two Masters, Dr. North and Dr. Montague, had produced its never-failing consequences, in impairing both decorum and learning: secondly, that distinguishing principle of Trinity College, admission to the founder's bounty upon the score of merit alone, had experienced an interruption in the times of civil discord, when Fellows were appointed by the nomination of parliamentary commissioners, and subsequently of the Protector. After the Restoration, Charles the Second, being probably urged to assume the same patronage as had been exercised by the Usurper, frequently sent Royal mandates for electing to fellowships; which, though plainly contrary to their statutes, the Society were constrained to obey. In the short reign of James the Second this exercise of arbitrary power was carried still further, *every* vacancy among the fellowships being filled by mandatory letters from the King. Although the College was delivered by the Revolution from further invasions of its privileges, yet some of the intruded Fellows, having obtained office by their seniority and not being indebted to industry or learning for their preferment, wanted both ability and disposition to encourage those qualifications in others. A third cause of the depressed and languid state of Trinity College may be found in the prevalent distaste for the old system of academical study; people had begun to neglect and despise the learning of the schoolmen, before a more vigorous and manly system of instruction had been substituted."[6]

When the young Newton left Woolsthorpe in June, 1661, and went up to Cambridge, he was engaged to marry Miss Storey. This obligation may have come from a sincere attachment or it may have resulted from the sentimental excitement incident to leaving home and early surroundings. Whichever may have been the cause, we have no reason to suppose that he did not expect to fulfill that contract when he had finished his education and had become financially able to support a family. He would, we may presume, expect to follow one of two professions; he could return to Woolsthorpe and as a small gentleman farmer manage his estates, or he might follow in the footsteps of his uncle and stepfather, take orders and become a parish priest. One can but wonder whether, if such had been his fate, he would have lived an obscure life, respected by his neighbours for ability and piety, or whether his genius for natural philosophy would have developed in spite of his occupation. It is, to me, a practical certainty that no circumstances could have repressed his creative ability. But all doubt as to what was to be his career was quickly set-

[6] Monk, *Life of Richard Bentley*, London, 1833, vol. I, p. 143.

tled, and he drifted unerringly into the scholarly and celibate life. At an age before most men have developed any maturity of thought, he had seen the vision unfold in his mind of that universal force which directs the cosmos,—he had solved one of the most baffling problems of the ages. It is no wonder, then, that his engagement to Miss Storey faded into mutual esteem and that he gave up all idea of a rural and family life. Instead, he remained at Cambridge for nearly forty years, the first seven years *in statu pupillari* until he received the degree of Master of Arts; the remaining time he spent as Fellow of Trinity College and Lucasian Professor of Mathematics.

During the period of his undergraduate days he would be under the direction of his tutor and must have conformed to the customary curriculum and rules of college. As soon as he had received an orderly intellectual training and was relieved from that discipline, he gave free rein to his creative genius and made in rapid succession his masterly discoveries.

Our direct knowledge of Newton's social life in Cambridge, even allowing for his detachment from current affairs, is very scant; and the record of his intellectual pursuits, owing to his secretiveness of mind and his abnormal sensitiveness to criticism, is meagre and confused. He kept no diaries and his later personal notes, except for scientific or theological meditations, are brief and hasty. His associates, in his early days, were evidently not deeply impressed by him, and even in later life there are surprisingly few references to him in contemporary records. We are forced to rely mainly on the occasional reminiscences of Newton, himself, after he had become old, and those which a few of his acquaintances committed to writing after his death. Such reminiscences are always more or less untrustworthy because of the unreliability of the memory and the tendency to magnify the early achievements of subsequently great men in order to make great boys of them as well. In Newton's case this is peculiarly true because of the concerted attempt of the English to make of him a national hero, without a blemish and without a rival, either morally or intellectually.

Picture the effect of Cambridge on a pious, reserved, diffident, and suspicious lad, fresh from the restricted and intimate life of a village and a country school, suddenly thrown into the distracting life of a great university town. Newton would find also a very different Cambridge from the one which his Uncle Ayscough may have described to him. It had but just passed through the hazardous and repressive experiences of the Puritan Commonwealth; and now it had suddenly become boisterous and riotous with the license which had come in with the Restoration.

Newton was not well, or even systematically, trained when he entered college where he was immediately placed in competition with young men from the great public schools. Even his passion and skill for mechanical construction, which would now find expression and distinction in experimental science, was then deemed to be of little significance in the educational plan. The problems, which we are told absorbed his youthful attention, have been carelessly assumed to be exercises in pure mathematics, but it is far more likely that they had to do with the elementary arithmetical calculations relating to simple trains of wheel-work, sun-dials, or other mechanical devices. The fact that he shunned all forms of physical exercise, played no games, and disliked boys, would not endear him to his fellow undergraduates. Neither would he appeal to the more studious men, as he was not sociable, witty, or talkative by nature. In addition, he was further handicapped by the fact that he was a Sizar and paid for his tuition and board by performing such menial tasks as procuring food from the kitchens, running errands, and waiting on his Tutor.[7] Lastly, his strict religious training and temperamental disgust for all forms of moral laxity would further isolate him from society, for the notorious looseness of morals of the Restoration had quickly spread from the Court to London, and from there to the universities. It is no wonder then that we can learn little about his college life, or that he seized every opportunity of a vacation to hasten back to Woolsthorpe where he was sure to find the sympathetic companionship of Miss Storey, of his family, and of his neighbours. We get a very significant glimpse of his life from the fact that he was driven out of his lodgings by the racket and riot of the companions of his room-mate and, while wandering disconsolately through the quadrangle, he met and agreed with another lad in the same trouble to change partners and room together, in order to secure peace and quiet.

[7] This class of students were required to perform various menial services. The following extract from the *Conclusion Book* of Trinity College, while it affords an example of one of their duties, will also serve to illustrate the rampant buoyancy of the academic youth at the period of the Restoration.—"Jan. 16.1660/1. Ordered also that no bachelor of what condition soever, nor any undergraduate, come into the upper butteries, save only a Sizar that is sent to see his Tutor's quantum, and then to stay no longer than is requisite for that purpose, under penalty of 6*d*. for every time; but if any shall leap over the hatch or strike a butler or his servant, upon this account of being hindered to come into the butteries, he shall undergo the censure of the Master and Seniors." Edleston's *Correspondence*, p. xli.

Brewster states that Newton had the advantage of letters of introduction from his uncle, the Rev. James Ayscough, to friends in Cambridge. This seems to be a purely imaginative statement, as we have no record of any such letters or of his uncle having any friends in Cambridge so many years after his graduation. Curiously enough Brewster overlooked other and more influential friends. Stukeley states that when Newton entered college "Dr. Babington was senior Fellow of Trinity, a person of learning and worth. He was own uncle to Mr. Vincent [and thus a close relative to Mr. Clark, the apothecary, with whom Newton had lodged], and that seems to be the reason why he went to Trinity College. The Doctor is said to have had a particular kindness for him which probably was owing to his own ingenuity."[8] Also Henry More, the Platonist and one of the most distinguished men in the University, was a native of Grantham and would probably assist him; later, they became intimate and had a very considerable influence on each other's thought. But Barrow was undoubtedly the most steadfast and important factor in his career: "The Doctor had a vast opinion of his pupil and would frequently say that he truly knew somewhat of mathematics still he reckoned himself but a child in comparison of Newton."[9] With such powerful backing it is not surprising that Newton advanced rapidly in his academic standing.

It is possible from several sources to present a rather more satisfactory narrative of Newton's intellectual activities than of his social life during his undergraduate days. We have a considerable knowledge of the current academic discipline from which to draw inferences; we have some of his own college note-books; and a few valuable anecdotes have been preserved.[10] Conduitt is the source of two anecdotes which have been generally accepted. The first is that Mr. Ayscough gave a copy of Sanderson's *Logic* to his nephew before he left home and told him it would be the first book he would be required to read. He studied it so thoroughly that, when he attended

8 *Portsmouth Collection.* Conduitt also notes that Humphrey Babington was one of the Senior Fellows when Newton was elected Fellow and may have been a Senior before his admission.

9 Stukeley, *Portsmouth Collection.*

10 The principal sources for this period are his nephew-in-law Conduitt's *Memoirs of Newton* which he sent to Fontenelle to correct statements made in his *Eloge* to the French Academy; his MSS. which he collected for a proposed life of Newton but never finished; Pemberton's *View of Newton's Philosophy;* and personal reminiscences of Newton himself which are scattered in a number of books. Brewster, who had access to all these sources, seems to have used little care in pointing out obvious errors and to have joined with Newton's uncritical eulogists in what De Morgan characterises "as their joint attempt to create a self-sufficient genius before there had been any dawn."

the college lectures on the subject, he was more familiar with it than was his tutor, Mr. Pulleyn.[11] So deeply impressed was the tutor by this independent industry that he invited the boy to attend readings of Kepler's *Optics* which he was about to give to some Gentlemen Commoners. Newton without waiting for the class took this book home and so mastered it that when the readings were commenced, the tutor again found the subject had been thoroughly grasped by his pupil.

Conduitt's second anecdote is that, in 1663, Newton bought a book on judicial astrology at the Stourbridge Fair, a festival held each autumn near Cambridge, and he soon found that he could not understand the astronomical problems without some knowledge of trigonometry. In his perplexity, he then bought an English Euclid with an index of all the problems. Having turned to two or three of those which seemed the most likely to be pertinent, he found the demonstrations of the theorems so self-evident that he expressed astonishment that anyone should bother to prove them and he threw it aside "as a trifling book." When he found Euclid to be beneath his notice he set himself to study Descartes's *Analytical Geometry* but gave up the attempt, as he found it to be quite beyond his depth. However, he soon returned to it and, by constantly poring over the text bit by bit, he mastered the whole work without assistance.

These stories are probably based on fact, but they are plainly mixed in their dates and quite misleading. In the first place, however much Newton's mastery of Sanderson's *Logic* before he went to college may have impressed his tutor, it would require a stretch of the imagination to see why the ability to read an elementary textbook on logic should lead to an invitation to attend readings on an advanced treatise on optics. No self-respecting tutor would recommend a boy, who had no knowledge of geometry, trigonometry, or optics, to read Kepler's *Optics*.

The story connecting Euclid and astrology, as it is told, is also patently absurd. It seems to have a basis of fact, as it was vouched for by Newton's friend, Demoivre, but if so, the date must be wrong. The whole course of mathematics at the University was based on Euclid's geometry; it is probable that some acquaintance with it was required for entrance, and it is certain that he must have studied the

[11] Benjamin Pulleyn, Regius Professor of Greek from 1674 to 1686. This professorship was one of the seven royal foundations established by Henry VIII in 1540. Its first incumbent was Erasmus and it has since been graced by a long line of eminent men, among whom are Widdrington, Barrow, Porson, Jebb, and Jackson.

subject during his first two years at College. It is far more likely that his purchases of the Astrology and the Euclid occurred at two different times. It would be better to date back the Euclid incident to his Woolsthorpe period in connection with some mechanical problem which involved a geometrical solution. A desultory student, looking for a royal road to learning, might well have glanced at one or two theorems and, finding them easy, have childishly tossed the book aside as beneath his serious attention.[12]

Since the knowledge of Newton's character and work is derived by most persons solely from Brewster's *Life,* it is necessary to prove, as occasions arise, how uncritically he has confused many of the incidents of his life. For example, in order to prove that Newton owed nothing to his teachers but reached the maturity of his genius entirely by his own unaided effort, Brewster adds this anecdote to the two just discussed. In 1664, three years after his matriculation Newton was elected to a scholarship: "On this occasion he was examined in Euclid by Dr. Barrow, who formed an indifferent opinion of his knowledge, and hence he was led not only to read Euclid, but to form a more favourable estimate of the ancient geometer when he came to the interesting propositions on the equality of parallelograms on the same base and between the same parallels."[13] Dr. Barrow, who was rated as having shown a compass of invention equal, if not superior, to any of his contemporaries, Newton only excepted, and who was Newton's teacher and most generous friend and patron, may very properly have made this criticism when Newton first entered college or when he first attended Barrow's lectures on geometry a year or so later. But, can anyone suppose that Barrow would consent to his election to a scholarship if Newton, after studying mathematics for three years, during which he had mastered Descartes's *Geometry* and the other most advanced analysis of the day, were still

[12] Amongst the books of Newton's library, recently discovered, is a copy of Euclid edited by Barrow. If he ever thought Euclid "a trifling book," he evidently changed his mind and followed Barrow's advice, "for the whole book is full of corrections and notes, most of which give the propositions in algebraic notation, doubtless as a help in its study." *Cf* Greenstreet, *Isaac Newton,* p. 169.

[13] Brewster, Vol. I, p. 24.—It should be noted that Demoivre, from whom the anecdote originated, gave the year as 1663 so the Euclid incident could not have occurred at the scholarship election. In justification of Brewster it should be noted that Conduitt confirmed the incident and added that Barrow did not examine him in Descartes as he did not imagine anyone could master it before knowing Euclid and Newton was too modest to mention it. As Conduitt did not collect his materials till after Newton's death we find a number of errors in dates and contradictions in facts about these early events. My criticism of Brewster does not rest on his inclusion of such anecdotes but on the fact that he does not observe and correct their errors.

deficient in Euclidean geometry? And what is there either especially attractive or difficult in the propositions on parallelograms such as to arouse his interest or to change a priggish opinion that "the ancient geometer" was a trifler?

This legend, that Newton had not studied Euclid during his undergraduate course and that he had read Descartes's *Geometry* when he first entered college and before he had any mathematical knowledge, is a striking instance of Brewster's uncritical attitude towards the Newtonian myth. It is especially glaring in this instance as on the preceding page he had quoted a statement of Newton which discredits the anecdote.

The fact of the matter is, Newton early in his career became one of the great masters of the classical, or Euclidean, geometry both on account of a passion for that form of mathematical expression and because of the influence of Barrow. Pemberton, who knew Newton intimately in his old age, has given us a valuable and convincing statement of his personal taste in mathematics. He says: "I found he had read fewer of the modern mathematicians than one could have expected. . . . I have often heard him censure the handling geometrical subjects by algebraic calculations. He frequently praised Slusius, Barrow and Huygens for not being influenced by the false taste, which then began to prevail. . . . But Sir Isaac Newton has several times particularly recommended to me Huygens's style and manner. He thought him the most elegant of any mathematical writer of modern times, and the most just imitator of the ancients. Of their taste, and form of demonstration Sir Isaac always professed himself a great admirer: I have heard him even censure himself for not following them yet *more closely* than he did; and speak with regret of his mistake at the *beginning of his mathematical studies,* in applying himself to the works of Descartes and other algebraic writers, before he had *considered the elements of Euclid with that attention,* which so excellent a writer deserves."[14]

Such a detailed discussion of Newton's personal taste in mathematics and the time when he studied Euclid was useful, in my opinion, as it afforded an excellent and concrete illustration of the care with which our sources for a life of Newton must be examined if a

[14] Pemberton, *A View of Sir Isaac Newton's Philosophy.* Preface. The portion italicised by me clearly proves that Newton had studied Euclid before he undertook to read Descartes, and regretted that he had not *fully* mastered that author before he turned to others. When such a geometer as Newton regrets that he had not considered Euclid with the attention the subject deserved we should take into account what standard of consideration would be in his mind.

just and accurate biography is to be written. The importance of such a careful consideration has been excellently expressed by Leibniz: "It is an extremely useful thing to have knowledge of the true origins of memorable discoveries, especially those that have been found not by accident but by dint of meditation. It is not so much that thereby history may attribute to each man his own discoveries and that others should be encouraged to earn like commendation, as that the art of making discoveries should be extended by considering noteworthy examples of it."[15]

When we are told that nothing is known of Newton's studies, the very obvious fact is overlooked that every undergraduate was required to follow an outlined and graded course of instruction under the direct guidance of his tutor, and there is no reason to suppose that Newton was an exception to the rule. In those days a tutor not only stood *in loco parentis* to his pupils, which means that he had the right to punish for disobedience, but he also taught them personally.[16] From Newton's note-books, some of his letters and conversations, and from our knowledge of the course of study then in vogue, we can give a reasonably accurate and full statement of his undergraduate work. As for science, the most important of his studies, we can give an almost complete account.

From Newton's own notes we know that he spent the first two years at college learning arithmetic, Euclid, and trigonometry. He also read or listened to lectures on the Copernican system of astronomy. For most of his work after the Easter Term in 1663, he was under the direction of Barrow,[17] the newly appointed Lucasian Professor, who also taught him natural philosophy and, most significant of all, optics. This science, which for the first time offered to him a serious opportunity to use his experimental skill, evidently fascinated him and first brought out his latent powers of invention. In addition to following the course of lectures on light, he read Kepler's *Optics* probably during the vacation, and that study was undoubtedly the cause of his interest in telescopes and the properties of light. His mastery of the subject was so thorough that, when Barrow shortly after-

[15] *Historia et Origo Calculi Differentialis*. *Cf.* Child, *Early MSS. of Leibniz*, p. 22.

[16] "The Statutes of 1560 which were in force till 1844 state: Pupilli Tutoribus pereant, honorumque paternum ac reverentiam deferant, quorum studium labor et diligentia in illis ad pietatem et scientiam informandis ponitur. Tutores sedulo quae docenda sunt doceant; quaeque etiam agenda instruant admoneantque." Greenstreet, p. 146.

[17] While the College records show that Pulleyn was his tutor when he entered Trinity, it is probable that Barrow took over that office. I found in the *Portsmouth Collection* the statement by Stukeley that Dr. Barrow was his tutor.

wards published his lectures, he turned to his youthful pupil for criticism and revision of the manuscript.

From a personal note-book (which contains an entry on the seventh page dated Jan. 1663/4), we have definite information when he first turned to the new analytical geometry invented by Descartes in which the properties of lines and surfaces are expressed by algebraic equations. We also learn that he attained his knowledge by studying the standard texts on the subject by Oughtred,[18] van Schooten,[19] Vieta,[20] and Wallis,[21] as well as Descartes. During the dispute, many years later, with Leibniz on the discovery of the calculus, Newton made the following entry which ought to settle the question as it was not dependent on memory.

"July 4, 1699.—By consulting an account of my expenses at Cambridge, in the years 1663 and 1664, I find that in the year 1664, a little before Christmas, I, being then a Senior Sophister, bought Schooten's Miscellanies and Cartes's Geometry, (having read this geometry and Oughtred's Clavis clean over half a year before), and borrowed Wallis's works, and by consequence made these annotations out of Schooten and Wallis, in winter between the years 1664 and 1665. At such time I found the method of Infinite Series; and in summer 1665, being forced from Cambridge by the plague, I computed the area of the hyperbola at Boothby, in Lincolnshire, to two and fifty figures by the same method.

Is. Newton."

Thus Newton progressed naturally and systematically from the mastery of algebra and geometry to the newer forms of analytical geometry and trigonometry which he first began to study in the sum-

18 William Oughtred (1574–1660). His most important work which long remained a classic text is his *Arithmeticæ in numeris et speciebus instituto, clavis est.* It contains his rule for abridged multiplication which is still taught in arithmetic courses. His other works are collected under the title: *Opuscula mathematica hactenus inedita.*

19 Frans van Schooten (d. 1661) wrote elementary textbooks to popularise the algebraic geometry of Vieta and Descartes.

20 François Viète or Vieta (1540–1603). Published in his *Isagoge in artem analyticam* (1591) an explanation how algebra could be applied to geometrical problems. Used letters to express both known and unknown terms and a notation for powers of terms. From his time elementary trigonometry was familiar to mathematicians.

21 John Wallis (1616–1703), Savilian Professor of Geometry in Oxford, was undoubtedly the foremost English mathematician of his time. His most important work, the *Arithmetica Infinitorum,* displays and greatly extends the methods of analysis introduced by Descartes and Cavalieri. It became the standard work on the subject and is constantly referred to by Fermat, Barrow, Newton, and Leibniz. His solution for finding the areas of curves by the use of infinite series was so close to the discovery of the calculus that Newton and Leibniz had principally to clarify and advance his method into a formal system.

mer of 1664 or about half a year before he graduated. There are also amongst his notes calculations relating to musical scales, and observations on the refraction of light, the grinding of lenses and their errors, which bore fruit later; and lastly problems on extracting mathematical roots which ultimately led to his discovery of the Binomial Theorem. In all this work, he was greatly helped, as Stukeley tells us, by his dexterity in drawing and handicraft. The extraordinary thing to bear in mind, in this catalogue of his undergraduate studies, is not so much that Newton thoroughly mastered these subjects as that he so digested them and meditated upon their inherent possibilities that they awoke his creative powers. In a few short years, each subject led directly and unerringly to a masterpiece of genius, and, a still more astonishing fact, these years provided the germ of all his discoveries.

Before leaving the subject of Newton's scientific training, we should pause for a moment to give a sketch of the extraordinary life of Barrow who, if he just failed to become one of the "Immortals," should be honoured as the intellectual father of a Newton. No youthful genius could have had a more excellent teacher and patron than did Newton, who owed to him his early training in science, philosophy and religion, his scholastic honours, and his professorship. If the facts could be known we undoubtedly should have had a charming record of kind acts and wise advice.

Isaac Barrow was born in 1630 in London, and was educated at the famous Charterhouse. Endowed with a restless body and a vivid mind, he so plagued his teachers and was so troublesome at home that his father, with lack of parental vision, prayed that if it pleased God to take away any of his children he could best spare Isaac. From the Charterhouse he went to Cambridge and became Bachelor of Arts, Trinity College, in 1648, and Fellow in 1649. He resided there till 1655 when he was driven out of the country by the Independents because of his political and religious views. The next four years were spent in travelling in Eastern Europe where he was attacked by pirates and had other exciting adventures. Shortly before the Restoration, when conditions became safe for him, he returned to England; was ordained to the ministry and elected professor of Greek in Cambridge. In 1662 he became professor of geometry in Gresham College; a position which he held for only one year as he returned to Cambridge where he had been chosen to be the first Lucasian Professor of Mathematics, a chair newly founded by Henry

Lucas. It is the second oldest of the non-royal foundations and one of the most illustrious chairs of science in the world; besides the first two, Barrow and Newton, its roll includes such eminent mathematical physicists as Whiston, Airy, Babbage, Stokes, and its present incumbent, Sir Joseph Larmor. Barrow resigned the professorship, after six years, to Newton whom he frankly acknowledged to be his superior and devoted the remainder of his life to theology. He was an excellent Master of Trinity from 1672 until his early death in 1677. He was noted for his strength, courage, and wit, and was a great favourite of Charles II. Courtiers could not forgive him for being slovenly in dress and an inveterate smoker. In appearance he was small, lean, and pale.[22]

Our knowledge of Newton's other collegiate work is not so full and, fortunately, it is not so important. We have to depend on our general information as to the subjects considered most valuable in the seventeenth century, and on casual hints made by Newton.

He certainly had a thorough grounding in Latin.[23] He would read the standard authors in that language and would listen to expositions and criticisms on their meaning and style. Much time would be given to grammar and composition. But, in addition to the classical literature, the student of the day would learn mediæval Latin as a living tongue as most works of importance were written in it and it formed a common medium of speech between scholars of different countries. It was, indeed, a most convenient, flexible, and universal form of communication; and one of the most unfortunate barriers to the interchange of scholarly work was raised when the growing influence of nationalism induced humanists and scientists to write, each in his native tongue. The burden, today, of learning indifferently well half a dozen languages as tools of scholarship has been discovered too late. An international language has been lost, and we turn a

[22] His most important scientific works were, a complete edition of Euclid, 1660; *Lectiones mathematicae,* delivered 1664–6, and published 1683; *Lectiones opticae et geometricae,* 1669. Barrow was also a great master of English and his Sermons rank with the best in the language.

[23] Hearne several times in his *Diaries* affirms that Newton "does not understand a bit of classical learning . . . nor can he, as I hear, write Latin." But Hearne was rabidly anti-Newton, both as an Oxonian and as an advocate of Hooke. He also in his *Diaries,* accuses Newton of not being able to keep his accounts at the Mint, of being a parodoxical chronologist, of having stolen Hooke's ideas on gravitation, etc. *Cf.* Hearne's *Diaries,* London, 1869, vol. II, pp. 216, 245, 277, 309, 310.—But Newton's library contained most of the Latin classics and an extraordinary collection of the Church Fathers. As most of the Greek authors were in editions giving a Latin translation it is probable that his knowledge of Greek was not thorough. Much of his correspondence is in fluent Latin and I found only one document where the language was defective; Conduitt states that he could converse in it.

deaf ear to the cacophonous inventions of modern enthusiasts who try to create new ones:

"Per lo cui mal coto
pure un linguaggio nel mondo non s'usa."

Newton also learned Greek but probably not so thoroughly, as interest in it had declined. He, apparently, if we can trust one of his note-books, learned the Hebrew alphabet and may have been able to puzzle out portions of the Old Testament in the original. Of German he knew nothing and he confessed, in a letter to Collins, that he was so deficient in French that the gift of a book in that language would be useless.

Both classical and Biblical history was much cultivated and carefully taught, as it was the common belief that all the examples of character and manners were better illustrated in ancient than in modern times. There was, I think, in Newton's day not one university professorship of modern history, as the lectureship founded by Fulke Greville had lapsed, and the students depended on their tutors for such current historical facts as were thought worth emphasising. Much attention was paid to logic and ethics, but in philosophy Cambridge still held fast to the mediæval interpretation of Aristotle and he would acquire little of the mechanistic philosophy of Descartes.

The period of three years, 1664–1666, is the most crucial one in Newton's life; during it, his power of scientific invention was at its highest and the foundation for all his future work was laid. He seems to have suffered from an illness during the year 1664, brought on, as he thought, by excessive work and the late hours he kept while observing the comet of that year. He also observed and noted a double halo about the moon.[24] From this illness, he is reported to have learned to keep early hours; but "early hours" must be thought of as an elastic term, for he certainly kept to no regular habits when he was engrossed in work. In the same year he was elected a Scholar of Trinity College with forty-four others. It was, as previously noted, at this examination that Barrow is reported to have found him deficient in Euclid.

In addition to the above facts of that year, it is stated in Conduitt's

[24] He afterwards referred to this phenomenon in his *Optics* (Bk. II, part IV, Obs. 13) and gave a correct explanation of it. He noted that he had observed the haloes Feb. 19th, 1664, at dusk and having, in 1692, seen the same effect from a vase of stagnant water, he assigned the cause to the light reflected from the moon's surface, and then refracted from drops of water in the air to the observer's eyes.

MSS. that Newton bought a prism at the Stourbridge Fair in August, 1665, to test Descartes's theory of light and soon discovered that author's error and his own true theory; the authority for this statement is an item in an expense-book which has since been lost.[25]

In January, 1664/5, three and a half years after his matriculation, Newton took his Bachelor of Arts degree with twenty-five other Trinity men.[26] It is unfortunate, Edleston notes, that the rank in graduation of the most illustrious candidate from Trinity College for a degree cannot be ascertained, as the *Ordo Senioratatis,* corresponding to the present Tripos list, of the Bachelor of Arts for the year is provokingly omitted in the Grace Book. His pupillage was finished; he had mastered his mathematical tools and his inventive genius had awakened. A few months later he committed to writing his first ideas on the method of fluxions, and occasionally placed dots over his algebraic symbols to indicate an infinitesimal quantity. While he probably did not attack at this time any original problems by his new method, and although the subject may have been in the air, yet it was an achievement of the greatest significance for a youth of his age to advance beyond the work of the veteran Wallis. He had, in effect, discovered a new and powerful mathematical method, which lay concealed in Wallis's work, worthy of a new and distinct form of notation. Judging from items in an expense-book given below, he relaxed somewhat the austere discipline of his life and joined in some of the festivities incident to graduation; at least he was at the tavern several times and twice lost money at cards. He had passed more than three years in hard study under the direction of others; his mind was filled with new ideas and for one of his temperament there was need for leisure, a time when he could arrange and digest his thoughts.

This golden opportunity came to him in the autumn of this year when the great plague[27] closed the University and forced him to live in seclusion at Woolsthorpe for the larger part of two years. There

[25] According to Edleston (*Cf.* infra) he left Cambridge before August and if so could not have attended the Fair.

[26] Apparently there was a rumour that Newton did not distinguish himself in his examinations. I found the following anecdote in a letter written by Stukeley to Dr. Mead: "I heard it as a tradition when I was student at Cambridge that when Sir Isaac stood for his bachelor of arts degree he was put to second posing, or lost his greats, as they call it, which is looked upon as disgraceful." *Cf. Portsmouth Collection.*

[27] The great bubonic plagues, known as the Black Death and so vividly described in Manzoni's *I promessi sposi,* swept over Europe in the fourteenth century and are reported to have killed one-fourth of the whole population. Successive outbreaks recurred in the fifteenth and sixteenth centuries, but they grew less frequent and severe in the seven-

are discrepancies in the statements as to when he was in Woolsthorpe, but the most reliable information has been given by Edleston who made a thorough examination of the College records.[28] With some slight chance of error, we can fix the absence of Newton from Cambridge and residence at home, omitting possible visits elsewhere, as being from about August first, 1665, to Lady Day, March 25th, 1666; and from June 22nd, 1666 to probably March 25th, 1667. As the plague decreased during the winter he may have been in Cambridge part of the period from March 25th to June 22nd, 1666; and as he received only five weeks' commons in the Lent Term of 1667, he may have returned to the University at any time after the middle of February, but it is likely that College did not reopen until the beginning of the Easter Term of that year.

There are no other examples of achievement in the history of science to compare with that of Newton during those two golden years. That a youth, who had shown no decided precocity of intellect in his boyhood and who had followed his college course with no more distinction or notice than have thousands of other collegians, should immediately after graduation retire to a lonely village and there, unaided, make three capital discoveries in science, is nothing short of the miraculous. The first of these inventions was the mathematical method of fluxions, the basis of all modern mathematics and the instrument by which all physical problems involving force and motion are now solved. The second was the law of the composition of light from which he later constructed a real science of optics. And the third was the law of universal gravitation.

While the first and second led to great results, they do not stir the imagination so deeply. But the conception of a universal force,

teenth century until the Great Plague of 1664–1665. Both Pepys and Defoe have given detailed and graphic pictures of its effects. Its onset was slow, until, in the summer of 1665, it began to spread more rapidly and became so terrible that in London alone the mortality was above 31,000. The following winter it declined, but it reappeared the next year in a less severe form.

[28] The College was dismissed on August 8, 1665, at the breaking out of the plague as shown by the *Conclusion Book:* "A month's commons allowed to all Fellows and scholars which now go into the country upon occasion of the pestilence." But Newton's name does not appear in the list of those who received *extra commons* for six and one-half weeks on the occasion, and Edleston concludes he must have left Cambridge before then. The students were again dismissed on June 22, 1666, on the reappearance of the plague. The Fellows and scholars were allowed compensation for their commons during their absence. Newton received on this account:

3*s*. 4*d*. weekly, for 13 weeks in the quarter ending Mich[s], 1666.
.... 12 .... Dec. 21, "
.... 5 .... Lady Day, 1667

Edleston, p. xlii.

as it slowly developed in his mind for a quarter of a century, and finally produced his incomparable *Principia,* is a unique achievement. Laplace, who disdained to praise other men, acknowledged that, since there can be but one cosmos, so there can be discovered but once its dominating law; and to Newton fate presented this gift. All others must be satisfied either to have prepared the way or to have extended his results; he must stand alone on the summit. To Newton, and to very few other mortals, could the verse of Halley be applied without arousing an inward sentiment of protest lest the gods be brought lower to earth.

"Nec fas est propius mortali attingere Divos."

Newton—when he was asked how his mind conceived and worked out his ideas—modestly replied that if he had any genius not common to other men it lay in the fact that when an idea first came to him, he pondered over it incessantly until its final results became apparent. One of the most puzzling traits of his character was his seemingly total lack of desire to disclose to others the fruits of his meditation. He never once acknowledged that he owed any obligation to the world or to the University which had so generously supported him. The consequences of fame, which brought with it the probability of criticism, were so repugnant that he time and again protested that he would abandon science or would, at least, withhold his work from publication until after his death. It may be said, without great exaggeration, that it was as difficult to force his mind to divulge his ideas as it had been for him to create them.

Although the detailed discussion of the discoveries Newton made during the two years he lived in Woolsthorpe will be postponed to later chapters, yet they should be noticed briefly now in order to fix their chronological order. During these two years he wrote five short papers on his new application of infinite series to a general method of solving the properties of curved lines and the areas included by them.[29] This method, which he later developed into what he called fluxions, is now known as the differential and integral calculus.[30] His first paper was written at Cambridge with the date,

[29] These papers were written by him in a common-place book and are listed in the youthful papers of Newton in the *Catalogue of the Portsmouth Collection,* pp. 1 and 2.

[30] The Rev. Dr. Derham, who was acquainted with Newton for thirty years, stated that Newton told him he had thoughts on fluxions when he was a Junior at College but was stopped by the plague. They came back to him when he read Mercator's *Logarithmotechnia* and Wallis's work.

May 20th, 1665; as the method depended on the summation of infinitesimal arcs of curves, he adopted the distinguishing notation of placing a dot over an algebraic symbol when it denoted such an infinitesimal quantity. On November 13th of the same year he finished a second paper at Woolsthorpe in which he solved problems involving tangents to curves and radii of curvature. He also found the area of one hyperbola, the first time it had ever been done, and with boyish enthusiasm he carried the calculation to fifty-two significant figures. The following year he prepared three more papers, the first probably in Cambridge, dated May 16th; the second in October; and the third in November while at home. So far as we know, he did not take anyone into his confidence; and while he is supposed to have used fluxions when he was engaged on the *Principia,* he destroyed all evidence of it by reworking the problems in the method of the classic geometry. Some of his results were published years later against his wish, and it was not until the end of the century that he made any public statement regarding them.

His second great discovery lay in the field of optics. Newton, as we have seen, had been interested in the Copernican theory and he had also read Kepler's treatise on light. We may be sure also that Barrow had taught his pupils the results of Descartes's important work on lenses and the telescope. The problem of the telescope was just such a one as would attract Newton; it involved both theoretical geometry and practical applications and must have revived the joys of his childish days when he was absorbed in constructing mechanical toys. He had, as early as 1664, bought a prism and had made some observations on the refraction of light. Now, while he was away from Cambridge on account of the plague, he prepared himself seriously to study the problem of lenses and the refracting telescope.

In the astonishingly short period of three months, he practised the exceedingly difficult operation of grinding lenses of surfaces other than spherical; he began an elaborate series of experiments with a prism to prove his capital discovery of the unequal refrangibility of the colours of the spectrum which mixed together give us the sensation of white light; he arrived at the correct deduction that lenses, even if so ground as to correct spherical aberration, would still have the defect of confusing the image by chromatic aberration, because the various colours would be refracted to different foci. As this seemed to involve an insuperable defect in telescopes using lenses, he left off his glass grinding and turned his attention to constructing an instrument equipped with concave mirrors instead of lenses, since chromatic aberration is not produced by reflected light. Such a reflecting telescope, as it is called, had been proposed and its details calculated by James Gregory of Scotland and by Cassegrain of France. Gregory was the first inventor of the instrument[31] and had commissioned Reeves and Cox, expert glass-grinders, to make for him the necessary mirrors but, as he was then preparing to go abroad, he neglected to attend to the matter and the telescope was never made. Newton frankly acknowledged that he had read the account of the Gregorian telescope and then explained why his own invention was an improvement on Gregory's and Cassegrain's arrangements of mirrors. He had hardly begun to construct a reflector before he was again "forced from Cambridge [in June] by the intervening plague, and it was more than two years before he proceeded further."[32] We get an interesting side-light on his habit of profound absorption when spurred by the pressure of new ideas; "to quicken his faculties and fix his attention, he confined himself to a small quantity of bread, during all the time, with a little sack and water, of which, without any regulation, he took as he found a craving or failure of spirits."

There is less uncertainty, although it too presents its problems, in regard to Newton's discovery of the law of gravitation. Conduitt states in his *Memoirs* sent to Fontenelle: "In the year 1665, when he retired to his own estate, on account of the plague, he first thought of his system of gravity, which he hit upon by observing an apple fall from a tree."[33] The story of the falling apple, as the trifling incident which first directed his thought to gravitation, is supported by Voltaire who had the story directly from Catherine Barton, Newton's favourite niece who lived with him for many years. "Un jour, en l'année 1666, Newton retiré à la campagne, et voyant tomber des fruits d'un arbre, à ce que m'a conté sa nièce [Madame Conduitt], se laissa aller à une méditation profonde sur la cause qui entraîne ainsi tous les corps vers une ligne qui, si elle était prolongée, passerait à

[31] Gregory described his reflecting telescope in his *Optica Promota* published in 1663. He had no idea of chromatic aberration but praised his instrument on the grounds that it would make telescopes shorter and less unwieldy than they had become.

[32] Edleston, p. xxi.

[33] "The apple tree is now remaining, 1727. [It later became weakened by age and was blown down in a storm.] In 1666 Sir Isaac was here [Woolsthorpe], for in that year he attended the Heralds visitation at Grantham, and entered three descents of his family, styling himself 'of Woolsthorpe, Æt, 23, Anno 1666.' Whilst he was here probably his half sister Hannah Smith was married to Mr. Pilkington." Turnor, p. 160.

peu près par le centre de la terre."[34] We have definite evidence that Newton was in Woolsthorpe in the late summer and early autumn of both these years, and this prime discovery was made in one of them. Brewster decides on 1665 in agreement with Conduitt, and Edleston follows Voltaire in placing 1666 as the date. Apparently, at this time, he made a rough calculation and satisfied himself that such a force would account for Kepler's laws of planetary motion. But, so far as we can learn, he dropped the subject and we hear nothing more about it for many years. The probable reason is that he immersed himself in his work on light. Judging however from his habit, the law of gravitation was frequently a part of his meditation.

Newton returned to Cambridge early in 1667 and it is probable that the University opened, the virulence of the plague having subsided, on Lady Day, March 25th, as that day marked the beginning of the Easter Term. On October first he was elected a Minor Fellow.[35] There were nine fellowships vacant that year, as no elections had been held in 1665 and 1666. One of them was made by the death of the poet, Cowley; two of the other vacancies were caused by Fellows falling down staircases—whether the result of defects in the stairs or of excessive conviviality may be left to the imagination. It is not probable that Barrow was one of the examiners as he was only thirteenth in the order of seniority of Fellows, and the first eight only usually examined for so important an occasion. One of the Senior Fellows was absent and another, Barton, had been ejected from college in the preceding June on the ground of insanity; even so Barrow only became temporarily the eleventh in order. A description of the examinations of the period is given in a memorandum by a student about twenty-five years later: "The fellowes on the 3[d] day of their sitting must have a theme given them by the Master, w[h] the chappel-clerk fetcheth for them: they sit 3 dayes being excused the 4th for their theme. They sit from 7 till 10, & from one to 4, each writing his name his age & his country; as doe the scholars, & also y[e] Mas-

[34] Voltaire, *Elémens de philosophie de Newton,* Pt. III, Ch. III.

[35] "The statutes only prescribe, that the persons chosen must be under the standing of Master of Arts. From the date of the statutes, 1560, to the year 1667, the Fellows were chosen promiscuously from the three years of Bachelors: but it is to be observed, that although the elections were sometimes held annually, they were more commonly biennial, or triennial. It was in 1667, the year made forever memorable in College annals, by the admission of Sir Isaac Newton to a fellowship, that the candidates were first confined to the third year of Bachelors. This continued the practice in all subsequent years, with two or three exceptions, till 1752." After that date Middle Bachelors were admitted to the competition; since 1819, Junior Bachelors have been permitted to be candidates. Monk's *Bentley,* Vol. II, p. 248.

ters of Arts, wch papers are carried to ye Master & Vice-M^{r}, the first morning so soon as all have written . . . Octob. I . . . by ye tolling of ye little bell at 8 in ye morning ye seniours are called & the day after at one o'clock to swear them y^{t} are chosen."[36]

As was the custom in Trinity College, rooms were assigned to the new Fellows in the order of their seniority as soon as any fell vacant; the room so assigned to a person was called his "seniority" or "fellowship chamber." In the schedule for September 30, 1667, bearing the signature of John Pearson, the Master, the last line runs: "to Sr Newton—Spirituall chamber." Edleston has been unable to find what room was so designated, but he conjectured that "it was the ground-floor apartment next the Chapel, at the north-east corner of the great Court." Although this was officially the room assigned to him, it is quite possible that he did not occupy it, as the Fellows had the privilege of sub-letting and receiving the rent.[37]

A few months later, on March 16, 1668, Newton was admitted as Major Fellow; and on July 7 of the same year, he was created Master of Arts, the twenty-third on the list of 148 signed by the Senior Proctor, Thomas Burnet, author of *Theoria Telluris Sacra.*[38] When he resigned his fellowship, shortly before December 21, 1701, he had risen to tenth on the list and, if he had held the fellowship for about two years longer, he would have succeeded to one of the eight senior fellowships.[39]

Thus, in seven or eight years, Newton had risen from exigent circumstances and the menial rank of a Sizar to affluence and the coveted position of Fellow of Trinity College, to be followed in a year by the Lucasian professorship of mathematics, one of the highest honours in the scientific world. Brewster echoes the old cry of the disgrace to the nation, that such a man was permitted to remain in the poverty and obscurity of a university position for so many years. There have been many cases where eminent men have been worried by poverty and lack of appreciation, but he fortunately escaped such a fate. In the first place, the rank and esteem of one engaged in the scholarly life are not, nor should they be, estimated by financial rewards; and in the second place, he was from now on in the permanent possession of a comfortable income with the freedom from all those harassing demands on his time which are the lot of those in commercial or public service; he had won the precious leisure to occupy himself fully in his meditations and scholarly work; and to

[36] Edleston, Preface, p. xlii. [37] *Ibid.*, p. xliii. [38] *Ibid.*, p. xliv. [39] *Ibid.*, p. lxxxii.

the end of his long life he enjoyed a respect and an admiration which have rarely been accorded to any human being.

No one should picture Newton as a typically abstracted scholar. He was scrupulously exact and regular in his business matters. He kept detailed and minute accounts of his expenses and his receipts; as an instance, he was only twice in arrears of the steward's bills. Though he was remarkably generous in gifts and loans, especially to his family, he steadily increased his fortune until he died a very rich man. While he was at the University he enjoyed excellent lodgings and board. From his fellowship, he received his share of the annual dividends accruing from the income of the College, his share of the pandoxator's dividend which came from the receipts of the College bake-house and brew-house, his allowance "pro pane et potu" of 3*s.* 4*d.* weekly during residence, and his livery allowance of £2 a year. In addition to the above, he had about £100 a year from his professorship, and £80 from his estates.[40] De Morgan estimated his income from all sources to have been not less than £250, over and above his board and lodging.[41]

While it may be difficult and misleading to translate the living value of an income at that time into terms of modern conditions, we can obtain a pretty fair knowledge of living expenses from contemporaneous diaries and letters. For example, a note in Pepys's *Diary* tells us that Phineas Pett, Clerk of the Cheque, a good position in the civil service of the navy, had a salary of £120.[42] Pepys refers to his own expenses, in 1662, "I find that I had spent above £250 this last half year."[43] Now the genial diarist lived well in a good house in London where he supported a wife and servants. Yet in spite of his complaint of extravagance, he had spent only at the rate of twice Newton's income. A century later, Dr. Johnson lived comfortably, maintaining a house and several inmates, on a pension of £300. The most significant statement I have found to support my opinion is a letter of David Hume written in 1751 in which he said: "I have £50 a year, a £100 worth of books, great store of linens and fine clothes, and near £100 in my pocket; along with order, frugality, a strong spirit of independence, good health, a contented humour, and an unabating love of study. In these circumstances I must esteem

40 Edleston, Preface, pp. lxxxii–lxxxiv.

41 De Morgan, *Essays,* p. 43. My estimate agrees with that figure. Col. de Villamil has recently in his *Newton: the Man* made an elaborate study of Newton's income which he places at £200.

42 Pepys's *Diary,* Vol. I, p. 64.

43 *Ibid.,* Vol. I, p. 261.

myself one of the happy and fortunate."[44] This evidence seems conclusive that Newton's income of at least £200, with board and lodging, was amply sufficient for a bachelor living in Cambridge, unless he had to use a considerable portion of it to support his relatives. This opinion is strengthened by the fact that the year after his fellowship was continued in 1676, and without any known addition to his income, he contributed £40 to the fund for building the Library, a sum in excess of his income from the fellowship.

It is probable that while Newton was in Woolsthorpe, or shortly after his return to Cambridge, the engagement with Miss Storey was broken off, or what is more likely, faded away. If he had married, it would have been necessary for him to renounce his university career; by this time he must have foreseen the bent of his mind and that a brilliant career was before him. A fellowship was immediately in sight; and Barrow, who had discovered his mathematical genius, may already have intimated his approaching retirement from the Lucasian professorship and his decision to recommend him as a successor. Certainly, there was no distressing rupture; Miss Storey remained his life-long friend; he aided her with money and gifts and, in her old age, she fondly recalled the incidents connected with her youthful lover.

With leisure and freedom from the routine of college lessons, Newton greatly extended his reading and his interests. We learn from his expense book and other sources, that he bought the *History of the Royal Society,* the *Philosophical Intelligences,* Gunter's *Book and Sector for Surveying,* Bacon's *Miscellany,* materials and apparatus for lenses, for the study of electricity and magnetism, and for chemistry. He took occasional trips to London and elsewhere, and engaged in a mild sort of social life.

We fortunately have preserved for us one of the few personal letters of Newton which I shall quote in full in spite of its length. In most of his correspondence he confined himself to the discussion of scientific or impersonal questions, and rarely alluded to his private affairs.[45]

[44] Burton's *Life of Hume,* Vol. I, p. 342.

[45] This letter was addressed to his college friend, Francis Aston, who was about to start on a foreign tour, and is printed in Macclesfield's *Collection,* Vol. II, p. 292.—Aston afterwards became Secretary of the Royal Society in 1678, and his manner of resigning that office in 1686 indicates that he did not profit from the cautious counsels of his friend. His successor Halley wrote to a friend: "On St. Andrew's day last, being our anniversary day of election, Mr. Pepys was continued President, Mr. Aston, Secretary, and Dr. Tancred Robinson chosen in the room of Mr. Musgrave; everybody seemed satisfied, and no dis-

Newton to Aston

Trin. Coll. Cambr. May 18, 1669.

Fr.

Since in your letter you give me so much liberty of spending my judgement about what may be to your advantage in travelling, I shall do it more freely than perhaps would otherwise have been decent. First, therefore, I will lay down some general rules, most of which I believe you have considered already; but if any of them be new to you, they may excuse the rest; if none at all, yet it is my punishment more in writing them than yours in reading them.

When you come into any fresh company, 1. Observe their humours. 2. Suit your own carriage thereto, by which insinuation you will make their converse more free and open. 3. Let your discourse be more in queries and doubtings than peremptory assertions or disputings, it being the design of travellers to learn, not teach; besides, it will persuade your acquaintance that you have the greater esteem of them, and so make them more ready to communicate what they know to you; whereas nothing sooner occasions disrespect and quarrels than peremptoriness. You will find little or no advantage in seeming wiser or much more ignorant than your company.

4. Seldom discommend any thing, though never so bad, or do it but moderately, lest you be unexpectedly forced to an unhandsome retraction. 'Tis safer to commend any thing more than it deserves, than to discommend any thing so much as it deserves. For commendations meet not so often with oppositions, or at least are not usually so ill resented by men that think otherwise, as discommendations. And you will insinuate into men's favour by nothing sooner than seeming to approve and commend what they like; but beware of doing it by a comparison.

5. If you be affronted, 'tis better in a foreign country to pass it by in silence, or with a jest, though with some dishonour, than to endeavour revenge: for in the first case, your credit is ne'er the

content appear'd anywhere, when on a sudden Mr. Aston, as I suppose willing to gain better terms of reward from the Society than formerly, on December 9th, in Council, declared that he would not serve them as Secretary; and therefore desired them to provide some other to supply that office; and that after such a passionate manner, that I fear he has lost several of his friends by it." Weld, *Hist. Roy. Soc.*, Vol. I, p. 303. In spite of the outbreak, the Council made him a gratuity of £60. Shortly afterwards Newton wrote to him that he and Mr. Charles Montague had failed to establish a philosophical society at Cambridge. Aston communicated a paper to the Royal Society which was published in 1692. At his death, he bequeathed an estate in Lincolnshire, to the Royal Society, still in its possession, and personal property to the value of £445. Weld, Vol. I, p. 428.

worse when you return into England, or come into other company that have not heard of the quarrel; but in the second case, you may bear the marks of your quarrel while you live, if you outlive it at all. But if you find yourself unavoidably engaged, 'tis best, I think, if you can command your passion and language, to keep them pretty evenly at some certain moderate pitch, not much heightening them, to exasperate your adversary or provoke his friends, nor letting them grow overmuch dejected to make him insult. In a word, if you can keep reason above passion, that and watchfulness will be your best defendants. To which purpose you may consider, that though such excuses as this,—He provoked me so much I could not forbear,—may pass amongst friends, yet amongst strangers they are insignificant, and only argue a traveller's weakness.

To these I may add some general heads for enquiries or observations, such as at present I can think on. As, 1. To observe the policies, wealth, and state affairs of nations, so far as a solitary traveller may conveniently do: 2. Their impositions upon all sorts of people, trades, or commodities, that are remarkable: 3. Their laws and customs, how far they differ from ours: 4. Their trades and arts, wherein they excel or come short of us in England: 5. Such fortifications as you shall meet with, their fashion, strength, and advantages for defense, and other such military affairs as are considerable: 6. The power and respect belonging to their degrees of nobility or magistracy. 7. It will not be time misspent to make a catalogue of the names and excellencies of those men that are most wise, learned, and esteemed in any nation. 8. Observe the mechanism and manner of guiding ships. 9. Observe the products of nature in several places, especially in mines, with the circumstances of mining and of extracting metals or minerals out of their ore and refining them; and, if you meet with any transmutations out of one species into another, (as out of iron into copper, out of any metal into quicksilver, out of one salt into another, or into an insipid body, etc.,) those above all others will be worth your noting, being the most luciferous, and many times lucriferous experiments[46] too in philosophy: 10. The prices of diet and other things: 11. And the staple commodities of places.

These generals, (such as at present I could think of,) if they will serve for nothing else, yet they may assist you in drawing up a model to regulate your travels by.

[46] This is one of the stock phrases of the alchemists to distinguish those experiments which advanced knowledge from those which added to the income.

As for particulars, these that follow are all that I can now think of, viz, Whether at Schemnitium in Hungary (where there are mines of gold, copper, iron, vitriol, antimony, etc.,) they change iron into copper by dissolving it in a vitriolate water, which they find in cavities of rocks in the mines, and then melting the slimy solution in a strong fire, which, in the cooling, proves copper. The like is said to be done in other places which I cannot now remember. Perhaps too it may be done in Italy; for about twenty or thirty years ago there was a certain vitriol came from thence, (called Roman vitriol,) but of a nobler virtue than that which is now called by that name, which vitriol is not now to be gotten, because, perhaps, they make a greater gain by some such trick as turning iron into copper with it, than by selling it. 2. Whether in Hungary, Sclavonia, Bohemia, near the town Eila, or at the mountains of Bohemia near Silesia, there be rivers whose waters are impregnated with gold; perhaps the gold being dissolved by some corrosive waters like *aqua regis,* and the solution carried along with the stream that runs through the mines. And whether the practice of laying mercury in the rivers till it be tinged with gold, and then straining the mercury through leather, that the gold may stay behind, be a secret yet, or openly practised. 3. There is newly contrived, in Holland, a mill to grind glasses plane withal, and I think polishing them too; perhaps it will be worth your while to see it. 4. There is in Holland one—Bory, who some years since was imprisoned by the Pope, to have extorted from him some secrets (as I am told) of great worth, both as to medicine and profit, but he escaped into Holland, where they have granted him a guard. I think he usually goes clothed in green: pray enquire what you can of him, and whether his ingenuity be any profit to the Dutch. 5. You may inform yourself whether the Dutch have any tricks to keep their ships from being all worm-eaten in their voyages to the Indies. Whether pendulum clocks be of any service in finding out the longitude, etc.

I am very weary, and shall not stay to part with a long compliment, only I wish you a good journey, and God be with you.

Is. Newton.

P. S. Pray let us hear from you in your travels. I have given your two books to Dr. Arrowsmith.[47]

[47] Brewster finds this letter a difficult matter to reconcile with his policy of presenting facts accurately and, at the same time of depicting Newton's character as the exemplar of all the virtues. He comments (see Vol. I, p. 34) on the author's advice in the following dry and cautious manner: "This 'letter' is a very interesting production. It does not evince much

If this famous letter had not been taken too seriously and often quoted as an early example of Newton's wise and noble character, there would be little need to comment upon it. Newton, like Washington, has been portrayed as a man with none of the ingenuousness or exuberance of youth. Should we not rather picture to ourselves two young men discussing the great event of a first trip abroad? The surprising thing is, that Aston should have looked to Newton for counsel and that he, in turn, should have considered himself capable of giving advice. Perhaps, also, the letter was a youthful bit of humour, disguised by ponderous seriousness, and I should like to think that Newton could occasionally unbend. If we take the letter seriously, Aston might have complained that he received little more than the standard seventeenth century "advice to travellers making the grand tour." But he would scarcely expect much valuable advice from a youth of twenty-four who had seen no more of the world than was comprised in his home and adjacent counties. He received the effusion of a young man assuming the pose of the worldly wise. I can thus agree neither with Brewster nor with De Morgan as the individualising parts of the letter throw but little light on Newton's own character, but they do reflect his interests.

The list of general things to be observed is such as any enquiring person might choose. But Newton picks out particularly two subjects, glass-work and chemistry, that he is interested in himself. There can be no doubt that chemistry was engrossing his mind or that he was a credulous alchemist. His naïve enquiries about the processes of changing iron into copper and of the charlatan, "one Bory, clothed in green," are indications of wide but desultory reading. So, too, they give us a glimpse of his youthful ambition to devote himself to luciferous experiments, and of his dreams of turning such knowledge into the lucriferous creation of gold. It was with great reluctance and after long years of labour that he finally became sceptical of the pretensions of alchemy.

Reference was made in the previous chapter to two note-books preserved by Newton which give an interesting account of his activi-

acquaintance with the ways of the world, but it shows some knowledge of the human heart, and throws a strong light on the character and opinions of its author." One wonders what light Brewster really thought it to be. Having asked a friend to read it, I was surprised by his opinion that Newton was writing either cynically or humorously. De Morgan, on the other hand, cites the advice on how to behave when insulted by foreigners as typical of Newton's grave defect of character such that "he had not within himself the source from whence to inculcate high and true motives of action upon others; the fear of man was before his eyes." *Essays*, pp. 132–134.

ties and expenses at this time. Sufficient abstracts were given of the items referring to his Grantham days. As he continued the entries for several years after he went to College I have taken some of the items when he first went up to Cambridge as they give a vivid glimpse of a student's expenses.

IMPENSA PROPRIA

	£ s d
Sewsterne	0—1—0
Stilton	0—2—0
Cambridge White Lion	0—2—6
Carriage to the College	0—0—8
A chamber pot	0—2—2
A table to set down the number of my clothes in the wash	0—1—0
A paper book	0—0—8
For a quart bottle and ink to fill it	0—1—7
Income for a glass and other things to my Chamberfellow	0—0—9
	0—12—4

He also seems to have had the habit of lending money to his schoolfellows; there are ten or more such entries and I suspect that he eked out his scanty income by charging for the accommodation.[48]

[48] As his list of expenses is valuble in giving an idea of his social life and of his work, I experienced a more personal contact with Newton when reading his little book than from any of his other papers in the *Portsmouth Collection*. The abstract which follows is also to be found in Brewster, Vol. I, p. 32.

1665

Received, May 23d, whereof I gave my tutor 5s.,	£ 5	0	0
Remaining in my hands since last quarter,	£ 3	8	4
In all,	£ 8	8	4

This account of expenses extends only to six and a half pages, and records many loans. The following are among the entries:

Drills, gravers, a hone, a hammer, and a mandril,	£ 0	5	0
A magnet,	0	16	0
Compasses,	0	3	6
Glass bubbles,	0	4	0
My Bachelor's account,	0	17	6
At the tavern several other times,	1	0	0

Probably with the approval of Barrow, and possibly with his advice, Newton undertook to expand his notes on his new calculus of fluxions into a connected essay, with the title of *On Analysis by equations with an infinite number of terms.* He then gave it to Barrow with the permission to send it to that scientific intermediary John Collins, but with his usual caution he stipulated that the name of the author was to be kept anonymous. In a letter, dated 20th June, 1669, Barrow merely announced to Collins that a friend staying at Cambridge had written an important mathematical paper. In his next letter, he forwarded the manuscript with the hope that it would delight him. Collins evidently expressed his warm approval, for Barrow then wrote a third letter on the 20th August and, having overcome the reluctance of the author, added that "the name of the author is Newton, a Fellow of our College, and a young man, who is only in his second year since he took the degree of Master of Arts, and who, with

Spent on my cousin Ayscough,	0	12	6
On other acquaintance,	0	10	0
Cloth, 2 yards, and buckles for a vest,	2	0	0
Philosophical Intelligences,	0	9	6
The Hist. of the Royal Society,	0	7	0
Gunter's Book and Sector to Dr. Fox,	0	5	0
Lost at cards twice,	0	15	0
At the tavern twice,	0	3	6
I went into the country, Dec. 4, 1667.			
I returned to Cambridge, Feb. 12, 1667.			
Received of my mother,	30	0	0
My journey,	0	7	6
For my degree to the College,	5	10	0
To the proctor,	2	0	0
To three prisms,	3	0	0
Four ounces of putty,	0	1	4
Lent to Dr. Wickins,	1	7	6
Bacon's Miscellanies,	0	1	6
Expenses caused by my degree,	0	15	0
A Bible binding,	0	3	0
For oranges for my sister,	0	4	2
Spent on my journey to London, and 4s or 5s more which my mother gave me in the country,	5	10	0
I went to London, Wednesday, August 5th, and returned to Cambridge on Monday, September 28, 1668.			
Lent Dr. Wickins,	0	11	0
April 1669			
For glasses in Cambridge.			
For glasses in London.			
For aquafortis, sublimate, oyle pink, fine silver, antimony, vinegar, spirit of wine, white lead, salt of tartar,	2	0	0
A furnace,	0	8	0
Air furnace,	0	7	0
Theatrum chemicum,	1	8	0
Lent Wardwell 3s., and his wife 2s.,	0	5	0

an unparalleled genius, has made very great progress in this branch of mathematics."[49]

Barrow, who had the wish to return to his theological studies, had now found one superior to himself; he resigned his professorship and secured his successor in Newton at the early age of twenty-seven years.

[49] Brewster, Vol. I, p. 35.

CHAPTER III

LUCASIAN PROFESSOR. LECTURES ON OPTICS. INVENTION OF REFLECTING TELESCOPE. HIS NEW THEORY OF LIGHT

1669–1673

UPON his appointment to the Lucasian Professorship, Newton flung himself into the intense creative work which was to absorb him for a score of years and raise him to a preeminent position in science. Assured of a competent income and of a commanding position in the University, he was free to follow his own inclinations and to develop his ideas. The prescribed duties of his professorship were light as they required him to give only one lecture a week during the Michaelmas term and two conferences a week with students while he was in residence. He had also the choice of any subject in the broad fields of mathematics and natural philosophy. His professorial obligations were even less burdensome as he usually had but very few auditors, and often none, at his lectures and hardly any conferences with students.

Any one of three topics might have attracted the young professor's interest. He had been thoroughly grounded in classical geometry by Barrow, and he had mastered by himself the new analytical geometry of Descartes and Wallis which had been developed as a means of solving the dynamical problems resulting from the discoveries of Galileo. His work, during his retirement at Woolsthorpe, had prepared him to create a systematic calculus fitted to deal with all problems of continuous motion. As a mathematician he was *sui generis* since he seemed to grasp the solution of a problem immediately and to have seen new methods of attack when the occasion demanded. But, as an end in itself, he considered mathematics to be a dry and barren subject; he valued it only as a tool and a language for the expression of natural law. Thus, while he made inventions of first-rate importance, he made them for his own use; he rarely developed them systematically and had no desire to publish them for the use of others. He seems, also, to have believed that the modern analytical methods, including his own, lacked the elegance and clarity which are the peculiar glory of the classical geometry.

Newton was also prepared to lecture on astronomy and mechanics. He had been deeply interested in the cosmical ideas of Copernicus, Kepler, and Galileo, which had been expanded into a universal mechanical system by Descartes. But he never attempted any astronomical observations and he was in his youth too near-sighted to make them efficiently. While he was convinced that he had found the long sought cosmical force of attraction it required the meditations of twenty years to prepare him to establish the universal law of attraction and work out its applications to natural philosophy. So the discovery remained in his mind as a more or less isolated problem which he jealously guarded till its general solution in the *Principia* became the crowning achievement of his life.

In spite of the attraction those subjects had, Newton chose optics for his maiden effort, and continued his lectures on light during the next two years. This branch of physics, following the discovery of the telescope, was a field of great activity and his choice was a wise one. He had made the fundamental discovery of the composite nature of white light which he thought disclosed an ineradicable defect in the refracting telescope. He had studied the geometrical properties of lenses; he had practised the art of grinding and polishing glass; and he had constructed a telescope which he thought avoided the faults of the type in use. Here, then, was a subject which combined skillful handicraft with the rigour and elegance of geometry; one in which he had been so systematically trained by Barrow that he was consulted during the preparation of his master's *Lectures on Light* for the press. That his topic was congenial to him is evident from the fact that it is the only one which awakened in him a burst of enthusiasm and pride when he disclosed his ideas to the world. The lectures were "deposited, at the time they were read, amongst the archives of the University: from whence many copies have been taken, and handed about by the curious in these matters."[1] The fact that they had been thus circulated and garbled was a matter of intense annoyance to their author, which he many years later gave as a reason for the publication of his treatise on *Optics*. The lectures were published posthumously in 1729[2] from a copy given by Newton

[1] Greenstreet, p. 70.

[2] *Lectiones Opticae, Annis MDCLXIX ad MDCLXXI, in Scholis Publicis habitae: et nunc primam ex MSS. in Lucem editae, Londini.*

to David Gregory, Savilian Professor at Oxford. An English translation, of the first part only, had been printed the year before with a preface by the anonymous translator. They are also included in Horsley's *Opera Omnia.*

In order to make clear the current knowledge of the phenomena and laws of light when Newton began his own investigations, we may conveniently glance at Kepler's *Paralipomena ad Vitellionem* which was published in 1604. While this treatise on light has all the verbosity and discursiveness so characteristic of the author's style and thought, we may be certain that he includes all that other men knew about the subject and adds new material of his own.

Kepler accepts the current idea that the velocity of light is infinite because the medium of its transference offers no resistance of friction. With the exception of a trial proposed by Galileo by noting the time of lantern signals passed from one observer to another, a method quite inadequate, no one had even attempted to measure its velocity. It was not until 1675 that Roemer used the indirect method of noting the variations in time between the observed and calculated eclipses of the moons of Jupiter at different positions of the earth's orbit and so obtained a fair approximation of the enormous speed of light.

The laws of reflection are stated accurately by Kepler, but the laws of refraction were not known, and he merely affirmed that its angle, when light passes from a rarer into a denser medium, increases less rapidly than the angle of incidence. By actual trial he worked out many practical problems for finding images in plane and spherical mirrors, and in lenses, but he could give no general formulæ for the positions of objects and images. When, in 1609, the invention of the telescope was brought to his attention, he quite erroneously claimed that it had been suggested by a diagram in this book of a concave and a convex lens accidentally drawn on the same axis. It was Kepler who, by these investigations, proved that a plano-convex lens brings rays, that are parallel to its axis, to a focus at a distance equal to the diameter of its curvature, and that the focal length of a double convex lens is just half that distance. But he did not investigate any rule for the foci of lenses unequally convex.

When we turn to the section dealing with the nature and causes of light and colour we find Kepler's ideas are purely speculative and quite typically obscure. In Proposition XV he states: "Colour is potential light buried in pellucid matter (if it may be considered as something independent apart from vision); and different properties in the nature of matter, because of rarity and density or of transparency and opacity, cause variety of colours. For since colours, which are observed in the rainbow, are of the same nature as colours in bodies, there must be the same cause of both. And indeed they all occur at the boundary of light and shadow, as it is certain that they owe their existence to the attenuation of light and a superinjection of watery material. There is only this difference, light is adventitious in the rainbow, and truly implanted in coloured bodies. Black is the limit of all colours and is related to colour as a point is to a line; that is, it pertains to a quantity although it is not a quantity." If this definition means anything, it is that colour is in some way a mixture of light and darkness, modified by the specific properties of the body through which it passes.

A knowledge of the laws of light was naturally of great importance to the astronomer; but it was the invention of the telescope, five years after the publication of Kepler's treatise, which first opened the eyes of the world to the possibility of applying science to practical uses. No more startling illustration of the slowness of communication in the seventeenth century, the little general interest in science, and the isolation of its scattered followers, could be given than the fact that the foremost astronomer of the day did not learn of the invention of the telescope until nineteen years after it had been discovered and was in use in the neighbouring country of Holland. Perhaps even more extraordinary is the possibility, although the evidence is doubtful, that Roger Bacon had made and used both telescopes and microscopes in the twelfth century and had acquainted John Der and others of his friends with their construction. If this be true, all knowledge of such instruments had completely vanished.

The credit for this marvellous aid to human vision apparently lies between two Dutch spectacle-makers, Zacharias Joannides (Jansen) and John Lippersheim, both of Middelburgh. The most circumstantial and authentic account of the invention of the telescope is to be found in the almost contemporaneous *De vero telescopii inventore* of Borellus. He assigns the honour of the discovery to Jansen who, in 1590, fortunately hit upon the combination of a double convex lens as an object glass and a double concave lens for an eye-piece. There is a legend that one of his children, while playing with some lenses, accidentally placed two of them in such a position as to make a telescopic combination and called to his father to look how large everything appeared. Whether the legend be true or not, it is certain that it was not due to chance, as Jansen was a diligent enquirer into nature and was trying to learn what uses could be made of lenses, other than for spectacles. As soon as he discovered the telescopic effect of this combination of lenses, he enclosed them in a tube and presented the instrument to Prince Maurice. As the Prince found that the instrument would aid him in his wars to observe the actions of the enemy, the inventor was ordered to keep it a secret. Though this was attempted for some time, the discovery leaked out and several persons in the city applied themselves to the making and selling of telescopes. Borellus also states that the son, John, observed the spots on the moon and the face of Jupiter, and "sometimes he perceived two, sometimes three, and at the most four small stars, a little above or below him; but this, he says, he leaves to the consideration of astronomers."

If this account be true, it took nineteen years for the rumour of a strange instrument which had been invented by a spectacle maker of Holland to reach Galileo. In spite of its length, I shall give Priestley's vivid story of the incident.

"About April or May, in 1609, it was reported at Venice, where Galileo (who was professor of mathematics in the university of Padua) then happened to be, that a Dutchman had presented to Count Maurice of Nassau, a certain optical instrument, by means of which, distant objects appeared as if they were near; but no farther account of the discovery had reached that place, though this was near twenty years after the first discovery. Struck, however, with this account, Galileo instantly returned to Padua, considering what kind of an instrument this must be. The night following, the construction occurred to him; and the day after, putting the parts of the instrument together, as he had previously conceived of it, and notwithstanding the imperfection of the glasses that he could then procure, the effect answered his expectations, as he presently acquainted his friends at Venice; to which place he, six days afterwards, carried another, and a better instrument that he had made, and where, from several eminences, he shewed to some of the principal senators of that republic, a variety of distant objects, to their very great astonishment. When he had made farther improvements in the instrument, he, with his usual generosity, and frankness in communicating his discoveries, made a present of one of them to the Doge, Leonardo Donati, and, at the same time, to all the senate of Venice, giving along with the instrument, a written paper, in which he explained the structure and wonderful uses that might be made of it, both by land and at sea. In return for so noble an entertainment, the republic, on the 25th of August, in the same year, more than tripled his salary as professor."[3]

With characteristic energy, Galileo made more than a hundred of these instruments with his own hands and turning them to the heavens he revolutionised our knowledge of the solar system. In March, 1610, he published an account of all his discoveries in his *Nuncius Sidereus,* dedicated to Cosimo, Grand Duke of Tuscany. As a reward for this honour, the Duke invited him to quit Padua, and assigned him a large salary as extraordinary professor at Pisa with no obligations to lecture or to reside there. His astounding discoveries were the cause of speculation and debate among the philosophers and astronomers. Many were sceptical and some refused to look through the tube lest it should shake their belief in Aristotle's philosophy. When the facts were settled beyond dispute, to save their faces they claimed that the discovery was concealed in the philosophy of their oracle. Galileo used to tell this story with his customary humour by comparing such men to alchemists who imagined the art of making gold was known to the ancients and lay hidden in the fables of the poets.[4]

It is an extraordinary fact that the Galilean telescope, which is the familiar opera glass, remained the only known form for twenty years. At best, it is an inferior instrument because the concave eyepiece diverges the light entering the eye and makes the field of view exceedingly small. Combinations of convex lenses are far more effective, since they converge the rays of light which enter the eye; and it was by following the theoretical work of Kepler that other and better types of telescopes were constructed.

These new instruments aroused an intense interest in astronomy and led to persistent study of the laws and grinding of lenses. The essential difficulty to be overcome was inherent in all spherical glasses. Rays of light refracted from portions near the rim of such a lens come to a focus closer to it than the rays through the middle portion. This fact, which is called spherical aberration, obviously blurs the image. Descartes not only published the general laws of refraction, but also devised a method for figuring and grinding aplanatic lenses having surfaces, other than spherical, which would not produce spherical aberration. However, he did not mention any other type of telescope

[3] Priestley, *Vision, Light, and Colours,* London, 1772, p. 60. [4] Priestley, p. 60.

than the Galilean as having been actually constructed. Although Kepler had suggested other possible combinations of lenses, the first person who actually made a telescope with a combination of two or three convex lenses was Father Scheiner,[5] about 1630. Since spherical aberration decreases as the focal length of a convex lens is increased, the desire for greater magnifying power and sharper images was met by steadily enlarging the length of the instrument, till it was proposed to make one in France two hundred feet long. Such is the history of this first practical and deliberate achievement of the new scientific method based on observation.

I have very little sympathy with the distinction commonly made between pure and applied science, or with the supposed superiority of those who plead for "science for science's sake." The chief value of science is that it increases our power over nature and adds to our safety and comfort. Unless the possibility of practical applications to the needs of society is very generally perceived, any branch of science is certain to languish except for the unappreciated work of a few investigators whose personal tastes lie in the field of abstract research. Although astronomy may seem, at first sight, to be the most remote of all the sciences from human problems, it is not difficult, however, to show why it was the first to feel the quickening impulse of the Renaissance.

In the first place, astronomy was the direct outgrowth of astrology which, with the exception of alchemy, was the only science generally cultivated during the Middle Ages because of its value to society. From the most ancient times, the influence of the stars on life was universally accepted as an established fact except by a few scoffers. And the dominating influence of the heat and light from the sun on physical and mental phenomena could be triumphantly pointed to as an illustration of celestial power. Even more forcibly the mysteries of the heavens touched the imagination and had been closely woven into religion and philosophy. The future fate of every person was believed to depend on the positions of the planets at the moment of birth. The most elaborate and intricate rules for taking horoscopes were devised and grave discussions were held in order to define what was the exact moment of birth, in itself a rather protracted period of

[5] The amusing story is told of Scheiner that he protested to his Provincial that he had observed the spots on the sun before Galileo and the credit of the discovery had not been given him. The answer was: Calm yourself, my son, I have read Aristotle through many times and he nowhere mentions any spots. Change your glasses; the imperfections are in them and not in celestial matter.

time. One of the common expedients was to station an astrologer on the roof of the house and to have the mid-wife notify him when the infant uttered its first wail of protest. The foresighted person of wealth and station maintained an astrologer in his household to advise him whether the aspect of the stars was propitious before any serious enterprise was undertaken. Medicines would not act properly; the chemical elements would neither transmute nor combine; beasts and plants would not propagate and grow satisfactorily, unless the stars were benign in their aspect. In spite of the chicanery and rascality which the astrologers practised in order to entice a livelihood from their ignorant patrons, there was also a genuine and enthusiastic investigation of the planetary motions. Thus astrology had a true scientific value and it needed only to be freed from its mythological swaddling clothes to develop into astronomy. And as astronomy advanced, the need for a greater knowledge of the sciences of light and mechanics became imperative, since the one was necessary for locating stars and the other for calculating their motions. These illustrations will, perhaps, serve to explain why astronomy and, with it, the correlated subjects of optics and mechanics were the fertile fields of science during the sixteenth and seventeenth centuries. We may now return to a brief statement of the prevailing ideas on the nature of light and colour.

Besides Kepler, I should mention Antonius de Dominis. In connection with his explanation of the cause of the rainbow, he gives in his treatise *De radiis visus,* published by Bartolus in 1611, his ideas on the nature of light. They are strictly Aristotelian. He explains colour in this fashion: "If there be in a body pure light, as in the stars or in fire, and it lose its brilliancy for any cause, it appears as white light. If some darkness be mingled with the light, which yet permits it a passage and is not completely absorbed, there then occur the intermediate colours. On that account our fire appears reddish because it is mixed with smoke which darkens it. . . . There are three intermediate colours. The least mixture of darkness which dims the glitter of white light produces red. This may be shown by passing sun-light through a three sided glass prism, the colour which passes through the least thickness of the glass is red. Then follows green which has passed a greater thickness of glass and so been more absorbed and mixed with black. Finally, we observe blue which has passed through the thickest part of the prism. If sun-light be still more absorbed there occurs darkness, although this is a privation of light rather than a positive colour.[6] The important fact to be noted is that the conception of "pure light, as in the stars or in fire" is identical with Aristotle's quintessence, his pure and incorruptible celestial matter of the stars. In its passage through space this elemental fire loses some of its brilliance and appears in its purest form as white light. Aristotle, according to his habit of resolving into contraries, then postulated darkness as an opposing entity. In the moral world, light and darkness were confused with good and evil, and physically they caused the sensations of whiteness and blackness; their mixture was greyness. Colours also resulted from their combination when light was affected by the action of the material substances through which it passed.

It would be wearisome and useless to quote the opinions on the nature of light of other contemporaneous writers. It was not until Descartes made his deliberate attempt to overthrow the Aristotelian science by portraying a universe which would involve only substance and motion, that a new hypothesis of light and colour was advanced. While his picture was purely fanciful, it had the result of directing attention to what later became the mechanical wave theory of light. The cause of light was attached to his theory of vortices in an ingenious way; and Descartes had the peculiar gift of using simple examples, which gave an air of verisimilitude to even his most fantastic ideas. He first accepted the Aristotelian idea of the impossibility of a vacuum and placed each star and planet at the centre of a vast vortex of cosmic matter whose motion in some way caused a drift of matter towards the centre. Now the substance of the sun and stars is celestial fire,—he was quite adept in using Aristotle's ideas while combating his philosophy. Although this celestial substance is constantly driven towards the centre of the vortex, yet, when it approaches that point, it experiences a tendency to press out to the equatorial surface because of its centrifugal motion. This conception of matter as endowed with both a centripetal and a centrifugal action, acting in opposite directions, is only a revival of the mysterious *tonos* of the Stoics. The effort, or tendency, to press out from the centre constitutes light. With such an hypothesis, Descartes found himself in a quandary when he later discussed the cause of colour but, rather than confess ignorance, he assumed that this light pressure causes two kinds of motion, one circular and the other rectilinear, in "globules" of terrestrial matter. If the circular motion of

[6] Chap. III, p. 9.

the "globules" is the more rapid of the two we experience the sensation of red when it agitates the retina; if it is the slower, the sensation is blue; and if they are equal, it is yellow. All other colours are compounded of these three primary sensations. As weird as this speculation may be, it was changed by Pardies, a distinguished professor of Clermont College, Paris, and by Hooke of London into a less fantastic scheme of vibratory motion; and later Huygens proposed a wave theory of light which in variously modified forms has persisted to the present time.

Newton had evidently been deeply interested in the subject of optics by his early study of Kepler and Descartes, and had mastered all the facts and hypotheses then known. His boyish love for, and skill in making, mechanical appliances had remained with him, and at the beginning of the year after his graduation, March 25, 1666, he devoted himself to the figuring and construction of lenses. Nothing is more significant of the ardour and industry of the men of science of that time than the labour and time spent by men like Galileo and Newton in the actual construction of apparatus. Such labour is almost incredible to us who have every facility of the expert apparatus maker at our disposal.

The defect of the Galilean telescope, or opera glass, had become only too evident. There was no method by which the field of vision could be made large, and we may justly express our admiration at the discoveries made with such an instrument. The future apparently lay with perfecting combinations of convex lenses. Such telescopes overcame the diverging defect of the concave eye-glass but they introduced the fault of spherical aberration which the concave eye-piece largely corrected. The great authority of Descartes led to the attempt to make lenses whose surfaces were ground either to parabolic or hyperbolic surfaces of revolution. It is a fairly easy matter to make accurate plane and spherical surfaces since their curvature is the same in all directions. The grinding tool can be held rigidly, and the irregularities which are produced in one line of motion are smoothed by the grinding along any other. The mechanical difficulty for other surfaces is to combine a circular motion of the tool with a simultaneous advance along the arc of a parabola or hyperbola so slowly and accurately as not to leave minute ridges which scatter the light.

Newton not only figured and ground lenses but he intimated to Conduitt that he constructed his grinding and polishing machines.

During this work he noticed an obscure effect which had escaped the attention of his predecessors; he found that the images of telescopes and lenses were bordered with a coloured edge which blurred their outline and made exact focusing even more difficult than did spherical aberration. The failure of others to note this defect, now called chromatic aberration, can be accounted for by the fact that the concave eye-piece of the Galilean telescope partially compensates the aberration of the object glass, and that the new type, with convex lenses only, was still in its infancy. But, one of the prime elements of Newton's genius was that he rarely overlooked apparently trifling phenomena, and when they were observed he never relaxed his attention until the cause was dragged into the clear light of day. In this case the seemingly unimportant observation that lenses produced coloured images led him to his capital discovery of the composition of white light.

Having encountered this new and unexpected complication, Newton came to the conclusion that it was useless to try to perfect the refracting telescope by improving lenses or by lengthening the tube. In the account of his work to the Royal Society in 1672, he gives the impression that when he began the grinding of lenses he procured a glass prism to try the "celebrated phænomena of colours" [just what he refers to by this phrase is obscure] and, having found the unequal refrangibility of colours, he left off his glass-works. Historians have assumed from this statement that he had first discovered the heterogeneity of white light by experimenting with a prism and then gave up the attempt to make "lenses with surfaces other than spherical" as it would be a waste of time. They have overlooked the quite obvious fact that, if he had discovered chromatic aberration beforehand, he would not have attempted to make lenses at all, whereas he did continue his work on lenses and gave it up only after he found their defect.

It is important to trace, if possible, the sequence of Newton's work on light. The problem is complicated by the fact that his biographers have depended on his reminiscences rather than on the evidence of his contemporaneous correspondence and publications. Now Newton was accurate in his recollections of what he did, but he was singularly careless in matters of dates and the sequence of his work. We have no evidence that he kept any orderly record of his scientific work and he certainly did not discuss it with his friends or his teachers. But, certain facts, given in his correspondence, seem to establish the sequence of the ideas which led to his discovery of the composition of white light.

We know definitely that in 1664, he made some observations with a prism and was interested in the subject of improving the refracting telescope, and the question is, which of the two lines of work led to his discovery of the nature of light. It is generally stated that it followed from his observation that the image of the sun through a prism was oblong instead of circular. The serious objection to this belief is that he continued to work on lenses for at least a year and if, as he believed, their chromatic aberration was unavoidable then all this labour was useless.

In his *Optics* and in his *Lectures on Light,* where Newton reviews all his work, he states that he observed the images in spherical lenses were bordered with colours which prevented a sharp focus. To find the cause of this defect in telescopes, he prepared an oblong strip of black paper by painting one half red and the other half blue; then he "lapped about it several times a slender thread of very black silk, in such a manner that the several parts of the thread might appear upon the colours like so many black lines drawn over them." He next illuminated the paper strongly with candle light. With a convex lens, he focused the black threads, which crossed the red strip, as sharply as possible, on a sheet of white paper and he observed that the black lines on the blue strip were out of focus and blurred. To bring the lines on the blue strip to a sharp image, he had to move the white screen an inch and a half closer to the lens; and then the black lines on the red strip were indistinct. The conclusion was obvious, the focal length of a lens depends on the colour of the light; blue is more refracted than red and there is no sharp focus for white light.

With this fact clearly demonstrated, Newton left off his glass-works as he believed that the unequal refrangibility of colours made it impossible to perfect the refracting telescope. During the next two or three years he carried on two lines of work; he made a little reflecting telescope, and he performed a long series of experiments with the prism, from which he derived his laws of light.

The first achievement of Newton in optics was his construction of a little reflecting telescope with a concave metallic mirror in place of an object glass. The details of this instrument and the success of the young inventor are described in the following letter.

Newton to ——

Trin. Coll. Cambridge,
Sir, Feb. 23, 1688/9.

I promised in a letter to Mr. Ent to give you an account of my success in a small attempt I had then in hand: and it is this. Being persuaded of a certain way whereby the practical part of optics might be promoted, I thought it best to proceed by degrees, and make a small perspective first, to try whether my conjecture would hold good or not. The instrument that I made is but six inches in length, it bears something more than an inch aperture, and a plano-convex eye-glass, whose depth is 1/6th or 1/7th part of an inch; so that it magnifies about forty times in diameter, which is more than any six feet tube can do, I believe, with distinctness. But, by reason of bad materials, and for want of good polish, it represents not things so distinct as a six feet tube will do; yet I think it will discover as much as any three or four feet tube, especially if the objects be luminous. I have seen with it Jupiter distinctly round and his satellites, and Venus horned. Thus, sir, I have given you a short account of this small instrument, which, though in itself contemptible, may yet be looked upon as an epitome of what may be done according to this way, for I doubt not but in time a six feet tube may be made after this method, which will perform as much as any sixty or hundred feet tube made after the common way; whereas I am persuaded, that were a tube made after the common way of the purest glass, exquisitely polished, with the best figure that any geometrician (Des Cartes, etc.) hath or can design, (which I believe is all that men have hitherto attempted or wished for,) yet such a tube would scarce perform as much more as an ordinary good tube of the same length. And this, however it may seem a paradoxical assertion, yet it is the necessary consequence of some experiments, which I have made concerning the nature of light.

[Is. Newton.]

This first telescope was lost, but a rumour of its success had leaked out and by urgent request he made a second and better one which he sent to the Royal Society. The letter itself is interesting, as it is one of his earliest which has been preserved. There are only two earlier, one written in January and the other in February of the same year. Both of these are addressed to Collins who was an amateur scholar, so enthusiastic and eager in the cultivation of correspondence that he became the scientific gazette of the time. They refer to questions of mathematics, acknowledging the receipt of Wallis's *Mechanics* which Collins had sent to Barrow for Newton, and explaining some of the problems involved in it. But it is also important in itself as the last sentence settles definitely the fact that he had discovered the unequal refrangibility of the spectral colours prior to the year 1669. This letter to an unknown correspondent came into the possession of Collins who wrote on it the following memorandum, describing the reception of the telescope by the Royal Society.[7]

"The telescope therein mentioned hath been lately sent up to the Royal Society, who gave Mr. Cox order to make one after the same manner of contrivance four feet long, the which hath been done; one end of the tube is open, at the other end is placed a concave metalline mirror, the diameter whereof is betwixt four and five inches; it was ground on a sphere of fourteen feet diameter, and about its focus, which is about four feet off, is placed a reflecting plate as big as a twopence, inclined at an angle of forty-five degrees to the axis, so that the reflected rays falling thereon, are again reflected upright to the side of the telescope, where the eye, through a small hole, wherein is placed a small plano-convex glass, beholds the object on the reflecting plate, as much magnified as it could have been done by an ordinary telescope of forty feet long or more, and void of colours. The mirror and reflecting plate are made to be taken out and wiped at pleasure; they are not yet pleased with the metal or polish of the reflecting plate, but are trying Lapis Osmandinus, a black stone that comes from mount Hecla in Iceland, and other materials, whereof you may afterwards hear the success.

"Mr. Hooke, seeing this telescope to obtain esteem, about a month since put in a proposal in writing to the Royal Society in words to this effect:

"The perfection of telescopes, microscopes, scotoscopes, and burning glasses, by figures as easily made as those that are plane or spherical, whereby the light and magnitude of objects is prodigiously increased, and whatsoever hath hitherto been attempted or almost desired in dioptrics accomplished———with a cipher containing the mystery, the which he disclosed to the Lord Brouncker and Dr. Wren, who report plausibly of it, and what is done in this way is performed by glass refraction.

[7] The letter and memorandum are printed in Macclesfield's *Collection,* Vol. II, p. 289. Collins was in error in stating that this first telescope was sent to the Society.

"Mr. Hooke moreover affirmed, *coram multis,* that in the year 1664 he made a little tube of about an inch long to put in his fob, which performs more than any telescope of fifty feet long, made after the common manner; but the plague happening which caused his absence, and the fire, whence redounded profitable employments about the city, he neglected to prosecute the same, being unwilling the glass grinders should know any thing of the secret."

Collins's memorandum was not added to the original letter until some time in the years, 1671 or 1672, when a second instrument was exhibited to the Society. Newton was in London on July 20, 1671, because he wrote to Collins on that day from there that he had proposed to visit him in Cambridge at the late solemnity of the installation of the Duke of Buckingham as Chancellor of Cambridge "but had been prevented by a sudden surprisal of a fit of sickness, which not long after (God be thanked) he recovered of."[8] It is possible that he was in the city on business connected with this telescope. We are told that it created a great stir and was examined by King Charles II; it now forms one of the most valued possessions of the Society.[9] The invention immediately brought Newton the honour of being proposed as a candidate for membership in the Society by Dr. Seth Ward, Bishop of Salisbury. He was elected a Fellow on January 11, 1671/2 when the telescope was the subject of discussion. "At that meeting mention was made of his improvement of telescopes, by contracting them, and that that, which himself had sent thither to be examined, had been seen by the King, and considered also by the President, Sir Robert Moray, Sir Paul Neile, Dr. Christopher Wren, and Mr. Hook, at Whitehall; and that they had so good an opinion of it, as that they concluded a description, and scheme of it, should be sent by the Secretary, in a letter on purpose, to Mr. Huggins [Huygens] at Paris, thereby to secure this contrivance to the author, who had also written a letter to Mr. Oldenburg from Cambridge (Jan. 6, 1671/2) altering and enlarging the description of his instrument, which had been sent hence for his review, before it should go abroad."[10]

Newton was immensely surprised and gratified with the enthu-

[8] Macclesfield, II, p. 308.

[9] Edleston, p. xlv. Collins writing to Vernon, English Secretary at Paris, December 26, says: "As to Mr. Newton's Telescope, I suppose Mr. Bernard (of Oxford) writ the same to you as he did to me upon the authority of one Mr. Gale of Cambridge [Fellow of Trin. Coll. and afterwards Dean of York]: since it hath been brought up for his Majesty's perusal, and I have seen an object in it."

[10] *Journ. Book,* R. S.

siasm which his invention had aroused. A detailed account of his plans for perfecting his telescope, and his attempts to find the proper alloy which would receive a high polish and be suitable for large metallic mirrors is preserved for us in a long series of letters, mostly addressed to Oldenburg.[11] I can thus give, by extracts from these letters, Newton's own account of his discovery and his efforts to make his ideas acceptable to the scientific world. Since the members of the Society had ordered their Secretary, Oldenburg, to protect Newton's rights of priority in his telescope by sending letters to learned men and, especially, to Huygens, he accordingly asked Newton to prepare a memorandum describing his instrument.

Newton to Oldenburg

Cambridge, Jan. 6, 1671/2.

Sir,

At the reading of your letter I was surprised to see so much care taken about securing an invention to me, of which I have hitherto had so little value. And therefore since the Royal Society is pleased to think it worth the patronising, I must acknowledge it deserves much more of them for that, than of me, who, had not the communication of it been desired, might have let it still remain in private as it hath already done some years. . . . I am very sensible of the honour done me by the Bishop of Sarum in proposing me candidate, and which I hope will be further conferred upon me by my election into the society. And if so, I shall endeavour to testify my gratitude by communicating what my poor and solitary endeavours can effect towards the promoting your philosophical designs.

Sir, I am
Your very humble servant,
I. Newton.

There followed a frequent correspondence relating mostly to the best method for grinding and polishing concave mirrors and preparing a metallic alloy which would take and preserve a sufficiently high polish. The Society had put this work into the hands of Cox, the most expert glass-worker in London—but the problem proved to be too difficult for him, and Newton was entirely too busy to devote

[11] These letters are published in Horsley's *Opera Omnia Newtoni* and in Macclesfield's *Collection*.

his own time to the practical work. As a result, reflecting telescopes of a large and useful size were not made until more than fifty years later. I shall omit the now uninteresting particulars of these attempts and abstract only those portions of the letters which throw light on Newton's character and life.

The first of these extracts is taken from a letter of date January 18, 1671/2 and is memorable as the first public announcement of his new discoveries as to the nature of light: "I desire that in your next letter you would inform me for what time the society continue their weekly meetings; because, if they continue them for any time, I am purposing them, to be considered of and examined, an account of a philosophical discovery, which induced me to the making of the said telescope, and which I doubt not but will prove much more grateful than the communication of that instrument, *being in my judgement the oddest, if not the most considerable detection, which hath hitherto been made in the operations of nature.*"[12]

This "detection," which I have italicised, refers, of course, to the heterogeneous character of white light. Nothing could better illustrate the general lack of interest in science and the isolation of the universities from London, than the fact that this great discovery had been made in Cambridge, and had been described in a public course of lectures for two successive years, and yet was still unknown to members of the Royal Society five years after it had been made. It is even more remarkable from the fact that Newton claimed the importance of what he had done and expressed satisfaction and enthusiastic pleasure in his work. At this time, he was eager to enjoy popular renown. Warmed by the flattering reception his telescope had received, he felt that he could show his appreciation for his election to the Royal Society in no way better than by offering a serious scientific communication. Accordingly, he sent a long letter to Oldenburg elucidating the hint of that "oddest, if not the most considerable detection, which hath hitherto been made in the operations of nature."

A Letter of Mr. Isaac Newton, Professor of Mathematics in the University of Cambridge; containing his New Theory of Light and Colours: sent by the Author to the Editor from Cambridge, Feb. 6, 1671/2; to be communicated to the Royal Society and published in their Transactions.[13]

[12] Macclesfield, Vol. II, 315; Horsley, Vol. III, p. 274. [13] *Phil. Trans.*, No. 80, p. 3075.

Sir,—To perform my late promise to you, I shall without further ceremony acquaint you, that in the beginning of the year 1666 (at which time I applied myself to the grinding of optic glasses of other figures than spherical,) I procured a triangular glass prism, to try therewith the celebrated phenomena of colours. And for that purpose having darkened my chamber, and made a small hole in my window shuts, to let in a convenient quantity of the sun's light, I placed my prism at his entrance, that it might be thereby refracted to the opposite wall. It was at first a very pleasing diversion to view the vivid and intense colours produced thereby; but after a while applying myself to consider them more circumspectly, I was surprised to see them in an oblong form; which, according to the received laws of refraction, I expected would have been circular. They were terminated at the sides with straight lines, but at the ends, the decay of light was so gradual, that it was difficult to determine justly what was their figure; yet they seemed semicircular.

Comparing the length of this coloured spectrum with its breadth, I found it about five times greater; a disproportion so extravagant, that it excited me to a more than ordinary curiosity of examining from whence it might proceed. I could scarcely think, that the various thickness of the glass, or the termination with shadow or darkness, could have any influence on light to produce such an effect; yet I thought it not amiss, first to examine those circumstances, and so tried what would happen by transmitting light through parts of the glass of divers thicknesses, or through holes in the window of divers sizes, or by setting the prism without, so that the light might pass through it, and be refracted before it was terminated by the hole; but I found none of those circumstances material. The fashion of the colours was in all these cases the same.

Then I suspected, whether by any unevenness in the glass, or other contingent irregularity, these colours might be thus dilated. And to try this, I took another prism like the former, and so placed it, that the light, passing through them both, might be refracted contrary ways, and so by the latter returned into that course from which the former had diverted it. For, by this means, I thought the regular effects of the first prism would be destroyed by the second, but the irregular ones more augmented, by the multiplicity of refractions. The event was, that the light, which by the first prism was diffused into an oblong form, was by the second reduced into an orbicular one, with as much regularity as when it did not at all pass through them.

So that, whatever was the cause of that length, it was not any contingent irregularity.

I then proceeded to examine more critically, what might be effected by the difference of the incidence of rays coming from divers parts of the sun; and to that end measured the several lines and angles, belonging to the image. . . .

Having made these observations, I first computed from them the refractive power of that glass, and found it measured by the ratio of the sines, 20′ to 31′. And then, by that ratio, I computed the refractions of two rays flowing from opposite parts of the sun's discus, so as to differ 31′ in their obliquity of incidence and found that the emergent rays should have comprehended an angle of about 31′, as they did, before they were incident. But because this computation was founded on the hypothesis of the proportionality of the sines of incidence and refraction, which though, by my own experience, I could not imagine to be so erroneous as to make that angle but 31′, which in reality was 2° 49′; yet my curiosity caused me again to take my prism. And having placed it at my window, as before, I observed, that by turning it a little about its axis to and fro, so as to vary its obliquity to the light, more than an angle of 4 or 5 degrees, the colours were not thereby sensibly translated from their place on the wall, and consequently by that variation of incidence, the quantity of refraction was not sensibly varied. By this experiment therefore, as well as by the former computation, it was evident, that the difference of the incidence of rays, flowing from divers parts of the sun, could not make them, after a decussation, diverge at a sensibly greater angle, than that at which they before converged; which being at most but about 31 or 32 minutes, there still remained some other cause to be found out, from whence it could be 2° 49′.

Then I began to suspect whether the rays, after their trajection through the prism, did not move in curve lines, and according to their more or less curvity tend to divers parts of the wall. And it increased my suspicion, when I remembered that I had often seen a tennis ball, struck with an oblique racket, describe such a curveline. For, a circular as well as a progressive motion being communicated to it by that stroke, its parts on that side, where the motions conspire, must press and beat the contiguous air more violently than on the other, and there excite a reluctancy and reaction of the air proportionably greater. And for the same reason, if the rays of light should possibly be globular bodies [Descartes's hypothesis], and by their oblique passage out of one medium into another acquire a circulating motion, they ought to feel the greater resistance from the ambient æther, on that side where the motions conspire, and thence be continually bowed to the other. But notwithstanding this plausible ground of suspicion, when I came to examine it, I could observe no such curvity in them. And besides (which was enough for my purpose) I observed, that the difference between the length of the image and diameter of the hole, through which the light was transmitted, was proportionable to their distance.

The gradual removal of these suspicions, at length led me to the *experimentum crucis,* which was this: I took two boards, and placed one of them close behind the prism at the window, so that the light might pass through a small hole, made in it for the purpose, and fall on the other board, which I placed at about 12 feet distance, having first made a small hole in it also, for some of that incident light to pass through. Then I placed another prism behind this second board, so that the light, trajected through both the boards, might pass through that also, and be again refracted before it arrived at the wall. This done, I took the first prism in my hand, and turned it to and fro slowly about its axis, so much as to make the several parts of the image, cast on the second board, successively pass through the hole in it, that I might observe to what places on the wall the second prism would refract them. And I saw, by the variation of those places, that the light tending to that end of the image, towards which the refraction of the first prism was made, did in the second prism suffer a refraction considerably greater than the light tending to the other end. And so the true cause of the length of that image was detected to be no other, than that light consists of rays differently refrangible, which, without any respect to a difference in their incidence, were, according to their degrees of refrangibility, transmitted towards divers part of the wall.

When I understood this, I left off my aforesaid glass works; for I saw, that the perfection of telescopes was hitherto limited, not so much for want of glasses truly figured according to the prescriptions of optic authors, (which all men have hitherto imagined,) as because that light itself is a heterogeneous mixture of differently refrangible rays. So that, were a glass so exactly figured, as to collect any one sort of rays into one point, it could not collect those also into the same point, which having the sáme incidence upon the same medium are apt to suffer a different refraction. Nay, I wondered, that seeing the difference of refrangibility was so great, as I found it, telescopes should arrive to that perfection they are now at. . . .

I shall now proceed to acquaint you with another more notable difformity in its rays, wherein the origin of colours is unfolded: concerning which I shall lay down the doctrine first, and then, for its examination, give you an instance or two of the experiments, as a specimen of the rest.—The doctrine you will find comprehended and illustrated in the following propositions:—

1. As the rays of light differ in degrees of refrangibility, so they also differ in their disposition to exhibit this or that particular colour. Colours are not qualifications of light, derived from refractions, or reflections of natural bodies (as it is generally believed,) but original and connate properties, which in divers rays are diverse. Some rays are disposed to exhibit a red colour, and no other; some a yellow, and no other; some a green, and no other; and so of the rest. Nor are there only rays proper and particular to the more eminent colours, but even to all their intermediate gradations.

2. To the same degree of refrangibility ever belongs the same colour, and to the same colour ever belongs the same degree of refrangibility. The least refrangible rays are all disposed to exhibit a red colour, are all the least refrangible; so the most refrangible rays are all disposed to exhibit a deep violet colour, and contrarily, those which are apt to exhibit such a violet colour, are all the most refrangible. And so to all the intermediate colours, in a continued series, belong intermediate degrees of refrangibility. And this analogy betwixt colours, and refrangibility is very precise and strict; the rays always either exactly agreeing in both, or proportionally disagreeing in both.

3. The species of colour, and degree of refrangibility proper to any particular sort of rays, is not mutable by refraction, nor by reflection from natural bodies, nor by any other cause, that I could yet observe. When any one sort of rays has been well parted from those of other kinds, it has afterwards obstinately retained its colour, notwithstanding my utmost endeavours to change it. I have refracted it with prisms, and reflected it with bodies, which in day-light were of other colours: I have intercepted it with the coloured film of air interceding two compressed plates of glass; transmitted it through coloured mediums, and through mediums irradiated with other sorts of rays, and diversely terminated it; and yet could never produce any new colour out of it. It would, by contracting or dilating, become

more brisk, or faint, and by the loss of many rays, in some cases very obscure and dark; but I could never see it change in specie. . . .

The Society: "ordered, that the author be solemnly thanked, in the name of the Society, for this very ingenious discourse, and be made acquainted that the Society think very fit, if he consents to have it forthwith printed, as well for the greater conveniency of having it well considered by philosophers, as for securing the considerable notices thereof to the author against the arrogations of others. Ordered also, that the discourse be entered in the register-book, and that the Bishop of Salisbury, Mr. Boyle, and Mr. Hook, be desired to peruse and consider it, and bring in a report of it to the Society."[14]

This first published article by Newton produced such an extraordinary effect on his contemporaries and had such an influence on his life and character that I shall examine it critically and show why it marked a new era in science. In the first place, it is an almost perfect model in both form and content. It is the more remarkable because Newton had no example to follow; it is significant of his genius that his first essay was as perfect as was his later work. His mind seemed to need no period of growth but to have reached its full maturity at once.

In form, the article is a work of art—clear, concise, and admirably arranged to lead the reader from a dramatic introduction straight to a convincing conclusion. He, certainly, made many observations which must have been useless; but from his notes he selected those which were pertinent and forbore to weary and confuse his readers by giving a mass of irrelevant details. That is, contrary to custom, he relied on a few carefully selected experiments to prove his thesis.

He opens with the apparently insignificant observation that the spectrum was oblong, whereas "the received laws of refraction" would lead him to expect that it would be circular in conformity with the shape of the source of light or of the aperture in the shutter. It is the business of science to investigate just such discrepancies between facts and ideas. As has been pointed out, he probably had his attention first drawn to this research by his work on lenses.

The correct procedure was then to determine the cause of this observed fact. He wisely examines first those causes which would be supported by the accepted laws of refraction. He carries through a

[14] *Jour. Book*, R. S.

series of experiments which prove that the unevenness and composition of the prism, the size and shape of both the source and the aperture, and the possible propagation of light in curved lines had no effect on the oblong form of the spectrum.

Having thus cleared away all the possible sources of error that he can imagine, he goes straight to the true cause. He prepares what he calls an *experimentum crucis,* one which will convince an impartial reader that it was due to an unsuspected property of light itself. Lastly, he sums up his whole work in three laws, which involve no speculation, or hypothesis, and can be denied only by proving that his experimental evidence was false or inexact.

Thus, at the very beginning of his career he had grasped the idea that the true function of science is to observe and classify a set of selected phenomena and from them to formulate laws which will predict, as accurately as possible, future events. To go further than this, to imagine the mechanism which operates to produce the phenomenon, is to pass from the field of physics into metaphysics[15] where there is no criterion of knowledge. His early distrust of metaphysics was intensified by the criticisms which his scientific method aroused. It seemed to him self-evident that the laws he had found could be attacked only by other experimental evidence which would give new facts or prove that his own were in error. Yet, to his amazement and chagrin, he found that even the masters of science refused to accept those laws because they did not conform to their preconceived hypotheses as to the nature and cause of light and colour. As a result, he discarded hypothesis from science altogether, and in the *Principia* he summed up his convictions in the famous phrase, *hypotheses non fingo.* He thus denied that we have any *à priori* knowledge of the constitution of nature; the world is as it is, and it is the business of the man of science to find the facts. A theory, to Newton, was a law based on indisputable facts, expressed in mathematical terms, which could be overthrown only by discovering new facts or by proving others to be false. An hypothesis was merely a speculation as to the cause or the method of phenomena. As all hypotheses ultimately, in his opinion, introduced occult forces or substances, they were not only incapable of verification, but many entirely different hypotheses could be imagined to explain any single set of phenomena. They, then, not only give us no positive knowl-

[15] The word metaphysics, as used here, must not be confused with philosophy. It refers to those speculations on natural phenomena which cannot be put to the test of experimental observation.

edge but they actually breed confusion and make men suppose they understand what they do not. If they are indulged in, they should be no more than the picture of a real scene, an aid to the memory. As we can mark the beginning of the scientific Renaissance by the work of Copernicus, so we can close that period and begin modern science with Newton's first published work.

It is usually stated that Copernicus, Kepler, Galileo, and Descartes were the inaugurators of modern science. That is true in part, but the older methods still clung to them. While they attacked the dogmatic and Aristotelian metaphysics, they often drew their own deductions from an *à priori* and inward sentiment of knowledge. Kepler's treatises are full of excursions into foreign fields; every observation he makes is detailed to our distraction, and wild speculation jostles his soberest description of facts. Galileo, marvellous experimentalist though he was, throws his two great works into the form of interminable dialogues, in which he devotes himself to attacking the Aristotelians by Aristotelian logic more earnestly than he gives the results of his observation.

As for Descartes and his school, I cannot contrast them better with the wholesome method of Newton than by quoting Lord Bolingbroke: "The notion he [Descartes] entertained and propagated, that there is, besides clear ideas, a kind of inward sentiment of evidence, which may be a principle of knowledge, is, I suppose, dangerous in physical enquiries as well as in abstract reasoning. He who departs from the analytic method, to establish general propositions concerning the phenomena on assumptions, and who reasons from these assumptions, afterwards on inward sentiments of evidence, as they are called, instead of clear and real ideas, lays aside at once the only sure guides to knowledge. No wonder then if he wanders from it. This DES CARTES did very widely in his construction of a world; and yet by dint of genius he gave a great air of simplicity and plausibility to his hypothesis, and he knew how to make even geometry subservient to error. . . . How slowly, how unwillingly have many philosophers departed from the cartesian hypothesis."[16]

If modern science, two hundred years after Newton, still debauches itself with hypotheses of æthers, electronic structures, and fantastic cosmogonies, we can easily imagine the opposition aroused by this young and unknown man who boldly and laconically challenged hypothetical dogmatism, who put the evidence of his experimentation

[16] *Letters or Essays Addressed to Alexander Pope, Esq., Works* (1754), Vol. I, pp. 62, 63.

against the accepted ideas of the day, supported by the weight of authority of Kepler, Descartes, and the other foremost men of science.

No wonder there was a controversy. Men of keen minds, even such as a Huygens and a Hooke, could not understand what Newton meant, and resented the fact that they were curtly forbidden to answer him with their opinions, coined from their inward sentiment of knowledge. His only reply to their arguments was; stop telling me what so and so thinks, but prove my results are wrong or provide new and different results. Newton's biographers refer to his opponents as being men who wearied Newton with foolish and silly objections. But they were not foolish men, they were merely opposing theory by hypothesis. They were doing exactly what the followers of hypothetical science today are doing, who create a fantastic world and maintain it against the stubborn facts of experience.

Newton, himself, became a marked man; he had introduced a new scientific method and henceforth treatises were expected to be pruned of redundant and extraneous matter. But the effect on Newton was disastrous. Totally unfit both by natural disposition, and by training, to encounter the egotistic hardness of men, he shrank from the hostility of vanity and the stolidity of custom. The attack made on him personally, and on his veracity—coming instead of the cordial reception of new ideas which he had expected—frightened him, and led him to desire Oldenburg to soften any harsh word that might escape him lest further opposition should be aroused. His naïve expression of pleasure changed to disgust, and he accused nature as well as men of being litigious; to enjoy peace of mind, he resolved in future to meditate, but not impart his cogitations to a carping public.

Before closing the chapter, a matter must be discussed which has never been explained and probably never will be. Barrow, before resigning his professorship, had edited his Lucasian Lectures on Light and published them in 1669, the year in which Newton began his course on the same subject. In the preface to the work, Barrow generously acknowledges his indebtedness to Newton, as a young man of excellent character and of great genius, who had criticised the manuscript and corrected the proofs.[17]

[17] "Verum quod tenellae matres factitant, a me depulsum partum amicorum haud recusantium nutriciae curae commisi, prout ipsis visum esset, educandum aut exponendum, quorum unus (ipsos enim honestum duco nominatim agnoscere) *D. Isaacus Newtonus,* collega noster (peregregiae vir indolis ac insignis peritiae) *exemplar revisit, aliqua corrigenda* monens, sed et de suo nonnulla penu suggerens quae nostris alicubi cum laude innexa cernes." *Epist. ad Lectorem.*

Now, the puzzle is this. Barrow's published lectures do not contain a single reference to the fact that Newton had worked independently in the subject of light; or show any acquaintance with his discovery of chromatic aberration, the construction of a reflecting telescope, the selective refrangibility of colours, and the composition of white light. Instead, the author gives the accepted and erroneous explanation of all of those subjects. Yet his young protégé, while the printing was in process, kept his own counsel and, from any evidence we have, never mentioned his work. Furthermore, when the book was first in the hands of the public and of the University students, Newton was delivering his lectures which contradicted and made much of his master's work false.

It is quite inconceivable that Barrow would have permitted his book to be published if he had known about Newton's work. He was too able a scientist not to have recognised its importance and at least to have alluded to it. And if Newton kept his work and its results absolutely to himself, what were his motives? Was it a case of that excessive modesty with which his biographers have endowed him? But Newton called his discovery "the oddest, if not the most considerable detection, which hath hitherto been made in the operations of nature"; and such a statement does not express any failure to recognise his own worth. Or, was it the first case of his sensitive and suspicious jealousy which made him regard his thoughts as his own and made him resent any intrusion of others in the same field?

The question just raised is more difficult to answer than, apparently, Brewster admitted. He easily explained the incident by simply denying the facts. "It does not appear," he says, "from any of the documents which I have seen, at what time Newton made his first optical discoveries. . . . And there is every reason to believe that he was not acquainted with the true composition when Dr. Barrow completed his *Optical Lectures,* published in 1669."[18] Whatever may be the answer, Brewster has certainly not given it. The incident will continue to be cited by some as an example of Newton's great modesty; by others it will be regarded as one of those exhibitions of jealousy, or vanity, which caused him such bitter quarrels in his later life.

[18] Brewster, Vol. I, p. 27. If Brewster did not see any documents which prove that Newton knew the composition of white light, etc., before 1669, he must have shut his eyes to Newton's letter of Feb. 23, 1668/9, to his Lucasian lectures on light published in Horsley, to the letter to Oldenburg of Jan. 18, 1671/2, and to his first paper published in the *Phil. Trans.,* which is a résumé taken from his lectures. No help can be obtained from the MSS. in the *Portsmouth Collection* as none of them refers to his early work on light.

CHAPTER IV

ARGUMENT ON THE NATURE OF LIGHT. NEWTON ON THEORY AND HYPOTHESIS

NEWTON'S conception of the scientific method was clearly brought out in his first published work on light, and the discussion which it aroused forced him to formulate his ideas on the mechanistic philosophy of physical phenomena. And while his *Principia* is his greatest achievement, he continued to experiment and meditate more consecutively on the subject of light than on any other except perhaps chemistry. He also chose to attach his general cosmical and philosophical meditations to his treatise on *Optics* in the form of Queries. As this book was not published till 1709, I shall devote this chapter to a connected outline of his theory of light and his philosophical method although it will necessitate a considerable amount of repetition when the events of his life are narrated chronologically. Only in this way can continuity of his ideas be presented, and in the career of such a man they are more important than his outward life.

The importance Newton, at the age of thirty, attached to his discoveries in light is clearly indicated in his letter to Oldenburg where he wrote of them as "the oddest, if not the most considerable detection, which hath hitherto been made in the operations of nature."[1] But I believe he was convinced that the method by which he had made these "detections" was more important than the "detections" themselves. He saw clearly that the revolt against the Aristotelian deductive method, begun by Galileo, could lead to but one conclusion; science is limited to experimentation and to formulation of laws which together constitute a theory. It is only by keeping this in mind that we can appreciate his long polemic against hypothetical reasoning.

We have seen in Chapter III that the first action of the Royal Society, when it received Newton's first great paper on light, was to appoint a committee to appraise the value of his new theory of light,

[1] *Cf.* Chapter III, p. 72.

and to safeguard his right of priority by instructing Oldenburg to communicate its contents to Huygens as the one whose opinions would carry the greatest weight. The committee, at once, brought in their report, which was written and read by Hooke, at the next meeting on February 15, 1671/2. The report, in my judgement, is eminently fair, giving Newton full credit for his ingenious experiment and differing from him only on the ground that he had not proved that a vibration theory would not also explain his results.

Hooke reported in part: "I have perused the discourse of Mr. Newton about colours and refractions, and I was not a little pleased with the niceness and curiosity of his observations. But, tho' I wholly agree with him as to the truth of those he hath alleged, as having, by many hundreds of trials, found them so; yet as to his hypothesis of solving the phenomena of colours thereby, I confess, I cannot see yet any undeniable argument to convince me of the certainty thereof. For all the experiments and observations I have hitherto made, nay, and even those very experiments, which he allegeth, do seem to me to prove, that *white* is nothing but a pulse or motion, propagated through an homogeneous, uniform, and transparent medium; and that colour is nothing but the disturbance of that light, by the communication of that pulse to other transparent mediums, that is, by the refraction thereof: that *whiteness* and *blackness* are nothing but the plenty or scarcity of the undisturbed rays of light: and that the two colours (than the which there are not more uncompounded in nature) are nothing but the effects of a compounded pulse, or disturbed propagation of motion caused by refraction.

"But, how certain soever I think myself of my hypothesis (which I did not take up without first trying some hundreds of experiments) yet I should be very glad to meet with one *experimentum crucis* from Mr. Newton, that should divorce me from it. But it is not that, which he so calls, will do the turn; for the same phenomenon will be solved by my hypothesis, as well as by his, without any manner of difficulty or training: nay, I will undertake to shew another hypothesis, differing from both his and mine, that shall do the same thing. . . .

"Nor would I be understood to have said all this against his theory, as it is an hypothesis; for I do most readily agree with it in every part thereof, and esteem it very subtile and ingenious, and capable of solving all the phenomena of colours: but I cannot think it to be the only hypothesis, nor so certain as mathematical demonstrations."

The report, after it was read, was ordered to be registered and a copy to be sent to Newton. "And that in the mean time the printing of Mr. Newton's discovery by itself might go on, if he did not contradict it; and that Mr. Hooke's paper might be printed afterwards, it not being thought fit to print them together, *lest Mr. Newton should look upon it as a disrespect, in printing so sudden a refutation of a discourse of his, which had met with so much applause at the Society but a few days before.*"[2]

Hooke has been severely blamed by the partisans of Newton for his harsh treatment of the young philosopher, but his early criticism is in a perfectly proper tone. Undoubtedly, two men of such irritable temperament were almost certain to disagree, but much of the bitterness which followed can be laid at the door of Oldenburg, who disliked Hooke and certainly did nothing to ease the situation. That Newton was quite satisfied with the reception of his discourse and had no fault to find with the criticisms of either Huygens or Hooke is shown by his answer to Oldenburg.

Newton to Oldenburg

Cambridge, Feb. 20, 1671/2.

Sir,

I received your's [of] Feb. 19th. And having considered Mr. Hooke's observations on my discourse, *am glad that so acute an objector hath said nothing that can enervate any part of it.* For I am still of the same judgement, and doubt not but that upon severer examinations, it will be found as certain a truth as I have asserted it. You shall very suddenly have my answer.

In Monsr. Hugenius's letter there are several handsome and ingenious remarks. And what he saith concerning the grinding parabolical conoids by geometrical rules, I do with him despair of; but I doubt not but that the thing may be in some measure accomplished by mechanical devices. This is all at present from

your faithful servant,

I. NEWTON.[3]

For some unknown reason, the published correspondence between Oldenburg and Huygens and the articles of Huygens and Newton on

[2] Birch, III, p. 9 seq.—It was not printed in the *Transactions.*
[3] Macclesfield, Vol. II, p. 318.

the subject suppress Huygens's name and he is referred to as "an ingenious person of Paris, or as Monsieur N." It is from his collected works that we find that Oldenburg kept him acquainted with the whole discussion.[4]

The attitude of Huygens presents a curious conflict of opinion arising from two different traits of his character. On the one hand, he was a great experimentalist and he immediately appreciated the elegance and rigour of Newton's observations. So he answered Oldenburg: "Concerning his new *theory* of colours, it seems to me most ingenious, but it is necessary to see whether it is compatible with all experience." This favourable answer was most gratifying to the young scientist. But Huygens was also strongly committed to the refracting telescope and Newton had, perhaps, irritated him by his rather brusque advocacy of the superiority of the reflecting type. He was, also, an adherent of the Cartesian philosophy; and he had expanded the Cartesian hypothesis of the nature of light into a tentative theory of wave transmission, which had the support of the ingenious experimentalist Robert Hooke. As it became more apparent to him that these new experiments were difficult to reconcile with his and Hooke's hypothesis of waves, and its corollary that two primary colours, red and blue, combined to produce all other colours including white light, his habit of relying upon "an inward sentiment of knowledge" began to confuse his judgement and he wrote three months later: "Concerning his new *hypothesis* of colours . . . I confess that it appears quite probable, and the *experimentum crucis* (if I understand it correctly, for it is expressed rather obscurely) confirms it well." Thus, even he could not grasp the idea of the finality of Newton's experiments and formulation of laws from them, since he believed their truth and value lay in whether they confirmed this or that hypothesis of the nature and cause of light. In other words, the diversity of colours was not an objective fact but something dependent on our preconception of the nature of light. So he again wrote to Oldenburg: "What you have published in a recent number of the *Transactions* greatly strengthens his doctrine of colours. At the same time the cause of light may be something quite different, and it seems to me that he should content himself that, what he had advanced, may pass for a probable hypothesis. Besides, if it should be

[4] *Cf. Œuvres d'Huygens, t.* VII; Macclesfield *Collections,* Vol. II, pp. 291–345 *passim.;* Horsley, Vol. III, Letters *passim.; Phil. Trans.,* Nos. 96, p. 6086; 97, pp. 6108, 6112.

true that the rays of light, in their original state, were some red, others blue, etc. there would still remain the great difficulty of explaining, by mechanical principles, in what consists this diversity of colours."

The inability of Huygens to grasp the significance of his work was a bitter disappointment to Newton. He had patiently explained his experiments. He had reiterated that they involved no hypothesis as to the cause or nature of light; that the function of real science was to discover a well thought out series of experiments and to classify them in laws; and that any ingenious person could imagine mechanical hypotheses of many kinds which were, at best, mere mental pictures and not science. If he could not convince Huygens, what chance was there with inferior men? In the bitterness of his disappointment, he rebuked, in a published article, this inability of Huygens to see his point of view: "I confess it was a little ungrateful to me to meet with objections which had been answered before, without having the least reason given me why those answers were insufficient." He also wrote in his familiar letters that he was minded to forsake science altogether or, at least, never again to expose himself to the litigious altercations which were the fate of any one who published new ideas.

Newton's first critic in print was Father Ignatius Pardies, the distinguished professor of natural philosophy in the College of Clermont at Paris. In a letter published in the *Philosophical Transactions,*[5] Pardies pointed out that this work, if substantiated, overturned the accepted hypothesis of the nature of light. Imbued with the practice of the day that a multitude of observations must be made before a correct conclusion may be drawn, he objected vigorously because so revolutionary a doctrine "is founded entirely on the experiment of the prism, in which rays entering a dark room through a hole in a window-shutter, and then falling on the wall, or received on a paper, did not form a round figure, as he expected according to the received rules of refraction." He then gave his own explanations why the spectrum should be oblong. He next considered the *experimentum crucis,* which he evidently misunderstood and with some justification since Newton's statement is not only too condensed but is somewhat obscure, and stated that it is explicable without recourse to his new theory of the heterogeneity of white light. He, lastly, maintained that Newton's experiments on the mixture of colours to

[5] No. 84 (1672), pp. 4087–4090.

produce white were not conclusive; but he admitted that he had ingeniously and properly refuted Hooke's ideas of primary colours.

The whole critique was so temperately and appreciatively expressed that Newton answered all the objections carefully and fully. He took the opportunity to close his letter with an admonition against trying to make the laws of nature conform to our preconceived speculations: "I do not take it amiss that the Rev. Father calls my theory an hypothesis, inasmuch as he is not acquainted with it. But my design was quite different, for it seems to contain only certain properties of light, which, now discovered, I think easy to be proved, and which if I had not considered them as true, I would rather have them rejected as vain and empty speculation than acknowledged even, as an hypothesis."[6] In a second letter[7] Pardies, although not convinced, acknowledged that he had not read the *experimentum crucis* carefully; apologised for calling the author's theory an hypothesis, and complimented the "excellent Newton" for his ingenious discoveries.

Newton was deeply touched with his critic's fairness and could "hardly determine whether there is more of humanity and candour, in allowing my arguments their due weight, or penetration and genius in starting objections." He, then, again explained his experiments fully and carefully. Warmed by so appreciative a critic, Newton laid aside his reserve and gave expression to his ideas on the scientific method in what may be justly called the Golden Rule of Science: "For the best and safest method of philosophising seems to be, first to enquire diligently into the properties of things, and of establishing those properties by experiments, and then to proceed more slowly to hypotheses for the explanation of them. For hypotheses should be subservient only in explaining the properties of things, but not assumed in determining them; unless so far as they may furnish experiments. For if the possibility of hypotheses is to be the test of the truth and reality of things, I see not how certainty can be obtained in any science; since numerous hypotheses may be devised, which shall seem to overcome new difficulties. Hence it has been here thought necessary to lay aside all hypotheses, as foreign to the purpose, that the force of the objection should be abstractedly considered, and receive a more full and general answer. . . . As to the Rev. Father's calling our doctrine an hypothesis, I believe it only proceeded from his using the word which first occurred to him, as a

[6] *Phil. Trans.*, No. 84, p. 4091. [7] *Ibid.*, No. 85, p. 5012.

practice has arisen of calling by the name hypothesis whatever is explained in philosophy: and the reason of my making exception to the word, was to prevent the prevalence of a term, which might be prejudicial to true philosophy."[8]

After Pardies had read this letter he appended the following note: "I am quite satisfied with Mr. Newton's answer to me. The last scruple which I had, about the *experimentum crucis,* is fully removed. And I now clearly perceive by his figure what I did not before understand. When the experiment was performed after his manner, everything succeeded, and I have nothing further to desire." So ended a controversy conducted with propriety and courtesy on both sides. But Newton had to submit to two other long-drawn-out altercations, which cut deeply into his precious time and meditations, and which the officious Oldenburg should have prevented. One was marked by stupidity, and the other was irritating because it arose from jealousy and vanity.

The enquiries and objections of Huygens had the desired effect of calling the attention of men of science to the revolutionary ideas of Newton, and Oldenburg, in one of his letters to Huygens, expressed his belief that the new ideas were gaining ground. But they were not to be accepted without protest. On October 6, 1674, a letter was published in the *Philosophical Transactions*[9] by the "learned" Francis Linus, professor of mathematics in the College of English Jesuits at Liége, sharply criticising Newton's experimental work. The author stated that he had performed similar experiments thirty years previously and many times since then, and had found the same lengthening of the spectrum. But he had traced the phenomenon to its true cause and found that it was due to scattered light, either because the prism had been placed at a considerable distance from the aperture admitting the sun-light, or because "the sun either shined through a white cloud, or enlightened some such clouds near unto it. Otherwise the spectral image of the sun was circular as the prevalent theory demanded."

Oldenburg, with his customary fussiness, immediately wrote to Newton urging him to reply to this criticism which would have died from its own folly if left alone. Newton flatly refused to become involved, and expressed his disgust of this frivolous intrusion on his time.

[8] *Phil. Trans.*, No. 85, p. 5014.

[9] *Ibid.*, No. 110, p. 217.

Newton to Oldenburg

Cambridge, Dec. 5, 1674.

Sir,

I am sorry you put yourself to the trouble of transcribing Fr. Linus's conjecture, since (besides that it needs no answer) I have long since determined to concern myself no further about the promotion of philosophy. And for the same reason I must desire to be excused from engaging to exhibit yearly philosophic discourses, but yet cannot but acknowledge the honour done me by your council, to think of me for one amongst that list of illustrious persons, who are willing to perform it, and therefore desire to have my thanks returned to them for the motion. If it were my lot to be in London for some time, I might possibly take occasion to supply a vacant week or two with something by me, but that's not worth mentioning.

If you think fit you may, to prevent Fr. Linus's slurring himself in print with his wide conjecture, direct him to the scheme in my second answer to P. Pardies, and signify (but not from me) that the experiment, as it is represented, was tried in clear days, and the prism placed close to the hole in the window, so that the light had no room to diverge, and the coloured image made not parallel, (as in his conjecture,) but transverse to the axis of the prism.

Your humble servant,

Is. Newton.[10]

It would be wearisome and useless to give the details of this controversy which dragged along intermittently for many years. Only enough need be told to show its unfortunate effect on Newton's character. Linus was evidently a typical example of the narrow-minded pedagogue who had grown conceited with the dictatorial authority of the teacher in the school-room. Instead of accepting the assurance that the experiments had been tried on cloudless days or of repeating them himself, he published a letter in the *Philosophical Transactions* accusing Newton of gross carelessness or of misrepresenting the facts. No insinuation could have been more exasperating to one, whose whole life proved his absolute and fearless intellectual integrity. Stung to the quick he published his *Considerations*.[11]

[10] Macclesfield, Vol. II, p. 368.—Newton had been invited to present before the Society a series of experiments.

[11] *Phil. Trans.*, No. 121, p. 501.

Newton to Oldenburg for the Royal Society

Cambridge, November 13, 1675.

Sir—When you showed me Mr. Line's second letter, I remember I told you that I thought an answer in writing would be insignificant, because the dispute was not about any ratiocination, but my veracity in relating an experiment, which he denies will succeed as it is described in my printed letters: for this is to be decided not by discourse, but new trial of the experiment. What it is that imposes on Mr. Line I cannot imagine: but I suspect he has not tried the experiment since he acquainted himself with my theory, but depends upon his old notions, taken up before he had any hint given to observe the figure of the coloured image. I shall desire him therefore, before he returns any answer, to try it once more for his satisfaction. . . .

And he very properly concluded this rebuke by requesting that the experiments may be repeated before the Royal Society, although Dr. Hooke had already given testimony that all these experiments had been verified by himself two or three years ago. Linus probably never saw this answer, since "the epidemic catarrh, which hath raged through so many countries, and taken away so many aged persons, hath also overcome him." The attack was continued by his colleague, Gascoines,[12] who was incapable of experimenting himself or of understanding what others had done. He merely asserted dictatorially the superiority of the experienced Linus over a rash youth who was conceitedly trying to upset the wisdom of his elders. This was the time to drop the matter, and Newton would have done so had he not been urged and nagged by Oldenburg to justify himself.

Linus was succeeded in his professorship by Antoine Lucas who proved to be an intelligent and open-minded opponent. He at once heeded Newton's plea to put the matter to the test of experience and published a set of eight experiments of his own. He verified the oblong form of the spectrum but found a very much less proportional elongation. If Newton had not been out of all patience with the controversy, he would easily have found that the discrepancy resulted from the different dispersive powers of various kinds of glass. In that case he would probably have discovered the simple remedy for chromatic aberration later found by Chester More Hall, who com-

[12] He is not to be confused with the mathematician, Gascoigne.

bined a weak concave lens of high dispersive power with a stronger convex lens of a low dispersion.

We may close this correspondence with the Belgian professors by quoting one more letter.

Newton to Oldenburg

18 November, 1676.

Sir,

I promised to send you an answer to Mr. Lucas this next Tuesday, but I find I shall scarce finish what I have designed, so as to get a copy taken of it by that time, and therefore I beg your patience a week longer. I see I have made myself a slave to philosophy, but if I get free of Mr. Linus's business I will resolutely bid adieu to it eternally, excepting what I do for my private satisfaction, or leave to come out after me; for I see a man must either resolve to put out nothing new, or to become a slave to defend it.

But to let this pass, I beg the favour of you to let your servant convey this, enclosed, to Mr. Boyle, I not knowing well how to direct it to him.

Sir, I am

your humble servant,

I. N.[13]

I cannot agree with those who dismiss the subject merely by saying that Newton's critics were "silly" or jealous. This is too easy a solution. The common experience in science has always been that new ideas must submit themselves to the most searching criticism; it is the glory of science that truth results from opposition. One has only to compare the considerate treatment of Newton with the savage attacks on Galileo who persevered in the publication of his ideas at the peril of his life. It is absurd to claim that Newton was opposed by weak or vicious men; they were scholars of recognised ability holding positions of responsibility. They were rightly supporting the ideas of the greatest authorities of their day,—Kepler, Huygens, and, above all others, the magic name of Descartes. How were they to anticipate that this young and unknown man was an antagonist of greater genius than all the authorities they cited?

Of Newton's critics, the Liégeois professors can be ignored since their criticism was unintelligent and irrelevant; of the others, Pardies

[13] Macclesfield, Vol. II, p. 405.

had been most open-minded, but the attitude of Huygens, the greatest living natural philosopher, was disheartening. Although impressed, at first, by the elegance and accuracy of Newton's observations, he finally opposed them because they did not agree with his hypothesis of the vibrational nature of light. Biased by his preconceived ideas, he shut his eyes to the value of the new experimental evidence and became offended when he was sharply reprimanded for not judging the facts on their own merit: "There were matter," he wrote to Oldenburg, "to answer them and to form new difficulties; but seeing that he maintains his opinion with so much concern, I list not to dispute." It is only fair, however, to add that Huygens and Newton later came to a mutual feeling of the highest respect and regard.[14]

It is impossible for us to understand the character of Newton or the state of the physical sciences in the seventeenth century, without referring at length to the life and work of Robert Hooke, or Hook, as his name is indifferently spelled. What manner of man was he whose personal opposition delayed the publication of Newton's *Optics* for thirty years and almost prevented the completion of the *Principia;* whose bitter tongue confirmed Newton's tendency to secrecy and isolation, destroyed his early enthusiasm for the Royal Society, and disgusted him with science?

Robert Hooke[15] was born in the Isle of Wight on the 18th of July, 1635. Like Newton, he was at birth very infirm and weakly; and for the first seven years his parents entertained but little hope of his living to maturity. Like Newton, also, his scientific aptitude first showed itself in his love and genius for inventing mechanical contrivances. He was educated under the famous Dr. Busby of Westminster School, whose name in literature is synonymous with the great efficacy of the rod and who boasted that sixteen of the living bishops had been birched with his "little rod"; later he entered Oxford as a Servitor.

This University, at that time, offered far better opportunities for a scientific training than were found by Newton at Cambridge. The cause of this early cultivation of the new experimental philosophy at Oxford came from the affiliation of a group of its Fellows with a Philosophical Society in London which had been formed in 1645

14 *Principia,* Ed. 1803, p. xlix.

15 Most of the material for this sketch is taken from the life of Hooke prefixed to his *Posthumous Works,* Edited by Richard Waller, Sec. R. S., and dedicated to Sir Isaac Newton, Pres. R. S., and to the Royal Society. London, 1705.

and later developed into the powerful Royal Society.[16] This Oxford group thus became almost an integral branch of the Royal Society which was formally chartered by Charles II in 1660. It was the custom for many years to communicate the more important papers to the respective members of both Societies; and such experiments as could not be carried on conveniently in London were made at Oxford, where meetings were held, more or less regularly, till 1690.

Hooke, even in his undergraduate days, attracted the attention of these eminent Oxford scholars who recognised and encouraged his inventive genius. He became the intimate friend and personal assistant of Boyle, who was not only the most distinguished man of science in England but was incomparable in the purity of his ideals and in his generous aid to the scientific work of others. As early as 1658, or 9, we find the claim of Hooke in his manuscript notes, that he had contrived and perfected the air-pump for Mr. Boyle whose reputation largely depended on its use. He also invented and made trials of flying machines and, when he found that they would not succeed because of the weakness of our arms, he attempted to overcome this defect by applying his mind to contrive a way to make artificial muscles.

While we must discount many of Hooke's claims, because a man of such a feverish mental activity is certain to speculate on almost every subject, and is too apt to confuse shrewd guesses with accomplished results, yet we can be certain that he had shown his experimental genius while an undergraduate, and had attracted the attention and support of influential men by the marvellous fertility of his inventive powers. It is on record that a company was formed, at that time, by Lord Brouncker, Robert Boyle, and Sir Robert Moray, all of whom were prominent members of the new Royal Society, to exploit the inventions of Hooke and, especially, his application of a coiled spring to drive clocks and pocket watches.

He was, however, soon called away from Oxford to a broader field of opportunity. On the 12th of November, 1662, he was proposed by Sir Robert Moray as willing to act in the capacity of Curator of the Royal Society, two years after it had received its Charter. He agreed to the astounding proposition recorded in its Journal-book, "to furnish the Society every day they meet [once a week] with three or four considerable experiments, expecting no recompence till the Society get a stock enabling them to give it." No place could have

16 *Cf.* Chapter XIII for the history of these two societies.

offered a better opportunity for a man of his temperament; he continued to hold this position until his death and he laid the foundation for the future usefulness and distinction of the Society. "The Journal-books record the trial by him of several hundreds of experiments, mostly new, by which 'facts multiplied, leading phenomena became prominent, laws began to emerge, and generalisations to commence.' Waller, in his *Life of Hooke,* states that it was 'observed by several persons, that whatever apparatus he contrived, for exhibiting any experiments before the Royal Society, it was performed with the least embarrassment, clearly, and evidently.' "[17]

In addition to the unremitting toil necessary to his position as official experimenter, he was also energetic in collecting curiosities for the cabinet. We have evidence of his industry from Cosimo III, Grand Duke of Tuscany, who visited the Society in 1669: "The cabinet, which is under the care of Dr. Hooke, a man of genius,—is full of the greatest rarities,—the Academicians contribute everything of value which comes into their hands. Amongst these curiosities, the most remarkable are: an ostrich, whose young were always born alive; an herb which grew in the stomach of a thrush; and the skin of a moor, tanned, with the beard and hair white: but more worthy of observation than all the rest, is a clock, whose movements are derived from the vicinity of a lodestone, and it is so adjusted as to discover the distance of countries at sea by the longitude."[18] The exhibits are enumerated in order to show that science was still in the period of credulous acceptance of the marvellous.

After the great fire of 1666, the advice of the Society was sought for plans to rebuild London. The esteem in which Hooke was held, at the early age of thirty-one, is evident from the fact that he was appointed City Surveyor and made a model for rebuilding the city. But his plan was not adopted because private interests blocked his attempt to realign and widen important thoroughfares.[19]

In Hooke, we have a striking illustration of a great intellect housed in a wretched bodily tenement and showing the contrast of an essentially noble character in large matters with an irritable, suspicious, and cynical temperament, in the familiar affairs of life. His col-

[17] Weld, *Hist. Roy. Soc.*, Vol. I, p. 138. [18] *Ibid.*, Vol. I, p. 219.

[19] According to Waller, it was as one of the city surveyors that Hooke acquired the greater part of his estate: "He might by this place acquire a considerable estate, every particular person being in haste to have his concerns expedited; so that, as I have been inform'd, he had no rest early and late from persons soliciting to have their grounds set out, which, without any fraud or injustice, deserv'd a due recompense in so fatiguing an employ." Weld, Vol. I, p. 362.

leagues disliked and feared him for his saturnine temper and his caustic tongue. He was notorious for his criticisms of their work and for his insinuations that they had stolen the fruits of his labour. He was morbidly sensitive about his physical appearance which was frail and undersized almost to the degree of a deformity. Yet in spite of handicaps of appearance and temper, he won the admiration of the world by his genius and intellectual industry. Although he suffered persistently from excruciating headaches and devastating illnesses, he never relaxed from his arduous labours which embraced the entire field of science. "He was," says his biographer Waller, "of an active, restless, indefatigable genius, even almost to the last; and always slept little, to his death, seldom going to sleep till two, three, or four o'clock in the morning, and seldomer to bed, oftener continuing his studies all night, and taking a short nap in the day. His temper was melancholy, mistrustful, and jealous, which more increased upon him with his years."[20] Like his great contemporaries, Boyle and Newton, he was deeply and sincerely religious and looked upon his scientific work as primarily important in disclosing the purpose of God towards man. He died on the 3rd of March, 1702/3, after a lingering and distressing illness. His suffering and infirmities, during the latter years of his life, were so great that one of his biographers speaks of him as "living a dying life."

The duties imposed on Hooke by his official position in the Society, and his impatient temperament, prevented him from the sustained labour necessary for connected and large work. He published only one connected treatise which, under the title of the *Micrographia,* appeared in 1665, three years after he went to London. The main part of this work is devoted to descriptions and engravings of minute bodies as viewed under a home-made microscope. It shows positively that he had a clear grasp of the combinations and principles of lenses to be used in making microscopes and telescopes. He also includes his experiments on various phenomena of light, of which those on the colours produced in thin films are the most important. In this work, he was influenced by Boyle who had also investigated the subject. Here, also, is to be found the development of his hypothesis of the vibratory nature of light to explain his experimental discoveries.

Although Newton referred only once, and then casually, to having read the *Micrographia,* an examination of his work shows conclusively that he was greatly influenced by Hooke's experiments on thin

[20] Weld, Vol. I, p. 359.

films and on diffraction. Newton rarely mentioned any of the sources from which he drew the inspiration for his work. In the *Optics,* for instance, he merely stated that Grimaldi had discovered a curious bending of light into the geometric shadow and gave no credit to Hooke although he had made and published many experiments in the subject. It was an unavoidable misfortune that Hooke's reputation should suffer an eclipse, and that Newton's incomparable glory should dim his rival's lesser achievements. But it is inexcusable that Newton's eulogists, amongst whom must be included Brewster, should have felt that they could add to the prestige of their hero by slurring the character and achievements of such a competitor. The tradition they have handed down to us that Hooke's hypothetical ideas on light were puerile and foolish is quite false, for he was in advance of his age and had almost grasped the idea of the wave theory of light.

We should rather learn to look upon Newton, not only as a consummate creative genius but also as a profound scholar who had read widely and had assimilated the work of others. His treatise on *Optics* may, by its omission of citation of others' work, give the impression that he conceived his experiments and ideas entirely from his own meditations; but his early papers in the *Philosophical Transactions,* and especially the one in which he vindicated himself against Hooke's charge of plagiarism, and surveyed the history of the hypotheses of light, prove conclusively, to the unbiased reader, that Newton was conversant with the history of science from ancient to contemporaneous times and that he had borrowed freely from all sources. Like Shakespeare, he found his material wherever it was to be had, and like Shakespeare he moulded it and built out of it an edifice more beautiful than its original discoverers could have imagined. But there is this difference between them; Shakespeare, from the character of his work, was not called upon to acknowledge his indebtedness to others, but Newton was placed in the position many times, particularly in his controversies with Hooke, Leibniz, and Flamsteed, when honour, or at least generosity, required him to be open and explicit in giving credit for their work. Too often, he remained silent or crushed his opponent with the weight of his reputation.

We could scarcely imagine two men more certain to disagree in personal and intellectual relations than Hooke and Newton. Both were temperamentally suspicious and jealous; both were impatient of opposition and sensitive to criticism. Newton, animated with a pure love of truth, never permitted himself to swerve from the high standard of his intellectual integrity. But he was not so guided in his personal standards; he met criticism by a covert attack on his critics or weakly threatened to abandon scientific work, lest by being induced to divulge his thoughts to an ungrateful world he should be disturbed in the pursuit of his private meditations. Hooke, on the other hand, blazed out into wrathful explosions, bitter recriminations, and accusations that his ideas had been stolen.

Also their environment would, of itself, keep them apart. Newton, living isolated and undisturbed, concentrated on a few subjects and, having seized on a few fundamental facts, never relaxed till he had wrung from them their deepest meaning. He made public a very small body of work, but each portion was an imperishable monument to his genius. Whereas Hooke, distracted by executive duties and required to complete three or four hurried experiments weekly, left a mass of undigested and scattered observations which have been swallowed up in the course of later and more accurate experimentation. He suffered from the exasperating experience of seeing his fertile hints developed by others and contributory to their fame. His work on light, which forms the bulk of his *Micrographia* and *Posthumous Papers,* is the only subject which shows any consecutive development, and he evidently regarded it as his chief contribution to science. And yet, although his hypothesis as to the nature of light was in advance of current ideas, history has characterised it as puerile in comparison with the work of Huygens and Newton.

Hooke, like Newton, was thoroughly in sympathy with the ambition of Descartes to substitute a purely mechanical universe, based on the experimental laws of matter and motion, for the teleological system of Aristotle. Both of them believed that the purpose of science was to discover and classify phenomena, and had a strong leaning to the application of science to practical problems; but they were also tinctured with the mediæval belief that God had created and continued to guide the world according to His will. The new discoveries in astronomy, mechanics, and light may have shaken their belief in the miraculous, and have substituted the idea that God, as an omnipotent geometer, had fashioned a universal machine subject to rigorous mechanical laws; but they also firmly believed that

God had endowed us with "an inward sentiment of knowledge" capable of understanding and exposing His plan and purpose, in order that, from a knowledge of His work, we should know Him.

Although Huygens, Hooke, and Pardies, the three principal opponents of Newton, were men of widely different temperament and achievement, they were all proponents of the Cartesian philosophy. We can easily imagine the general attitude of the scholarly world; on the one side, there was a young, and unknown, man who had proposed a revolutionary method based on a few simple experiments; on the other side was entrenched the dogmatic authority of accepted procedure, buttressed by the glittering and grandiose cosmical system of Descartes. Can we doubt to which side the rank and file leaned? It was not until Newton had proved himself a greater genius than Descartes that the world accepted his leadership. And then, such is the irony of fate, his basic definition of the limitations of the scientific method was more or less ignored or forgotten; while his merely tentative queries about the nature of the universe were seized upon, that out of them might be erected a new and even more glittering cosmogony than that of Descartes.

Descartes, as has been noted previously, had included in his cosmical system a purely imaginative explanation of the nature of light and colour unsupported by any experimental evidence. He merely asserted that light, in essence, was a pressure transmitted instantaneously through space from a cosmic vortex. The action of this pressure on matter was to give a translational motion to certain particles which he first created and then named "light globules." The impact of these globules on the retina produced the sensation of whiteness; but if, in their passage through matter, the globules had also acquired a rotatory motion, then we experienced a sensation of colour.

The only possible value of this hypothesis was the attempt to explain light in terms of mechanical ideas. But Hooke, following up some observations of Boyle, approached the subject from its experimental side and had made a large number of observations on the colours produced by light reflected from transparent films of mica, soap bubbles, etc. By a masterly analysis of the facts, he recognised that the succession of colours which he observed was produced by the combination of a beam of light reflected from the upper surface of the film with a second beam which had penetrated the film and had been reflected from its lower surface. He then saw that Descartes's hypothesis, of the conversion of light (whiteness) into colour by adding a rotatory motion to the linear propagation of globules, was fundamentally at fault and untenable. His conclusion should be given in his own quaint language: "Here we have all kinds of colours generated in a pellucid body, where there is properly no such refraction as Descartes supposes his globules to acquire a *verticity* by; For in the plane and even plates it is manifest, that the second refraction does regulate and restore the supposed *turbinated globules* unto their former uniform motion. This experiment will prove such a one as *our thrice excellent Verulam calls experimentum crucis.*"[21]

Hooke had discovered the fundamental phenomenon of the interference of light, and had noted the correct succession of colours. But he failed to take the final, and decisive, step of submitting his observations to quantitative measurement which Newton happily accomplished by observing the colours produced in the measured film of air between a glass plate and a superimposed plano-convex lens. And by that failure, the credit of the whole discovery passed to Newton.

As a result of his observations, Hooke then drew three conclusions: first, the parts of all fiery burning bodies are in motion; secondly, the motion is exceeding quick and vibrative; thirdly, it is a very short vibrative motion. This first explanation was later modified to conform to the ideas of Newton, for in his lectures on light, delivered in 1680, he shifted to the idea that light is a corporeal substance, a kind of uncompressible fluid capable of motion like all other bodies. This motion of the "light substance" is propagated in the medium either by waves of motion spreading out in rings or else by the extrusion of the part of the fluid medium of light that lies between the solid particles of the shining body, like water from a sponge. It seemed in some cases, according to him, to be the one way; and in other cases, the other way.[22]

In their general ideas, Hooke and Newton were never far apart. They both hoped to express the phenomena of light either as the action of a substance or as a vibratory motion, and each influenced the other's ideas. They split on the question of what constitutes a primary colour and it will not be difficult to show that the cause of their difference arose only from their incompatible definitions of colour.

Hooke had discovered the psychological effect that the mixture of

[21] *Micrographia*, p. 54.

[22] Hooke, *Posthumous Papers*, p. 115.

two complementary colours, such as scarlet and blue, produced a sensation of white which could not be distinguished from sun-light. He therefore assumed them to be the only primary colours, and that all others are mixtures of these two with light and darkness. He then, without any basis of fact, followed the fashion and formulated a hypothetical cause for colour. He says: "The phenomenon of colour depends on the obliquity of the orbicular pulse [i.e., the wave-front] to the lines of radiation. The ray which constitutes the scarlet has its inner parts, namely those which are next to the middle of the luminous body, precedent to the outermost which are contiguous to the dark and unradiating sky. And that the ray, which gives a blue, has its outward part precedent to the pulse from the innermost part."[23]

Just here lies the evidence of the genius which separated Newton from his competitors. He, in the first place, refused to make an hypothetical explanation of colour and, in the second place, he refused to adopt the psychologic or subjective sensation of colour as a criterion for physical or objective phenomena of light. To him, a primary colour was one which had a definite angle of refrangibility, whatever sensation of colour it might cause, and could not be decomposed by passing it through a prism. The eye thus is merely a recording instrument for certain phenomena of light and may not be sensitive to others which can properly be classed as invisible light. To instance only one example: we know that radiation is not limited by the visible spectrum; beyond the blue end invisible energy can be detected by a photographic plate and beyond the red end by a thermometer and, except for their inability to affect the eye, such radiations are identical with those which are visible. And in fact phenomena pertaining to visible light are frequently observed, and accurately measured, by thermometers or electrical instruments whose responses can be determined by the sense of touch. While our contact with the external world is necessarily by our sensations, the physicist has successfully discarded the sensation immediately concerned for one which is less liable to be thus confused. While for phenomena of light the eye may often be used, an instrument is interposed whose record will not depend on the same class of phenomena. The "white" which was created by Hooke's primary red and blue colours was not by Newton's criterion equivalent to the "white" which could be spread out into the indefinite number of colours of the continuous

[23] *Micrographia,* p. 59.

spectrum; each of these constituents of the rainbow was therefore a primary colour. This may seem to be a trifling difference but it involves the essential problem of what constitutes the scientific method.

While physicists have more and more discarded the psychologic sensations as criteria and have, as far as possible, formulated objective laws, they still confuse subjective sight and objective light, or radiation; in text-books they discuss colour as if it were an objective reality and yet explain it subjectively by the supposition of a nerve reaction to three primary colours, altogether ignoring the fact that in another portion of the book they define a primary colour as any one of the indefinite number of lines in a continuous spectrum. On the other hand, psychologists endeavour to measure subjective phenomena of sight with physical instruments as though they were independent of the sensation of vision. Neither realises that there is no common ground of fact or theory. To the physicist, the problem ends when light energy is physically absorbed by the retina; for the psychologist the problem begins with that absorption. What happens in the interval between the physical absorption of energy and the mental translation into vision is a process to which science can give no clue. The phenomena of sight and light form two irreducible and incommensurable categories.

As another example of the gulf between psychology and physics, I may instance the phenomenon of after-images. If the eye becomes fatigued by steady gazing at an intense red light and is then closed, there appears to the mind the subjective image of the same object changed to the colour complementary to red. However the psychologists may attempt to explain such a phenomenon, their explanation will not fall under any known physical law of optics. The variation they are studying occurs not in the active agent but in the receiving instrument which records an action of its own contrivance.

An even more convincing illustration may be given of the fundamental difference between the points of view of the psychologist and the physicist. Let us consider the well-known phenomenon of colour blindness which prevents certain persons from distinguishing between redness and greenness. The assertion by the psychologists, derived from the sense perception of sight, that there are the two qualities of redness and greenness is one which must always remain a pure matter of opinion to be decided by the fact that the majority of people possess the ability to make such a distinction. Because the majority is large, the minority are content to conform to their opinion and to confess an abnormality of vision although they have no possibility of perceiving the difference. It would not be difficult to imagine all human beings to be thus colour blind. Granted such a condition, the possibility of distinguishing between these two colours, visually or psychologically, could never have arisen; yet the physicist with a prism would have no difficulty in distinguishing them by their specific refrangibilities.

I am not one who indulges in the vain fancy of imagining what the world would have been without intelligent and self-conscious beings like ourselves to observe and interpret its phenomena, or of speculating whether it could be said to exist independently of a sentient organic being; I look upon such pictures (so often given us by evolutionists and metaphysicians) as idle dreams and impossible speculations made by one who first of all postulates the state of non-existence of himself. But it is possible to imagine a world like ours except for the fact that no organic being on it possessed the sensation of sight,—in the language of evolution, that the eye had never developed. Would it be an exaggeration to say that the idea of colour would never have been conceived and that there would have been no phenomena of light so far as either psychology or physiology is concerned? But there could still be an objective science of light radiation, because many of the phenomena, which we, possessed of vision, now fuse with the sensation of colour and light, could be discovered by the physicist by other means even if the whole race of men had always been blind. I am, of course, merely stating the old and trite question; is there a sound if a tree falls in a forest when there is no one near enough to hear it? To the physicist, a sound is only a particular form of vibratory motion in the air, or other medium, which can be detected and measured by any suitable apparatus whether or not it be audible; to the psychologist, audibility is the essence of such radiation. Are we not justified in agreeing with Newton that the sensation of colour is not a criterion in establishing the physical laws of light? To avoid confusion of thought, all theories of colour sensation should be omitted from the science of physics. There are no primary colours, except in the sense that there are primary sound-tones. Any colour which cannot be decomposed by Newton's criterion of the laws of refrangibility is a primary colour, just as a tone is acoustically primary if it is due to a simple harmonic motion. Newton has, once for all, enunciated the fundamental difference between physics and all the biological sciences,—between objective and subjective phenomena.

The controversy between Hooke and Newton is thus fundamentally important, since it, for the first time, raised the issue between the hypothetical and the theoretical methods. It is fortunate that, on the whole, the Newtonian method has prevailed and has made possible the growth of physics into the most nearly exact of the sciences. But it is unfortunate that the hypothetical method in science still confuses the issue, and prevents us from distinguishing between the objective and subjective worlds,—between science and humanism.

After this long digression, we can discuss Newton's attack on hypothetical reasoning with the better hope of clearing up some of the misconceptions which still persist in regard to his ideas. His conviction, that the scientific method is dependent on an intuitive belief in the objective reality of natural phenomena and is limited to mathematical formulation of laws derived from their observation and classification, was undoubtedly temperamental, as it clearly showed itself in his earliest years.

The source of the opposition to Newton, as has been previously noted, sprang from the dogmatic acceptance of Descartes's cosmical hypothesis. While Newton may have been too sensitive to any criticism, he was morbidly so, when the opposition was supported by the bare authority of a great name. I have little doubt that his persistent depreciation of even Descartes's solid scientific work may be assigned to this cause, and is the answer to Biot's surprise when, in his essay on Newton, he comments: "It is singular, however, that Newton, in his writings, has never mentioned Descartes favourably; and, on more than one occasion, has treated him with injustice. Particularly in his *Optics,* where he attributes the discovery of the true theory of the rainbow to Antonius de Dominis, leaving to Descartes only the merit of having 'mended the explication of the exterior bow'; and yet every impartial reader, who refers to the original works, will see that the theory of Descartes is exact and complete.—And the book of Dominis contains absolutely nothing but explications entirely vague, without any calculation or real result."

Newton not only grasped the fundamental principle of the scientific method and defined the limits beyond which exact sciences cannot go, but he also warned men of science against the confusion of thought which results from the careless use of words. From the beginning he recognised that the gravamen of the criticism was directed against deductions made from his observations rather than against the facts themselves. He also saw clearly that the source of disagreement in scientific arguments is often to be found in laxity of expression. Thus he insisted on the fundamental distinction between hypotheses and theories: "As to the Rev. Father's [Pardies] calling our doctrine an hypothesis, I believe it only proceeded from his using the word which first occurred to him, as a practice has arisen of calling by the name hypothesis whatever is explained in philosophy: and the reason for my taking exception to the word, was to prevent the prevalence of a term, which might be prejudicial to true philosophy." It cannot be denied that there is a real distinction between ideas about the objective world which are deduced from phenomena by experiment, or are verifiable by experiment, and ideas which are not; and it would be an invaluable aid to clear thinking if we should emphasise this difference by preserving the distinction between an "hypothesis" and a "theory" which Newton introduced. If the warning against looseness of diction was needed in Newton's day, when learned men used Latin in familiar conversation and employed a nicer discrimination in English, it is far more necessary today when our conversation is slovenly, and men of science as a class are ignorant of Latin, and disdainful of literary training. If the student of science spent a little less time in the laboratory, and more time in learning a correct use of his native tongue and greater care in expressing his thoughts accurately, the controversial literature of science would be greatly reduced in bulk, and the world at large could distinguish between the solid ground of scientific truth and the vagaries of pseudo-science.

The young Newton began his long polemic against "hypotheses" in the mild form of expressing his preference for the experimental method. Thus he wrote to Pardies: "Give me leave, Sir, to insinuate that I cannot think it effectual for determining truth, to examine the several ways by which phenomena may be explained, unless where there can be a perfect enumeration of all these ways. You know that the proper method for enquiring after the properties of things, is to deduce them from experiments."[24] And again: "Hypotheses should be subservient only, in explaining the properties of things, but not assumed in determining them; unless so far as they may furnish experiments."[25]

[24] *Phil. Trans.*, No. 85, p. 5004. [25] *Ibid.*, No. 85, p. 5014.

It was only when he found that even such critics as Huygens and Hooke would not accept his experiments on their own merit, but judged them adversely because of a disagreement with their psychologic hypothesis of two primary colours,—it was then that he stiffened in his opposition to including imaginative concepts of the objective world in the scientific method. He rebuked Hooke in print. First, he sarcastically declared that he could imagine many hypotheses which will explain all the known experimental facts as satisfactorily as does Hooke's hypothesis. Then he showed that Hooke's hypothesis will not really explain the observations of either of them; and lastly, he dismissed the subject as unimportant, after pointing out certain fundamental objections to a wave theory of light. "It is true that from my theory I argue the corporeity of light; but I do it without any absolute positiveness. . . . But I knew that the properties which I declare of light, were in some measure capable of being explicated, not only by that, but by many other mechanical hypotheses. And therefore I *chose to decline them all,* and to speak of light in general terms. . . . You see therefore, how much it is beside the business in hand to dispute about hypotheses."[26]

Newton had encountered a common failing from which men of science are not exempt; the hypothetical children of the mind are objects of such tender solicitude to their parents, that they are more anxious to safeguard them than to examine impersonally the truth of experimental facts. He came to the conclusion that his contemporaries were absolutely unable to understand the fundamental difference between hypothesis and experimental law. As a result of this conviction, painfully borne in on him by altercation after altercation, he determined to discard the hypothetical method altogether in the *Principia* and in his treatise on *Optics*. The classic statement of this determination is given in the General Scholium at the end of the *Principia:* "Hitherto I have not been able to discover the cause of those properties of gravity from phenomena, and I frame no hypotheses, *hypotheses non fingo;* for whatever is not deduced from the phenomena is to be called an hypothesis; and hypotheses, whether metaphysical or physical, whether of occult qualities or mechanical, have no place in experimental philosophy. In this philosophy particular propositions are inferred from the phenomena, and afterwards rendered general by induction. Thus it was that the impenetrability, the mobility, and the impulsive force of bodies, and

[26] *Phil. Trans.,* No. 88, p. 5084.

the laws of motion and of gravitation, were discovered. And to us it is enough that gravity does really exist, and act according to the laws which we have explained, and abundantly serves to account for all the motions of the celestial bodies, and of our sea." [27]

While Newton excluded hypothesis from the field of science, he, as is the habit of anyone with imagination, indulged in much private speculation as to the causes of phenomena and the nature of the physical universe. His excellence lay in the fact that his mind was so disciplined that, while such fancies might delight his power of invention and spur him to continued effort, he never confused them with the permanent acquisition of knowledge which follows from a careful investigation of phenomena and natural laws.

To turn from a discussion of general differences between the two philosophers to the specific cause of their mutual hostility, we should remember that Hooke had been appointed a member of a committee of the Royal Society to consider the new work of Newton. His report was appreciative of Newton's experimental work, but in it he had the bad taste to advise him, as a novice, to continue his useful labour of improving the telescope and to leave the general field of experimental light to those who had perfected a thoroughly satisfactory hypothesis. He also indulged in his customary and obnoxious habit of claiming that most of the discoveries had been made by himself. He, lastly, brushed aside Newton's disclaimer of neither proposing, nor needing, an hypothesis since he had, on the contrary, really advanced the notion that "light is a body, and that as many colours or degrees as there may be, so many bodies there may be; all which compounded together would make white."

Oldenburg, the Secretary, promptly reported to Newton what had occurred in the Council of the Society, and urged him to defend himself against what he termed a secret attack. The motive for the advice may have been a sincere interest in his friend's welfare, but it was undoubtedly influenced by the evident jealousy which existed between himself and Hooke. As a consequence of his own antipathy, he exaggerated the Curator's irascibility and gave the impression that matters were worse than they actually were. This time he succeeded, and Newton prepared a long letter for publication in which he vindicated his own work and criticised in detail Hooke's hypothesis and his unjust attitude.

27 Andrew Motte's translation of the *Principia*, Vol. II, p. 314, London, 1803.

In this memoir[28] Newton acknowledged that, from his theory, he had argued the corporeity of light but did so without any absolute positiveness. He had foreseen that his discoveries were explicable in some measure by that supposition, but as they were equally well explained by vibrations and by many other mechanical hypotheses, he chose to decline them all and to speak of light only in the most general terms. Why, he asked, does Hooke become so agitated against such an hypothesis, since a belief in vibrations as a cause of colour is as applicable to it as to his own?

He thus admitted that he had vaguely defined light as some *thing* or some *power* propagated in straight lines. And he had proposed a corpuscular hypothesis, if one could call it by such a name, because he believed it had a close affinity to Hooke's own hypothesis of vibratory motion and not as a substitute to it. Unfortunately, however, he had spoken loosely of colours,—a term in common use for rays of light,—as if they were objective qualities of light instead of the subjective sensation excited in our minds by specific variations of a light substance or of its mechanical motion. Such light corpuscles, when they impinge on a reflecting or refracting material surface, would excite vibrations in the æther "as stones do in water when thrown into it," and we may assume these vibrations to be of various wave lengths according to the sizes and velocities of the corpuscles causing them. How these different vibrations account for reflection and refraction, heat, phenomena of colours in thin films, vision, colours of bodies, etc., "I shall leave to their consideration, who may think it worth their endeavour to apply their hypothesis to the solution of the phenomena."

Newton next stated Hooke's hypothesis as he understood it: "The parts of bodies, when briskly agitated, do excite vibrations in the æther, which are propagated every way from those bodies in straight lines, and cause a sensation of light by beating and dashing against the bottom of the eye, something after the manner that vibrations in the air cause a sensation of sound by beating against the organs of hearing." This, he claimed, can mean only that the agitated parts of luminous bodies differ in shape, size, and motion, thus producing vibrations of various depths and sizes in the æther. A mixture of these vibrations excites a sensation of whiteness, whether by two complementary colours or by the whole spectrum. But, if the different vibrations are sorted out by any means, such as by a prism,

[28] *Phil. Trans.*, No. 88, p. 5084, July 11, 1671.

the largest beget the sensation of a red colour; the least, or shortest, a violet; and similarly for the intermediate colours of the spectrum. This seemed to Newton a necessary corollary to Hooke's hypothesis and he should therefore welcome the new discovery of selective refrangibility and of decomposition of white light into an indefinite number of primary rays, or of primary colours if we translate the objective phenomena into their subjective sensation of vision.

Newton finally gives his reasons why he believes in a corporeal, or corpuscular, nature of light to which must be added the ancillary effect of æthereal vibrations. It was his settled conviction that the rectilinear propagation of light *in vacuo* cannot be explained except by the hypothesis of corpuscles moving with a great velocity in straight lines; it is impossible "that waves or vibrations in any fluid can, like the rays of light, be propagated in straight lines, without a continual and very extravagant spreading and bending every way into the quiescent medium, where they are terminated by it." According to the knowledge of the day, he was correct. From observation of waves in water and of sound in air, he knew that waves do not progress in straight lines; water waves bend around an obstacle, and sound waves encroach deeply into the shadow; but the shadow cast by an obstacle placed in a beam of light was believed to be bounded by geometrically straight lines drawn from a point source to a screen. To be sure, the obscure phenomenon of diffraction had been discovered by Grimaldi, but no one then knew that it could be explained by a similar bending of rays of light. Before the diffraction of light, as an evidence of the bending of light rays into a shadow, could be incorporated into a wave theory, Huygen's celebrated mathematical theorem of the rectilinear propagation of waves, combined with the principle of secondary point sources and interference, had to be developed. Even this support of a wave theory left its author's hands defective and more than a century passed before a rigorous solution of the problem was discovered. Even now an insuperable objection to a pure wave hypothesis persists; an æthereal medium must be imagined whose mechanical properties are absolutely contrary to our experience of material substances,—a fluid so fictitious, and so impossible of visualisation, that it became a burden, instead of an aid, to science.

Thus Newton made no objection to the hypothesis that light is, in a general way, either moving corpuscles or æthereal waves. For, in fact, if one attempts to define all physical phenomena in terms of mechanical action, light must be one or the other, or a combination of both, since they are the only known methods by which mechanical energy can be transmitted through space. So he pointed out that his experimental results could be taken as a support to Hooke's, or any other, hypothesis of a mechanical nature. But the habit of giving *specific* properties to an occult corpuscle or to an occult æther was abhorrent to him. From these general considerations, he then turned on his critic and, in a few sentences, demolished Hooke's particular hypothesis that there are only two colours, red and blue, which are themselves explained "by the splitting and rarefying of æthereal pulses,"—an explanation that his own experiments had made futile. "If," he concluded, "I would proceed to examine these his explications, I think it would be no difficult matter to show that they are not only insufficient, but in some respects, to me, at least, unintelligible."

We can easily imagine that Newton's vindication of his own ideas, and crushing counter-attack on Hooke's cherished hypothesis, produced a profound effect on the abler members of the Royal Society. We can, also, be sure that it vastly increased Hooke's irritable temper. From the correspondence between Oldenburg and Newton, we are certain that Hooke used the advantage of his constant attendance and official influence to prejudice the members against the absent Cambridge professor by accusing him of taking from the *Micrographia* whatever was of any real value in his work. Newton endured these attacks for three years and then answered them only in a personal letter to Oldenburg which he forbade to be published; but, it is altogether probable that his correspondent showed it to some, at least, of his fellow-members.

From the following entries in the Journal-book of the Society we can appreciate how far Hooke had progressed in his opposition and why Newton finally broke his silence to vindicate himself in such a crushing manner.

"On December 9, 1675, Newton sent a manuscript, giving the principal phenomena connected with the colours produced in thin plates by refraction."

On December 16, 1675: "The sequel of his [Newton's] hypothesis, which was began [sic] to be read the last day, was read to the end. To which Mr. Hook said, that the main of it was contained in his

Micrographia, which Mr. Newton, in some particulars, had only carried further." This communication was not published and presumably because of Hooke's objection.

At the meeting of January 20, 1675/6, Newton's letter to Oldenburg of 21 December, 1675, was read in which he sharply criticised Hooke.

The portion of a letter to Oldenburg, dated 10 January, 1675/6, which refers to Hooke is as follows:[29]

"I am obliged to you, Sir, for your candour, in acquainting me with Mr. Hook's insinuations. It is but a reasonable piece of justice, I should have an opportunity to vindicate myself from what may be undeservedly cast on me; and therefore, since you have been pleased to be my representative there, and I have no means of knowing what is done but by you, I hope you will continue that equitable candour; though I think the present business of no great moment as to me, not imagining that the Royal Society are to be imposed on in a thing so plain, or that Mr. Hook himself will persist in a mistake, when he hears the difference stated. The only thing I said he could pretend taken from his hypothesis, was the disposition of æther to vibrate; and yet whilst he grasps at all, he is likely to fall short of this too. That æthereal vibrations are light, is his; but that æther may vibrate (which is all, I suppose) is to be had from a higher fountain: for that æther is a finer degree of air, and air a vibrating medium, are old notions, and the principles I go upon. I desire Mr. Hook to shew me, therefore, I say not only the sum of the hypothesis I wrote, which is his insinuation, but only part of it taken out of his *Micrographia;* but then I expect too, that he instance in what is his own. It is most likely he will pretend, I had from him the application of vibrations to the solution of the phenomena of thin plates: and yet all the use I make of vibrations, is, to strengthen or weaken the reflecting power of the ætheral superficies; which is so far from being in his *Micrographia,* that the last spring, when I told him of the reflecting power of the æthereal superficies, he took it for a new notion; having till then supposed light to be reflected by the parts of gross bodies. To the things that he has from Descartes, pray add this, *that the parts of solid bodies have a vibrating* motion, least he should say I had from him what I say about heat. And his having from Descartes the reduction of all colours to two, you may, if need

[29] A part of this letter referring to Linus's criticisms was published in the *Phil. Trans.*, but the portion which I have given was suppressed. The whole letter is printed by Horsley, *Opera Omnia,* Vol. IV, p. 355.

be, explain further for me thus. That as Descartes puts every *globulus* to be urged forward on one side by the illuminated medium, and impeded on the other by the dark one; so Mr. Hook puts every vibration to be promoted at one end, and retarded at the other by those mediums; and thence both alike derive two modifications of light, on the two sides of the refracted beam, for the production of all colours."

Although Newton sent no more communications to the Society after 1675 on the subject of light, he continued his experimental work, extending his knowledge of refraction, colours in thin plates, diffraction, and the new phenomenon of double refraction produced by crystals of Iceland spar. He also pondered deeply on the nature of light. While he still maintained his early conviction that light, itself, was material, yet he became more and more influenced by the ideas of Huygens and Hooke, whose experimental ingenuity he fully appreciated and whose hypothesis of vibrations had steadily progressed in public estimation. So, when he published his *Treatise on Optics* many years later, he limited the body of his work to a discussion of the experimental phenomena and laws of light; but he ventured to add, as an appendix, a set of Queries, in which form he could state his matured ideas on the nature and mechanism of light and yet not incorporate them as an integral part of a scientific treatise. I shall, by an analysis of these Queries, attempt to give an untechnical view of his conception of light, and to clear up some of the mistakes which his followers attached to it. Such an analysis is facilitated by the fastidious care he exercised, as always, in the choice of words and clarity of diction. We may disagree with his ideas, and he certainly is not always consistent in his opinions, but we are rarely at a loss to comprehend what he has attempted to express.

Newton rather roughly grouped his Queries into three general divisions; the first section treats of the nature of light, its emission from luminous bodies, and its relation to matter; this is followed by an enquiry into the absorption of light by material bodies and its interpretation as vision; the conclusion, which forms the longest and most important portion, is concerned with the method of the transmission of energy through space, and with the general properties of an æthereal transmitting medium.

I have frequently read and meditated upon these Queries, and each time I am more profoundly impressed with Newton's consummate genius, his pure intellectual integrity, and his reverent humility in the presence of the infinite complexity of nature. In them, he is at his best, far removed from the petty jealousies and intrigues which marred so frequently his personal relations. They are the choicest fruit of almost a half-century of meditation. I know of no other such scientific document so perspicuous, so restrained, and so conscious of the inherent limitation of our thought to penetrate the essence of things. I have wondered why he should have appended to a rigorous treatise on light such questionings on so many diverse topics; perhaps it was the same feeling which animated his Platonic friends to regard Light as a mystical personification of God.

He had early insisted that a mechanical model could readily be devised for any limited set of phenomena; in fact, he said that many models could be imagined for the same set of phenomena. But, when we attempt to insert several groups of related phenomena into a larger frame, then these models invariably fail to fit together. At best, therefore, all such models or hypotheses are but pictures and aids to memory, or concrete modes of verbal communication. Their fault and grave danger lie in the tendency they have to make us confuse what is real with what is fictitious, a confusion peculiarly obnoxious to him. Worst of all, the history of thought and his own experience clearly prove that hypotheses always become static and dogmatic so that new experimental data are judged, and accepted or condemned, according as they confirm, or contradict, such preconceived and cherished children of the mind; whereas if they are indulged in at all, they should remain so fluid and tentative as to be abandoned or modified so soon as new data are discovered. Admitting this limited use of mechanical hypotheses, he would still deem them to be merely fictitious pictures of the material world and absolutely irrelevant to problems involving life.

Newton[30] postulated that the essence of Light is a Corporeal Substance in so far, at least, as to have the mechanical properties of extension and motion. Every body is a combination of a material and of a luminous substance, both of which are granular in structure; the corpuscles of the latter are very much smaller in size than atoms of matter; they occupy the interstitial spaces between the material atoms of bodies and fill vacuous space as a luminiferous medium or æther. As material atoms by their motions, create the sensations of tangibility, sound, etc.; so light corpuscles, by their motion, produce the sensations of sight and temperature and, perhaps, of weight. In

[30] Digest of thirty-one Queries appended to the *Optics*, 4th edition, 1730, pp. 313–382.

other words, it was inconceivable to him that there could be motion without something substantial which could move. In this respect he was dualistic, since he held that energy was the combination of two irreducible factors, substance and motion.

Atoms and corpuscles, by the impacts of their motion, act mutually upon one another; that is to say, bodies upon light, causing its emission, reflection, refraction, and inflection; and light on bodies by putting their parts into a vibrating motion wherein heat consists. This identification of heat with motion he adopted from Descartes. If this vibratory motion be communicated to our own bodies, we recognise it as temperature; if it be sufficiently rapid it also affects the optic nerve, and we perceive the object as luminous. Corpuscles and atoms act on one another not only by impact but they also mutually attract each other with a force varying inversely as some power of the distance between them,—the cause, perhaps, of the attractions of gravitation, electricity, magnetism and other phenomena. This supposition of the mutual attraction of matter and light has been revived by Professor Einstein as one of the fundamental postulates of his theory of the gravitational field. While it has not been conclusively verified, observations on the positions of stars very near the sun made during eclipse are believed by many astronomers to confirm it.

The proposal to fill both free space and the pores of bodies with light corpuscles, everywhere individually of the same order of size and differing only in density of spatial distribution, involved Newton in an insuperable dilemma. Either the corpuscles, emitted at enormous speed from luminous bodies, must be able to travel the immense distances of interstellar space in straight paths without encountering other corpuscles, although they are assumed to be the densest *in vacuo:* or, the corpuscles must persist in the bodies in which they are enmeshed and merely transmit a vibratory, or wave, motion to an æther which, itself a substance, would thus involve the existence of a third elemental substance,—an hypothesis untenable in his opinion because of its incompatibility with the rectilinear propagation of light by waves. As Newton's corpuscular hypothesis breaks down in explaining the transmission of light, so all vibrational hypotheses equally fail to provide a comprehensible material source of light (the moving thing) and a mechanism for transferring energy from the luminous object to the æther. As he illogically advanced the one supposition or the other, as the exigencies of the problem required, so we now, after long vacillation, are vainly trying to combine a corpuscular theory, under the pseudonym of quanta of energy, to explain the cause of light, and a wave theory to account for any phenomenon which involves interference. The mechanism for the absorption of light, in Newton's scheme, agrees closely with that of emission. Corpuscles, after their expulsion from a luminous source and excursion through space, agitate the atoms of bodies, which they strike, and give to them their energy.

In order to account for vision, he asks the questions, "do not the rays of light in falling upon the bottom of the eye excite vibrations in the *Tunica Retina?* Which vibrations, being propagated along the solid fibres of the optic nerves into the brain, cause the sense of seeing. . . . Do not several sorts of rays make vibrations of several bignesses [wave-lengths], which according to their bignesses excite sensations of several colours, much after the manner that the vibrations of the air, according to their several bignesses excite sensations of several sounds? And particularly do not the most refrangible rays excite the shortest vibrations for making a sensation of deep violet, the least refrangible the largest for making a sensation of deep red, and the several intermediate sorts of rays, vibrations of several intermediate sorts to make sensations of the several intermediate colours? May not the harmony and discord of colours arise from the proportions of the vibrations propagated through the fibres of the optic nerves into the brain, as the harmony and discord of sounds arise from the proportions of the vibrations of the air?"

Newton was deeply interested in the problem of vision and wrote several long and elaborate letters on the subject which the curious may find given at length in Brewster. As his facts were meagre and faulty and his conclusions of no present value, it is sufficient to state that he thought binocular vision was due to the crossing and uniting of the nerve fibres from the two eyes, in such a fashion that the fibres meet in the brain to make but one entire picture, half of which in the right side of the Sensorium [the organ of appreciation, of life and of the soul] comes from the right side of both eyes, and the other half similarly from the left side. But he had been much more influenced by the later work of Huygens, who had improved and extended the wave theory, than has been supposed; we should not then be surprised when, in a later Query, he questions whether, in spite of certain advantages of the corpuscular hypothesis, vision is not caused chiefly by the vibrations of an æther.

A mechanical model must simulate consistently and satisfactorily the three principal actions of bodies on light,—reflection, refraction, and diffraction. The mechanism proposed by Newton depends upon the modification of a stream of light corpuscles by two subordinate actions. The first of these is a mutual attraction between atoms and corpuscles which increases as the distance decreases. And the second is caused by vibrations produced in the æther when corpuscles impinge on a body; the velocity of the æthereal wave being assumed to be greater than that of a corpuscle, it alternately accelerates or retards the speed of light, according as the to-and-fro motion of the vibration aids or opposes the direction of propagation of the corpuscle.

The first action being granted, he puts the questions: Do not bodies act upon light at a distance, and by their action bend the rays; are not the rays of light, in passing by the edges and sides of bodies, bent several times backwards and forwards, with a motion like that of an eel; and do not the three fringes of coloured light, seen in the phenomena of diffraction, arise from three such bendings? We should accept this explanation if, as he suggests, rays which differ in refrangibility differ also in flexibility. In that case, their different degrees of flexibility would separate the colours, when white light grazed the edge of a body, in the same manner as a prism does by selective refrangibility. It would also follow that the angles of reflection and refraction are not abrupt but slightly curved at their apex. Rays of light, because of this bending, are reflected, refracted, and inflected by one and the same principle, acting variously in various circumstances.

Newton was driven to propose this ancillary wave hypothesis, in spite of his reluctance, in order to provide a mechanism which would, at times, increase the velocity of light sufficiently to make a ray penetrate a transparent body and, at other times, retard it enough to make it rebound from an opaque surface or even prevent it from reaching the body. It will be best to give this famous doctrine of "Fits" in the author's own words: "When a ray of light falls upon the surface of any pellucid body, and is then refracted or reflected, may not waves of vibrations, or tremors, be thereby excited in the refracting or reflecting medium at the point of incidence, and continue to arise there, and to be propagated from thence? And are not these vibrations propagated from the point of incidence to great distances? And do they not overtake the rays of light, and by overtaking them successively, do they not put them into the *Fits of easy*

Reflection and Easy Transmission described above? For if the rays endeavour to recede from the densest part of the vibration, they may be alternately accelerated and retarded by the vibrations overtaking them."[31]

Newton devotes the third book of his *Optics* to the phenomena of colours produced by successive reflections and refractions in thin transparent plates. While it may have been the custom of the day to refer only casually to the work of others, Newton unfortunately gives the impression that the whole subject, excepting its bare discovery, was the result of his own labour. Hooke's name is not even mentioned, and no one would suppose that he had described all the essential phenomena of these colours in his *Micrographia* almost a half century earlier, or that he had been the source from which Newton had derived his composite-wave hypothesis. Since these colours are the result of successive reflections and refractions, Newton added the property of fits of easy reflection and of easy transmission occurring at equal intervals to his corpuscular hypothesis as a substitute to his rival's device of the interference of æthereal waves. It is, however, a satisfaction, to me at least, that he concludes these futile speculations with the caution: "But whether this hypothesis be true or false I do not here consider. I content myself with the bare discovery, that the rays of light are by some cause or other alternately disposed to be reflected or refracted for many vicissitudes."

Such is Newton's ingenious and famous hypothesis of light. We ought not to object to it on the obvious ground that it is based on an absolutely false assumption of fact or that its mechanism is often unintelligible, so long as men of science are still guided by the belief that hypotheses are valuable, whether their assumptions are true or false and whether their mechanisms are intelligible or not. For scientists to hold that knowledge can be furthered by a false assumption,

[31] There has been assumed, in the minds of many physicists, a rather contemptuous attitude towards Newton's invention of "Fits." It is worth while to quote the opinion of so eminent an authority on optics as Biot. In his *Life of Newton,* page 11, he says: "We have here an admirable example of the universal application of scientific definitions when framed in strict accordance with experiment. For, though the term *fits,* inasmuch as it seems to imply a physical property, is applicable in its first intention to material particles only, and thus involves the assumption of the materiality of light (a fact of which we may reasonably doubt, though Newton has never treated it as doubtful), yet the characteristics of these fits are described in such exact conformity with experiment, that they would exist without any change, even were it discovered that light is constituted in any other manner—that it consists, for instance, in the propagation of undulations: such is the point of view in which Newton regards these fits in his *Optics,* 1704, limiting himself to deduce from them his profound inductions, on the intimate constitution of bodies, and on the cause which renders them apt to reflect or transmit a particular colour."

if only the intention be good, is a curious commentary on their pretension that science is based on objective facts. At a time when Römer had just discovered the finite velocity of light, it could not be dreamed that we would some two centuries later be able to measure so swift a speed in the short stretches of our laboratories. Descartes, with no experimental data on the velocity of light at his disposal, had stated that the transmission of light was instantaneous, and yet when he attempted to explain the phenomenon of refraction he quietly assumed that its velocity is greater in transparent bodies than *in vacuo* where he had assumed it to be infinite. In a moment of relaxed conscience, Newton forsook his fixed principle that science must be based on observed facts and measurements only, and incorporated this fiction into his hypothesis. Now, if hypotheses are valuable aids to the investigation of scientific laws, we should have to admit that this one advanced truth for two centuries during which it was *supposed* that light travels faster in material media than *in vacuo;* after that its acceptance would have promoted error because light had been experimentally observed to have just the opposite property. If any moral obligation can be attached to scientific enquiry, such a principle of thought comes perilously close to the famous doctrine that the end justifies the means. But we can, nevertheless, claim for Newton's hypothesis that, in spite of false premises and obscure reasoning, it is as satisfactory an explanation as later ones,—for we are still in total darkness as to why, and how, light penetrates some bodies and is reflected from others.

We are sure of but four facts when a luminous source and its receiver are separated by vacuous space,—the mechanical energy of light and heat is not absorbed; it is transmitted rectilinearly and with a finite velocity; its colour and temperature are not affected. Römer had discovered this time-interval to be seven or eight minutes for a distance equal to the earth's orbit. This distance, of about 92,000,000 miles, divided by the time is called the mechanical velocity of light. The problem, before Newton, was to invent a mechanical substance capable of transmitting such a velocity. Experience teaches us of only two ways of transmitting such an action by mechanical means, either by a stream of projectiles like bullets fired from a gun or a periodic motion transmitted as a wave along some elastic material. The Greeks pictured light by the first method. Descartes had proposed a pressure method; space was like a rigid rod, if you tapped one end of it, a ball (his light *globulus*) resting against the other end would fly off as a result of the transmitted shock. Huygens and Hooke had changed this idea of instantaneous pressure into a vibratory action impressed on a fluid medium, whose motion was similar to the waves impressed on air or water by a tuning fork or an organ pipe.

Newton returned to the projectile hypothesis because he found a compressional wave incapable of explaining the rectilinear propagation of light and certain phenomena of double refraction in crystals. He then added a vibratory æther as a contributing cause of other known phenomena.

He pictured to himself the æther as an excessively rare gas, atomic in structure and capable of vibrating by alternate condensation and rarefaction. With his customary thoroughness he made many experiments on the velocity of sound by timing the echo in Neville's Court of Trinity College. He found it to be about 1140 feet per second and derived a formula expressing the velocity in a gas to be equal to the square root of the ratio of the elasticity to the density of the medium ($v=\sqrt{e/d}$). From Römer's observation, the velocity of light is very roughly 700,000 times that of sound. As the simplest composition for an æther, he assumed it to be a fluid, 700,000 times more rigid than air and, at the same time, with a density of only 1/700,000 that of air. We must also bear in mind that it must be so rare as not to retard, by its friction, the motion of the planets to an appreciable amount, and, at the same time, immensely more rigid than steel.

At times, Newton identifies the light corpuscles with the æthereal atoms, and at other times he writes as if the corpuscles were of a smaller order of magnitude and shot through the pores of the æther without collision or deviation. However that may be, light while traversing the æther creates no waves; it is only when corpuscles impinge on matter that waves occur, as when a stone strikes water, and then they progress through the æther much faster than light in order to produce *"fits."*

If one is engaged in creating a mechanism to explain light, there is no apparent reason why the æther should not be forced to serve as the cause of other phenomena; so Newton, having taken the first step, lets his fancy have full sweep in order, as I think, to show that his condemnation of hypothesis was not due to a paucity of imagination, but to a settled conviction of method. No one can believe that he expected to be taken seriously.

In brief, this universal medium of action must have a composition so complex as to be capable of answering his queries: Is not this medium much rarer within the dense bodies of the sun, stars, planets, and comets, than in the empty celestial spaces between them? And in passing from them to great distances, doth it not grow denser and denser perpetually, and thereby cause the gravity of those great bodies towards one another; every body endeavouring to go from the denser parts of the medium towards the rarer? . . . Doth it not cause the attraction of electrical and magnetic actions? . . . Is not vision performed chiefly by the vibrations of this medium, and also, in general, is not animal motion performed by its vibrations, excited in the brain by the power of the will and propagated through the capillaments of the nerves into the muscles for contracting and dilating them? . . . Nay, even [why not go the limit,] are not gross bodies and light convertible into one another, the changing of bodies into light, and light into bodies, is very conformable to the course of nature, which seems delighted with transmutation?

Newton could not have deceived himself to the extent of not knowing that such an æther would be merely that kind of an occult substance endowed with an occult power of doing all those things which we wish it to do. Like Proteus, in Greek mythology, it changes its form according to the necessities of the case; it is merely a fiction, an explanation which does not explain. And so he would have us regard it: "To tell us that every species of things is endowed with an occult specific quality by which it acts and produces manifest effects, is to tell us nothing: but to derive two or three general principles of motion from phenomena, and afterwards to tell us how the properties and actions of all corporeal things follow from those manifest principles, would be a very great step in philosophy, though the causes of those principles were not discovered: And therefore I scruple not to propose the principles of motion above mentioned, they being of very general extent, and leave their causes to be found out."

This long discussion of the controversy, which arose in the seventeenth century and which is immensely important in its formulation of the scientific method, can be best closed by tracing briefly its subsequent history. A great injustice has been done to Newton. He did not propose a purely corpuscular theory of light and is not responsible for the fact that his followers fastened his name to it. He found, as he thought, insuperable objections to the wave hypothesis of Huygens and Hooke which were well founded and tried to avoid those difficulties by a combination of corpuscles and vibrations. The problem before the scientists of the eighteenth century was to choose between occult light corpuscles and an occult æther, which like a gas vibrated longitudinally; they chose the former as the less repugnant to experience. At the opening of the nineteenth century, Young and Fresnel, almost simultaneously, gave a new impetus to the wave theory by the hypothesis of assuming that light vibrations were transverse to the direction of propagation, although it was necessary to give to the æther the impossible attributes of being, at the same time, the rarest of gases and the most rigid of solids. For a time it was claimed that every problem of light had a satisfactory explanation, and the development of the elastic-solid theory of light was regarded as the greatest achievement of the age. It was, unfortunately, an edifice dazzling in appearance but built on sand. With each new phenomenon incorporated in its walls, the æthereal substance of its foundation became more occult. The literature of the subject, for the first half of the nineteenth century, is a monument to the effort and ingenuity of physicists to patch up this material æther.

The quietus was given to every type of a material medium for light when Maxwell published his prediction that an electro-magnetic oscillation would be propagated through space with the velocity of light. His significant conclusion was: "If my calculations are correct [and they were shortly confirmed by experiment], there are now two forms of energy, light and electricity, propagated through space with the same velocity. Since the only function of an æther is to provide a vehicle which will propagate energy at a specific velocity, it would be foolish to fill space with two æthers when one is sufficient." The æther, as a kind of elastic-solid has served its purpose, let us therefore assume light to be an electro-magnetic vibration of particular wave-lengths and the æther, a something capable of being electrified and magnetised but with no material attributes of density or elasticity. It was this hypothesis of Maxwell which called forth the witticism of Lord Kelvin, that the æther had become merely a personification of the verb, to wave.

The accumulation of experimental data, especially in the fields of radio-activity and of the discharge of electricity in gases, has rapidly forced even this pseudo-substantial æther further and further into the pale limbo of discarded ideas. There was little protest made when Lorentz, and later Einstein, quietly buried it with the remark that the æther with its complex of Faraday lines of force was merely a mathematical formula. With the passing of a substantial æther, matter as an objective reality has gone also. The world is portrayed as merely a manifestation of disembodied energy, active and passive at the same time, and we are drifting rapidly towards the dogma of the relativists, that truth is to be found only in the mathematical formula. In a certain way, this idea is true; but it is only a half-truth and no philosophy, and especially no science, can persist which does not take cognisance of the equally true objective world of brute fact.

If we contemplate the history of the science of optics during the two centuries since the death of Newton, we find, on the one hand, a steady and permanent advance in our knowledge of the phenomena and laws of light and of its interactions with matter, electricity, and heat, but, on the other hand, the chronicle of our hypotheses has been a record of vacillation and defeat. The best efforts for two centuries have not advanced our real knowledge of the nature of light one step; in essence, light is still nothing to us but light. If Newton, at the beginning of modern science, despaired of teaching his contemporaries the unavoidable limitations of the scientific method, he would have renounced science today altogether as the most litigious and dogmatic of task masters.

CHAPTER V

TRINITY COLLEGE. CHARACTER OF NEWTON. CORRESPONDENCE WITH COLLINS AND OLDENBURG ON LIGHT AND MATHEMATICS

1669–1674

THE physical aspect of Trinity College in 1669, when the young Newton succeeded Barrow as Lucasian Professor of Mathematics, differed greatly from its present appearance. The Great Court, the most impressive of all college quadrangles, had been completed at the beginning of the century, except for some minor changes. Loggan's general view of the College shows a garden laid out between it and Trinity Street, with a high wall around the garden on the right hand of the Great Gate as one enters, and buildings, as at present, between the College and the street on the left side. Only the two wings of Neville's Court, extending westward, had been partially completed, and, where Sir Christopher Wren's Library now stands, there was a wall penetrated by a gate admitting to the Backs. These buildings provided all the accommodations for the College except the small court forming the Bishop's Hostel, which had just been completed. As the College was practically a self-supporting community it had also a range of low buildings for stables, brew-house, bakery, and other domestic purposes.

Although the College had given to the Royalist cause much of its plate and money, its finances were now on the mend and its students growing in number. The result was serious overcrowding, sometimes as many as three or four students shared a single room, and some of the Junior Fellows had roommates instead of each having as now a suite of rooms; certainly this is true of Newton in his early days. During most of his tenancy, building was going on in Neville's Court; the two wings were extended in length, and Wren's imposing library was erected to join them across the open end. Funds, however, seem to have come in slowly, and the whole Court was not completed until 1690. Besides obtaining outside donations, the

College drew heavily on its own resources, and its Fellows contributed from their personal funds; amongst the latter items, we have the record that Newton, at one time gave £50, and at another loaned £100.

The number of members on the Foundation was then about the same as now, and consisted approximately of sixty Fellows, sixty Scholars, and sixteen Sizars. But the number of undergraduate students was much smaller, as only forty were admitted in Newton's first year, instead of the two hundred, or more, who now enter annually.

The College was governed by the statutes instituted in Queen Elizabeth's reign, and under them the Master, who was appointed by the Crown, had almost unlimited authority. Associated with him in the government were the eight Senior Fellows ranked according to length of appointment. The progress of the Fellows in rank was slow, so slow that, when Newton resigned his fellowship in 1701, he had risen only to be tenth on the list after an occupancy of thirty-three years, and he would not have attained his seniority until a year and a half later. This unfortunate delay in promotion to seniority, and an active part in administering the College, was due to an abuse of the purpose of the fellowships. They were intended, primarily, to be an aid to young scholars while they were preparing themselves for the church. Able men, after graduation, were supposed to be elected to the Foundation for a period of seven years, thus assuring them an income sufficient to secure them leisure and opportunity to study, till they could proceed to their divinity degrees, and obtain a parish under the patronage of the College. Only a relatively few of the Fellows who were appointed to a university professorship or other office, or to a college tutorship, were expected to remain with the College permanently. Unfortunately, an increasing number showed a reluctance to proceed to their divinity degrees or to exchange the comforts of college life, and the enjoyment of an intellectual community, for the wretched accommodations of the average rural parsonage and the dull society of the squire's house, where often the parson ranked scarcely above the butler. They persisted in maintaining their quarters in the College; with but few required duties, they lapsed too frequently into an idle life, dawdling over trifles and blocking those who were eager and able to manage the community vigorously.

There are many stories current in Oxford and Cambridge about the extraordinary vagaries of some of these half-mad recluses who had developed eccentricities during a long life of dull laziness, unrestrained by contact with life and work. One may laugh at these anecdotes, but the humour is tinged with regret at the spectacle of the degradation of such a distinguished body of men. One of them, although it does not refer to Newton's time, is too good not to repeat. A Fellow, well over eighty years of age, had become a pure eccentric; after years of academic idleness, he had absolutely secluded himself in his chambers and was hardly seen by any one, day or night. At dusk he would creep down his stairs and, armed with a stout stick to support his tottering steps, make the round of the Quadrangle for exercise. Each time that he discovered a worm during his walk, he would stop, peer at it anxiously with purblind eyes, and then jab at the wriggling symbol of mortality with his stick; meanwhile muttering in quavering accents, "Damn you, you haven't got me yet." These comfortable life tenures have long since been abolished even at King's College, where they persisted longest and led to the worst abuses; and today Cambridge Fellows enjoy their privileged life so long as they are worthy of their office and contribute to the reputation of the College and University.

In this community of scholars, Newton held a distinguished position though he took little part in the management of the College. It has already been mentioned that living quarters were first assigned to him in what was known as the "Spirituall chamber" and which was conjectured by Edleston to be the ground-floor room next the Chapel in the north-east corner of the Great Court. We do know, however, that Newton and his friend John Wickins, a Fellow two years his junior and later pastor of the church at Stoke Edith near Monmouth, still roomed together in 1673. In that year they seem to have separated, and it may be guessed that it was Newton who went into other quarters for a grandson of Wickins states: "The whole furniture of the chambers devolved upon my ancestor upon Sir Isaac's leaving the college, and hath with some other articles remained in the family ever since." In 1678, he had a sizar living with him as the Junior Bursar's Books contain an entry that Mr. Newton's sizar's chamber was mended over. The first specific notice of the location of his rooms is an entry in the same book for the year ending Michaelmas, 1683: "For mending the wall betwixt Mr. Newton's garden and St. John's." Edleston offers as the most probable supposition, that he went into them in the summer of

1679. These are the rooms pointed out to the stranger, on the first floor of the entry to the north of the Great Gate. It is a distinguished entry, for the ground-floor chambers were later occupied by Macaulay and Thackeray. And I recall with pleasure the feeling, almost of reverence, which came over me when I once, years ago, took after dinner coffee with the Fellow who then occupied them. While the analysis of light may not have been made there, a far greater thing occurred; in them Newton meditated and wrote his *Principia,* and spent the long and silent hours in contemplation on the mysteries of the universe.

Besides his living rooms, Newton had assigned to him a room which he fitted as a chemical laboratory and where he spent days and nights at certain seasons of the year, oblivious to other duties and occupations. At the head of his staircase, he had mounted one of his own reflecting telescopes, and from one of his windows a flight of stairs permitted him to descend to the little garden laid out between the college and the street. This garden plot seems to have been reserved for his private use; and one gets the impression that in its short length, the great and lonely scholar paced up and down for the little exercise he was willing to abstract from his hours of study.

An interesting anecdote of these rooms comes down to us from a grandson of Bentley, who was a freshman in 1747; speaking of the kindness of Walker, the Vice-Master, who then occupied them, he wrote: "He frequently invited me to his rooms, which I had so often visited as a child, and which had the further merit with me as having been the residence of Sir Isaac Newton, every relic of whose studies and experiments were respectfully preserved to the minutest particular, and pointed out to me by the good old Vice-Master with the most circumstantial precision. He had many little anecdotes of my grandfather [Bentley], which to me at least were interesting, and an old servant Deborah, whom he made a kind of companion, and who was much in request for the many entertaining circumstances she could narrate of Sir Isaac Newton, when she waited upon him as his bedmaker, and also of Dr. Bentley, with whom she lived for several years after Sir Isaac left college, and at the death of my grandfather was passed over to Dr. Walker, in whose service she died."[1] Thus fate has preserved the name of Deborah, whose association with such great erudition was not capable of teaching her to

[1] Edleston, p. xliv.

write her own name, and whose interesting memories the negligence of others has failed to transmit to us.

When Newton was appointed Lucasian Professor, at the age of twenty-seven years, he was mature in mind and character. As our interest in such a man naturally centres about his intellectual life, it is important to give a sketch of his appearance, habits, and character before narrating the events of his life which follow after this definite recognition of his genius; and especially so, because the traditions and stories which gathered about him have come down to us very often undated and confused.

We have no description or likeness of Newton's personal appearance in his youth; there is, to be sure, a portrait by Lely said to have been painted when he was a bachelor of arts, but it is probably not authentic as it shows little resemblance to his later portraits, and also Newton was at that time too obscure and too poor a man to have engaged the brush of so eminent an artist.[2]

With the exception of the portrait painted by Kneller, in 1689, shortly after the publication of the *Principia,* all the extant pictures of Newton were done when he was an old man living in London; and most of them are so evidently idealised to express the artist's conception of an heroic thinker that one gets but a vague impression of the man. In addition, the figure is stiffly posed, and the full-bottomed wig conceals the shape of the head. The most faithful likenesses are the one painted by Gandy in 1706, and the three by Thornhill shortly afterwards; in spite of rather striking differences, they agree in general appearance.

Newton's most notable features are the power and expanse of the forehead, and the appearance of concentrated meditation in the brow and eyes. The profile, as drawn by Thornhill, makes the forehead high and receding and shows a most extraordinarily long and unbroken curve from the chin to the crown of the head. The nose is long, thin, and prominent, and the line of the bridge is wavy. But,

[2] The following list of important portraits is given by Professor D. E. Smith, who has probably the largest collection of Newtoniana in existence. (*Cf.* Greenstreet, p. 171.)

Portrait by Lely, date 1665–8. Original in possession of Viscount Cremorne, probably not authentic.

By Kneller, 1689. In possession of Earl of Egremont.

By Gandy, 1706. Formerly in possession of J. A. Walter, Esq.

By Thornhill, 1709. In possession of Trinity College.

By Thornhill, two other portraits. Original of one of them in Hurstbourne Park.

By Vanderbank, 1725. In possession of Royal Society.

By Vanderbank, 1725 [?]. In possession of National Gallery of London.

By Seeman, 1726. In possession of Thomas Hollis, Esq.

By Roubiliac, statue in antechapel of Trinity College.

the lower part of the face is in strong contrast with the strength and nobility of the upper half. The chin is square and broad, while the lower jaw appears to be underhung, and the lower lip is pinched and drawn in; so that the expression is one of excessive cautiousness; and one infers him to have been of a suspicious and obstinate temperament. In height, he was not above middle size, and he became stout in his later years as would naturally result from his sedentary habits.

Conduitt tells us that Newton "had a lively and piercing eye, a comely and gracious aspect, with a fine head of hair as white as silver, without any baldness, and when his peruke was off was a venerable sight." A lock of his hair, silver white and unusually fine in texture, is still preserved amongst his relics in Hurstbourne Park. He was gray headed when he was thirty, which Stukeley quaintly attributed to a hot and dry constitution. Quite the contrary is a description by Bishop Atterbury who, in a letter, wrote: "In the whole of his face and make, there was nothing of that penetrating sagacity which appears in his compositions; he had something rather languid in his look and manner, which did not raise any great expectation in those who did not know him." And this opinion is confirmed by Hearne who found "Sir Isaac was a man of no very promising aspect. He was a short well-set man. He was full of thought, and spoke very little in company, so that his conversation was not agreeable. When he rode in his coach one arm would be out of his coach on one side, and the other on the other." As Newton owned a sedan chair, and not a coach, this odd habit which seems to have made his passage in town noticeable would be easier in that narrow vehicle.

These different opinions may perhaps be reconciled, as the meditative, inward look of the scholar may, to the casual observer, give the impression of an abstracted and dull appearance; but, when aroused, he may have had the intent, piercing eye which Conduitt remembered. His eyes were full and protuberant, and he several times mentions that he was near-sighted, too near-sighted to make astronomical observations; Flamsteed insinuates that he would guess at words rather than confess his inability to read small print, or wear spectacles. Newton believed that his eyes were normal when he was a child because he remembered being able to see Grantham church spire like a stick six miles away. His eyes, however, were strong and were never tired by reading, so that to the end of his life he could read the smallest print by the light of a coal fire without spectacles.

During his Cambridge days he was inattentive, even to slovenliness, in his dress and habits. There are many references to this carelessness, such as "Newton hath come into the Hall without his band, and went towards St. Mary's in his surplice"; this indifference to dress grew into a legend, as indicative of the great scholar, for there is a Staffordshire figure of him, in my possession, in which the neckband is loose, the stockings ungartered, and the breeches unbuttoned at the knee. But, when he moved to London, he adopted a more seemly costume and, on occasions, considerable elegance. With the later authority and full recognition of his genius, his whole aspect grew in power and dignity, and his latest portraits indicate a man fully conscious of his achievements and position.

In spite of his untoward birth and delicate infancy, the life on the farm must have established Newton's health at a fairly early age and have given to him a rather extraordinary constitution. Even as a boy, he shunned rough sports and, from manhood on, we have no intimation that he diverted his mind with amusements or felt the need of any bodily exercise except the slow pacing of his little college garden enclosure. Yet he had only two serious attacks of illness; once as an undergraduate, he had a temporary break-down from too persistent observations of a comet for many nights, and when, after the exorbitant labour he had put into the composition of the *Principia,* he suffered from insomnia and such excessive nervousness that reports were spread of his being mentally deranged. As often happens with solitary men, he took much interest in his health, and both doctored himself during his minor ailments, and suggested simple remedies to his friends. A significant indication of his prevailing good health is that even in those days of reckless tooth-pulling he lost but one from his entire set. A constitution, which could stand irregular hours, irregular meals, a sedentary life, and yet each morning experience no dullness of the mind, is as baffling as are some of the traits of his character. It is noteworthy that four of the most distinguished natural philosophers of the time, Newton, Whiston, Flamsteed, and Hooke, attained fame in spite of an unpromising birth and, with the exception of Newton, persistent ill-health.

He was abstemious and regular in his diet, except when he was so immersed in the fascination of creative work as to be forgetful whether he had eaten or not. As a young man, he enjoyed wine and beer and, if we can credit a legend, he occasionally smoked. As he grew older, he limited himself to a little wine at meals, and gave up tobacco because he would not be dominated by habits. He, also, said of himself that he learned to go to bed early, but then he considered midnight, or later, as early and, during strenuous times, he frequently worked all night, finding that a short nap entirely refreshed his mind. He was not interested in travelling and lived almost constantly in the College as is shown by the record of the Exits and Redits of Bachelor Fellows and Scholars. During the long vacations, and occasionally during term time, he returned to Woolsthorpe; his attachment to the scenes of his youth and to his family, especially his mother, seems to have been by far the strongest impulse in his social life. Very rarely, he went to London or visited acquaintances elsewhere; there is no indication of the least curiosity to inspect the historic or artistic monuments of England, to enjoy its scenery, or of any desire to relieve the monotony of a fixed abode.

In his social life, Newton living at a time when class distinctions were very rigid, was in the anomalous position of one whose family, by occupation and income, were ranked practically as yeoman farmers but at the same time had the rights theoretically belonging to the gentry. To be a lord of a manor and, at the same time, a sizar at college would make a proud youth avoid the companionship of humble students and uncomfortable in the society of gentlemen. His first opportunity to associate with men of gentle birth came from his intimacy with Charles Montague, afterwards Earl of Halifax. And from that time it is easy to note a change in his disposition. He grew restive in the academic life and sought a political position which would bring social recognition. He cultivated acquaintanceship with such distinguished men as Boyle, Bentley, Locke, Pepys, Henry More, and stood for Parliament as frequently as an opportunity presented. He wearied of Cambridge society and, with almost abject submissiveness, petitioned his friends to secure him an office in London. And when he finally succeeded, he left Cambridge, his colleagues, and his work, without an expression of regret; he cultivated the society of the nobility, was a welcomed guest at Court, and derived the greatest satisfaction from the respectful attentions of eminent foreigners whom he entertained frequently and handsomely. This attitude, which links together Newton and Shakespeare,—that the reward of genius in any line is to be found in social and political distinction,—is peculiarly British and has been one of their sureties of high principles in government. At bottom, it comes from the same conviction which animated Rome in her greatest days, that the first and highest concern of the citizen is the State.

Newton never lost his interest in Woolsthorpe; he returned there whenever his duties at Cambridge permitted, and most of his greatest discoveries came to his mind as he meditated in the quiet seclusion of his farm. He helped to restore the church at Colsterworth and intended to establish and endow a school there. After his mother's death, he kept a close watch over his tenants and his rights as lord of the manor, and desired to trace his genealogy to the county family of a Sir John Newton. His love for his mother was the strongest tie in his life and he felt it to be so intimate that he left no word, or letter, about their tender relationship. With the exception of his niece, Catherine Barton, the rest of his immediate family were more of a concern and worry to him than a pleasure. She, alone, was in any way comparable to him; she has come down to us as the beautiful, witty, and virtuous Mistress Catherine Barton; she presided over his house and entertained the best society of London; and she, finally by the marriage of her daughter, became the ancestress of the Earls of Portsmouth. As Newton advanced in fortune, he continued to aid his stepsisters and their children, setting the nephews up in business and making large gifts to his sisters and nieces when they married.

With the exception, perhaps, of Montague, Newton had no intimate and personal friends who penetrated the ivory tower in which he jealously guarded his inner life. How aloof he wished to be is epitomised in his almost agonised cry that he would publish nothing more as it would result only in attracting acquaintance, what he most sought to avoid. Towards Boyle and Wren he showed a deep respect, and next to Montague his most congenial friends were Henry More and John Locke; but even they regarded him as difficult and "nice" to approach. Men of science, such as Hooke, Flamsteed, and Leibniz, who ventured in the same field of work and who felt themselves competent to criticise him, were met by chilling rebuffs. The altercations with them were due to the interference with his time which their criticism caused; and to his almost morbid sensitiveness to any opposition, which to him was synonymous with a reflection on his personal integrity and honour, rather than to a scholarly difference of opinion. If an explanation of his ideas was not sufficient to meet with acquiescence, he abruptly stopped his correspondence; and if he was further opposed, he became an implacable and, even at times, an unscrupulous antagonist.

Newton's relations with his Cambridge colleagues can be described as formal. He must have been intimate with his chamber-fellow, Wickins, and he entertained at times; but we get the impression that he rarely mixed in the academic social life. If one were to present him at his best, it would be in his intercourse with young men. He had the power of arousing in them devoted admiration and loyalty; and he, in return, showed towards them a certain grave courtesy which was altogether admirable. From the nature of their relationship, he would not fear intrusion on his time or criticism of his ideas; he gave them wise and kindly advice, and was indefatigable in promoting their success. Collins, Gregory, Halley, Cotes, Fatio, Keill, Demoivre, Montague, and others, were his ardent partisans, and they resented any criticism of him or of his work. This power of attracting young and brilliant scholars is the best and most genuine tribute which can be given to his character. To them he showed that integrity of mind, purity of thought, and generosity of spirit, which made Bishop Burnet designate him as the whitest of souls. Because of the publicity in which he lived, his altercations have been engraved on our minds; and we forget that they were but incidents in a long life, which on the whole was one of uniform kindliness and of high principles.

If we except Newton's affection for his mother and for his niece, Catherine, women had no influence in his life; esteem he may have had for a few, but passion had been omitted from his nature. He visited occasionally at country houses but scarcely a reference to any woman is to be found in his correspondence or in his affairs. To break off his boyish engagement with Miss Storey left his serenity unruffled, and their friendship unembarrassed. On the strength of a letter, dubious in meaning, some have supposed that he proposed marriage, late in life, to a Mrs. Norris, but the affair seems incredible. There is another legend which has all the ear-marks of the invention and wit of the undergraduate mind with its stock conviction of the absent-mindedness and absorption of the scholar. An apocryphal scene has come down to us, afterwards illustrated by the ingenious Cruickshank. Some of his colleagues are said to have induced Newton to propose to a young lady. During what should have been an absorbing conversation, while tenderly holding her hand, the philosopher's mind wandered into other fields of thought; instead of raising her hand to his lips, he absent-mindedly used her little finger as a tamp for his pipe. Aroused by her sudden exclamation of pain from the heat of the embers in place of the pleasure which should have come from the warmth of love, Newton exclaimed, "Ah, my dear Madam, I beg your pardon! I see it will not do! I see, I see that I am doomed to remain a bachelor."[3]

With these exceptions, Newton's inner and real life might have been passed in a world destitute of women and but rarely populated with men. It is little wonder that his contemporaries have passed on to us the impression that he was not a mortal man, but rather an embodiment of thought, unhampered by human frailties, unmoved by human ambition. We can offer this remoteness as a possible cause for the legends which grew up about his Trinity days. His fellows, feeling his aloofness from human society and unable to understand how a man could live without intimate companionship, would naturally invent, or transfer to him, stories of a fondness for animal pets to comfort his loneliness. So we have the pathetic story of the little dog Diamond who, on upsetting a candle and burning a mass of important manuscript, drew on himself only the stilted reproof: "Diamond, Diamond, thou little knowest the damage thou hast done." So also we may regard the legend that, bothered by the restless entrances and exits of a favourite cat, he cut a hole in his room door for her convenience. When, after the habit of female cats, she presented him with kittens, he foresaw a new disturbance to his peace and philosophically cut another, and smaller, hole in the door for them. Of themselves, they are undoubtedly trivial fictions; he never had either dogs or cats in his rooms, or any fondness for them; but they are of value as they express in a striking and homely manner the unofficial attitude of students and colleagues towards him during his long years of college life.

Most of the authentic stories of Newton's absent-mindedness cluster about his indifference towards food. He seldom went to Hall for dinner but had his victuals brought to his chamber, and was often so deeply engaged in study that he neglected to eat them till supper; if he entertained and went for wine, there was danger of his forgetting his guests. Even in London this habit persisted, and

[3] This story must have been widely spread during Newton's life-time. John Bernoulli told Professor Björnstahl that: "sagte uns, Newton sey ebenfalls sehr zerstreut gewesen, und habe einmahl den Finger eines Frauenzimmers genommen, um seine Tabakspfeife nachzustopfen." Edleston, note 196, p. lxxx.

his niece must have made special arrangements for him as one separate from the regular domestic régime. The following note given to her husband indicates that he led a solitary life in his personal apartments: "He was always called a half hour before dinner, and would let his dinners stand two hours; his gruel, or milk and eggs, that was carried to him warm for supper, he would often eat cold for breakfast." It would, however, be quite erroneous to think of him as the perplexed dreamer who commits ludicrous blunders. It may be true that: "After he printed his *Principia,* the students at Cambridge said, as he passed by, there goes the man who has writ a book that neither he nor any one else understands." Most men did not understand it, but he did; and his occasional absent-mindedness was due to concentration, not to distraction, of mind.

It is easy to summarise Newton's character as habitually generous, pure-minded, pious, and self-disciplined:—but how to reconcile other qualities usually attributed to him; modesty with his assurance of the superiority of his discoveries; his intellectual integrity with his mutability of temper and inconstancy of conduct; his stiff insistence on an exclusive right to his ideas which he kept secret, with his indifference, even repulsion, towards popular fame; his moral principles with his treatment of friends and rivals. Such contradictions can be accounted for only as the result of antagonistic traits of character. The gods had showered on him, at birth, extraordinary gifts such as have been given to almost no other man, but some evil fate cursed him with a suspicious and jealous temperament which marred his life. This taint in his blood did not show itself in the form of ordinary vanity, but in an inordinate sensitiveness to any personal criticism or to a reflection on his personal honour. In spite of his love of meditation and of peace free from all distractions, it involved him in constant quarrels and altercations; and during a long and illustrious life it raised an impenetrable barrier between him and other men. To his friends, he was never more than lukewarm and he kept them constantly uneasy lest they had offended him; to his rivals he was, at times, disingenuous, unjust, and cruel.

In his intellectual character also, Newton presents this same baffling problem of conflicting tendencies. Since his powers as a natural philosopher, both as a theorist and as an experimentalist, were so supreme, it is not strange that his contemporaries, seeing him immersed in scientific work for thirty years, should have supposed science to have been congenial to his temperament, and to have been regarded by him as of the greatest importance as an end in itself. Nor is it surprising that his later biographers have echoed the same opinion. But how can we make this judgement conform with his statements that mathematics was a dry and barren subject; that science was such a litigious taskmaster that one might as well be perpetually engaged in law-suits; that he grudged the time he had spent on it to the hindrance of other matters dearer to him? On the other hand, during those years, apparently devoted to science, he was deeply interested in history and religion; and during his last thirty years in public life, he was rarely without a pen in his hand writing draught after draught of his meditations on those subjects. Is it not probable that his mental endowment made his entry into science, as a profession, inevitable, and the discoveries which came to his mind drove that wonderful machine to work out their solution, as it were, independently of his will or desire? Because of the rare quality of his genius, he was able to transcend other men in science and yet regard it for its own sake as of little more value than an intricate game of chess. In common with the scientists and divines of the day, he believed that, natural laws having been ordained by God, their discovery would be a support to religion by disclosing the divine will and purpose. Our chief duty and interest were to be found in the study of the relations of man to God and in the reconciliation of the new mechanistic philosophy with the doctrines of Christianity. Whatever had been his early training, he became a convinced believer in the Protestant tenet of the ultimate responsibility of the individual towards doctrines of faith. Intellectually sceptical of the plenary inspiration of the Bible, he yet devoted immense labour to the task of proving its moral inspiration and authority, and its prophetic revelation of future events. Heterodox towards some of the fundamental articles of faith of the Church of England, he still maintained unquestioningly his connection in that Church.

Of Newton's minor characteristics, the one to show itself first was his manual dexterity. It began with the fashioning of toys, and was continued in the habit of making apparatus and of experimentation; he also loved penmanship and cultivated a variety of hands which in his old age developed into a fatal facility for mere writing. So, also, Newton, as a boy, was fond of drawing, and Stukeley thought the practice had been continued, as he asked Conduitt to send a sketch to him as a remembrance of his friend. He is represented to us as having been totally indifferent to art, but in his boyhood he certainly had a taste for pictures, and he once made the unexpected statement that he could have been a poet, as he excelled in writing verses. There are many examples of men who found pleasure in the arts during the emotional period of their youth, which later became dulled by the occupations and interests of later life. The belief in his complete indifference to art and literature rests on a few anecdotes. He once said that he had heard but one opera, and was bored at the end of the second act; again, when the Earl of Pembroke's collections were praised, he spoke sarcastically of him as a lover of stone dolls. Too much weight should not be attached to such casual statements, taken out of their setting, as Newton could not have been quite so unhuman a character as tradition has made him; and some sparkle of humour and sarcasm should be left to him. The other instance, which has been often cited, occurred during an acrimonious quarrel which arose as a result of Bishop Hare's critique of Bentley's edition of the *Fables of Phædrus*. It was carried on with such asperity as to cause much scandal, and Newton is said to have complained that two eminent divines were "fighting with one another about a play-book." But, this expression of contempt was not directed against poetry, but against the impropriety of two divines thus lowering their sacred calling, a matter towards which he was very tender. Probably, the safest opinion is, that art and literature played a very minor part in his life.

In all the ordinary affairs of life, Newton was notably patient and gentle; traits which showed themselves particularly in his sympathy towards suffering. He could not bear the sport of hunting, and he objected to one of his nephews, because he killed birds. Whiston spread the report that he abstained from eating rabbits because they were strangled and from black puddings because made of blood. But his niece denied the report, and said he followed the rule of St. Paul to take and eat what comes from the shambles without asking questions for conscience's sake.

Before concluding this sketch of Newton's character a word should be said about the causes of the quarrels which plagued his life. They should not bulk too large in our estimate of his character as, after all, they occupied but a small part of a long life which was, on the whole, exemplary; and we must also make allowances for his constitutional irritability when criticised, a trait which such inordinate flattery as was given to him could not fail to intensify.

The first cause of his troubles was a result of his own high standard of work and of his reluctance to publish. He maintained through life the high ideal that no work should be made public until the utmost possible finish had been given it. This desire is not unique with him but he also thought that no work should be criticised until the reader had prepared himself for the task with the same exhaustive meditation. As a consequence, he was puzzled and exasperated by hasty opposition; and he justly complained that he was misunderstood because his critics had failed to grasp his purpose. The same is true of his habits of composition. He sought with painstaking care for the right word and for a lucid style.

In contrast with the diffuse treatises on scientific topics, his own work was cast in the form of geometrical theorems and was expressed with excessive brevity; it is not an exaggeration to state that it required the efforts of the greatest mathematicians for a century to grasp and elucidate fully his *Principia,* and few scientists today have a correct idea of his theory of light, and still fewer, of his philosophy. This obscurity does not result from laxity of expression; but from the omission of illustrations and explanatory clauses which are aids to ordinary men. His style is accurate, clear, and concise, and he was exacting in his use of words.

Where he felt his exclusive rights of discovery to be involved, no one could be more determined to assert himself. He held jealously to the conviction that if he had made a discovery, it was his personal property for all time, even if he kept it locked in the secret chambers of his own mind. If another should later make the same discovery and publish it first, he held to the opinion that no rights were attached to priority of publication; the author had merely trespassed unwittingly on Newton's property and should receive no credit.

The second cause of Newton's troubles came from the state of science which his inherent reluctance to publish, and his ideas on priority of rights, greatly accentuated. Before the middle of the seventeenth century there were no scientific journals in which the progress of invention could be quickly disseminated and credit be properly assigned. The only methods of publication were the writing of books, or of letters. Neither method was appropriate, the composition of a book was too slow, and letters were ephemeral, restricted in circulation, and had their unsavoury side. At the same time, the advance of science was then extraordinarily rapid, especially in pure and applied mathematics. Discoveries came so easily, and so rapidly, that it would have been difficult, under the best of circumstances, always to assign them to their proper source. Accusations of plagiarism, and even its prevalence, were common and widespread. Efforts were frequently made to protect rights by announcing, and at the same time concealing, a discovery in the form of an anagram, or jumble of letters, till the finished work could be published in a book. Newton's inherent reluctance to publish kept his suspicions aroused and aggravated his disputes.

If Newton's character were such as has been described, one can imagine his anxiety when he was suddenly called upon to succeed the veteran and distinguished Barrow. There must be no failure, he must not only maintain the high standard set by the first Lucasian Professor but he must bend every effort to surpass his predecessor. He had chosen optics for his subject and there, also, he came in direct competition with Barrow who had just published his own lectures on the same subject. It is not surprising that these first years are barren of incident. In addition to his professorial work, he carried on with unremitting energy his experimental work in light, grinding and polishing of lenses, working on his reflecting telescope, and investigating the best alloys for his metallic mirrors. He must have been spurred to even greater effort by the appearance of Hooke's *Micrographia* with its wealth of material on the various phenomena of refracted light and the composition of colours. Hooke was a competitor to be feared as so keen a mind might at any moment snatch from him the fruits of his own incomplete work.

Besides treating in his lectures the subject of geometrical optics in a concise and elegant manner, Newton added his own new discoveries and described in detail his experiments to prove the specific refrangibility of colours and the composition of white light. He also discussed the advantages of the reflecting telescope. The lectures, with the title of *Lectiones Opticae,* were written and delivered in Latin. The style is lucid and condensed; but his exposition would tax the ability of his auditors since he here, as in his later work, omitted intermediate steps and illustrations. The course comprised thirty-one lectures delivered consecutively, and without repetition, between January 1669/70 and the end of 1672. The manuscript, except for the last two or three pages and marginal notes, is not in the author's hand-writing. It was, as required by statute, given to the Vice-Chancellor and delivered by him to the Librarian, Robert Peachey, to be preserved in the University Library. Though much of the material was later incorporated in his *Optics,* the lectures were not published till 1729.

The specific duties of the chair were not onerous as the professor was required to lecture only once a week during term-time on some portion of geometry, arithmetic, astronomy, geography, optics, statics or other mathematical discipline. On two days a week during term-time, and on one day during vacation, if he was in residence, he was expected to confer with students in his chambers. That Newton carried out this provision, at least occasionally, is known because Henry Wharton states in his autobiography that: "He attained . . . no mean skill in mathematics. Which last was much increased by the kindness of Mr. Isaac Newton, Fellow of Trinity College, the incomparable Lucas-Professor of Mathematics in the University, who was pleased to give him further instructions in that noble science, amongst a select company in his own private chamber."[4] It is easy to understand that the novelty of subject and rigorousness of treatment of his lectures would repel most college students. And we know that he had few to attend them; often finding no one present, he left the room and returned to his private work. This small attendance at his lectures occurred in spite of the official letter of Charles II confirming the Lucasian statutes, by which all undergraduates after their second year and all Bachelors of Arts to their third year ("usque ad annum tertium") were required to attend them. The Professor could continue to hold a fellowship, but he was forbidden to receive pay for any other university office, except that he might be a Tutor to Fellow-Commoners.[5]

How closely Newton remained at his work in Cambridge, during these first years, can be seen from the record of Exits and Redits of Bachelor Fellows and Scholars which were kept in the book of the Muniment Room. With the exception of a short absence from November 26 to December 8, 1669, he lived in College continuously between September 29, 1668 and April 17, 1671. As his published correspondence begins with the year 1669 we can glean from his letters something of his personal life and intellectual pursuits. His first correspondent was John Collins whose letters have been preserved for

[4] Edleston, p. xlv.

[5] This prohibition will account for our not finding Newton's name at any time among the College or University Officers. He availed himself of the privilege of taking Fellow-Commoners as pupils in two instances only: Mr. George Markham, afterwards Baronet and F. R. S., entered June 26, 1680, and Mr. Robert Sacheverell, whose mother was daughter of the second Sir John Newton, and sister of the third Baronet of the name, entered September 16, 1687. Edleston, p. xlv.

the most part in the very valuable collection of the letters of scientific men made by the Earl of Macclesfield.

Collins was an important and useful member of the scientific world of his time. He was a self-educated man, who lamented that he had been unable to attend a university. But he had, from a love of mathematics and science, become proficient in those subjects and had eagerly developed a large correspondence with the notable men of his time. He tells us that he lived in London and held the position of secretary and member of the Council of Plantations. He, like other public servants of the time, suffered from the genial habit of the Stuarts of restricting the payment of actual money to those who ministered to their personal interests rather than to the public welfare. In a letter to Dr. Beale, he laments: "I have been employed near 2¼ years under Mr. Slingesby, mint master, as secretary (and a member) of the Council of Plantations, and have received but little more than the tithe of my pay. A pension I had of £50 per annum, half my salary, a little while of the King, for the loss of my place as an accountant in the Excise Office, by reason of altering the administration thereof since the late Lord Treasurer's death, and that hath been stopped these twelve months, as is likewise my wife's pay as laundress of the table linen to the Queen; the King's debts and occasions for the war diverting the money. Albeit I am exceedingly obliged to Bp. Ward for speaking to the Lord Clifford for his kindness to me, as I am to Sir Robert Moray in the like kind. And now the Council of Plantations is likewise to be a Council of Trade; and Mr. Slingesby, conceiving the trouble will be great, and the pay as uncertain, leaves his secretary's place, and advises me to leave that employment and to manage the Farthing Office, to deliver out all, that are coined, on Tuesdays, Thursdays, and Saturdays, in the mornings, in crown-papers ready tied up; the salary £50 per annum, and a fair dwelling house which I think may be in or near Fenchurch-street: where, having a convenient shop, I intend, God willing, to set up a stationer's trade, (and have a promise of serving the Mint,) and afterwards hope to fall into the printing of books, especially some of the copies of the members of the Royal Society and some of my own, particularly one of the modern advancement of mathematical sciences, and an account of the best authors of that kind, and some others which I intend, of which more hereafter."[6] He also tells us that he had a wife

[6] The writer's diction may be slovenly, but it is lively and the reader can, if he wishes, get an intimate picture of the confusion existing in the government of Charles II. Macclesfield, I, p. 201.

and children, and that his wife was the younger daughter of Mr. William Austin, who had been one of His Majesty's cooks when he was Prince of Wales, but had served as master cook of Wadham College, Oxford, during the interregnum. After the Restoration he had returned to the post of master cook to Charles II; and Collins was then living with his father-in-law in Petty France, Westminster, over against the Adam and Eve.

It is greatly to his credit that, although of humble origin, Collins became the familiar friend and counsellor of such a distinguished circle. At a time when there were no journals giving scientific news and articles, he became a sort of clearing house, spreading the news of recent work and answering enquiries. He regularly supplied information of new work and purchased books, especially from the continent, for his friends. Communication was slow and he once wrote that, "We are here so unhappy that we cannot get books that are common to be had in Paris," and he mentions "two which were extant six years before Dr. Wallis heard of either, though he was not a little concerned in both." He tells us, also, there was so little sale for books in England that treatises by the most distinguished authors could not secure a publisher. For that reason he determined to become a publisher himself, to assure the publication of important works, to attend to correcting the proofs, and to arrange for their sale.

He at once perceived Newton's genius and was largely responsible for spreading his reputation outside of Cambridge. With great tact, he constantly urged Newton to publish his mathematical work, and in such a way as not to offend his sensitive nature. This tact was especially noticeable when he acted as intermediary in a correspondence between Gregory and Newton concerning the reflecting telescope; it was no easy task to cement a friendship between the inventor of the instrument and its successful creator. So long as he lived the relations between Newton and Leibniz also were dignified and amicable, and we may be sure his influence would have been exerted to counteract the advice of more indiscreet and less scrupulous partisans.

Collins's acquaintance with Newton began with a curious and typical incident. The *Biographia Britannica*[7] gives the story in the following form. Lord Brouncker had arrived at a method of finding the area of an hyperbola in terms of an infinite series. With the help of this hint, and the use of Wallis's method of division by series, Mercator published in his *Logarithmotechnia,* in 1668, the actual

[7] Art. Newton.

solution of the problem. As it was the first time that the area under a curve had ever been calculated by the use of the new analytical geometry, it attracted much attention and came under the notice of Barrow. He remembered that Newton had been interested in infinite series during his retirement at Woolsthorpe because of the plague. But he did not know what had been the exact nature of the young student's work, and he certainly never dreamed that the same problem had been solved not only theoretically but that, with boyish enthusiasm, the area of the hyperbola had been actually computed, in 1665, "to two and fifty figures by the same method." When Mercator's work was thus communicated to Newton, he brought to light those papers of his which had remained for four years entirely unknown to his teacher, and which included the essential portions of his celebrated tract *De Analysi per Aequationes Numero Terminorum Infinitas.* "The doctor perusing it, stood amazed at the prodigious performance, and immediately acquainted his friend Collins with it; at whose request he afterwards obtained leave of Mr. Newton to send him the papers." Thus it was Collins who was the first to make Newton known to the world, since he made, and dispersed, copies to all the eminent mathematicians of his acquaintance. And this incident is supposed to have persuaded Barrow to recommend him as his successor in the Lucasian professorship.

During the years 1669–1670, we have preserved for us nine letters between Collins and Newton which give us some interesting details on his occupation and character.[8] Collins was quick to press a friendship by asking for the solution of some problems, and by sending him a copy of the new Kinkhuysen's *Algebra.* Newton made some notes upon it, at his leisure, and solved approximately the annuity problem: "To know at what rate (N per cent) an annuity of B is purchased for thirty-one years at the price A." But when he found that Collins wished him to revise the book, he answered that, as it was only a moderately useful one, he did not care to do more than to review it and to point out where it was amiss or defective.

News travelled slowly in those days and apparently Newton did not learn until a year later that Hooke had made light of his discovery of the reflecting telescope, and had claimed to have antedated the invention by several years. At least I cannot account for the contents and date of the following letter in any other way.

[8] Macclesfield, Vol. II, pp. 281–308.

Newton to Collins

Sir, Feb. 18, 1669/70.

Two days since, I received yours and Mr. Dary's letter with a book, for which I thank Mr. Dary, and have, here enclosed, sent him my thoughts of what he desired. That solution of the annuity problem if it will be of any use, you have my leave to insert it into the Philosophical Transactions, so it be without my name to it. *For I see not what there is desirable in public esteem, were I able to acquire and maintain it. It would perhaps increase my acquaintance, the thing which I chiefly study to decline.* Of that problem I could give exacter solutions, but that I have no leisure at present for computations. I now see a way, too, how the aggregate of the terms of musical progressions may be found, (much after the same manner,) by logarithms, but the calculation for finding out those rules would be still more troublesome, and I shall rather stay till you have leisure to do me the favour of communicating what you have already composed on that subject.

Your much obliged servant,

I. NEWTON.[9]

We have been led to believe that Newton's distaste for publicity, and his threats to abandon science, were caused by the persistent and ignorant criticisms of his papers on light. But this letter was written a year or more before he sent his first paper to the Royal Society and yet it expresses his sentiments as strongly as he ever did afterwards. The only reason that can be given for his disillusionment is that he may have heard, although it hardly seems probable, that Hooke had made some extravagant claims.

A closer examination of Kinkhuysen's *Algebra* had changed Newton's opinion of its value, and he now spent considerable time revising, and making additions to it. By July, 1670, the notes were finished and sent to Collins. But he is very doubtful whether they should be printed with the translation as he had changed and added so much: "There remains but one thing more, and that's about the title-page, if you print these alterations, which I have made in the author. For it may be esteemed unhandsome and injurious to Kinkhuysen to father a book wholly upon him, which is so much altered from what he had made it. But I think all will be safe, if

[9] Macclesfield, Vol. II, p. 296. Italics mine.

after the words, *Nunc e Belgico Latine versa,* be added, *Et ab alio authore locupletata* or some other such note."[10]

Collins at once expressed his hearty thanks and wrote "I received yours with Kinkhuysen's Introduction, and perceive you have taken great pains, which, God willing, shall be inserted into the translation and printed with it. Hereby you have much obliged the young students of algebra, and the bookseller."[11] He had not, as yet, become thoroughly acquainted with Newton's reluctance to subject himself to criticism and quite naturally ends his letter with the query, "Why you should desire to have your name unmentioned I see not; but if it be your will and command so to have it, it shall be observed."

Two other letters passed between them in the same month. Newton's thoughts had turned to expanding his notes on algebra into a book of his own, and he asked for their return. This was exactly what Collins desired, and he returned the manuscript with the handsome and neat compliment that his "pains will be acceptable to some very eminent grandees of the Royal Society, who must be acquainted therewith" as he considers him more likely than any man he knows to oblige the republic of learning.[12]

The answer to Collins's letter was delayed till the end of September, as Newton was waiting for Dr. Barrow's return from London that he might consult his library on some matters connected with the solution of cubic equations. A passage in this letter is worth quoting at length. It shows, in his own words, the early trend of his mind to avoid particular solutions, and to meditate on a subject till he had arrived at a general synthesis which would embrace a whole category of problems. This trait of mind accounts, in part, for the breadth of the work which he did publish; but it also accounts for the fact that, since the boundaries of his thoughts continually widened, he never felt satisfied that his work should be published till he had been teased by others to end his speculations. The passage is as follows: "I sometimes thought to have set upon writing a complete introduction to algebra, being chiefly moved to it by this, that some things I had inserted into Kinkhuysen were not so congruous as I could have wished to his manner of writing. Thus having composed something pretty largely about reducing problems to an equation, when I came to consider his examples, (which make the fourth part

[10] Macclesfield, Vol. II, p. 298. [11] *Ibid.,* Vol. II, p. 299.
[12] Macclesfield, Vol. II, p. 303.

of his book,) I found most of them solved, not by any general analytical method, but by particular and contingent inventions, which, though many times more concise than a general method would allow, yet, in my judgement, are less proper to instruct a learner, as acrostics, and such kind of artificial poetry, though never so excellent, would be but improper examples to instruct one that aims at Ovidian poetry. But considering that, by reason of several divertisements, I should be so long in doing it as to tire your patience with expectation, and also that, there being several introductions to Algebra already published, *I might thereby gain the esteem of one ambitious among the crowd to have my scribbles printed,* I have chosen rather to let it pass, without much altering what I sent you before."[13]

Newton passed the year, 1671, in his study, not leaving Cambridge except for a short visit to the country, probably Woolsthorpe, on business from 17 April to 11 May. He had finally been persuaded by Collins to publish some of his work under his own name and commenced the preparation of twenty lectures on light for the press; but, before they were ready, he became involved in the long controversy which followed from his discovery of the composition of light and he abandoned the project in disgust. He also decided to publish his papers on infinite series, including his new method of the fluxions, but this book also was never finished. It first appeared in 1736, in Colson's translation, with the title of *The Method of Fluxions and Infinite Series.* Pemberton tells us that he induced Newton "to let it go abroad. I had examined all the calculations and prepared part of the figures; but as the latter part of the treatise had never been finished, he was about letting me have other papers in order to supply what was wanting. But his death put a stop to that design."[14] Horsley included it in his edition of Newton's Works under the title of *Geometria Analytica.*

Newton to Collins

(London)

Sir, July 20, 1671.

I purposed to have given you a visit at the late solemnity of our Chancellor's creation; but I was prevented in that journey by the

[13] Macclesfield, Vol. II, p. 307. Italics mine.

[14] Pemberton's *View of Newton's Philosophy,* Lond., 1728. Preface.

sudden surprisal of a fit of sickness, which not long after, (God be thanked,) I again recovered of. And since I am prevented from a verbal acknowledgement of your undeserved favours, I must be yet contented to do it in writing. In which respect I find, by your last letter, that I am still become more your debtor, both for the care you take about my concerns, and for Borellius *De Motionibus*. But for Borellius I beg that I may be accountable to you at our next meeting, and that you would not, for the future, put yourself to the like trouble in sending any more books. I shall take it for a great favour, if in your letters you will only inform me of the names of the best of those books which newly come forth.

The last winter I reviewed the Introduction [Kinkhuysen], and made some few additions to it. And, partly upon Dr. Barrow's instigation, I began to new methodise the discourse of infinite series, designing to illustrate it with such problems as may (some of them perhaps) be more acceptable than the invention itself of working by such series. But being suddenly diverted by some business in the country, I have not yet had leisure to return to those thoughts, and I fear I shall not before winter. But since you inform me there needs no haste, I hope I may get into the humour of completing them before the impression of the Introduction, because, if I must help to fill up its titlepage, I had rather annex something, which I may call my own, and which may be acceptable to artists, as well as the other to tiros.

. . . .

Farewell,

Your most obliged servitor,

I. NEWTON.[15]

Elated by the performance of his first little telescope, Newton spent much time in the autumn improving his method of polishing metallic mirrors and, in December, sent a new and better instrument to the Royal Society where it is still displayed amongst its treasures. We know about the instrument's reception, and that it led to his nomination for membership by Bishop Ward.[16] At the meeting of 11 January, 1671/2 the brief statement was recorded, "Mr. Isaac Newton was elected." The fame of his telescope soon spread to the continent and, in a book of this period, he is called an *Artifex quidam Anglus*

[15] Macclesfield, Vol. II, p. 308.

[16] *Cf.* Chap. III, p. 70 seq.

nomine Newton, a title which well illustrates the fact that experimental science was not then rated as a learned profession.

An anecdote, if authentic, which appeared in *The Gentleman's Magazine,* gives a picture of Newton's truthfulness and inexperience in worldly affairs: "One of Sir I. Newton's philosophical friends abroad had sent him a curious prism, which was taken to the Custom-house, and was at that time a scarce commodity in this kingdom. Sir Isaac, laying claim to it, was asked by the officers what the value of the glass was, that they might accordingly regulate the duty. The great Newton, whose business was more with the universe than with duties and drawbacks, and who rated the prism according to his own idea of its use and excellence, answered 'That the value was so great, that he could not ascertain it.' Being again pressed to set some fixed estimate upon it, he persisted in his reply, 'That he could not say what it was worth, for that the value was inestimable.' The honest Custom-house officers accordingly took him at his word, and made him pay a most exorbitant duty for the prism, which he might have taken away upon only paying a rate according to the weight of the glass!!"[17] This story may be founded on a conversation which Dr. Stukeley reports as having taken place in 1721. "He showed us [Halley and Stukeley] at that time the famous Huygenian glass lens of 170 ft. radius which he had lately bought and since presented to the Royal Society. He complained of the custom-house officers making him pay £20 for the duty. He bought soon after, the great Maypole set up in the Strand and had it carried to Wanstead for Mr. Pound to use this glass upon, in astronomical observations."[18]

This year may be regarded as an important one in Newton's life. His paper on infinite series, and his general solution for finding the area subtended by curved lines, had been circulated by Collins. It was recognised by mathematicians that a general solution of the most important problem of the day had been found and Newton became a marked man. The veteran Wallis wrote to Collins that he thought it would be better for Mr. Newton to "publish what he hath as a treatise of his own, rather than by way of notes on him [Kinkhuysen]." And again, "I would very fain that Mr. Hooke and Mr. Newton would set themselves in earnest for promoting the designs about telescopes, that others may not steal from us what our nation invents, only for our neglect to publish them ourselves." So also

[17] Weld, *History of the Royal Society,* Vol. I, p. 238.
[18] Stukeley's *Mem. to Mead, Ports. Coll.,* File Add 4007.C.U.

James Gregory and Richard Towneley urged Collins to use his influence to get these discoveries into print.

The Royal Society had been aroused to the keenest enthusiasm by the little telescope which had been sent to them, and by the grasp the young man had shown of the principles of light and lenses. Newton had, at once, shown himself to be the peer of Descartes, Hooke, and Huygens. The Secretary, Henry Oldenburg, was directed to thank him and did so in the following flattering terms: "It [the telescope] having been considered, and examined here by some of the most eminent in optical science and practice, and applauded by them, they think it necessary to use some means to secure this invention from the usurpation of foreigners. And they request me to send a description of the instrument in a solemn letter to Paris to Mr. Huygens, thereby to prevent the arrogation of such strangers."

There is not the least doubt but that Newton was genuinely surprised and gratified by this reception of what he had looked upon as the exercises and diversions of his youth. His surprise has generally been ascribed to his modesty and diffidence. But it is far more likely that he felt they were mere preliminary sketches for the great problems which were ripening in his mind. If these slight things would attract attention, what might not he expect from his meditations on the nature of light and the cosmogony? His early letters to Oldenburg in January and February, 1672, indicate clearly his attitude. Extracts from these letters have already been given.[19] In them he mentioned his new discoveries in light as a matter really of importance and hoped to show his gratitude for the honour of his election by submitting other papers. Not only was he anxious to establish cordial and ingenuous relations with members of the Society, but he wished to have the advice of Oldenburg about the form of his communications.

Newton to Oldenburg

Jan. 29, Cambridge, 1671/2.

Sir,

. . . .

The publishing a description of the telescope in the Transactions I wholly leave to your pleasure, being willing to submit my private considerations in any thing that may be thought of public concernment. I have sent you, by the bearer, John Stiles, 40s for admission

[19] *Cf.* Chapter III, p. 71 seq.

money: and I hope I shall get some spare hours to send you also suddenly that account, which I promised in my last letter. In the mean time I rest

your very faithful servant,
I. NEWTON.[20]

During March, Newton wrote four letters to Oldenburg giving further particulars about his telescope and directions how to make the necessary mirrors; he further reported that one of the Fellows of the College was busy making another telescope.

But, these amicable feelings were not destined to endure. Huygens and Hooke had stiffened in their objections to the new doctrine, and a new critic had appeared in the person of Fr. Pardies of Paris. The scientific world, also, was beginning to take sides in the controversy. On April 9, James Gregory wrote to Collins: "I was exceedingly surprised with these experiments of Mr. Newton; they will cause great changes throughout all the body of natural philosophy, by all appearance, if the matter of fact be true, which I have no ground to question. I would gladly see what Mr. Hooke can say against the doctrine raised upon them, and am most willing to be at all the charges for the Transactions containing that debate, if you will be pleased to send them to me."[21] But Flamsteed, the astronomer royal, aligned himself against the theory and wrote to Collins: "I have perused Mr. Newton's letter concerning colours, but cannot think them to proceed from difform rays, capable of different refractions."[22]

In addition to his burden of correspondence, Newton was still trying to find time to prepare other work for the press. We learn from a letter of Collins, written to him on April 30: "Dr. Barrow informed me you were busy in enlarging your general method of infinite series, or quadratures, and in preparing twenty Dioptric lectures for the press; and lately meeting with Mr. Jonas Moore, he informed me that he heard you had something at the press in Cambridge, possibly about the same argument: . . ." He also expressed his pleasure that Newton had been elected a member of the Royal Society, but was chagrined to learn that he is expected to pay dues which should not be required of one who is so fitted "to enrich learning with your excellent contemplations about the same."[23]

[20] Macclesfield, II, p. 316.
[21] *Ibid.*, II, p. 237.
[22] *Ibid.*, II, p. 134.
[23] *Ibid.*, II, p. 319.

Newton to Collins

Sir, Cambridge, May 25, 1672.

This day fortnight I received your letter accompanied with part of the Remains of Mr. Horrox, two tracts of Honorato Fabri, and four or five copies of a Synopsis of Mr. Kersey's Algebra. For these and Dr. Wallis's Mechanics, together with many other civilities, I must acknowledge your obligingness and affection to me, and shall be ever ready to testify as much. Nor is your mathematical intelligence less grateful; for I am very glad that Dr. Barrow's book is abroad, and that the world will enjoy the writings of the excellent astronomers Mr. Horrox and Hevelius, and those complete mathematicians M. Huygens and Slusius.

Your kindness to me also in proffering to promote the edition of my lectures, which Dr. Barrow told you of, I reckon amongst the greatest, considering the multitude of business, in which you are involved; but I have now determined otherwise of them, finding already, by that little use I have made of the press, that I shall not enjoy my former serene liberty till I have done with it, which I hope will be so soon as I have made good what is already extant on my account. Yet I may possibly complete the discourse of resolving problems by infinite series, of which I wrote the better half the last Christmas with intention that it should accompany my Lectures, but it proves larger than I expected, and is not yet finished.

The book here in the press is Varenius his Geography, for which I have described schemes, and I suppose it will be finished about six weeks hence. The additions to Kinkhuysen's Algebra I have long since augmented with what I intended, and particularly with a discourse concerning invention, or the way of bringing problems to an equation; and those are at your command. If you have not determined any thing about them, I may possibly hereafter review them, and print them with the discourse concerning infinite series.

I take much satisfaction in being a member of that honourable body the Royal Society; and could be glad of doing any thing which might deserve it; which makes me a little troubled to find myself cut short of that freedom of communication, which I hoped to enjoy, but cannot any longer without giving offence to some persons whom I have ever respected. But it is no matter, since it was not for my own sake or advantage that I should have used that freedom. . . .

For my tardiness in returning you this answer I have no excuse, but that I staid four or five days, in hopes to send you some of those subscriptions, and being intent upon the duty of this term, the time slipped on faster than I was aware of. But I promise myself, by your so much testified friendship, that you will pardon it, and believe that I think myself really

your most obliged debtor,

I. NEWTON.[24]

Edleston records an anecdote which if, as is probable, it refers to the action between the English and Dutch fleets in Southwold Bay on the 28th of May, shows Newton's great acuteness of hearing and observation: "There is a traditional story at Cambridge . . . that Sir Isaac Newton came into the hall of Trinity College and told the other fellows that there had been an action just then between the Dutch and English, and that the latter had the worst of it. Being asked how he came by his knowledge, he said that being in the observatory [should be the great gateway], he heard the report of a great firing of cannon, such as could only be between two great fleets, and that as the noise grew louder and louder he concluded that they drew nearer to our coasts and consequently that we had the worst of it, which the event verified."[25]

Early in June, he wrote a long letter to Oldenburg to be transmitted to Pardies, explaining more fully his experiments in light. And he soon had the pleasure of an answer that this more detailed description of his work had fully satisfied Pardies, who now unreservedly accepted the conclusions and had no further criticism to make. During the controversy which followed, Newton vacillated between scorn for the obtuseness of his critics, who seemed to him unable to recognise that his work was a permanent contribution to knowledge which could be disproved only by other experimentation and not by speculation, and a hopeless feeling that however carefully he might express himself no one would take the trouble to think before making rash objections. In a mood for conciliation he wrote

[24] Macclesfield, Vol. II, p. 321.—It is clear from this letter, and from one given later, that Newton believed there was a cabal formed against him in the Royal Society by Hooke which deliberately tried to prevent his work from receiving a just consideration. From the sources at my disposal which unfortunately do not include the private memoranda of the Society, his suspicion was without foundation.—One can but wonder when he acquired the knowledge to lecture on geography as we know he did, or when he found time to undertake so laborious a task as preparing such a book for the press.

[25] Edleston, p. xlvii.

to Oldenburg to revise his recent letters and to soften any expressions which might cause offense. At such times, he shows himself as one would wish so great a man always to be, patient and considerate.

Newton to Oldenburg

June 11th, 1672.

S^r.

I have sent you my Answers to Mr Hook & P. Pardies, wch I hope will bring with y^m y^t satisfaction wch I promised. And as there is nothing in Mr Hooks Considerations wth wch I am not well contented, so I presume there is as little in mine wch he can excep against, since you will easily see that I have industriously avoyded ye intermixing of oblique & glancing expressions in my discourse. So y^t I hope it will be needlesse to trouble the R. Society to adjust matters. However if there should possibly be any thing esteemed of y^t kind, I desire it may be interpreted candidly & with respect to the contents of Mr Hooks Considerations, & I shall readily give way to ye mitigation of whatsoever ye heads of ye R. Society shall esteem personall. And concerning my former Answer to P. Pardies, I resigne to you ye same liberty wch he hath done for his Objections, of mollifying any expressions that may have a shew of harshnesse.

Yo^r Servant

I. Newton.

These
To Henry Oldenburg Esq: *at his house*
about ye middle of ye old Pall-maile
in Westminster London.[26]

Shortly after writing this letter, Newton left Cambridge for a month of rest and visiting. He first went into Bedfordshire and then home, to Woolsthorpe, where he always regained his composure. Oldenburg continued to press him to keep up the attempt to satisfy his critics, but Newton wisely wrote him that he would wait till he had had time to prepare a convincing and temperate reply. After a short stay at those places, he paid a visit of almost a month at the house of Mrs. Arundell, in Stoke Park, Northampton-

[26] Edleston, p. 248.—A curious instance of the license in spelling in those days is shown by the fact that Newton spelled and capitalised "Pall-Mall" in as many different ways as the sound of the words could suggest to an ingenious mind. I have noted, without much attention, five forms. Although I have generally transcribed most of the letters into modern spelling, I have left this as Newton wrote it. His letters show that he wrote hurriedly and frequently dropped words and letters.

shire. While there, he wrote to Oldenburg that excellent statement of the scientific method which should, I think, be learned and followed by every man of science:

"In the mean while give me leave to insinuate that I cannot think it effectual for determining truth to examine the several ways, by which phenomena may be explained, unless where there can be a perfect enumeration of all those ways. You know the proper method for enquiring after the properties of things is to deduce them from experiments: and I told you that the theory, which I propounded, was evinced to me, not by inferring 'tis thus because not otherwise; that is, not by deducing it only from a confutation of contrary suppositions, but by deriving it from experiments concluding positively and directly. The way therefore to examine it is by considering the experiments, which I propound, do prove those parts of the theory, to which they are applied, or by prosecuting other experiments, which the theory may suggest for its examination.[27]

He also asked Oldenburg to keep him informed about the progress of the war with Holland, as he is "at a place where the quick arrival of news is a rarity." To Collins, he wrote to inform him that he had finally decided not to publish his lectures on light and was hesitating about the advisability of finishing his work on infinite series. As soon as he returned to Cambridge he wrote again to him, on July 30, that Varenius[28] was newly off the press, and he had sent a complimentary copy by the university carrier, John Stiles. Towards the end of the year, Dr. Barrow was appointed Master of Trinity, and Newton expressed his pleasure in welcoming the return of his patron and teacher in a letter to Collins in which he said that no one rejoiced more than he did.

The years 1673 and 1674 were a time of little incident. The records of the Royal Society rarely mention Newton's name. He

[27] Macclesfield, Vol. II, p. 326.

[28] Bernhardi Vareni Geographia generalis, in qua affectiones generales Telluris explicantur, summâ curâ quam plurimis in locis emendata, et XXXIII Schematibus novis, aere incisis, unâ cum Tabb. aliquot quae desiderabantur aucta et illustrata. Ab Isaaco Newton Math. Prof. Lucasiano apud Cantabrigiensis. Cantabrigiae 1672. "The first edition had appeared in Holland in 1650, and was considered the best book on geography of that time. Another Cambridge edition, with Newton as editor, came out in 1681. A third edition, in English translation, was issued after the death of Newton, in 1736, in which the translator remarked: 'The reason why this great man took so much care in correcting and publishing our author, was because he thought him necessary to be read by the audience while he was delivering lectures upon the same subject from the Lucasian chair.' " *Sir Isaac Newton*, Baltimore, 1928, p. 168. This is, I think, the only reference to the fact that he delivered lectures on geography.

wrote only a few letters on light, and these were sent to Huygens who had become dissatisfied with his own attempt to include the new work in the wave theory of light.

Early in March, 1673, there occurred a contest for power between the Heads of the Colleges and the Senate over the appointment of Public Orator. In spite of the effort of the Chancellor to effect a compromise and of a protest on the morning of the election by a large number of the Senate, amongst whose names was that of Newton, the Heads gained the day and installed their choice.

Newton, apparently, this year became apprehensive about his income. In the ordinary course of events, his fellowship would expire in the autumn of 1675. He had been advised to take orders so that he might continue as Fellow, but he finally refused on the ground that he could give better service to religion out of the church. On February 14, a law-fellowship became vacant which was open to lay members of the College. The story has come down to us "that Newton and Robert Uvedale were candidates for the fellowship in question; and that Mr. Barrow, who had been admitted Master of Trinity on February 27, decided it in favour of Mr. Uvedale, saying that Mr. Uvedale and Mr. Newton being equal in literary attainments, he must give the fellowship to Mr. Uvedale as senior."[29] Brewster makes much of this story to excite sympathy for Newton in order to show that he was a much neglected young man. But, as Edleston remarks, since this fellowship required the holder *"operam dare juri civili,"* its duties could hardly be undertaken by a professor of mathematics. Brewster thought this was a mere technicality as such fellowships have frequently been occupied by men who had no qualifications for the law; but Barrow and Newton were the type of men who would take their word and their work seriously. It is simply absurd to put in Barrow's mouth that he thought Newton and Uvedale equal in attainments. As the story originated with a great-grandson of Robert Uvedale, we can assign it to a family tradition that Uvedale was appointed to a lay-fellowship and that Newton had desired it.

Rightly or wrongly, Newton was worried about his living; however, even if he had lost his fellowship, it will be shown later that he was not in any serious difficulties. In my opinion his sudden decision to resign from the Royal Society should not be laid to poverty as has been very generally assumed; but he had been dis-

[29] Edleston, p. xlviii.

illusioned, he had never as yet attended a meeting and was constantly fretted by the rumours Oldenburg sent him that he was criticised and attacked by Hooke and his protéges. At any rate he startled Oldenburg by sending him the following letter.

Newton to Oldenburg

Cambridge, March 8, 1672/3.

Sir,

I received both your letters, and thank you for Hecker's Mercurius in Sole. As for M. Huygens' observations, I conceive they are but the abstract of a private letter sent to you, and therefore concern not me to take notice of them. But yet if he expect an answer, and intends that this should be made public, I will return you my thoughts upon them, if you please to send me the original letter, and procure from M. Huygens that I may have liberty to publish what passeth between us, if occasion be.

Sir, I desire that you will procure that I may be put out from being any longer Fellow of the Royal Society: for though I honour that body, yet since I see I shall neither profit them, nor (by reason of this distance) can partake of the advantage of their assemblies, I desire to withdraw. If you please to do me this favour you will oblige

your humble servant,

I. NEWTON.

P. S. I have presumed to put you once more to the trouble of receiving my quarterly duty as Fellow of the Royal Society. At next Lady-day I am behindhand for half a year, and have therefore sent you 1£.6s. by John Stiles. I hope you will excuse this trouble, it being the last. I shall be henceforth absent from Cambridge for about a month.[30]

Oldenburg was much disturbed by this letter and at the idea of the Society losing so valuable a member; perhaps, also, he was chagrined by the consciousness that he may have been partly responsible. He answered at once to express surprise "at his resigning for no other cause than his distance, which he knew as well at the time of his election. Offering withal my endeavour to take from him the trouble of sending hither his quarterly payments without any reflection."

[30] Macclesfield, II, p. 348.

After sending this letter, Newton left Cambridge, probably for a short visit home, and did not return until the 1st of April. His correspondence with Collins was mostly as a go-between with James Gregory over the merits of their forms of reflecting telescopes. Collins so managed it that Gregory became a warm friend and admirer of Newton, and there was no break in their friendship. Newton states in one of these letters that he was unable to read French without the continual use of a dictionary.

He also confides to Collins his troubles with the Royal Society in a manner which I think makes it certain that the payment of dues was an excuse for the true reason. He wrote: "Concerning the expenses of being a member of the R. S. I suppose there hath been done me no unkindness, for I met with nothing in that kind besides my expectations. *But I would wish I had met with no rudeness in some other things.* And therefore I hope you will not think it strange, if, to prevent accidents of that nature for the future, I decline that conversation which hath occasioned what is past. I hope this, whatever it may make me appear to others, will not diminish your friendship to me."[31]

Late in the year Gregory went to London and, on his way back to Scotland, stopped in Cambridge to pay Newton a visit during which the two indulged in long and intimate talks on telescopes, mirrors, and mathematics.

Newton passed almost the entire year, 1674, in Cambridge. There is nothing to record accept the final flare up over his experiments on light. This time, the objection came from the Liégeois professors, who were pompous in their conceit and exasperating in their dullness; nor did Oldenburg help matters, for he could not understand that they were not critics in the same class with Hooke and Huygens, and he continued to pester his friend with urgent requests to defend himself instead of letting their opinions die from their own foolishness. The discussion dragged on for two years more and ended with the death of Oldenburg.

Added to the irritation which the long-drawn-out and, of late, futile controversy on light had engendered, there had arisen a new injury to his feelings, for Oldenburg had hinted that it would be unnecessary for him to resign from the Royal Society as a promise of experiments and discourses from him would be accepted in lieu

[31] Macclesfield, II, p. 360.—The word "conversation" was used to express any social intercourse. Its use in that sense will be an important matter in an incident in his later life. Italics mine.

of the payment of dues. In this frame of mind he wrote, in 1674, that he wished to be excused from giving any discourses, or demonstrations, to the Society as he was seldom in London.[32] Though he did not insist on his resignation being accepted, he for many years rarely attended meetings. It was not till the Society received his *Principia* with such enthusiasm that he recovered from his wounded feelings; and so long as Hooke lived, Newton showed but little interest in its affairs and had no place in its councils.

[32] For the full text of the letter, *cf.* Chap. IV.

CHAPTER VI

ALCHEMY AND CHEMISTRY. HIS PERSONAL LIFE. RELATIONS WITH HOOKE. EARLY MATHEMATICAL WORK. INVENTION OF CALCULUS. CORRESPONDENCE WITH LEIBNIZ

1674–1676

TOWARDS the end of the year, 1675, Collins made the casual remark in a letter to Gregory: "Mr. Newton, I have not writ to or seen these eleven or twelve months, not troubling him as being intent upon chemical studies and practices, and both he and Dr. Barrow beginning to think mathematical speculations to grow at least dry, if not somewhat barren."[1] As has been remarked before, Newton suffered from irritation and depression when circumstances compelled him to confine himself to mathematical, or speculative, work and he then sought solace in what we should now call experimental science. The need for such diversion was pressing upon him; he was weary of the contentions of men and the criticism of work which afforded him no interest.

In comparison with his other work, what Newton achieved in chemistry has been rather slighted. While it is true that he made no striking discoveries or enlarged the knowledge of chemical action, one has merely to glance through the manuscripts of the *Portsmouth Collection* to be convinced that he was a master of the subject. He left a mass of notes and data relating to the experiments he had tried. According to his habit, he was indefatigable in making notes in his common-place books and draughts of attempts to ally molecular forces with gravitational attraction of bodies. His own books were annotated on the margins and passages marked by his customary habit of folding the corners of the pages; and he frequently borrowed from the University Library. An examination of his own library shows a comprehensive collection of books on chemistry and the very large proportion of works on alchemy and magic is significant of his interest.[2] Since his efforts were concentrated on finding a general

[1] Macclesfield, Vol. II, p. 280. [2] *Cf.* R. de Villamil, *Newton: The Man*, London, 1932.

synthesis of chemical combinations and on the transmutation of the elements which we now contemptuously class as alchemy, it is probable that having accomplished neither, he did not think it advisable to publish his disconnected and tentative results.

We are justified in saying that Newton's interest in chemistry began with his boyish days in Clark's apothecary shop; his first notebook preserved in the Morgan Library is largely filled with recipes referring more or less to the subject. During the thirty-five years he lived in Cambridge he experimented intermittently, but with an almost passionate energy, in the college room he had fitted as a laboratory. In London, after he had given up all other scientific work, he still found pleasure in the chemical problems relating to metals and alloys which were involved in the operations of the Mint. Humphrey Newton of Grantham, who served for some years as his assistant and amanuensis, has left us this interesting description of Newton's method of relaxation when fatigued with the composition of the *Principia*. "About six weeks at spring, and six at the fall, the fire in the laboratory scarcely went out, which was well furnished with chemical materials as bodies, receivers, heads, crucibles, etc., which was [sic] made very little use of, the crucibles excepted, in which he fused his metals; he would sometimes, tho' very seldom, look into an old mouldy book which lay in his laboratory, I think it was titled Agricola de Metallis, the transmuting of metals being his chief design, for which antimony was a great ingredient."[3]

The fact of the matter is, Newton was an alchemist, and his major interest in chemistry, in his earlier years, centred in the possibility of transmuting metals. He begged his youthful friend, Aston, in the letter previously quoted,[4] to find out all he could on the subject during his travels and not to be too scrupulous in his method of enquiry. Humphrey Newton found him absorbed in the search in 1685, and still later in life he carried on a correspondence about it with Locke and Boyle. There was a mystical strain in his character which has been quite overlooked. It showed itself not only in his persistent reading of the esoteric formulæ of the alchemists, but also in his sympathy for the philosophy of the Cambridge Platonists and in his extended interpretations of the prophecies of the Books of Daniel and of the Revelation. Nor did his enquiry stop at these bounds, there is evidence that he studied the writings of Jacob

[3] *Portsmouth Collection*. Letter of H. Newton to Conduitt.—This work and others of Agricola are to be found in the catalogue of his library.

[4] *Cf*. Chap. II, p. 49.

Boehme and became, more or less, a follower of the mystical shoemaker. "The Rev. Mr. Law has stated that there were found among Sir Isaac's papers large extracts out of Jacob Boehme's works, written with his own hand, and that he had learned from undoubted authority, that in a former part of his life he was led into a search of the philosopher's tincture from the same author."[5] There can be no doubt that he not only seriously sought the transmutation of metals into gold and the universal panacea for disease and old age, but also believed them to be the chief goal of the chemist.

Because of our facile identification of alchemists with charlatans and prostituters of pure science for the sake of wealth, Newton's eulogists, although they must admit that he was an ardent adept, attempt to explain his motive as only a desire to expose the errors of those "great pretenders" of the Hermetic philosophy as he once termed them.[6] Why should Newton not be an alchemist? All his contemporaries, even Boyle, Locke, and Hooke were, and if he desired to study the composition of bodies, he would without hesitation

[5] Brewster, Vol. II, p. 371. Boehme's works were in his library.

[6] *Cf.* Brewster, Vol. II, p. 374. "The alchemy of Boyle, Newton, and Locke cannot be thus characterised [as commencing in fraud and terminating in mysticism]. The ambition neither of wealth nor of praise prompted their studies, and we may safely say that a love of truth alone, a desire to make new discoveries in chemistry, and a wish to test the *extraordinary pretensions* of their predecessors and their contemporaries, were the only motives by which they were actuated. In so far as Newton's enquiries were limited to the transmutation and multiplication of metals, and even to the discovery of the universal tincture, we may find some apology for his researches; but we cannot understand how a mind of such power, and so nobly occupied with the abstractions of geometry, and the study of the material world, could stoop to be even the copyist of the most contemptible alchemical poetry, and the annotator of a work [by Agricola], the obvious production of a fool and a knave."—Brewster obviously did not know the reputation of that author, and it is a gross injustice to class alchemists as knaves and fools. The assertion that Newton was engaged in alchemical research and studied its treatises only in order "to test the *extraordinary pretensions*" of the alchemists rests on a single statement in a letter in which he says (see infra, Chap. VI, p. 162), "there being other things besides the transmutations of metals (if those *great pretenders* brag not) which none but they understand." Brewster evidently thought that he used the word "pretender" to mean one suspected of fraud and falsehood. But Newton used it to characterise one who earnestly sought to obtain knowledge. Its restriction to a false claimant came into the language only after it had been applied by the Whigs to the claims of the son of James II in order to throw discredit on their legitimate claims. The pitfalls of language which await the historian of the seventeenth century are many. For instance one of the most recent writers on Newton makes the following remarkable deduction. Newton once, when indulging in an extravagant speculation, checks himself with the simple statement, "I am not satisfied about it for want of Experiments." The essayist makes this delightful comment, "Note the capital E. Do we not have here a glowing example of Newton the experimental natural philosopher?" (*Sir Isaac Newton, 1727–1927,* p. 222. Essay by Professor Lyman Newell.) One can but believe that the essayist was quite unacquainted with the laxity of capitalisation and spelling of Newton and of all writers of that century. If he had considered even one example he would have drawn no inferences from a capital E. I claim the highest admiration for Newton, but I trust that I may not fall under the hypnotic spell which seems to be the fate of those who discuss his great personality.

class himself as one of them. Alchemy, in name, is probably the Arabic translation of the Greek word to mix or to fuse, and it was applied to designate all the known chemical processes; the new term, chemistry, was but just beginning to come into use.

During the Middle Ages, and well down into the seventeenth century, all matter was believed to be composed of the four elementary substances or essences,—earth, water, air, and fire,—combined in different proportions and actuated by the qualities of heat and cold, dryness and moisture. Thus, there was every reason for the conviction of alchemists that proper chemical and physical reagents would alter the relative proportions of those elements in any given compound and so change one substance into another. For example, alchemists considered gold and lead to be compounds of the four elements in different proportions and therefore could be transmuted by proper chemical reagents; on the other hand, chemists during the nineteenth century confidently declared that gold and lead were two amongst ninety-odd immutable elements which combined in varying proportions to form all other substances. It is difficult, in a scientific sense, to distinguish between the theories of alchemy and chemistry, however greater the practical knowledge of what elementary substances now may be. The certainty of the ideas of chemists of the last century seemed to have been thoroughly established; this certainty, however, no longer pertains to at least all of their elementary substances,—one of them, uranium, without artificial aid decomposes into radium and it, in turn, into the element, lead. It is safe to say that many chemists now assume there is but a single primary element,—a protion of electricity,—as hypothetical as the primary elements of alchemists; and they are diligently trying to transmute what they formerly claimed to be fixed elements. Also, if we grant the postulates of alchemists that the human body is composed of the four classic elements and that illness, and even death, result from a disturbance of their just balance, then it is a perfectly rational and scientific conclusion that a chemical method, an elixir of life, might be found which would restore their balance and be a cure for disease and senility.[7]

[7] The emperor Diocletian "caused a diligent enquiry to be made 'for all the ancient books which treated of the admirable art of making gold and silver, and without pity committed them to the flames; apprehensive, as we are assured, lest the opulence of the Egyptians should inspire them with confidence to rebel against the empire.' But if Diocletian had been convinced of the reality of that valuable art, far from extinguishing the memory, he would have converted the operation of it to the benefit of the public revenue. It is much more likely that his good sense discovered to him the folly of such magnificent pretensions, and that he was

The mere fact that natural cupidity for health and wealth led many alchemists to seek especially the philosopher's stone and the transmutation of lead into gold has nothing to do with the question. The difference between alchemy and chemistry is a difference in time and experience rather than of concept or method. Is it not one of the glories, and I venture to say the chief glory, of modern chemistry that it has vastly increased our power and wealth? Is not radioactivity but the science of the transmutation of the elements? There is a vast deal of nonsense talked about science for science sake, just as there is about art for art's sake. Newton, Boyle, and Locke desired to apply their knowledge to obtain practical results, and would have welcomed power and wealth as men of science do today. Francis Bacon esteemed science only for its fruits. And it is a commentary on human blindness for anyone in this age, absorbed as it is in the pursuit of mechanical power and with its ideals confused with material welfare, complacently to apologise for Newton's practical tastes lest his scientific reputation be smirched. As he grew older, he seems to have lost his faith in the practicability of transmutation. At least, in his letters to Locke, he expressed a doubt that Boyle had found an alchemical recipe and had kept it a secret for twenty years.

Boyle's own ideas on alchemy and on science for science's sake can be given in his own words. For example, Boyle published a paper in the *Philosophical Transactions* in 1675 on "An experimental Discourse of Quicksilver growing hot with Gold." In this paper he described how, "through God's blessing, my trials afforded me positive proof about the year 1652" and a preparation of mercury had been found which when mixed with powdered gold made the mass become noticeably warm. In conclusion he states: "I will not so much as affirm, that every mercury obtained by extraction, even from the perfect metals themselves, must needs be more noble and fit, as alchemists speak, for the *philosophic work*, than that, which common mercury skilfully freed from its recrementitious [superfluous] and heterogeneous parts, and richly impregnated with the subtle and active one of congruous metals or minerals." This discourse occasioned the following comment from Newton.

desirous of preserving the reason and fortunes of his subjects from the mischievous pursuit. It may be remarked that these ancient books, so liberally ascribed to Pythagoras, to Solomon, or to Hermes, were the pious frauds of more recent adepts. The Greeks were inattentive either to the use or to the abuse of chemistry. In that immense register, where Pliny has deposited the discoveries, the arts, and the errors of mankind, there is not the least mention of the transmutation of metals; and the persecution of Diocletian is the first authentic event in the history of alchymy." Gibbon, *Roman Empire,* Chap. XIII.

Newton to Oldenburg

Cambridge, April 26, 1676.

Sir,

. . . .

Yesterday I reading the two last *Philosophical Transactions* had the opportunity to consider Mr. Boyle's uncommon experiment about the *incalescence of gold and mercury.* I believe the fingers of many will itch to be at the knowledge of the preparation of such a mercury; and for that end some will not be wanting to move for the publishing of it, by urging the good it may do in the world. But, in my simple judgement, the noble author, since he has thought fit to reveal himself so far, does prudently in being reserved in the rest. . . . Because the way by which mercury may be so impregnated, has been thought fit to be concealed by others that have known it, and therefore may possibly be an inlet to something more noble, not to be communicated without immense damage to the world, if there should be any verity in the Hermetic writers; therefore I question not, but that the great wisdom of the noble author will sway him to high silence, till he shall be resolved of what consequence the thing may be, either by his own experience, or the judgement of some other that thoroughly understands what he speaks about; that is, of a true Hermetic philosopher, whose judgement (if there be any such) would be more to be regarded in this point, than that of all the world beside to the contrary, there being other things beside the *transmutation* of *metals* (if those *great pretenders* brag not) which none but they understand. Sir, because the author seems desirous of the sense of others in this point, I have been so free as to shoot my bolt; but pray keep this letter private to yourself.

Your servant,

ISAAC NEWTON.[8]

That Boyle did not have any contempt for the practical fruits of science may be seen from an extract from a letter written towards the close of his life.

Boyle to a Friend

Sir,

. . . .

To those that think it strange, that among my other experiments about metals and minerals, I have not produced those gainful ones,

[8] Boyle's *Works,* Vol. I, p. cv; and Macclesfield, Vol. II, p. 395. Italics mine.

that chemists call *particulars,* it may, I hope, suffice to represent, that being a bachelor, and through God's bounty furnished with a competent estate for a younger brother, and freed from any ambition to leave my heirs rich, I had no need to pursue lucriferous experiments, to which I so much preferred luciferous ones, that I had a kind of ambition (*which I now perceive to have been a vanity*) of being able to say, that I cultivated chemistry with a disinterested mind, neither seeking nor scarce caring for any other advantages by it, than those of the improvement of my knowledge of nature, the gratifying the curious and industrious, and the acquist of some useful helps to make good and uncommon medicines. . . . But, however, since I find myself now grown old, I think it time to comply with my former intentions to leave a kind of Hermetic legacy to the studious disciples of that art, and to deliver candidly, in the annexed paper, some processes chemical and medicinal, that are less simple and plain than those barely luciferous ones I have been wont to affect, and of a more difficult and elaborate kind than those I have hitherto published, and more of kin to the noblest Hermetic secrets, or, as *Helmont* styles them, *arcana majora.* Sir,

Your most faithful and most humble servant,

ROBERT BOYLE.[9]

Hooke was so eager for money that he constantly dunned the Royal Society for more salary and lived as a miser, that he might fill his iron-bound chest: Newton was generous, but he was careful enough to leave a large fortune at his death.

In spite of Newton's interest and persistent work in chemistry, he published only one strictly chemical paper. This work, *De Natura Acidorum,* is only about two pages long and is a succession of speculations on chemical affinity rather than a detailed account of acids. As it contains references to the *Principia,* it must be dated after 1685. If the reader be interested in Newton's chemical work, he should read carefully Queries 30 and 31 in the *Optics,* since he gives in them his ideas on chemical affinity and the cause of chemical action in a less technical form than elsewhere.

Query 30 is a veiled apology for the search for the transmutation of metals. He pictures Nature as delighted with transmutations, and gives examples to show that all bodies are composed of the same hard particles which differ in nature only because of their arrangement and

[9] Boyle's *Works,* Vol. I, p. cxxx.

their mutual forces of attraction. He even carried his belief in transmutability so far as to query whether gross bodies and light are not convertible into one another.

Query 31 is a review of the general question whether all physical and chemical phenomena, and perhaps even the phenomena of life are not due to a mechanical attraction between all particles of matter,—a generalisation from his discovery of gravitation. A few quotations from it will show the drift of his ideas:

"Have not the small particles of bodies certain powers, virtues or forces, by which they act at a distance, not only upon the rays of light for reflecting, refracting and inflecting them, but also upon one another, for producing a great part of the phenomena of Nature? . . . For Nature is very consonant and conformable to herself. How those attractions may be performed, I do not here consider. What I call attraction, may be performed by Impulse, or by some other means unknown to me. I use that word here to signify only in general any force by which bodies tend towards one another, whatsoever be the cause. For we must learn, from the phenomena of Nature, what bodies attract one another, and what are the laws and properties of the attraction, before we enquire the cause by which the attraction is performed. The attractions of gravity, magnetism and electricity, reach to very sensible distances, and so have been observed by vulgar eyes; and there may be others which reach to so small distances as hitherto escape observation; and perhaps electrical attraction may reach to such small distances, even without being excited by friction."

"For when salt of tartar runs *per deliquium,* is not this done by an attraction between the particles of the salt of tartar, and the particles of water, which float in the air in the form of vapours? . . . When salt of tartar *per deliquium,* being poured into the solution of any metal, precipitates the metal, and makes it fall down to the bottom of the liquor in the form of mud: does not this argue, that the acid particles are attracted more strongly by the salt of tartar than by the metal, and by the stronger attraction go from the metal to the salt of tartar?"

"The parts of all homogeneal hard bodies, which fully touch one another, stick together very strongly. And for explaining how this may be, some have invented hooked atoms [Democritus], which is begging the question; and others tell us, that bodies are glued together by rest [Descartes]; that is, by an occult quality, or rather by nothing: and others, that they stick together by conspiring motions;

that is, relative rest amongst themselves. I had rather infer from their cohesion, that their particles attract one another by some force, which in immediate contact is exceeding strong, at small distances performs the chemical operations above-mentioned, and reaches not far from the particles with any sensible effect."

"All bodies seem to be composed of hard particles: for otherwise fluids would not congeal."

"And thus Nature will be very conformable to herself, and very simple; performing all the great motions of the heavenly bodies by the attraction of gravity, which intercedes those bodies; and almost all the small ones of their particles, by some other attractive and repelling powers, which intercede the particles."

"And therefore that Nature may be lasting, the changes of corporeal things are to be placed only in the various separations, and new associations, and motions of these permanent particles."

It seems quite evident that Newton found in chemistry the scientific work most congenial to his personal tastes and aptitude; it satisfied best his fondness for working with tools and for experimentation, and at the same time gave full play for his predilection for wide generalisations. Though he performed a multitude of separate experiments, they were done for his own satisfaction, and he saw no reason for making them public. They would be of use to the world only if, by them, he could arrive at some general and fundamental principle of chemical action, such as he had found in the universal force of attraction. Thus his eager enquiry in alchemy was for the purpose of finding some essential substance, or quality in matter, which by its variations would link together all chemical actions, such as the postulates of inertia and attraction had in the physical world. His successful synthesis in mechanics was made possible by the work of his great predecessors, but he could find in chemistry no such material. He certainly had pictured in his mind an atomic theory in which the variety of elements was due to the geometrical groupings of a universal atomic substance. He had gone even further in that he queried whether the force which held together, and acted on, those atomic groups were not the same attractive force which bound the planets into a solar system; and he had also queried whether chemical affinity were not a manifestation of electricity. But to Newton, queries were not science till they were supported by experimental demonstration. If the accumulation of chemical data had permitted Newton to formulate the modern atomic theory, as it did Dalton, we may not know what would have been the history of chemistry, but we can be certain that the intimate connection between physics and chemistry would have been established much earlier. Newton would not have advanced an atomic theory in the simple and statistical form that it left Dalton's hands. He would surely have given it a dynamic basis, and have attempted to express chemical forces by mathematical formulæ. In fact, there is reliable evidence that he had undertaken such a work. I found in the *Portsmouth Collection* the following memorandum by Stukeley: "He wrote likewise a piece of chemistry, explaining the principles of that mysterious art upon experimental and mathematical proofs and he valued it much, but it was unluckily burnt in his laboratory which casually took fire. He would never undertake that work again, a loss much to be regretted."[10]

This brief survey of Newton's chemical work will be closed by quoting an estimate of it by Professor H. E. Armstrong: "Newton . . . considering the operation of the force of residual affinity, which is not only unexplained to the present day but rarely considered. In his subsequent discussion of the interactions of acids and metals, and of acids and salts, he is dealing with the subject of ordinary chemical change. Speculation on these subjects to-day is not less vague than it was in Newton's time. Modifying his language but slightly, to reduce it to modern terms, we can but realise that little advance has been made in our understanding of the phenomena—although we have an exact and abounding knowledge of fact which is astounding compared with that of Newton's day. We need a Newton with the perspicacity to order our knowledge into a philosophy."

Professor Armstrong also points out that Newton, when he described the air as abounding "with acid vapours fit to provide fermentations,"[11] anticipated Lavoisier, and then ends with this drastic criticism of modern ideas and practice:

"Today, we have reduced the conception 'Acid' to the most miserable of dimensions—to a figment of the imagination, the lonely hydrogen ion. Verily, is our ignorance far greater than that of Newton, near two hundred years ago, because, having eyes to see and a vast

[10] Though the statement adds another to the confusion of the Newtonian fires, I believe it is correct as it occurs in Stukeley's *Memorandum to Mead,* one of the most trustworthy documents we have. I found it also in a draught of *Fragments of Conduitt's intended Life of Newton.*

[11] He means by fermentations all such oxidation processes as the rusting of metals, combustion, the heat from respiration, etc.

mass of recorded fact to consider, we will take no notice of fact and are but worshippers of faiths which have no secure basis?

"Whether we study diamond, whether we study colour, whether we study acids or other characters, we are always faced with this one problem that which struck Newton's attention, the problem of chemical affinity. We now believe it to be electrical in its origin. Further it is impossible to go at present—the speculation thus far indulged in seems trivial in face of the complexities the subject presents. We are told that the electron does everything but *how* it does anything we are not informed.

"We need, indeed, to follow Newton's advice—to argue from phenomena with less feigning of hypotheses and to deduce causes more from effects. Never was superstition more rife in scientific circles than it is to-day—the apostolic injunction, 'Prove all things, hold fast that which is true,' is not practised, at least among chemists and physicists. Above all, we need to clear our minds by argument, if there be any left to argue, with reasonable attention to the facts."[12]

It is time to turn to Newton's personal affairs. We have been led to believe that he was much worried during 1675 about his finances, and the cause has been ascribed to the fact that, in the natural course of events, his fellowship which he had held for seven years would lapse in the coming autumn. If he was so worried, it was the only time in his life of which we have any record; the probable loss of his fellowship does not seem sufficient to have caused any acute anxiety. The monetary value of a fellowship, apparently, was unusually small at that time. The new Master of Trinity, Dr. Barrow, had just called attention to the fact that, "a fellowship with us is now so poor that I cannot think it worth holding by an ingenuous person upon terms of so much scruple."[13] While this statement is somewhat vague as we may find it difficult to capitalise the scruples of an ingenuous person, Edleston estimated the annual income of his fellowship to be less than £30. From the analysis of his income previously given,[14] he would still have, in addition to his free lodgings and dinners, £80 a year from his estates and about £100 from his professorship. Such an income would have been considered opulence by Hooke, Flamsteed, and most of the scholars of the time.[15]

[12] *Isaac Newton*, ed. by Greenstreet, p. 15.

[13] Edleston, p. L.

[14] *Cf.* Chapter II, p. 47.

[15] Brewster, (vol. I, p. 100) draws an absurdly pathetic picture of the ingratitude of the British nation towards men of science in general, and Newton in particular. In comparison with the poets and other literary men, science has been liberally rewarded and Newton is

The only authentic evidence of Newton's financial worry rests on the interpretation by Oldenburg of a letter in which he asked to have his resignation presented to the Royal Society. The only reasons given there for this request were that his scientific contributions were not valued by the members and that he lived too far from London to be able to attend the meetings. The only reference to money was that he had forwarded his dues for half a year, which merely indicated that he was in arrears and had not previously been pressed for their regular payment. Oldenburg, who was impetuous and tactless, at once jumped to the conclusion that these specious excuses had been given to conceal Newton's embarrassment in not being able to pay the annual dues of fifty-two shillings.

The Secretary of the Society had good cause to be interested in the dues as it was a serious question during the early years of the Society. The Treasurers' reports were most discouraging and by 1674, only fourteen years after the foundation, the arrears amounted to the astonishing figure of £1957. The Record frequently called attention to this embarrassing situation and many severe regulations were adopted to compel members to be more prompt, but without much success. Nothing better illustrates the little interest in science, and the few workers, than the financial difficulties of the Society during its early history. The Secretary was much distressed at the defection of so promising a member, and further embarrassed Newton by recommending, without first obtaining his approval, that his dues should be compensated for by giving discourses and demonstrations to the Society. As a result of this recommendation the Council, at the meeting of January 28, 1674/5, voted that: "Mr. Oldenburg having mentioned, that Mr. Newton had intimated his being in such circumstances, that he desired to be excused from the weekly payments [one shilling], it was agreed by the council, that he should be dispensed with, as several others were."

When Newton received notice of this generous proposal, he was placed in a most awkward position. He had not asked to have his dues remitted and he could hardly tell the Council that his real motive for resigning was caused by his belief in their personal opposition and their indifference to his work. He sharply declined to

certainly not an example of neglect. He was generously and freely supported by the University for a period of almost forty years as sizar, scholar, fellow, and professor. When his reputation was established, he represented her in the Court of Commission and in Parliament. When he desired to leave Cambridge, he received a lucrative position and became a rich man, honoured by the whole nation as its most distinguished citizen.

serve as lecturer and demonstrator; and he apparently withdrew his resignation and ignored the subject of dues. Meanwhile to Collins, with whom he was franker and less reserved than with anyone else, he specifically stated that he had been treated rudely, and could not expect an impartial hearing. Lest he might be blamed by others, he hoped his friend at least would not think it strange that to avoid such treatment he "declines that conversation which hath occasioned what is past."[16]

Newton, this year, made one of his rare visits to London, staying there from February 9 to March 19. He attended, for the first time, a meeting of the Royal Society on February 18, as the record states that he and James Hoare, Esq., were admitted and signed the Register on that day. He also attended the meetings on March 11 and 18 in order to be present when Hooke was expected to repeat his experiments with the prism to settle the objections of Fr. Linus. For some unknown reason, however, he was disappointed as Hooke failed to try the experiment, and instead read a paper of his own on diffraction and interference of light. The test was delayed for more than a year, and it was not until April 27, 1676, that the Society could inform Fr. Linus and his colleagues at Liége that the experiment had been tried and had succeeded as Newton had all along asserted it would. A trifling incident occurred at one of the meetings which is typical of Newton's thoughtfulness and amiability. When he returned to Cambridge, he wrote to Oldenburg that he had met at the Society an ancient Gentleman, who, being thick of hearing, had enquired of him about Mr. Mace's Otocousticon, or improved ear trumpet.[17] Owing to a pressure of business he had neglected to attend to the request and was now enclosing a description of the instrument which he begged might be forwarded with his apology.

But, the trip to London had been undertaken for another and much more important purpose. Either by the advice and backing of his friends (amongst whom we should undoubtedly include the Master of Trinity), or on his own initiative, a petition of indulgence had been prepared for the Crown that he be permitted to retain his fellowship without entering into orders so long as he held his professorship. Edleston thought that the patent had been drawn up by

[16] It should be remembered that the word, *conversation,* was not then limited to oral communication but was the common expression for all social intercourse. We can, I think, dismiss the idea that Newton was at any period of his life in serious financial straits.

[17] Conduitt states that Newton was much interested in making, and improving, ear trumpets. *Portsmouth Collection.*

Newton, himself, as a copy of it in his handwriting was found among the Lucasian manuscripts.[18] Following the body of the text there is the memorandum, also in Newton's hand:

Whitehall, March 2, 1674 O. S.

His Majesty being willing to give all just encouragement to learned men who are and shall be elected to the said Professorship, is graciously pleased to refer this draught of a Patent unto Mr. Attorney General to consider the same, and to report his opinion what his Majesty may lawfully do in favour of the said Professors as to the indulgence and dispensation proposed and desired. And then his Majesty will declare his further pleasure.

A. COVENTRY.

The draught was adopted: the actual instrument, (coinciding with the draught except in two unimportant particulars), with the broad seal attached, is in the Registry's office (Box 21. G. 1.2) entitled:

A grant to the Mathematical Professor in Cambridge

PIGOTT.[19]

This was a great, and unusual, distinction paid to Newton in recognition of his high attainments. Just a few months previously, Francis Aston had failed to obtain a similar dispensation on his own account, although it was backed by the powerful interest of Sir Joseph Williamson, Principal Secretary of State. This honour and the favourable reception he had evidently received from the Royal Society did much to restore his tranquillity of mind, and we hear nothing further of his desire to resign.

Newton's correspondence of the year was confined to some technical notes on the solution of equations, and letters to Oldenburg relative to his optical work. In one of these latter he mentioned an experiment in electricity which immediately aroused the curiosity of the Society. He supported a glass plate, four inches broad and a quarter of an inch thick, on a wooden frame so that it should lie about one-sixth of an inch from a table. Under the glass, he placed some tiny, triangular bits of very thin paper, the wings of flies, etc. He

18 This hardly seems conclusive as Newton may well have made a copy of such a document even if it were drawn up by someone else.

19 A transcript of the patent is preserved in the College Archives, with the heading: "Indulgentia Regia Professori Mathematico concessa, dignissimo Viro Mro Isaaco Newton, hujus Collegii Socio, istud munus tunc temporis obeunte." This note and the full text of the patent is given in Edleston, p. xlix.

then rubbed the glass with a cloth to electrify it; whereupon, the papers jumped to the glass and then back to the table, "the motion of the papers would continue sometimes while I counted a hundred; every paper leaping up about twenty times more or less, and down as often." The explanation of this electric hail, as it is sometimes called, is that the papers are attracted to the electrically charged glass and, having received a like charge from contact with it, they are then repelled. When they touch the table, this little charge leaves them and the operation is repeated until the electricity has leaked from the glass plate. To Newton, the experiment was important, as he thought it was a confirmation of his belief that electricity might be a universal force which caused cohesion, chemical affinity, and all other molecular phenomena.

Such was the lack of experimental skill of the members of this most learned society in comparison with Newton's, that the simple experiment repeatedly failed when they tried to perform it, and several letters[20] passed before the demonstrator, presumably Hooke, succeeded in verifying it at the meeting on Jan. 13, 1675/6: "Mr. Newton's experiment of glass rubbed, to cause various motions in bits of paper beneath, being made according to his more particular directions, succeeded very well. The rubbing was made both with a scrubbing brush, made of short hog's bristles, with a knife, the haft of the knife made of whalebone, and with the nail of one's finger. It appeared, that touching many parts at once with a hard and rough body, produced the effect expected. It was ordered, that Mr. Newton should have the thanks of the Society, for giving himself the trouble of imparting to them such full directions for making the experiment."[21]

Newton, relieved from the worry of losing his fellowship and encouraged by the attentions paid him by the Royal Society, decided to tempt criticism again by offering a new discourse on colours. This communication was the longest and most elaborate paper which he submitted to the Society. He reviewed his past work, added an outline of an hypothesis on the nature of light and on a luminiferous æther, and described his most recent experiments on diffraction and the colours produced in thin transparent plates by interference or, as he called it, by fits of easy reflection and transmission. The discourse was so long that its consideration occupied several sessions. The ideas contained in it have been discussed at length in a previous

[20] Horsley, vol. III, p. 375 *et seq.*

[21] Birch, *Hist. Roy. Soc.*, III, p. 271.

chapter, but some personalities were indulged in which should be touched upon.

He evidently felt that an hypothesis on the nature of light, coming from him after his categorical refusal to consider the speculations of others as not being germane to science, needed a word of explanation and apology. His letter to Oldenburg, accompanying the paper, is worth quoting as it seems to indicate that he wished to show that his stand against hypothetical reasoning did not come from an inability to meet his opponents on their own ground. It shows also how insidiously the desire for speculation steals into the mind when once the doors have been opened to it.

Newton to Oldenburg

[1676]

Sir,—I have sent you the papers I mentioned, by John Stiles. Upon reviewing them I find some things so obscure as might have deserved a further explication by schemes [diagrams]; and some other things I guess will not be new to you, though almost all was new to me when I wrote them. But as they are, I hope you will accept of them, though not worth the ample thanks you sent. I remember in some discourse with Mr. Hooke, I happened to say that I thought light was reflected, not by the parts of glass, water, air, or other sensible bodies, but by the same confine or superficies of the æthereal medium which refracts it, the rays finding some difficulty to get through it in passing out of the denser into the rarer medium, and a greater difficulty in passing out of the rarer into the denser; and so being either refracted or reflected by that superficies, as the circumstances they happened to be in at their incidence make them able or unable to get through it. And for confirmation of this, I said further, that I thought the reflection of light, at its tending out of glass into air, would not be diminished or weakened by drawing away the air in an air-pump, as it ought to be if they were the parts of air that reflected; and added, that I had not tried this experiment, but thought he [Hooke] was not unacquainted with notions of this kind. To which he replied, that the notion was new, and he would the first opportunity try the experiment I propounded. But upon reviewing the papers I sent you, I found it there set down for trial; which makes me recollect that about the time I was writing these papers, I had occasionally observed in an air-pump here at Christ's College, that I could not perceive the reflection of the inside of the glass diminished in drawing out the air. This I thought fit to mention, lest my former forgetfulness, through my having long laid aside my thoughts on these things, should make me seem to have set down for certain what I never tried.

Sir,—I had formerly purposed never to write any hypothesis of light and colours, fearing it might be a means to engage me in vain disputes; but I hope a declared resolution to answer nothing that looks like a controversy, unless possibly at my own time upon some by-occasion, may defend me from that fear. And therefore, considering that such an hypothesis would much illustrate the papers I promised to send you, and having a little time this last week to spare, I have not scrupled to describe one, so far as I could on a sudden recollect my thoughts about it; not concerning myself, whether it should be thought probable or improbable, so it do but render the paper I send you, and others sent formerly, more intelligible. You may see by the scratching and interlining it was done in haste; and I have not had time to get it transcribed, which makes me say I reserve a liberty of adding to it, and desire that you would return these and the other papers when you have done with them. I doubt there is too much to be read at one time, but you will soon see how to order that. At the end of the hypothesis you will see a paragraph, to be inserted as is there directed. I should have added another or two, but I had not time, and such as it is I hope you will accept it.—Sir, I am your obedient servant,

Is. Newton.[22]

At the conclusion of the reading of the first portion of Newton's paper the Record stated: "After reading this discourse, Mr. Hooke said, that the main of it was contained in his *Micrographia,* which Mr. Newton had only carried farther in some particulars.[23] There is some basis of truth in Hooke's criticism. The fundamental ideas and experiments of Newton, on both diffraction and colours in thin plates, had undoubtedly been suggested by the work of Grimaldi and Hooke, and he had been, to say the least, not generous in his acknowledgement of his indebtedness to them. He had also modified his early ideas of the nature of light and had incorporated, in part, Huygens's and Hooke's conception of the rôle of æthereal waves. A full statement of his indebtedness to others would probably have gained Hooke's support and would certainly have soothed his

[22] Brewster, I, p. 133. *Cf. supra,* Chapter IV, p. 116.

[23] Birch, III, p. 269.

irritable vanity. Newton had so far surpassed the work of his predecessors that he could well have afforded to give them ample credit for their work. Hooke's criticism may have been made with a slurring tone; he may even have been offensive in manner; and Oldenburg, who had no love for him, dispatched an account to Newton which lost nothing in the telling. Newton, stung to the quick, interpolated in his paper, when it was published, a bitter attack on Hooke's own work and attitude towards himself. He accused him of borrowing most of his own ideas from Descartes and others, merely changing that philosopher's pressing or progressive motion of the medium into a vibrating one. Then he asserted, that Hooke's and his hypotheses had little in common; while his own two main experiments, "without which the manner of the production of those colours is not to be found out, were not only unknown to him [Hooke] when he wrote his *Micrography,* but even last spring, as I understood, in mentioning them to him." His first assertion is open to question, but his second is an indisputable fact, and is the factor in Newton's work which makes him stand out from his contemporaries. He closed his vindication in these words: "He left me to find out and make such experiments about it, as might inform me of the manner of the production of those colours, to ground an hypothesis on; he having given no further insight to it than this, that the colour depended on some certain thickness of the plate; though what that thickness was at every colour, he confesses in his *Micrography,* he had attempted in vain to learn; and therefore, seeing I was left to measure it myself, I suppose he will allow me to make use of what I took the pains to find out. And this I hope may vindicate me from what Mr. Hooke has been pleased to charge me with."[24]

We may judge that the discourse excited the admiration of the Society but that many, at least, still favoured the opinions of their Curator, Hooke. After the close of the reading of the paper, there followed a formal debate on the question whether "the rays of light, which, though alike incident in the same medium, yet exhibit different colours, may not reasonably be said to owe that exhibition of different colours to the several degrees of the velocity of pulses, rather than, as Mr. Newton thought, to the several connate degrees of refrangibility of the rays themselves? Mr. Hooke was of opinion, that the former of these ways was sufficient to give a good account of the diversity of colours."[25]

[24] Birch, III, p. 279.

[25] *Ibid.,* III, p. 295.

The controversy had reached an acute stage, and we can assume that pressure was put on Hooke to appease the wounded feelings of the younger man. At least he, although he had not been the one to indulge in personalities, took the first step towards a conciliation by sending the following letter:

Hooke to Newton

Robert Hooke—These to my much esteemed friend, Mr. Isaac Newton, at his chamber in Trinity College in Cambridge.

S^r,—The hearing a letter of yours read last week in the meeting of the Royal Society, made me suspect that you might have been some way or other misinformed concerning me; and this suspicion was the more prevalent with me, when I called to mind the experience I have formerly had of the like sinister practices.[26] I have therefore taken the freedom, which I hope I may be allowed in philosophical matters to acquaint you of myself. First, that I do no ways approve of contention, or feuding or proving in print, and shall be very unwillingly drawn to such kind of war. Next, that I have a mind very desirous of, and very ready to embrace any truth that shall be discovered, though it may much thwart or contradict any opinions or notions I have formerly embraced as such. Thirdly, that I do justly value your excellent disquisitions, and am extremely well pleased to see those notions promoted and improved which I long since began, but had not time to complete. That I judge you have gone farther in that affair much than I did, and that as I judge you cannot meet with any subject more worthy your contemplation, so I believe the subject cannot meet with a fitter and more able person to enquire into it than yourself, who are every way accomplished to complete, rectify, and reform what were the sentiments of my younger studies, which I designed to have done somewhat at myself, if my other more troublesome employments would have permitted, though I am sufficiently sensible it would have been with abilities much inferior to yours. Your design and mine are, I suppose, both at the same thing, which is the discovery of truth, and I suppose we can both endure to hear objections, so as they come not in a manner of open hostility, and have minds equally inclined to yield to the plainest deductions of reason from experiment. If, therefore, you will please to correspond about such matters by private letters, I shall very gladly embrace it; and when I shall have the happiness

[26] These references are, of course, to Oldenburg.

to peruse your excellent discourse, (which I can as yet understand nothing more of by hearing it cursorily read,) I shall, if it be not ungrateful to you, send you freely my objections, if I have any, or my concurrences, if I am convinced, which is the more likely. This way of contending, I believe, to be the more philosophical of the two, for though I confess the collision of two hard-to-yield contenders may produce light, [yet] if they be put together by the ears by other's hands and incentives, it will [produce rath]er ill concomitant heat, which served for no other use but . . . kindle—coal. S^r^, I hope you will pardon this plainness of, your very effectionate humble serv^t^,

ROBERT HOOKE.[27]

1675/6.

Newton to Hooke

Cambridge, February 5, 1675/6.

Dr Sir,—At the reading of your letter I was exceedingly pleased and satisfied with your generous freedom, and think you have done what becomes a true philosophical spirit. There is nothing which I desire to avoid in matters of philosophy more than contention, nor any kind of contention more than one in print; and, therefore, I most gladly embrace your proposal of a private correspondence. What's done before many witnesses is seldom without some further concerns than that for truth; but what passes between friends in private, usually deserves the name of consultation rather than contention; and so I hope it will prove between you and me. Your animadversions will therefore be welcome to me, for though I was formerly tired of this subject by the frequent interruptions it caused to me, and have not yet, nor I believe ever shall recover so much love for it as to delight in spending time about it; yet to have at once in short the strongest objections that may be made, I would really desire, and know no man better able to furnish me with them than yourself. In this you will oblige me, and if there be any thing else in my papers in which you apprehend I have assumed too [. . .] if you please to reserve your sentiments of it for a private letter, I hope you [will find that I] am not so much in love with philosophical productions, but that I can make them yield. . . . But, in the mean time, you defer too much to my ability in searching into this subject. What Descartes did was a good step. You have added much several ways, and especially in considering the colours of thin plates. *If I*

[27] *Portsmouth Collection.*

have seen farther, it is by standing on the shoulders of giants.[28] But I make no question you have divers very considerable experiments beside those you have published, and some, it's very probable, the same with some of those in my late papers. Two at least there are, which I know you have often observed,—the dilatation of the coloured rings by the obliquation of the eye, and the apparition of a black spot at the contact of two convex glasses, and at the top of a water-bubble; and it's probable there may be more, besides others which I have not made, so that I have reason to defer as much or more in this respect to you, as you would to me. But not to insist on this, your letter gives me occasion to enquire regarding an observation you was [sic] propounding to me to make here of the transit of a star near the zenith. I came out of London some days sooner than I told you of, it falling out so that I was to meet a friend then at Newmarket, and so missed of your intended directions; yet I called at your lodgings a day [or] two before I came away, but missed of you. If, therefore, you continue . . . to have it observed, you may, by sending your directions, command . . . your humble servant,

IS. NEWTON.[29]

These two letters have all the earmarks of an attempt towards a formal reconciliation which had been urged by others, and recognised as proper by themselves. Each of the writers expresses great admiration for the other's ability; each deprecates the public and partisan discussion of their opinions; and each requests the other to criticise rigorously his work, but to do it privately.

Two such men may indulge in general sentiments of a high and abstract order, and use elaborate expressions of personal esteem; but there could not be found two men, who were so temperamentally incapable to form a lasting friendship. Both were suspicious and sensitively vain. In Hooke, these qualities showed themselves by wrathful explosions and by reiterated accusations that he had been

[28] This celebrated saying is usually quoted as being original with Newton, but it really goes back much earlier. Burton, in his *Anatomy of Melancholy,* quotes Didacus Stella, In Luc. 10. tom. 2, as saying, "Pigmei Gigantum humeris impositi plusquam ipsi Gigantes vident." The idea, that pygmies can see farther than giants merely by being elevated on their shoulders, is a specious one. We should remember that, however high a pygmy may be raised, he will still interpret what he sees with the mind of a pygmy. Newton saw farther and he understood better because he was Newton. Perhaps, even, our complacent idea that we see farther, and thus better than the giants of earlier times may also be specious,—unless there be a modern Newton. Italics mine.

[29] *Portsmouth Collection.*

robbed of the fruits of his work; in Newton when opposed, they were equally apparent in a cold assumption of a disdain for fame and a silent retirement into his ivory tower. It is needless to say that their correspondence was limited to official communications; the embers of hostility still existed and needed only a new occasion to make them blaze up in public. They never forgave each other; Hooke continued to claim that he had anticipated Newton's work, and Newton maintained his aloof attitude towards the Society till Hooke's death relieved him from the fear of his insinuations.

It is not necessary to dwell on Hooke's letter but there is a need for criticising Newton's as it impresses me differently from the common opinion.[30] The point in question is his striking illustration of having seen farther because he stood on the shoulders of giants. This sentence is universally quoted as a generous tribute to the genius of others, and an extraordinary example of his own modesty. I confess that I cannot agree with such an opinion. We should bear in mind that this was the expression of a young man who was known to the world for having done one piece of work excellent in itself, but one whose far reaching effects could not then have been foreseen. If it had been made towards the close of his life when the world recognised him as having seen farther than the giants of intellect, and when he had fulfilled to his own satisfaction the promise of his youth; then I might agree that it could be termed modest, although I should rather deem it a cold and exact statement of fact.

Consider also how little credit, and in how slighting a manner, Newton concedes to the giants, on whose shoulders he was standing. To Descartes, whom he persistently ignored or slighted, he admits only that he had taken "a good step" and Hooke, who had enriched the whole field of science, he compliments only to the extent of

[30] Brewster, and his opinion as the standard biographer of Newton has been unquestionably accepted, comments: "These beautiful letters, emulous of good feeling and lofty principle, throw some light on the character and position of two of the greatest of our English philosophers." He lays entirely too much blame on poor Oldenburg, who may have increased, but who did not cause the enmity. His only criticism of Newton is the mild statement "that he did not do justice to the valuable communication of this rival." The fact is, that Newton had given him *no* credit, and had persistently either ignored or condemned his work. Brewster, however, dealing with Hooke, lamely says that he cannot give his sanction to so harsh a judgement as that pronounced by a distinguished philosopher who "ventured to describe him as a 'bad man' "; but "that influenced by the charity which thinketh no evil, we may find in the physical constitution and social position of Hooke, and to a certain extent in the injustice of his enemies, some apology for that jealousy and quickness of temper which may have been more deeply regretted by himself than it was felt by others." Certainly the faults of character of the two men are very differently treated, and Brewster is a flagrant example of those whom he accuses of having tried to add "to the intellectual fame of Newton by the moral depreciation of his rival." *Cf.* Brewster, vol. I, pp. 143–145.

having "added much in several ways," and especially in one limited field. It should be remembered that in addition to those two, the other giants were Copernicus, Kepler, Galileo, and Huygens; was it modest, or calculated to promote peace, to say that he then saw farther than they? Those who have approved Newton's modesty so unreservedly may have forgot that their judgement is one of retrospect, and might have been different if they, like Hooke, had read the letter when it was written. It should be borne in mind that I am not seriously criticising Newton's use of the phrase. In my opinion it was but a more or less stereotyped reply to Hooke's formal compliment to him. Just as the signature of "your humble and obedient servant" was a social custom of the day and not meant to be taken literally, so also the mutual depreciation of their work was merely a form of politeness. The need for discussion arises from the fact that Brewster, following the example of Newton's contemporaries, cites the phrase as a proof of his extreme modesty, and it is frequently quoted in the same spirit today as a rebuke to the pretensions of mediocrity. Newton was piously humble in the presence of God; but he had no illusions of what would have been false modesty when he compared his work with that of other men.

Two minor incidents of this year may be noted. On December 1st, he gave a copy of St. Irenaeus, just published in Paris, to the College Library. This is the first instance of a donation of a book to his College; the giving of books to the College, and to the Royal Society, became a frequent occurrence. And Mercator stated in his new *Astronomical Institutions* that the celebrated Isaac Newton had explained to him most elegantly the cause of the moon's libration. Newton had discovered in 1673 that, if the rotation of the moon on its axis corresponded exactly with the period of its revolution about the earth, then we could see only the same hemisphere of its surface; but, owing to irregularities in its orbital motion, we can observe somewhat more than half the surface.

The year, 1676, was an important and busy time in Newton's life. He carried on a long correspondence with Oldenburg and the Royal Society in connection with his electrical experiment which has been described. His long hypothesis on the nature of light and the æther was read to the Society,—the last paper he communicated to it on that branch of science. The discussion with Hooke had ended with a temporary truce, but the personalities indulged in had left a feeling of bitterness with both; and the controversy with Linus and his colleagues had also drifted into a disagreeable phase. One of them, Gascoines, had accused him of deceit by sending private directions which differed from the printed accounts of his experiments; and this charge Newton indignantly and truthfully denied. He had also insinuated that both Newton and Oldenburg had maliciously tried to involve him in an unpleasant controversy. To meet this charge, he wrote to Oldenburg: "This is the history of Mr. Linus's business, so far as I know it; which I have set down that his friends may see he has not been dealt with obliquely, as they seem to apprehend. All that I think they can object to you is, that you were at a stand, because you could not engage me in the controversy, and to me, that I had no mind to be engaged: a liberty every body has a right to, and may gladly make use of, sometimes at least, and especially if he want leisure, or meet with prejudice or groundless insinuations. But I hope to find none of this in Mr. Gascoines. The handsome genius of his present letter makes me hope it for the future. In the mean time I desire, with him, that you would publish Mr. Linus's letters as soon as you can conveniently, to prevent further misapprehensions."[31]

In spite of the fact that Newton was displeased with the attitude of some of the members of the Royal Society and absented himself from the meetings, he maintained a theoretical interest in its welfare and, at some period of his life, drew up a memorandum for improving and enlarging its usefulness. The scheme was found by Brewster amongst the *Portsmouth Papers* and was never published. His main idea was to appoint a small number of Fellows, perhaps three or four, in each of the principal branches of science, who should devote themselves to the advancement of their specialties. They would be obliged by pensions, or forfeits, to attend the meetings, report on books and experiments of others, and demonstrate new inventions and experiments of their own. It is quite evident that Newton had been influenced by Bacon and was advocating a closer adherence to his scheme for enlisting a concerted scientific army, divided into companies and led by captains for each science. The plan has never been adopted and, as the Society increased in age and in importance, the honour of being elected a member, and of presenting papers, has become so great, that there is no lack of voluntary contributions.

Newton's mind was groping for a general explanation of the

[31] Macclesfield, II, p. 387.

cause of phenomena, and he was evidently turning to the conception of a mechanistic universe in which a universal æthereal substance would, by its actions, account for all phenomena, both organic and inorganic. Since he later amplified and perfected his first outline of a cosmical hypothesis, it will be sufficient here to give only its main features. According to his ideas, the nature of this medium is assumed to be similar in "constitution with air, but far rarer, subtiler, and more elastic." It is not to be supposed, however, that this medium is one uniform matter, since it is composed partly of the main phlegmatic body of æther, and partly of other various æthereal spirits, much after the manner that air is compounded of the phlegmatic body of air intermixed with various vapours and exhalations. "For the electric and magnetic effluvia, and the gravitating principle, seem to argue such variety. . . . Nature is a perpetual circulatory worker, generating fluids out of solids, and solids out of fluids, fixed things out of volatile, and volatile out of fixed, subtile out of gross, and gross out of subtile, some things to ascend and make the upper terrestrial juices, rivers, and the atmosphere, and by consequence others to descend for a requital to the former, and as the earth, so perhaps may the sun imbibe this spirit copiously, to conserve his shining, and keep the planets from receding further from him." Not only do the protean changes of this medium produce all the phenomena we perceive in the physical world, but this æther also composes the animal spirits which he says are "of an æthereal nature, subtile enough to pervade the animal juices as freely as the electric, and perhaps magnetic, effluvia do glass. . . . Thus may therefore the soul, by determining [driving] this æthereal animal spirit or wind into this or that nerve, perhaps with as much ease as air is moved in open spaces, cause all the motions we see in animals. . . . And what is said of muscular motion may be applied to the motion of the heart, only with this difference; that the spirit is not sent thither as into other muscles, but is continually generated there by the fermentation of the juices with which its flesh is replenished and as it is generated, let out by starts into the brain, through some convenient *ductus* to perform those motions in other muscles by inspiration, which it did in the heart by generation."[32]

In an explanatory letter to Oldenburg, which accompanied this scheme and was not to be published, he added his idea of God, as

[32] Brewster I, p. 390 *et seq.*—Printed in full from the paper which Newton submitted to the Royal Society on December 9, 1675.

creator and governor of this mechanistic universe; who first created the fermental æther and its principles of action, and then assigned to a lesser power, Nature, the duty of forming and operating the perceptible mechanical universe. This idea bears a close resemblance to the Platonic hypothesis of dual real and imaginary worlds as decribed in the *Timaeus;* and it leads one to suspect the influence of Henry More and the Cambridge Platonists. His conception of Nature, as "a perpetual circulatory worker," is the Renaissance echo of the universal flux of Heraclitus as interpreted by the Stoics.

"Where I say that the frame of nature may be nothing but æther condensed by a fermental principle, instead of those words write, that it may be nothing but various contextures of some certain æthereal spirits, or vapours, condensed as it were by precipitation, much after the manner that vapours are condensed into water, or exhalations into grosser substances, though not so easily condensible; and after condensation wrought into various forms, at first by the immediate hand of the Creator, and ever since by the power of Nature, who by virtue of the command, 'Increase and multiply,' became a complete imitator of the copies set her by the Protoplast. Thus perhaps may all things be originated from æther, etc."[33]

For one who reproached his critics with the rebuke that hypothesis was not science, Newton could match the best of them in unbridled speculation, when he gave free rein to his imagination; but, in justice to him it should be added, that he rarely confused such speculations with science.

The personal incidents of Newton's life are so meagre that a biographer should be pardoned if he makes too much of a rather trifling matter about the planting of apple trees and the making of cider. At least it shows that he was, as a country gentleman, keen about agriculture. He enquired of Oldenburg for information about the best kind of apple trees for cider which could be obtained from a Mr. Austin, an Oxonian planter. The growers about Cambridge made good profit from cherry trees but had not succeeded with apples for cider. The difficulty was "that Red Streaks" [the famous fruit for cider in other parts] did not maintain their reputation in that country. "The tree," he wrote, "thrives well here, and bears as much fruit, and as good to look as in other countries; but the cider made of it they find harsh and churlish" and also the cider will not keep above a year whereas that made of "Red Streaks" in other

[33] Macclesfield, II, p. 389.

places will keep three years or more. So he enquired whether he could obtain grafts, rather than sprags, from Mr. Austin for improving their trees. His letters show an intimate knowledge of the subject. It would be interesting to know whether the cider of Cambridge is, at present, improved, and, if so, whether the improvement is due to Newton's efforts.

During this year, Newton's correspondence with Collins was limited to one or two letters, and the only news of a general nature is his denial of a rumour that he was finally about to publish a book on mathematical series. He supposed the rumour had its origin from the fact that his edition of Kinkhuysen's *Algebra* had been declined by the University Press on account of other work on hand, but was now in the hands of a Cambridge book-seller who had undertaken to get it printed. It should be a satisfaction to writers of rejected manuscripts to learn that a work by Newton was declined by the University Press because of other work on hand. He also advised James Gregory to publish his work on infinite series, and not to wait for the appearance of anything of his own: he adds that Gregory's improvement of the method of infinite series does not interfere with his ideas and is, also, of a limited usefulness. He, therefore, approved the publication lest the public should be hindered from "enjoying a thing so valuable."[34]

This same year is also memorable in the history of science as the time when the seeds of the great controversy on the invention of the calculus were sown between Newton and Leibniz. This unfortunate dispute smouldered for a third of a century before it burst into a blaze of recrimination which smirched the reputation of the two greatest philosophers of the age. Even at the risk of some repetition this controversy must be touched upon currently, although a detailed discussion of its tangled history will be given in a later chapter.

Previous to the Renaissance, mathematicians had followed the Greek method of regarding a curved line as a series of points placed as closely together as one wished. Thus, a curve was to them a series of geometric points connected together by imaginary straight lines. In consequence of this static idea the length of a circle, or other curved line, was merely the limit between the lengths of two inscribed and circumscribed polygons of an indefinitely large number of sides. Beginning with the Renaissance, interest had shifted from

[34] Macclesfield, II, p. 397.

problems relating to such static lines to an enquiry of how they had been made; that is, to regarding them as the truly curved paths of a continuously moving small body. The chief creator of this new field of dynamics was Galileo, whose principal work lay in determining the laws of motion of bodies, and the nature and measure of force. The problem of geometry had thus been changed from a consideration of straight lines to the necessity of finding an expression for the lengths and properties of continuously curved paths of motion. If one desires to study the path of a stone whirled on the end of a string it is easy to see that there is then no question of rectilinear jumps from position to position, but a steadily flowing motion. One of the important results of Galileo's dynamical discoveries was the invention of the analytical geometry by Descartes. The purpose of this geometry was to express the paths of moving bodies in terms of algebraic equations, and it developed into an efficient aid in solving these new problems in mechanics. The advance of mathematics during the seventeenth century was extraordinarily rapid and, especially, in those branches which were concerned with the problems involved in the sciences of astronomy and mechanics. It will be sufficient to point out that it was quickly recognised that such problems of moving bodies were associated with the expansion of functions in infinite series. In England, Wallis had advanced so far in this analysis that he had reached the threshold of the discovery of the infinitesimal calculus.

When considering Newton's early mathematical work, we should bear in mind that he studied chiefly the work of Descartes, Wallis, and his master, Barrow. He, himself, acknowledged that he had been led to his first discoveries in analysis and fluxions by Wallis's *Arithmetica Infinitorum*. It is now thoroughly established that during his undergraduate days, and especially during his period of leisure at Woolsthorpe because of the plague, he had extended Wallis's work on the expansion of quantities into infinite series, had found expressions of a general nature for the lengths and tangents of curves, and had evolved a method for calculating the areas subtended by curved lines. Extraordinary as were these extensions to Wallis's work by a youth in his twenties, Newton had far surpassed them by his capital discovery of what he termed Fluxions. The basis of this discovery lay in his clearly recognised idea that the path of a moving body should be regarded, not as a series of points, but as the graph made by a continuously moving point. Since the velocity of a point moving in a direction *x* is the distance traversed, divided by the time, or x/t, we can express the same velocity by constantly reducing the length, *x*, if we at the same time reduce, *t*, proportionately; thus, a continuous and finite motion is equal to the quotient of an infinitesimal distance and an infinitesimal time. To the moving point, he gave the name of a fluent, and for the velocity, he used the term, fluxion, which he sometimes indicated by the symbol $\dot{x}$, and sometimes by the letter *o* placed before it. For changes in velocity, or acceleration, he at times used the symbol $\ddot{x}$.[35]

Professor Child[36] who has made a very careful study of the sequence of Newton's mathematical ideas is of the opinion that in 1669, when his tract *De Analysi* was sent by Barrow to Collins and by him to other scholars, "wonderful as is the work that has been accomplished, yet the methods employed are merely a correlation of what he has learned from Descartes, Wallis and Barrow, combined with his original methods of infinite series and their reversion. In the true sense of the word, he could not differentiate or integrate, except, as we say nowadays, by first principles." He places the discovery of the fluxions or calculus seven years later, on the ground that the *De Analysi* contained all Newton knew at the time and does not present the Binomial Theorem in its generalised form,[37] without which the development of a differential caculus, in any real sense, is impossible. Now, the first authentic statement of this Theorem occurs in a letter to Oldenburg, dated June 13, 1676. That this statement fixes the date of the discovery of the Binomial Theorem is supported by another letter to Oldenburg written just four months later, in which occurs the following passage italicised by me: "This is my first entry into these meditations; and truly I should have forgotten it, but that, *some weeks ago,* I once more referred to certain notes.

[35] I found in the *Portsmouth Collection,* Sect. I, § XI, No. 30, the draught of a letter which has never been published. As it gives an important, and new light, on the sources from which Newton derived the fluxions I shall give an extract from it at this time. The document is most carefully written with many erasures and variants: "I had the hint of this method from Fermat's way of drawing tangents and by applying it to abstract equations, directly and invertedly, I made it general. Mr. Gregory and Dr. Barrow used and improved the same method in drawing of tangents. A paper of mine gave occasion to Dr. Barrow [who?] showed me his method of tangents before he inserted it into this 10th Geometrical Lecture. For I am that friend which he then mentioned." As I stated in a previous chapter, Laplace and Lagrange both give the credit to Fermat as the inventor of the calculus. But this is the first time that direct evidence has been given of Newton's indebtedness to Fermat.

[36] Greenstreet, p. 117, *et seq.*

[37] The generalised form of the Binomial Theorem gives the expansion of a binomial $(x + y)^n$ into the infinite series, $x^n + nx^{(n-1)}y + \frac{n(n-1)}{1.2}x^{(n-2)}y^2 +$ etc., where *n* is any integer or fraction.

. . . And thus became known to me, a general reduction of radicals to infinite series, by the rule which I placed at the beginning of the former letter, *before that I had found the extraction of roots.*" Professor Child's opinion carries the more weight since these two letters were written to be forwarded to Leibniz, who had enquired about Newton's new method as he himself was interested in the same subject. As we shall see later, Newton was, in these letters, describing the sequence of his work accurately and, at the same time, protecting his rights of discovery for fear that Leibniz would anticipate the same method. The date of the discovery of the complete Binomial Theorem seems settled without doubt as 1676; there remains only the question whether a real differential calculus could be evolved without the aid of that Theorem, a question which must be decided by mathematicians.

The relations between Newton and Leibniz, which ended so shamefully, began pleasantly enough with mutual esteem. They were both young men, nearly of the same age, and on the threshold of those remarkable careers which bulked so large in the history of the thought of the seventeenth century. Leibniz had entered the service of the Elector of Mainz and, in 1672, was summoned to Paris by Louis XIV to explain a plan for an invasion and conquest of Egypt, drawn up by him, it is said, to distract Louis from a threatened attack on Germany. He had early been interested in mathematics and while he was in Paris he cultivated the friendship of its learned society and, especially, of Huygens, who directed his attention to mathematics and taught him the new Cartesian analysis. The year before, he had sent a short tract, entitled *Theoria Motus Abstracti,* to the Paris Academy of Sciences which Dr. Hales thought contained "no obscure seeds of his differential calculus."

In 1673, Leibniz travelled to London[38] in the train of the Duke of Hanover and there he met the distinguished men of science, Boyle,

[38] It will be of interest to give the intercourse of Leibniz with the Royal Society from the actual records of the year, 1673. "At this meeting (January 22) was present Mons. Leibniz, the author of the printed discourse, intitled, *Hypothesis Physica Nova,* dedicated by him in 1671 to the Society. He now shewed them a new arithmetical instrument, contrived, as he said, by himself, to perform mechanically all the operations of arithmetic with certainty and expedition.—He gave some proof of what he said. but acknowledged the instrument to be imperfect, which he promised to get perfected, as soon as he should be returned to Paris, where he had appointed a workman for it."

On February fifth, the irrepressible Hooke mentioned, "that he intended to have an arithmetical engine made, which should perform all the operations of arithmetic, with great expedition and certainty, without making use of the rhabdology [computation by means of

Pell, Oldenburg, and others, and eagerly enquired into the new matters occupying their attention. He was admitted to the Royal Society, and presented for their criticism an intricate calculating machine which he had invented. He stayed in London but a brief time and returned to Germany where he was shortly afterwards appointed librarian at Hanover. He maintained, however, his interest in English scholarly work, and corresponded frequently with Oldenburg.

In order to prepare the reader to follow the tangled story of the early relations between Leibniz and Newton, a brief summary of Newton's mathematical work prior to the year, 1673, is now given.

Newton's attention was first directed to the study of infinite series in 1663, the year he graduated, by reading Wallis's *Arithmetica Infinitorum* and Barrow's lectures. The year following, he derived a method of determining lengths of curves, tangents, and the area of circular sectors by the use of these series; and in 1669 he calculated the area of an hyperbola.

He also discovered, in the same period, the essentials of the Binomial Theorem, which, besides its general importance, ultimately provided him with the apparatus for inventing his fluxions; although Professor Child believes he did not develop the theorem to its complete statement until 1676.

In 1665 and 1666, during his retirement to Woolsthorpe on account of the pest, he made his great discovery of fluxions and wrote several short papers which he laid away because he thought that others would certainly discover the same method before he would be old

small rods, called Napier's bones] and that much more simply than that of Mons. Leibniz." A month later, he produced his arithmetic engine and showed the manner of its operation. He was asked to explain how it differed from Mons. Leibniz's. In answer to this request, he read a discourse on May seventh discussing such engines in general and remarked caustically: "As for the arithmetical instrument [of Leibniz] it seemed to me so complicated with wheels, pinnions, cantrights, springs, screws, stops, and truckles, that I could not perceive it ever to be of any great use, especially common use.—The design, indeed, is very good, which is the only thing I was able to understand of it.—But I have an instrument now making, which will perform the same effects with the German, which will not have a tenth part of the number of parts, and not take up a twentieth part of the room." I doubt whether either instrument was ever made, although I have not discoverd notices of their further history.

At the meeting of February 19, "Mr. Oldenburg produced and read a letter in Latin, left with him by Mons. Leibniz, dated at London, $\frac{10}{20}$th February, 167$\frac{2}{3}$, containing his desire of being received into the Society.—This gentleman having been lately present at several meetings of the Society, and at one of them having produced and shewed an ingenious arithmetical engine, and in other respects given testimony of his abilities, and of his great esteem for the Society, Sir Robert Moray having taken public notice hereof proposed him as candidate.—April 9. Mr. Edward Barnard and Mons. Leibniz were unanimously elected into the Society.—June 11. Mr. Oldenburg read a Latin letter to the Society from Mons. Leibniz, dated at Paris, 1st June, 1673, giving them thanks for his election into their body." Birch, vol. III, pp. 76, 82, 92.

enough to write for the public. In these papers he sometimes used dots above the letters to indicate a fluxion, but more often a small letter in place of a capital. He, apparently, did not attach much importance to specific notation; a serious error since appropriate symbols are as important in mathematics as an alphabet and written words are to a language.

His *De Analysi per Aequationes* was sent by Barrow to Collins in 1669. This work contained probably all he knew about series up to that time. There is much difference of opinion as to whether this work contained anything on fluxions or the calculus. Newton's partisans hold that it did, and that an able mathematician could have worked out his secret from it. Brewster, who was sufficiently biased, is doubtful, but such critics as De Morgan, Professor Child, and the continental mathematicians, hold that it did not. No part of it was published until 1693 when Wallis, "having learned that Newton's Method of Fluxions passed in Europe as Leibniz's Differential Calculus," inserted a notice of Newton's claim to the method in the preface of the first volume, and some extracts in the second volume of his *Works*. Collins had, however, made the existence of the work known, and had intimated that an important discovery had been made. The curiosity about the secret was widespread as he had written of it to James Gregory in Scotland; Bertet and Vernon in Paris; Slusius in Holland; Borelli in Italy; Strode, Oldenburg, Dary, and others, in England. It has been established that Leibniz was acquainted with the work, and extracts from it have been found in his note-books.

At this point, Leibniz enters the scene. His visit in London had established an intimacy with the leading scholars of the country, and he maintained an active correspondence with Oldenburg to keep in touch with them. During the year 1673, we have preserved for us two letters of his, dated at London, and four written from Paris. These letters treat of mathematical subjects and describe freely and fully his discoveries in the properties of numbers. The following year, in two letters, he indicated clearly that he was becoming interested in the problem of determining the lengths and areas of curved lines by the method of infinite series as developed by Wallis. In an answer to these letters, Oldenburg hinted at the extensions and improvements which James Gregory[39] and Newton were then

[39] James Gregory (1638–1675), born in Aberdeen, became professor of mathematics at St. Andrews, and later at Edinburgh. His reputation rests on his discovery of the reflecting

busied with. Leibniz became keenly interested and asked for further information. In reply, Oldenburg forwarded a communication, of date December 10, 1672, from Collins describing the results which Gregory and Newton had sent him in 1671.[40] Leibniz answered that he was distracted by other business, and could not compare the results with a certain method of great power upon which he had hit. In the meanwhile, Oldenburg and Collins had been urging Newton to disclose his astonishing discoveries, and especially his fluxions, as it was evident that his rival was rapidly advancing along the same lines and might eventually supplant him in the honour of the discovery.

Newton, overborne by these entreaties, wrote his *epistola prior* to Oldenburg, dated 13 June, 1676, and requested him to forward it to Leibniz. This he did, and enclosed in it extracts from Gregory's work. In the letter, while Newton explained his new method of series and included a number of important examples, he did not make any reference to his secret discovery of fluxions. He did, however, give a vague hint that he had a more important method in his mind: "From these examples, it may be seen how far the limits of analysis are extended by infinite series of this sort: in fact their aid may be employed for almost all problems excepting some numerical ones similar to those of Diophantus. But, it still lacks being a universal method without some further method of extending infinite series.—How this may be done, there is not now time to explain (jam non vacat dicere)."

Such an evasion naturally whetted Leibniz's curiosity the more keenly, and he sent an answer to Oldenburg for Newton, on 27 August, 1676, asking for further information and adding a theorem for transmuting figures into one another. This theorem made it evident that he had travelled far towards the discovery of the calculus. He must have guessed that his and Newton's methods were

telescope and on his work in the new geometry. He was an admirer and friend of Newton. His nephew, David Gregory (1661–1708), was also a distinguished mathematician. He was first appointed professor at Edinburgh and afterwards Savilian professor of astronomy at Oxford, largely on the recommendation of Newton. He was one of the heartiest admirers and friends of Newton, and supported his new gravitational mechanics.

40 This letter figured largely in the final phase of the controversy. It was used as one of the principal documents against Leibniz by the investigating Committee of the Royal Society. It is now generally agreed that the letter could not have given a clue to the invention of the calculus. But the discussion on the point is academic as it has been proved by De Morgan that Oldenburg sent only a review of the letter to Leibniz and omitted the illustrative example on which the charge of plagiarism rested. For proof of this statement, *cf.* De Morgan, *Essays,* p. 69, and also *infra,* Chapter XV.

probably similar in principle and would hope that he might have a frank reply. It succeeded so far as to arouse Newton to write a long and elaborate letter to Oldenburg on 24 October, 1676, to be forwarded.

This celebrated *epistola posterior* gave in detail the history of Newton's first discovery of the method of series and its later developments. In it also, he enlarged on his tract *De Analysi* and gave the solution of several problems; and then, having reached the point when an explanation of his method of fluxions, or calculus, would logically follow, he abruptly broke off with the statement, "the basis of these operations, sufficiently obvious (since now I cannot continue my explanation) I have thus rather concealed 6a 2c d æ 13e 2f 7i 3l 9n 4o 4q 2r 4s 9t 12v x."[41] After the solution of certain problems by series he, at the end of the letter wrote: "But yet, lest I seem to have said too much, the inverse [integration] problem of tangents is more difficult to expand in powers than the others. For solving them I use a double method; the one more elegant, the other more general. It seems best to write down both, at present, in transcribed letters, lest if others should discover the same, I should be compelled to change the method into another. 5a 2c d æ 10e 2f h 12i 4l 3m 10n 6o 2q r 7s 11t 10u 3x: 11a b 3c 2d 10e æ g 10i 2l 4m 7n 6o 3p 3q 6r 5s 11t 7u x, 3a c æ 4e g h 6i 4l 4m 5n 8o q 4r 3s 6t 4u, 2a 2d æ 5e 3i 2m 2n 2o p 3r 5s 2t 2u."[42]

On the same day he wrote the following letter which lacks an address.

Newton to [*Collins or Oldenburg?*]

October 24, 1676.

. . . .

To M. Leibniz's ingenious letter I have returned an answer, which I doubt is too tedious. I could wish I had left out some things, since to avoid greater tediousness I left out something else, on which they may have some dependence. But I had rather you should have it

[41] The sentence published later by Wallis from this jumble of letters was "Data Æquatione quotcumque, fluentes quantitates involvente, fluxiones invenire, et vice versa,"—given any equation, involving fluent quantities, to find the fluxions, and *vice versa.*

[42] The sentence to be derived is, as given by Wallis: Una Methodus consistit in extractione fluentis quantitatis ex æquatione simul involvente fluxionum ejus: altera tantum in assumptione Seriei pro quantitate qualibet incognita ex qua cætera commoda derivari possunt, et in collatione terminorum homologorum æquationis resultantis, ad eruendos terminos assumptæ Seriei (Commercium Epistolicum, ed. 1722, p. 144).

any way, than write it over again, being at present otherwise encumbered. Sir, I am in great haste,

yours,
Is. NEWTON.

P. S. I hope this will so far satisfy M. Leibniz, that it will not be necessary for me to write any more about this subject; for having other things in my head, it proved an unwelcome interruption to me to be at this time put upon considering these things.[43]

The correspondence, from which I have derived my account of the friendly and appreciative relations between Newton and Leibniz, is of the greatest importance in his life. The letters are all preserved in the Letter-Books of the Royal Society and were, when the controversy about the invention of the calculus broke out, examined and certified by its Committee appointed to decide on the question of priority. They were printed, in whole or in extracts, in the *Commercium Epistolicum* and were adduced as the principal evidence of Newton's priority, and of Leibniz's plagiarism. Of Newton's priority, there could have been little doubt and Leibniz had frankly admitted it; but the partisans of Newton, with his approval, attempted to disgrace Leibniz's reputation on evidence taken principally from the *epistola prior* and the *epistola posterior* from which I have just given extracts. It was claimed that a man of Leibniz's genius could have discovered the secret of the fluxional method from the *epistola posterior* of October 24th; although it is now generally conceded that it does not refer to that method. It is evident Newton was certain that he had successfully concealed his method by his jumble of letters and had, at the same time, given warning of his priority to possible other discoverers, or why should he have employed that stratagem? These jumbled letters have been frequently referred to, even by so recent writers as Brewster, as ciphers, or anagrams, or transposed letters, which of course they are not. The significance of such a designation is only too obvious. A cipher has a key, and is not only capable of solution, but often is worked out by others; thus the impression is made on the mind of the unwary that

[43] Macclesfield, vol. II, p. 400.—Rigaud, the editor of the *Collection* remarks in a foot-note, "There is no address to this letter. It seems to have been written to Collins, from the subject of the preceding communication; and there are a number of figures in Collins's handwriting on the back." To me, however, it seems far more likely to have been written to Oldenburg. It was dated the same day as the *epistola posterior* to Oldenburg and has all the signs of being a personal note referring to the letter to be forwarded to Leibniz. Edleston (*cf*. p. li, note 55) is also of the same opinion.

in some way Leibniz might have deciphered the sentences and so have got information from them. Now, it is evident that no translation could by any possibility be made, and it was intended by the author that no one should be able to make any sense out of it till he chose to publish his key sentences. Furthermore, no mathematician could have obtained any help from such brief and obscure sentences if they had been written in plain English. While the partisans of Newton hinted that, in some way, Leibniz had received a clue from Newton which enabled him to hit upon the invention of the calculus, they were cautious enough to avoid being explicit in the charge, only Raphson had the audacity to state that Leibniz had re-distributed the jumble of letters and from the hidden sentences had found his method. Raphson, in 1715, published a short *History of Fluxions* and, with the permission of Newton, added some of the correspondence and documents on the controversy. In the Preface is the following outrageous statement: "He [Newton] communicated the same [his general method of quadratures] in a letter in the year 1676 to Mr. Leibniz (of Germany) in letters *transposed* [sic] as underneath [6a, etc.], which Mr. Leibniz having deciphered, found this sentence contained under them, viz. [Data . . . vice versa]: In English thus, [Having . . . *vice versa*]; and, some time after, he perceived his meaning in it, and writ in answer that he had found out a method not unlike it, as Sir Isaac himself had *hinted,* p. 253, *Princ. Phil. Nat. Math.,* but deferred publishing anything of his own invention, till the month of October, in the year 1684."[44]

Unfortunately for the reputation of the partisans of Newton and even more unfortunately for his own, the above does not cover the facts. The time between Newton's *epistola posterior* of 24 October,

[44] Raphson, *History of Fluxions,* London, 1715. In the same year, a Latin translation was published. Some copies have letters of Wallis, Leibniz, and Newton, added as an appendix. I was able to secure copies of the Latin edition with, and without, the letters. But the English edition is extremely rare and I desire to thank the Director of the British Museum for his courtesy in sending me a photostatic copy of the part I needed. De Morgan calls Raphson the unscrupulous man of the time. His unscrupulous statement of the deciphering the sentences, and the equally false one that Newton had *hinted* in the *Principia,* whereas he had generously acknowledged, Leibniz's independent discovery, justify the epithet. It may be added, that Raphson changed and softened the charge of plagiarism in his Latin edition. In that edition he omitted the statement that Leibniz "deciphered" the sentence and uses only the expression, "Mente Newtoni ex epistolis ejus percepta"; also he omitted the word *hinted* and merely states, "Newtonus ergo Ann. 1665, et 1666, methodum adinvenerit, et anno 1676, notitias suæ inventionis inter caeteros[e] [[e]foot-note. Princ. Nat. Ph. Math. p. 253] cum Leibnitio communicaverit." Raphson was sly enough to think that English readers would stand a stronger dose than foreigners. As Newton gave to Raphson the documents, which he published, it is more than probable that he knew, and approved of, the contents of the book.

1676, and the announcement to Oldenburg by Leibniz of his discovery of the Differential Calculus on 21 June, 1677, would have been absurdly short for him to have invented the calculus even if he had deciphered Newton's sentences. But, the fact is, the forwarding of Newton's letter was delayed for months. This is verified by incontestable evidence. Brewster, whose integrity forbade him to ignore facts and yet whose partisanship was so strong that his entire account of the controversy favours Newton or, at least, softens the faults of his own, and of his British contemporaries' conduct, can be quoted with safety. "This letter," he states, "though dated 24th October, (1676), had not been forwarded to Leibniz on the 5th March, 1676/7. At the time Newton was writing it, Leibniz spent a week in London, on his return from Paris to Germany; but it must have reached him in the spring of that year, as he sent an answer to it dated June 21, 1677."[45] In other words, Leibniz had at his disposal less than four months to force a meaning out of a mere jumble of letters, which if straightened out would give but a vague hint, and to develop out of this hint a finished mathematical analysis! For, in his answer he frankly described his differential calculus, gave its algorithm, or symbolic nomenclature, so perfectly that it is used today, and expressed his opinion that the method of drawing tangents which Newton wished to conceal did not differ from his own.

We may assume that, during his week's visit in London, Leibniz enquired for further information about Newton's method and, if so, he must have become convinced that he could not expect to overcome Newton's innate reluctance to disclose his thoughts. He could then, with perfect propriety, feel that the field was open to anyone interested in the subject. So many were engaged along similar lines that, if he would reap the honour of his great discovery, he must disregard the fact, which he suspected, that Newton's method was essentially similar to his own, and not delay longer to complete his own work.

Be this as it may, Leibniz had invented the differential calculus by his own efforts, as is now admitted by all unbiased and competent critics. Soon after the receipt of Newton's delayed *epistola posterior,* he sent his answer on 21 June, 1677, addressed to Oldenburg. He began the letter with a compliment to Newton: "I received your long expected letter with the enclosed most excellent one from Newton, which I shall read at once with the care and attention that it

[45] Brewster, vol. II, p. 26.

certainly merits, no less than it needs. Now, I shall note down immediately a few points that occurred to me at a first glance. I am immensely pleased that he has described the method by which he arrived at some of his truly elegant theorems." He then, as frank as Newton was secretive, gave a full and clear statement of his complete differential calculus, with the notation still in use, so that others could readily work with it. This letter, undoubtedly, marks an epoch in pure mathematics as notable as that of Newton's *Principia* in the physical sciences.

We should bear in mind that the relations between Newton and Leibniz, at this time, were friendly and harmonious. Their correspondence was carried on through the intermediation of their mutual friends Collins and Oldenburg, the latter of whom was the countryman and deep admirer of Leibniz. The letters which passed were couched in the stately manner of the day, and expressed full recognition of each other's commanding ability. Leibniz was frank and eager in his desire to know what Newton had done; he showed no jealousy, and readily admitted the claims of Collins and Oldenburg that Newton had been first in the field. On the other hand, Newton was surprisingly indifferent, he never once asked his rival to explain his method; he had to be urged to write at all and, when he did so, the impression is given that he was bored and looked upon the subject as of little interest. Certainly, we can find no trace of a feeling, that he felt any obligation to give to the public a new, and powerful, mathematical tool. It is one of the most baffling and inexplicable incidents in the history of science.

It was years later, after the calculus of Leibniz had established its value on the continent, that the friends of Newton published his prior claim, and he was aroused sufficiently to assert himself. Even then, he did not publish his method with a notation so that others could use it, he merely claimed that it was his property, and that no other person was entitled to any share of the honour. The friends, who urged him to assert himself, were the companions of his later years, and the active ones amongst them, Fatio de Duillier, Raphson, and Keill, were flatterers who could profit from his great reputation. Their aim was not to establish Newton's priority of discovery, that was not disputed, but to strip from Leibniz every shred of merit by accusing him of plagiarism of the most inexcusable kind,—of having stolen Newton's ideas from personal letters solicited from him, and from private conversations with his friends. If Collins and Oldenburg had been alive at the time, those jackals of the lion would not have dared to pursue their concerted plan to smirch the reputation of one of the greatest ornaments of the age.

We shall have to apportion blame, and much blame, to both of the principals of the controversy but we fortunately do not have to question the direct statements of fact of either of them. If there had been no documentary evidence that Newton had discovered the germ of the fluxional calculus in 1665 or 1666, our knowledge of his intellectual integrity would lead us to give full credit to his assertion. And we ought also to give an unqualified acquiescence to the solemn statement of Leibniz: "Il n'y a pas," he wrote in a letter to the Abbé Conti,[46] "la moindre trace ni ombre du calcul des Differences ou Fluxions dans toutes les anciennes Lettres de M. Newton que j'ai vûes, excepté dans celle qu'il a écrite le 24 d'Octobre 1676, où il n'en a parlé que par enigme; et la solution de cette enigme, qu'il n'a donnée que dix ans après, dit quelque chose, mais elle ne dit pas tout ce qu'on pourroit demander."

This belief in their direct statements does not preclude the belief that they may have received, unconsciously, aid from each other. The subject was in the air. It was from reading the *Arithmetica* of Wallis, and the work of Fermat, that Newton turned his attention to the subject of infinite series and found the idea of his calculus; Leibniz had his interest aroused in the same subject by Huygens and Pascal, and the mere knowledge, that Newton had found a new method, may have given him an additional stimulus. The opinion of the mathematician, Bernoulli, should be given weight; it was his belief that, of the two, Newton received more assistance from Leibniz. I am inclined to agree with that opinion so far as the later development of fluxions is concerned. The work of Leibniz was much more systematically developed; it could be quickly understood and extensively used by others. Newton's methods were *sui generis,* he could use them, but others could not. He never worked out his methods in detail and it took years for others to learn to follow his processes. There can be no doubt that some, at least, of the theorems of his *Principia* were worked first by the fluxional method and that he destroyed the evidence of its use when he recast them in the classic geometric form. Before he was engaged on that work, he had had Leibniz's letter giving clearly his method of the calculus, which he acknowledged in a Lemma. Would he not

46 Gerhardt, *Briefwechsel Liebniz,* Bd. I, p. 283.

have improved his own method by adopting something from the more systematic method and notation of his rival?

There is but little to add, at this time, to this episode in Newton's life. He had exhausted any interest he had had in the subject when he wrote his *epistola posterior* of over fourteen folio pages to Leibniz; and he announced his purpose to be quit of it forever in the note of the same date which has been quoted. Although Collins then tried to move him from this unfortunate decision, his plea was unavailing; the following reply left no doubt that Newton's decision was final.

Newton to Collins

Sir, Cambridge, Novemb. 8, 1676.

. . . .

You seem to desire that I would publish my method, and I look upon your advice as an act of singular friendship, being, I believe, censured by divers for my scattered letters in the Transactions about such things, as nobody else would have let come out, without a substantial discourse. I could wish I could retract what has been done, but by that I have learned what is to my convenience, which is to let what I write lie by till I am out of the way. As for the apprehension that M. Leibniz's method may be more general, or more easy than mine, you will not find any such thing. His observation, about reducing all roots to fractions, is a very ingenious one, and certainly his way of extracting adfected roots is beyond it: but in order to series they seem to me laborious enough in comparison of the ways I follow, though for other ends they may be of excellent use. . . . I say there is no such curve line, but I can, in less than half a quarter of an hour, tell whether it may be squared, or what are the simplest figures it may be compared with, be those figures conic sections or others. And then, by a direct and short way, (I dare say the shortest the nature of the thing admits of, for a general one,) I can compare them. And so, if any two figures expressed by such equations be propounded, I can by the same rule compare them, if they may be compared. This may seem a bold assertion, because it is hard to say a figure may or may not be squared or compa[red] with another, but it is plain to me by the fountai[n I] draw it from, thou[gh] I will not undertake to prove it to others. The same method extends to equations of four terms, and others also, but not so generally. But I shall say not more at present, but that I am,

your's to serve you,

IS. NEWTON.[47]

This determination to avoid making public his ideas had gone much further than merely to break off his correspondence with Leibniz; it made Newton resolve to forsake science altogether as a profession, and it foreshadowed his later eagerness to leave Cambridge and to enter public life. Lest there should be any doubt of the finality of his decision, he wrote a few days later to Oldenburg the letter previously quoted[48] which expresses only too clearly the bitterness that had replaced his ingenuous enthusiasm: "I see I have made myself a slave to philosophy, but if I get free of Mr. Linus's business, I will resolutely bid adieu to it eternally, excepting what I do for my private satisfaction, or leave to come out after me; for I see a man must either resolve to put out nothing new, or to become a slave to defend it." The pity of it is that, judged on ordinary standards, we can feel no justification for his disgust but, under the cold and restrained demeanour of Newton there must have lain hidden a hypersensitive spirit which shrank from the rough contacts of life. And while we must, at times, judge his conduct adversely, we must not forget the delicate organisation of his mind, nor the self-discipline which overcame his natural temperament. In spite of the fact that he was spurred on neither by ambition nor pleasure, he later gave to the world his incomparable *Principia* and *Optics*. And we can be grateful that his genius was recognised, and that he was given during his life the homage which he deserved.

This year Newton contributed £40 towards the building of the new college library which was slowly approaching completion. One other incident may be mentioned; Collins wrote to him that Loggan had reported that he was engraving a portrait of Newton which was to be prefixed to a treatise on light and colours.[49]

Newton's determination to be quit of scientific correspondence,

[47] Macclesfield, II, p. 403.

[48] *Cf.* Chapter IV, p. 91.

[49] David Loggan was then engaged in making his plates for his *Cantabrigia Illustrata.* His Plate of St. Mary's Church was dedicated to Newton in the following style: "Clariss°. Viro D°. Isaaco Newton Matheseos apud *Cantabrigienses Professori Lucasiano SS*tae *Trinitatis Coll*ii ibidem, et *Regiæ Societ*s *Socio, Mathematico Philosopho, Chymico* consummatiss°. Nec minus suavitate Morum et Candore Animi, Cum rerum Humanarum Divinarumq: Peritiâ spectabili, *Hanc Tabulam* Observantiae ergo D. D. C. Q. Dav. Loggan." Edleston, note 61. Loggan has left little unsaid in praise of his patron.

which he had so often before threatened, he now carried out literally, and for some years his life is practically concealed from us. Although Leibniz wrote at least two more letters, they were not answered. The death of Oldenburg may have been partly the cause, but it is more probable that the correspondence would have stopped under any circumstances.

During the next two years he was absent from college several times but where he was, or what engaged his time and thoughts, we do not know.

CHAPTER VII

LIFE IN CAMBRIDGE. ON THE NATURE OF THE ÆTHER. FRIENDSHIP WITH MONTAGUE. EARLY WORK ON GRAVITATION

1676–1685

HOWEVER retired and isolated Newton's life in Cambridge undoubtedly was, he had, till the age of thirty-five, three sources of contact with the scientific world,—Barrow, Oldenburg, and Collins; but he was destined to lose all three in the short space of a year. The unexpected death of Isaac Barrow, in 1677, at the early age of forty-seven was noted by Collins in a letter to a friend: "Lamentation makes the next paragraph. The most learned and pious Dr. Barrow, Master of Trinity College in Cambridge, coming up to make the customary Easter election of some Westminster boys, to be admitted into the University, did here fall sick of a malignant fever, which ended his days, to the very great grief of all, that either knew or heard of his worth." He was one of the most versatile and distinguished men of his age: as a theologian, his sermons are masterpieces of virile English and are still read with interest and profit; as an administrator, he was rapidly restoring Trinity College to its former prestige; as a mathematician and classical scholar he attained a leading position. But his value to the world came no less from the fact that he was the patron and friend of Newton. That his unfailing help was appreciated is shown by the brief statement made by Newton to Conduitt, many years later, when he remarked that no one had greater cause to regret Barrow's death than he.[1] Barrow was Master of Trinity only five years, too short a period to effect a permanent reform and, after his death, the College declined in influence during the remainder of Newton's life in Cambridge. It is reasonable to suppose that this state of affairs contributed to his desire to leave the University and the scholarly life. In spite of Newton's apparent detachment from society, he must already have impressed influential men not only with his profound

[1] *Portsmouth Collection.*

scholarship, but also with his common sense and executive ability. In confirmation of this opinion, I found the hitherto unpublished memorandum by Conduitt in the *Portsmouth Collection:* "Archbishop Tenison offered him the Mastership [of Tri]nity College when it was given [to John M]ontague if he would take orders." As Montague was the successor of Barrow, this offer must refer to this time. It certainly throws a new light on Newton's standing and influence in the University.

Till the year 1678 all of Newton's correspondence with the Royal Society, and with men of science, had been conducted through the friendly mediation of Henry Oldenburg and John Collins. The almost simultaneous loss of their stimulating influence accounts for the sudden cessation of his correspondence till he found their successor in Edmond Halley, two years later.

Oldenburg (1626–1678) was born in Bremen and according to the fashion of the day, assumed sometimes the transliterated name of Grubendol. For several years, he acted as agent, or consul, for the republic of Lower Saxony in England, and afterwards continued to live in that country. His interest in science dates from his entry in Oxford as a student; in 1662 he became Secretary of the Royal Society. Much of the growth and success of the Society in its early days is due to his love and indefatigable zeal for its interests. For years, he worked for no compensation but the proceeds from the sale of the *Transactions* which never amounted to more than £40 a year; afterwards he received an additional salary of the same amount. He was a voluminous correspondent, serving as the medium of scientific news between England and the Continent, and he edited the first twelve volumes containing 142 numbers of the *Transactions.*

A letter from him to Boyle throws an interesting light on the terrors of the plague and shows that he, like Pepys, was ready to risk death in the discharge of his duties: "If the plague should come into this row where I am, I think I should then change my thoughts and retire into the country, if I could find a sojourning corner. In the meantime, I am not a little perplexed concerning the books and papers belonging to the Society that are in my custody; all I can think of to do in this case is, to make a list of them all, and to put them up by themselves in a box, and seal them together with a superscription, that so in case the Lord should visit me, as soon as I find myself not well, it may be sent away out of mine to a sound house, and *sic deinceps.*"

Oldenburg's passion for letter writing involved him in an unexpected and serious difficulty. His large foreign correspondence awoke the suspicions of government officials who, in those corrupt and unsettled times, could imagine no reason for communicating with foreigners except to betray political information for money. He was arrested on the following warrant:

C. R.

Warrant to seize the person of Henry Oldenburg for dangerous designs and practices, and to convey him to the Tower.

June 20, 1667

By order
ARLINGTON.

Pepys, who rarely missed a bit of gossip, noted in his Diary five days later: "I was told, yesterday, that Mr. Oldenburg, our Secretary at Gresham College, was put into the Tower, for writing news to a virtuoso in France, with whom he constantly corresponds on philosophical matters; which makes it very unsafe at this time to write, or almost do any thing." [2] He was not released until August 26, and even a short imprisonment on a vague political charge was a matter likely to have serious results. "I was so stifled," he wrote to Boyle, "by the prison-air, that, as soon as I had my enlargement from the Tower, I widen'd it, and took it from London into the country, to fan myself for some days in the good air of Craford in Kent. Being now returned, and having recovered my stomach, which I had in a manner quite lost, I intend, if God will, to fall to my old trade, if I have any support to follow it. My late misfortune, I fear, will much prejudice me; many persons unacquainted with me, and hearing me to be a stranger, being apt to derive a suspicion upon me. Not a few came to the Tower, merely to enquire after my crime and to see the warrant, in which when they found that it was for dangerous designs and practices, they spread it over London, and made others have no good opinion of me."

Oldenburg not only did yeoman service in promoting the scientific reputation of the Society, but he had to struggle against its imminent dissolution from poverty. Dues were always sadly in arrears, and he and Hooke were given a mere pittance, in spite of the devotion of their entire lives to its furtherance,—their ability to

[2] Weld, who quotes this passage from Pepys's Diary, wrongly gives the date June 28.

live on £80 a year, or less, is an interesting side-light on the supposition of Newton's resignation from inability to pay the fees. In addition, he had to meet criticism from within and from without. He and Hooke, his rival in the active management of the Society's affairs, were jealous of each other and caused dissensions amongst the members. Once, at least, their mutual dislike broke out into an open accusation by Hooke, that his invention of the coiled spring for driving clocks had been maliciously assigned to Huygens and so published by the Secretary in the *Transactions*. It is significant that the Council publicly exonerated Oldenburg. Some, also, of its members were doubtful of the wisdom of an organised scientific body, which might become the dictator of scientific thought and publication. The most influential man of science of the day, Robert Boyle, was certainly luke-warm towards it and, in letters to him, Oldenburg tried to remove his scruples. Boyle, like Hooke and Newton, was intensely religious and considered the chief purpose of scientific discovery to be the means of disclosing the design and laws of God. The imminence and awe of the Divine Power were so real and so constantly present with Boyle that he is said never to have failed to make a distinct pause in his conversation before uttering the name of God, and he had conscientious scruples against binding himself by an oath. He, gradually, became a supporter of the Society, but he declined the presidency "for reasons which shew his extreme tenderness and delicacy in all matters of conscience." He wrote to his much respected friend, Hooke, "hearing that an acquaintance of mine was come to town, whose eminent skill in the law had made him a judge, if he himself had not declined to be one, I desired his advice (which because he would not send me till he had perused the Society's charter, I received not till late last night) and by it I found, that he concurred in opinion with the two lawyers already mentioned, and would not have me venture upon the supposition of my being unconcerned in an act of parliament, to whose breach such heavy penalties are annexed. His reasons I have not now time to tell you, but they are of such weight with me, who have a great (and perhaps peculiar) tenderness in point of oaths, that I must humbly beg the Royal Society to proceed to a new election, and to so easy a thing, as among so many worthy persons, that compose that illustrious company, to choose a president, that may be better qualified than I for so weighty an employment."[3]

[3] *Life of Boyle—Boyle's Works,* Vol. I, p. cxix.

Besides the indifference of many of the members and the reluctance to pay their dues, the Society aroused the jealousy and the fears of the fundamentalists of the day, who accused the Fellows, in print, with undermining the Universities, destroying the established religion, and upsetting the ancient and solid learning. To meet such attacks, Bishop Sprat published a history of the Royal Society and Glanville wrote his *Plus Ultra,* in which he affirms that "the impertinent taunts of those who accused the Society of doing nothing to advance knowledge, were no more to be regarded than the little chat of idiots and children." The amiable John Evelyn did not hesitate to implicate the Devil in these plots against the New Learning. "There is nothing," we find in his Diary, "which does more confirm me in the nobleness of the design, than this spirit of contradiction which the Devil (who hates all discoveries of those false and proestigious ways that have hitherto obtain'd), does incite to stir up men against it." Oldenburg, also, came to the defense of the Society in his preface to the fifth volume of the *Transactions.* "Let envy snarl," he wrote, "it cannot stop the wheels of active philosophy in no [sic] part of the known world." He then gave a list of the nations which had felt the stir of the new science, and added, "even the frozen Muscovite and Russian, have all taken the operative ferment, and it works high, and prevails every way to the encouragement of all sincere lovers of knowledge and virtue."

Oldenburg's death naturally caused changes in the Royal Society. Dr. Nehemiah Grew and Robert Hooke were elected joint Secretaries, and the publication of the *Transactions* was suspended the following year. In 1679, Hooke commenced publishing the *Philosophical Collections,* "a sheet or two every fortnight, of such philosophical matters as he shall meet with from his correspondents." This abbreviated edition continued until 1683, when the *Transactions* were started again under the editorship of Dr. Plot, the successor of Hooke, and have continued without a break to the present time.

The permanent break-down in health of Collins was perhaps an even greater loss to Newton than the death of Oldenburg. Collins writing to the mathematician, Thomas Strode, mentioned that he had been prevented from being with Leibniz during his short visit to London in October, 1676, because, "troubled with a scorbutic humour, or saltness of the blood, and, taking remedies for it, they made me ulcerous and in an uneasy condition." And again, three months later, he was still suffering: "In this severe winter I have been troubled with an ebullition of the blood caused by its thinness and saltness, whence ensued a great itching, to remove which taking physic before phlebotomy, it caused boils and an inflammation in my right arm, which hindered not only all correspondence with you ever since August last, but likewise my private affairs, being out of the farthing office, or public concern, on account of tin farthings that are to ensue." Although Collins lived until November 10, 1683, the drastic physicking of the day had done its deadly work; his correspondence ceased, and his last years were evidently a period of suffering and debility. His last relation with Newton was characteristic of him, as he offered to print his *Algebra* along with Wallis's and Barrow's if the Royal Society would agree to subscribe for sixty copies.

No history of science in the seventeenth century would be satisfactory which did not take notice of the activities of John Collins. Although he was a self-educated man, knowing no Greek and but little Latin, he attained to a mastery of science such that he corresponded constantly, and on terms of easy familiarity, with nearly all the important scientists. He criticised their work with skill and with the greatest tact; and he had a genius for getting information about new books, passing it on to his friends and acting as an agent for their purchase and sale. Styling himself a "midwife for the press," he published and edited scientific books, which were too limited in sale to tempt the commercial printers and publishers. He left behind him a large correspondence, docketed and annotated with clerkly neatness, which now forms a part of the valuable scientific correspondence known as the *Macclesfield Collection.* Collins had an unerring flare for detecting and appreciating genius. He quickly estimated Newton to be the greatest mathematician of the age; but he also recognised the genius of Leibniz and could appreciate that, as a creator of a new calculus, his systematic mind would carry him further than the too individualistic temperament of Newton. This may explain his apparently contradictory statement that Leibniz outtopped English mathematicians as a moon amongst the lesser stars.[4] With his just estimate of the mental characteristics of the two rivals, and his intimate knowledge of the opening scenes of the invention of the calculus, he would certainly have prevented the tragic ending of the controversy. In my judge-

[4] Macclesfield, vol. II, p. 454.

ment, Collins was the most valuable of Newton's friends. One needed to possess a cheerful disposition, a total lack of vanity, and an unqualified appreciation of his transcendant powers, to penetrate the reserved and timid shell which encrusted Newton's otherwise amiable character. Too many of those who sought his friendship did so by unqualified flattery, in order to advance their own interests.

At this time, John Wickins was still the chamber-fellow of Newton and perhaps continued so until he was presented to the living of Stoke Edith, near Monmouth, in 1684.[5] Shortly after Newton's death, Conduitt began collecting materials for a proposed life of his uncle and requested, by letters, any information that could be given. It was natural to suppose that Wickins not only would have made memoranda about their common life, but also would have passed on to his family many anecdotes of their Cambridge days. Professor Smith, then Lucasian Professor, wrote to his son for information. To the everlasting reproach of the Wickins family the following meagre account is all that could be extracted. It is exasperating that the idea of preserving the habits and familiar talk of a Newton was neglected for the duties of a rural parish, and that their most vivid remembrance was of being aided in their dispensing of many dozens of Bibles. The following letter is his reply:

Nic. Wickins to Professor Smith

Stoke Edith, Jan. 16th, 1827/8.

Dear Sir,—It was an unspeakable pleasure to me to see the hand of my old acquaintance; and I wish, in return, I could send something considerable to give you a pleasure relating to the great man you write about, but I am so unhappy as to find very little under Sir Isaac's own hand of what passed between him and my father.

I guess from a small book I found among my father's papers, that he had a design to collect into one all that he had of Sir Isaac's writing, but he went no farther than transcribing three short letters he received from him, and a Common Place of his, part of which I find under Sir Isaac's own hand; the rest, with the original of these three letters, is lost. Besides these transcribed letters and the Common Place, I can meet with nothing but four or five letters under Sir Isaac's own hand, very short, and relating to dividends and chamber

[5] Humphrey Newton, secretary to Newton, in 1685, states that he had no room-mate at that time.

rent, which he was so kind as to receive for my father when at Monmouth, where he was most part of the time he continued Fellow. There being so little in these letters, I do not now send them, but wait for your commands; for whatever I can meet with of this worthy man, shall be at your service.

My father's intimacy with him came by mere accident. My father's first chamber-fellow being very disagreeable to him, he retired one day into the walks, where he found Mr. Newton solitary and dejected. Upon entering into discourse, they found their cause of retirement the same, and thereupon agreed to shake off their present disorderly companions and chum together, which they did as soon as conveniently they could, and so continued as long as my father staid at college.

I have heard my father often say that he has been a witness of what the world has so often heard of Sir Isaac's forgetfulness of his food when intent upon his studies; and of his rising in a pleasant manner with the satisfaction of having found out some proposition without any concern for a seeming want of his night's sleep, which he was sensible he had lost thereby.

He was turning grey, I think, at thirty, and when my father observed that to him as the effect of his deep attention of mind, he would jest with the experiments he made so often with quick-silver, as if from hence he took so soon that colour.[6]

He sometimes suspected himself to be inclining to a consumption, and the medicine he made use of was the Leucatello's Balsam,[7] which, when he had composed himself, he would now and then melt in quantity about a quarter of a pint, and so drink it.

It is now eight years since my father's death, in which time many things my father used to relate of him are slipped out of my memory; but being mostly of such a nature as I have now mentioned, I suspect would be of no service could I recollect any more.

But there is one thing, upon account of which not only my father, but myself also, shall always pay a peculiar regard to his memory, which was a charitable benefaction which has privately passed from

[6] Stukeley also refers to his white hair and assigns the cause to a hot and dry temperament. *Cf. Portsmouth Collection.*

[7] Newton evidently thought the Balsam was a sovereign remedy for many ills since he preserved its recipe in his papers. Its principal ingredient was what he calls Venus turpentine, a curious misspelling for Venice. He recommends "For the measell, plague, or small-pox, a half an ounce in a little broth; take it warm, and sweat after it. And against poison and the biting of a mad dog; for the last you must dip lint and lay it upon the wound, besides taking it internally. There are other virtues of it; for wind, cholic, anoint the stomach, and so for bruises."

him through my father's, and since his death through my own hands. We have been the dispensers of many dozens of Bibles sent by him for poor people, and I have now many by me sent from him for the same purpose, which, as it shows the great regard he had for religion, I cannot but desire that by you it may be made public to the world.

Dear Sir, my thoughts dwell with wonderful delight upon the memory of this great and good man, and therefore I have troubled you with so long a letter, which I now beg pardon for, and in hope of again hearing soon from you, conclude with my brother's hearty service and respects to you. I beg my humble service to all my old acquaintance, and am,

Dear Sir, your much obliged humble servant,

NIC. WICKINS.

To Mr. Professor Smith, at
Trinity College, Cambridge.[8]

Like many a bachelor scholar, Newton cultivated apprehensions about his health, and had a fondness for dosing himself; Dr. Stukeley, whom I have already quoted, says that "his breakfast was orange-peel boiled in water, which he drank as tea, sweetened with sugar, and with bread and butter. He thinks this dissolves phlegm." And Lord Pembroke told the Doctor that when Newton "got a cold, he lay in bed till it was gone, though for two or three days' continuance, and thus came off the illness by perspiration."[9] One can but wonder what kind of a constitution he had. He was probably not robust, and he was certainly lethargic in habit. He took no exercise, indulged in no amusements, kept no regular hours and was indifferent to his food. Yet he lived to what, in that time, was an extraordinarily old age with but one known serious illness, and his mind could work indefinitely without any ill effects from lack of sleep or food. His exemption from illness may be partly attributed to the simples he concocted, and his avoidance of the drastic dosing and phlebotomy of medical practice.

Newton had now attained a position of authority, and he was frequently solicited for advice and criticism. He was invariably courteous in his answers to such enquiries and spared no pains to give his opinions fully and clearly. It was a marked trait of his character that he became bored by a scientific correspondence which in-

8 *Portsmouth Collection.*

9 *Portsmouth Collection.*

volved any enquiry or critical discussion of his own work; and he soon declined to continue it on the plea that it distracted him. Yet he would cheerfully interrupt his work in order to answer any requests for information or help by others. Also, while correspondence of the first sort was invariably carried on by an intermediary so that we have scarcely a letter addressed to a well-known man of science, letters of the second sort were, on the contrary, sent direct to the enquirer.

A Dr. Maddock had hit upon the idea that there might be radiations which would not affect sight, and sent to Newton some speculations on the properties of such *dark rays*. I should hardly look upon this supposition of Dr. Maddock as a prophecy of our now known electro-radiation any more than I think Anaximander was a corner stone of evolution, because he opined that all life originated in the ocean. In fact, Maddock seems to have based his hypothesis on the legend that Tiberius, with his enormous protruding eyes, could see at night and in the dark. Newton's answer was eminently kindly and tactful. He wrote that, unless some experimental evidence of such rays could be given, and it could be shown whether they have the same laws of refrangibility as visible rays, or if not, how they differ, then their existence must be doubtful. If, however, he concluded, one grants the existence of such rays, the remainder of your thesis is correct.

At what time Newton became interested in the problem of vision, we do not know. But, that he had made dissections and careful measurements of the optical system of the eye was proved by Brewster, who found amongst the family papers a drawing to scale of an enlarged sheep's eye with the dimensions tabulated. He had also developed a theory of binocular vision which was later published as Query 15 in his *Optics*. In 1682, Dr. William Briggs, Fellow of Corpus Christi College, Cambridge, published a new theory of vision in Hooke's *Philosophical Collections*. He included a fantastic explanation of binocular sight, according to which the optic nerves from corresponding points of the two retinas go to the brain in pairs of equal length and tension. The nerve fibres, he further assumed, are stretched like the strings of two harps and each pair of fibres of equal length and tension give but one impression to the mind, as two strings struck in unison seem but one sound. The author appealed to Newton for criticism and, to his surprise, found that he had been far surpassed in accuracy and breadth of knowledge of the subject. Newton answered with the freedom of a friend, praising portions of what he politely named an ingenious theory, but making it quite clear that he found this explanation of binocular vision to be quite untenable. When Briggs pressed him to put his objections in writing, he generously took the time to answer in a long letter, covering in detail the whole subject, and incorporating his own explanation of binocular vision. According to his usual custom, he began the letter with an apology, and a request that it be considered confidential. "Though I am," he wrote, "of all men grown the most shy of setting pen to paper about any thing that may lead into disputes yet your friendship overcomes me so far as that I shall set down my suspicions about your theory, yet in this condition, that if I can but write plain enough to make you understand me, I may leave all to your use without pressing it further on. For I design not to confute or convince you but only to present and submit my thoughts to your consideration and judgment." He then, first, criticises adversely the hypothesis that the optic nerve fibres are under different tensions according to their lengths by using a homely illustration from the fibres of bent apple trees, a fact which must have come under his acute observation in his boyhood. His own idea of binocular vision was, that the object does not appear as one to the mind because of the same colour, form, and bigness of the image in each eye, but because the two images fall in the same relative situations or places on the two retinas. His proof was that pressure on one eye causes such coincident images to separate and one of them will seem to move upwards, downwards, or sideways according to the direction of the pressure applied to that eye. He then, wisely, excluded the explanation of vision from the field of physics as being a question to be answered only by a knowledge of the processes of the mind.

In some unknown way, he thought the sensorium of the brain interprets the two images as one, [perhaps by analogy to the inverted images on the retina being interpreted in their correct position by the mind]. "But you will say, how is this coincidence made? I answer, what if I know not? Perhaps in the sensorium, after some such way as the Cartesians would have believed, or by some other way. Perhaps by the mixing of the marrow of the nerves in their junction before they enter the brain, the fibres on the right side of each eye going to the right side of the head, those on the left side to the left." After giving what facts he can to support his ideas he concluded: "You have now seen the sum of what I can think of worth objecting, set down in a tumultuary way, as I could get time from my Stourbridge Fair friends. If I have anywhere exprest myself in a more peremptory way than becomes the weakness of the argument pray look on that as done not in earnestness but for the mode of discoursing. Whether any thing be so material as that it may prove any way useful to you I cannot tell. But pray accept of it as written for that end. For having laid philosophical speculations aside, nothing but the gratification of a friend would easily invite me to so large a scribble about things of this nature."

As usually happens, the author paid little attention to his critic, but continued in his own opinion. He published his *Theory of Vision* in 1685, and prefixed to it a Latin letter by Newton. In the same spirit with which Dr. Johnson wrote laudatory prefaces for all sorts of books, Newton extolled Briggs's theory of binocular vision as similar to consonance of sounds, because Nature loves to accomplish different ends by the same means.[10]

Whenever a great advance is made in a particular subject of physics, it naturally absorbs the attention not only of physicists, but its influence spreads into the other sciences. Today, for example, electrical phenomena are the most fertile field of study, and we are making rapid advances in the discovery of new phenomena, the formulation of new laws, and their application to the arts. During such a period of expansion, there seems to be no limit to what may be accomplished. In spite of past experience, we indulge the hope that, at last, we have found a universal substance whose attributes will account for all phenomena. Such systems were evolved in the past with atoms of matter as the substratum of reality and, although they failed, yet we are willing to begin again the same course of speculation under the delusion that electricity, as a substance, may evade the limitations which were discovered in matter. To be sure, ions of electricity seem to be merely atoms of matter, reduced to a smaller size and given a greater velocity; and their essential similarities are disguised only by a change of name. Not only has electricity sup-

[10] This correspondence is printed in full in Edleston, pp. 264, 273, from the original MSS. in the British Museum. Brewster also prints it with a comprehensive critique. Vol. I, pp. 218–236, 420–436. Those interested in the subject will find it well worth the study. In my judgement, the subject of binocular vision lies, for the most part, outside the field of physics and mechanics. After the image is formed on the retina, its future history and interpretation as vision have no mechanical explanation.

planted matter as a basis of physical and chemical phenomena but it somehow pleases us, or at least gives an anodyne to scepticism, to say that nervous stimuli, the processes of life, and even consciousness, are merely electrical actions. In the seventeenth century, due to the invention of the air pump which enabled Boyle to vary, and to measure, the pressure of gases, the properties of matter in the gaseous state were enthusiastically investigated, and all phenomena, both of the inorganic and organic worlds, were ascribed to modifications of a subtile gas, or æther.

In Newton's mind, there was gradually evolving a universal mechanical system which would embrace all physical phenomena; the postulates for this system required only the specification of inertia, motion, and a force of attraction by a material substance. He had found, from the criticism of his published work on light, that he must postulate a luminiferous æther in order to account for such phenomena as diffraction and the colours shown by thin transparent films; his search for a general chemical principle had carried him back to an atomic theory of matter; and lastly his discovery of an universal law of gravitation had forced on him the dilemma of either assuming for bodies an occult property of attracting at a distance, or of postulating a gaseous medium which caused these attractions by its pressure. Newton had met Robert Boyle, the acknowledged master of chemistry and the discoverer of the laws of gases, but a few times. Their conversation turned on the properties of material gases and on those of a universal æthereal gas which would serve as a sort of *deus ex machina* of the physical world. Newton mentioned to him his own idea of such an æther, and, at Boyle's solicitation, he sent to him an elaborate statement of his views of the constitution of such a medium. The letter was first published in Boyle's *Works* and, while it is quite long, it should be given with only the omission of unimportant details as it is the fundamental document of the mechanistic philosophy of the seventeenth and eighteenth centuries.

Newton to Boyle

Honoured Sir,—I have so long deferred to send you my thoughts about the physical qualities we spoke of, that did I not esteem myself obliged by promise, I think I should be ashamed to send them at all. The truth is, my notions about things of this kind are so indigested, that I am not well satisfied myself in them; *and what I am not satis-*

fied in, I can scarce esteem fit to be communicated to others; especially in natural philosophy, where there is no end of fancying.[11] But because I am indebted to you, and yesterday met with a friend, Mr. Maulyverer, who told me he was going to London, and intended to give you the trouble of a visit, I could not forbear to take the opportunity of conveying this to you by him.

It being only an explication of qualities which you desire of me, I shall set down my apprehensions in the form of suppositions as follows. And first, I suppose, that there is diffused through all places an æthereal substance, capable of contraction and dilatation, strongly elastic, and, in a word, much like air in all respects, but far more subtile.

2. I suppose this æther pervades all gross bodies, but yet so as to stand rarer in their pores than in free spaces, and so much the rarer, as their pores are less; and this I suppose (with others) to be the cause why light incident on those bodies is refracted towards the perpendicular; why two well-polished metals cohere in a receiver exhausted of air; why mercury stands sometimes up to the top of a glass pipe, though much higher than thirty inches; and one of the main causes why the parts of all bodies cohere; also the cause of filtration, and of the rising of water in small glass pipes above the surface of the stagnating water they are dipped into; for I suspect the æther may stand rarer, not only in the insensible pores of bodies, but even in the very sensible cavities of those pipes; and the same principle may cause menstruums [solvents] to pervade with violence the pores of the bodies they dissolve, the surrounding æther, as well as the atmosphere, pressing them together.

3. I suppose the rarer æther within bodies, and the denser without them, not to be terminated in a mathematical superficies, but to grow gradually into one another; the external æther beginning to grow rarer, and the internal to grow denser, at some little distance from the superficies of the body, and running through all intermediate degrees of density in the intermediate spaces; and this may be the cause why light, in Grimaldo's experiment, passing by the edge of a knife, or other opaque body, is turned aside, and as it were refracted, and by that refraction makes several colours. . . .

4. When two bodies moving towards one another come near together, I suppose the æther between them to grow rarer than before,

[11] Italics mine. One wonders whether those who are today so fancifully describing the universe have satisfied themselves. If not, they might heed Newton's advice with profit to themselves and others.

and the spaces of its graduated rarity to extend further from the superficies of the bodies towards one another; and this, by reason that the æther cannot move and play up and down so freely in the strait [narrow] passage between the bodies, as it could before they came so near together. . . . And as the other body approaches more and more, I suppose the æther between them will grow rarer and rarer. These suppositions I have so described, as if I thought the spaces of graduated æther had precise limits. . . . But really I do not think they have such precise limits, but rather decay insensibly, and, in so decaying, extend to a much greater distance than can easily be believed or need be supposed.

5. Now, from the fourth supposition it follows, that when two bodies approaching one another come so near together as to make the æther between them begin to rarefy, they will begin to have a reluctance from being brought nearer together, and an endeavour to recede from one another; which reluctance and endeavour will increase as they come nearer together, because thereby they cause the interjacent æther to rarefy more and more. But at length, when they come so near together that the excess of pressure of the external æther which surrounds the bodies, above that of the rarefied æther, which is between them, is so great as to overcome the reluctance which the bodies have from being brought together; then will that excess of pressure drive them with violence together, and make them adhere strongly to one another, as was said in the second supposition. . . . Now hence I conceive it is chiefly that a fly walks on water without wetting her feet, and consequently without touching the water; that two polished pieces of glass are not without pressure brought to contact, no, not though the one be plain, the other a little convex, that the particles of dust cannot by pressing be made to cohere, as they would do, if they did but fully touch; that the particles of tingeing substances and salts dissolved in water do not of their own accord concrete and fall to the bottom, but diffuse themselves all over the liquor, and expand still more if you add more liquor to them. Also, that the particles of vapours, exhalations, and air do stand at a distance from one another, and endeavour to recede as far from one another as the pressure of the incumbent atmosphere will let them; for I conceive the confused mass of vapours, air, and exhalations which we call the atmosphere, to be nothing else but the particles of all sorts of bodies, of which the earth consists, separated from one another, and kept at a distance by the said principle.

From these principles the actions of menstruums upon bodies may be thus explained: suppose any tingeing body, as cochineal or logwood be put into water; so soon as the water sinks into its pores and wets on all sides any particle which adheres to the body only by the principle in the second supposition, it takes off, or at least much diminishes, the efficacy of that principle to hold the particle to the body, because it makes the æther on all sides the particle to be of a more uniform density than before. And then the particle being shaken off by any little motion, floats in the water, and with many such others makes a tincture; which tincture will be of some lively colour, if the particles be all of the same size and density; otherwise of a dirty one. For the colours of all natural bodies whatever seem to depend on nothing but the various sizes and densities of their particles, as I think you have seen described by me more at large in another paper.[12] . . .

Nor does the size only, but the density of the particles also, conduce to the permanency of aërial substances; for the excess of density of the æther without such particles above that of the æther within them is still greater; which has made me sometimes think that the true permanent air may be of a metallic origina; the particles of no substances being more dense than those of metals. This, I think, is also favoured by experience, for I remember I once read in the Philosophical Transactions, how M. Huygens at Paris, found that the air made by dissolving salt of tartar would in two or three days time condense and fall down again, but the air made by dissolving a metal continued without condensing or relenting in the least. If you consider then, how by the continual fermentations made in the bowels of the earth there are aërial substances raised out of all kinds of bodies, all which together make the atmosphere, and that of all these the metallic are the most permanent, you will not perhaps think it absurd, that the most permanent part of the atmosphere, which is the true air, should be constituted of these, especially since they are the heaviest of all other, and so must subside to the lower parts of the atmosphere and float upon the surface of the earth, and buoy up the lighter exhalations and vapours to float in greatest plenty above them. Thus, I say, it ought to be with the metallic exhalations raised in the bowels of the earth by the action of acid menstruums,

[12] Here follows a long passage giving many illustrations from various chemical actions to show that they depend on the size of the particles, or atoms as we would say, and whether the constituent substances are "sociable" or "unsociable" towards each other. These illustrations are ingenious, but obsolete, and may be omitted.

and thus it is with the true permanent air; for this, as in reason it ought to be esteemed the most ponderous part of the atmosphere, because the lowest, so it betrays its ponderosity by making vapours ascend readily in it, by sustaining mists and clouds of snow, and by buoying up gross and ponderous smoke. The air also is the most gross unactive part of the atmosphere, affording living things no nourishment, if deprived of the more tender exhalations and spirits that float in it; and what more unactive and remote from nourishment than metallic bodies?

I shall set down one conjecture more, which came into my mind now as I was writing this letter; it is about the cause of gravity. For this end I will suppose æther to consist of parts differing from one another in subtilty by indefinite degrees; that in the pores of bodies there is less of the grosser æther, in proportion to the finer, than in open spaces; and consequently, that in the great body of the earth there is much less of the grosser æther, in proportion to the finer, than in the regions of the air; and that yet the grosser æther in the air affects the upper regions of the earth, and the finer æther in the earth the lower regions of the air, in such a manner, that from the top of the air to the surface of the earth, and again from the surface of the earth to the centre thereof, the æther is insensibly finer and finer. Imagine now any body suspended in the air, or lying on the earth, and the æther being by the hypothesis grosser in the pores, which are in the upper parts of the body, than in those which are in its lower parts, and that grosser æther being less apt to be lodged in those pores than the finer æther below, it will endeavour to get out and give way to the finer æther below, which cannot be, without the bodies descending to make room above for it to go out into.

From this supposed gradual subtilty of the parts of æther some things above might be further illustrated and made more intelligible; but by what has been said, you will easily discern whether in these conjectures there be any degree of probability, which is all I aim at. For my own part, I have so little fancy to things of this nature, that had not your encouragement moved me to it, I should never, I think, have thus far set pen to paper about them. What is amiss, therefore, I hope you will the more easily pardon in

Your most humble servant and honourer,

ISAAC NEWTON.

Cambridge, Feb. 28, 1678/9.[13]

[13] First published in *Boyle's Works,* Vol. I, p. cxii. Copied in Brewster, Vol. I, p. 409, and Macclesfield, Vol. II, p. 407.

This year can be marked as a fortunate and influential one for Newton, as it saw the beginning of a new relationship which was destined to have a profound effect on all his future life. On November 8, Charles Montague matriculated at Trinity College as a Fellow-Commoner and, between the brilliant young man and the Lucasian Professor nineteen years his senior, there quickly grew up a friendship which was broken only by the death of Montague. It is difficult to understand what drew two such unlike men together. It must have been a strong tie, because in the beginning, one occupied the position of an undergraduate student, and the other was one of the distinguished scholars of the world; while later the positions became reversed, and the younger man grew to be a great nobleman and statesman, the patron and employer of his former master. Such a reversal of fortune is not conducive to ingenuous friendship and, in this case, it would have seemed to be especially unexpected, for one was vain and arrogant, and the other vain and sensitive. Yet it did last and, so far as we know, there was but one temporary display of ill temper between them. To understand Newton's life rightly, we must know what manner of a man Montague was, and follow his dazzling career.

Charles Montague, the fourth son of a younger son of the first earl of Manchester, was born at Horton, Northamptonshire, in 1661, the year Newton went to college. He was educated at Westminster School, and then entered Trinity College. As a younger son, of a younger branch of the family, he was not wealthy and was, like many younger sons, intended for the church. He early showed great ability and had evidently a warm and generous nature, for it was told of him that he went to college a year before the proper time, as he was unable to bear the thought of being separated from his "dearest friend." Although the cold facts of dates prove the story to be apocryphal, we may rely on it as an expression of his unspoiled temperament and attribute his later pride and unpopularity to his heady successes in politics. As a Fellow-Commoner, he would meet the Fellows of the College intimately in hall and commons, and it was during those times that his friendship with Newton would grow. His career at College was a brilliant one as he surpassed his competitors in logic and ethics, and read widely in the classics. At the same time, his attention was applied sufficiently to mathematics and science for him to turn from the Cartesian system in vogue to the new philosophy then being so brilliantly developed by Newton. His biographers say that "he was one of the small band of students who assisted Newton in forming the Philosophical Society of Cambridge"; but we shall see, at the proper time, that the attempt failed. In 1681, he was made M.A. by Royal Mandate, as befitted a young gentleman of a noble family.

However able as a student Montague may have been, it was his talent for fluent verse-making which opened up the way to fortune. A clever and absurdly eulogistic ode, written on the death of Charles II,[14] secured him favourable notice of the earl of Dorset, the great patron of the day, who took him to London and introduced him to the principal wits of the town. Although he had been a Fellow of his college for some years past, we can be sure that he now spent most of his time in London and, with powerful patronage behind him, began to look forward to making his fortune by his pen. The opportunity came to him, and nothing is more surprising to us than the sort of opportunities which then opened the road to political preferment; a clever lampoon or eulogy, an amorous intrigue, or a genuine literary ability, all were regarded as the equipment for a statesman, and oddly enough often correctly. Such an opportunity came to him and to seize it he did not hesitate to enter the lists against Dryden, the dictator of letters. With the accession of James II, Dryden had become a Roman Catholic, some say from conviction, and others to gain royal favour. However that may be, he wrote and published *The Hind and the Panther* in which, with all the fervour of a new convert, he portrayed the Roman Church as a timid and innocent hind drooping in the cruel jaws of a carnivorous and vengeful Church of England. Montague saw his chance and, with the collaboration of Matthew Prior whom he had recently met, he wrote a parody on this ode, in 1687, which was called the *Country Mouse and the City Mouse*. The burlesque carried the city by storm, and

[14] As this ode started Montague on a career which incidentally made Newton Master of the Mint, the reader may wish a specimen of it:

"Farewell, Great Charles, Monarch of Blest Renown,
The best Good Man that ever fill'd a Throne:
Whom Nature, as her highest Pattern, wrought
And mixt both Sexes Virtues in one Draught.
Wisdom for Councils, Bravery in War,
With all the mild Good-Nature of the Fair,
The Woman's Sweetness, temper'd Manly Wit,
And Loving Power, did crown'd with Meekness fit;
His awful Person Reverence engag'd,
Which mild Address and Tenderness assuag'd:
Thus the Almighty Gracious King above,
Does both command our Fear, and win our Love."

his reputation was made, not only as a man of letters but as a potential statesman. The following year, he resigned his fellowship and left Cambridge. As a further step towards fortune he married, at about the same time, the Countess Dowager of Manchester, his uncle's widow. We can be fairly certain that it was ambition rather than affection which influenced him, as his wife was from ten to twenty years older than himself and had borne nine children to her first husband. In 1689, he became a member of the Convention Parliament for Malden through the patronage of Dorset. Dr. Johnson says that when he entered Parliament he still intended to take orders, but his success as a debater turned him permanently to public life. As during the sessions, he again met Newton, who had been elected to represent the University, we can defer his future history.[15]

The attention of the world has been so concentrated on Newton as the scholar and man of science that another side of his character has been neglected. He was known as a man of sound judgement and of executive ability by his colleagues before he attained his commanding reputation in science or he would not have been selected by the University to serve as its representative during a delicate and dangerous religious controversy with James II before the High Court of Commission, and also in the Convention Parliament which reorganised the government after the Revolution of 1687. We should also remember that Montague, in his student days, had been so impressed with the same qualities as later to entrust to him the complicated and hazardous problems of the recoinage. That he had a strong pride of family and longed to be a gentleman of social rank and gentle birth, as that title then signified, rather than to be a scholar, is equally certain. He held stiffly to the distinction of his lordship of a manor, insignificant as the manor was; he acted generously towards the members of his family, whether they were worthy or worthless, as would be becoming of the head of a county family; and he endeavoured to trace his genealogy to another county family of the same name, but of higher rank, on very doubtful evidence. And, lastly, he showed in the later period of his life the greatest satisfaction as the dispenser of an easy hospitality, as the companion of the gentry and nobility, and as the favourite of a very dull Court. And when he became a gentleman, he abandoned science and scholarship without any apparent regret. This opinion is given

[15] See the *Works and Life of the Earl of Halifax*. Printed for E. Curll, London, 1715. A rare and not altogether reliable history as it was written in a tone of uncompromising eulogy.

without the least intention to cast a slur on Newton's reputation or character. If so, I should have to include Shakespeare, who also abandoned his career and literary fame to be a landed gentleman; to be a gentleman in those days meant much more than it does now, and to be a scientist meant far less. Newton had the unusual distinction of satisfying both ambitions.

It was this side of his character which his intimacy with Montague brought to self-consciousness and to maturity. It was the first time that the scholar had come in contact with what we call the great world. The wit, the buoyancy of spirits, and the social manners of this brilliant youth attracted and fascinated the college don. The reminiscences we have give no details of this intimacy, but the scholar's long vigils of work must have been frequently broken by conversations with his young friend. Although it is natural that his scholarly habits should have been emphasized, he was not quite the solitary figure he has been depicted, and his time was not entirely absorbed in his laboratory and study. There were the almost daily meetings with the Fellows in the Combination Room; he had a small circle of acquaintances in the other colleges and occasional guests from out of town; he frequently took part in the philosophical discussions of the Platonists who made Christ Church their rendezvous. Then, too, it should not be forgotten that Wickins, who was his room-mate for many years and thus his constant companion, would also bring his friends to their rooms. But most significant of all, the intimacy with Montague points to frequent and familiar visits. We can imagine that the brilliant young man would delight and charm the older scholar with his wit and with his accounts of the country life of a great house. And, in return, he would receive from Newton a first hand knowledge of the new philosophy and the new science which was stirring in the scholarly world. Nor should we doubt that Newton described his personal work and sketched those ideas of a cosmical system which were unfolding in his mind; and if so, there were few to be more envied than he, who had the unique opportunity of hearing those profound ideas at first hand, and in their inception. The influence of Halley in giving us the publication of the *Principia* has been frequently extolled; but no one has linked Montague's name with it; and yet his sympathy and eager enthusiasm may have done much to encourage Newton during the early days of its incubation. We have suffered an irreparable loss by the failure of Montague to leave us a record of his long and intimate association with

Newton; how many disputed points such a record would have solved.

The reconciliation with Hooke, which resulted from the exchange of the courteous letters previously quoted, was only a temporary truce. Their natures were too incompatible to endure any contact with patience, and the first indication that Newton gave of a renewed willingness to make public his ideas was certain to arouse the watchful and jealous irritation of Hooke. The cause of the final and permanent break between them arose from a casual suggestion made by Newton to the Royal Society that it would be useful to undertake an experiment on falling bodies. Although the result of the suggestion led to bitterness, it must be looked upon as one of the greatest and most fortunate of events, since it was the direct cause of the composition of the *Principia.*

Before giving the history of this episode, a summary of the principal questions involved will be useful.[16] A month after Oldenburg's death, Hooke, the new Secretary, wrote a courteous letter, at the request of the Royal Society, begging Newton to continue his correspondence on scientific matters with its members, as it was feared that his interest in its affairs might cease with the death of his friend.

Hooke to Newton, Nov. 24, 1679

Sir,

Finding by our registers that you were pledged to correspond with Mr. Oldenburg, and having also had the happiness of receiving some letters from you myself make me presume to trouble you with this present scribble—Dr. Grew's more urgent occasions having made him decline the holding correspondence. And the Society hath de-

[16] The sources of this most important event in Newton's life are seven letters which passed between Newton and Hooke in the years 1679 and 1680 and seventeen between Newton and Halley in the years 1686 and 1687. Ball has published the Hooke-Newton correspondence with the exception of two letters which had not been found; fortunately one of these, Newton to Hooke, Dec. 13, 1679, has just been discovered and published with an interesting comment on the whole incident by M. Pelseneer. This leaves only one letter, Hooke to Newton, Dec. 9, 1679, unaccounted for, and its tenor is known from an extract in the R. S. *Record.* Of the seventeen letters of Halley and Newton relating to the publishing of the *Principia* all but one, which was lost, are given in Ball's *Essay.* The quarrel between Newton and Hooke which occurred in the years 1679 and 1680 can be described from the contemporary first series; as it flared up again when the *Principia* was published, Newton's attitude can be seen in retrospect from his letters to Halley. The reader should consult: W. W. Rouse-Ball, *Essay on Newton's Principia,* Macmillan, 1893.—Rigaud, *First Publication of the Principia,* Oxford, 1838.—Jean Pelseneer, *Une lettre inédite de Newton, Isis,* Vol. XII (2), No. 38, 1929.

volved it on me. I hope therefore that you will please to continue your former favours to the Society by communicating what shall occur to you that is philosophical, and for return I shall be sure to acquaint you with what we shall receive considerable from other parts or find out new here. And you may be assured that whatever shall be so communicated shall be no otherwise further imparted or disposed of than you yourself shall prescribe. I am not ignorant that both heretofore, and not long since also, there have been some who have endeavoured to misrepresent me to you, and possibly they or others have not been wanting to do the like to me, but difference in opinion if such there be (especially in philosophical matters where interest hath little concern) me thinks should not be the occasion of enmity—'tis not with me I am sure. For my part I shall take it as a great favour if you shall please to communicate by letter your objections against any hypothesis or opinion of mine; and particularly if you will let me know your thoughts of that of compounding the celestial motions of the planets of a direct motion by the tangent and an attractive motion towards the central body, or what objections you have against my hypothesis of the laws or causes of springyness.

I have lately received from Paris a new hypothesis invented by Mo^r^ Mallemont de Messanges, D^r^ of the Sorbonne, who desires much to have what can be objected against it. He supposes then a centre of this our vortex about which all the primary planets move in perfect circles, each of them in his own equal spaces in equal times. The next to it he places the Sun; and about the Sun, Mercury as a satellite; the next Venus; the next the earth, about which the Moon as a satellite; then Mars; then Jupiter and his satellites; and Saturn with his. He supposes the Sun to make its revolution in about half the time the earth makes its, and the plane of it to be inclined to the plane of the ecliptic as much as the trepidation requires. He is not precise in defining any thing, as reserving a liberty to himself to help him out where objections might stick.

I am informed likewise from Paris that they are there about another work, viz. of settling the longitude and latitude of the most considerable places: the former of those by the eclipses of the satellites of Jupiter. Mr Picart and De la Hire travel, and Mo^r^ Cassini and Romer observe at Paris. They have already found that Brest in Brittany is 18 leagues nearer Paris than all the maps make it. I have written to a correspondent in Devonshire to see if we can do somewhat of that kind here, and I should be glad if by perpendicular observations, we could determine the difference of latitude between London and Cambridge. If you know of any one that will observe at Cambridge, I will procure it to be done here very exactly.

Mr Collins shewed me a book he received from Paris of De la Hire containing first a new method of the conic sections and secondly a treatise *De locis solidis.* I have not perused the book but Mr Collins commends it. Mr Flamsteed by some late perpendicular observations hath confirmed the parallax of the orb of the earth.

But I fear I have too much trespassed, and therefore to put an end to your further trouble I shall subscribe myself, Sir,

Your very humble Servant,

R. H.

Gresham Colledge, Nov. 24, 1679.[17]

As a personal document, this letter is important as it shows Hooke's better nature and amounts almost to an apology for his, and the Society's, past treatment of Newton. Philosophically it is much more important. Hooke's question about the law of attraction turned Newton's attention to his early work on the subject and induced him to take it up again in a serious manner; the reference to Picart's work may have led him to substitute the more correct diameter of earth in his former calculations of the attraction of the moon although I have shown this not to be probable; and lastly, the hypothesis of Messanges[18] was the direct cause of the discovery of the law of attraction of a solid sphere on an exterior or interior point—a theorem essential to expanding the law of gravitation into one of universal applicability.

Newton answered Hooke's letter almost immediately. It is one of the most revealing documents we have from him, because of the light it throws on his intentions for the future. There can be no reason to doubt that he had determined to abandon science and philosophy permanently. What his plans were, we shall probably never know, but we can guess that he intended to follow Barrow into the

17 *An Essay on Newton's Principia,* W. W. Rouse-Ball, p. 139.

18 The hypothesis of Messanges can be explained somewhat more clearly than it is in the letter. Mallemont de Messanges published his *Nouveau système du Monde* in 1679, and immediately sent a copy to the Royal Society for criticism. He imagined that there was a fixed centre of the solar system and that about it the planets were carried in exact circles by a Cartesian vortex. The Sun, with Mercury as its moon, was the nearest of the planets to this imaginary centre and the others at increasing distances were Venus, Mars, Earth, etc. The revolution of the Sun required something more than six months. The whole idea is, of course, absurd; and when he later wrote a dissertation on comets, the astronomer Lalande caustically remarked that "il n'est pas aussi absurde que de coutume."

field of theology or to try to join Montague, as he afterwards did, in some public career.

Newton to Hooke

Nov. 28, 1679.[19]

Sir,

I cannot but acknowledge my self every way, by the kindness of your letter, tempted to concur with your desires in a philosophical correspondence. And heartily sorry I am that I am at present unfurnished with matter answerable to your expectations—for I have been this last half year in Lincolnshire cumbered with concerns amongst my relations till yesterday when I returned hither; so that I have had no time to entertain philosophical meditations, or so much as to study or mind any thing else but country affairs. And before that, I had for some years last been endeavouring to bend myself from philosophy to other studies in so much that I have long grutched the time spent in that study unless it be perhaps at idle hours sometimes for a diversion; which makes me almost wholly unacquainted with what philosophers at London or abroad have of late been employed about. And perhaps you will incline the more to believe me when I tell you that I did not, before the receipt of your last letter, so much as hear (that I remember) of your hypothesis of compounding the celestial motions of the planets, of a direct motion by the tangent to the curve, and of the laws and causes of springyness, though these no doubt are well known to the philosophical world. And having thus shook hands with philosophy and being also at present taken of with other business, I hope it will not be interpreted out of any unkindness to you or the R. Society that I am backward in engaging my self in these matters, though formerly I must acknowledge I was moved by other reasons to decline, as much as Mr Oldenburg's importunity and ways to engage me in disputes would permit, all correspondence with him about them. However I cannot but return my hearty thanks for your thinking me worthy of so noble a commerce and in order thereto frankly imparting to me several things in your letter.

As to the hypothesis of Monsr Mallemont, though it should not be true yet if it would answer to phenomena it would be very valuable by reason of its simplicity. But how the orbits of all the primary

[19] Rigaud in his *Essay on the Principia* gives a surprisingly accurate account of this episode although he was compelled to reconstruct the story from very scanty materials since the letters here quoted had not then been discovered. Brewster gives it but little space.

planets but Mercury can be reduced to so many concentric circles through each of which the planet moves equal spaces in equal times (for that's the hypothesis if I mistake not your description) I do not yet understand. The readiest way to convince the world of this truth would be I conceive to set forth first in some two of the planets, suppose Mars and the earth, a specimen thereof stated and determined in numbers.

I know nobody in the University addicted to making astronomical observations: and my own short sightedness and tenderness of health makes me something unfit. Yet it's likely I may sometime this winter when I have more leisure than at present attempt what you propound for determining the difference of latitude between Cambridge and London.

I am glad to hear that so considerable a discovery as you made of the earth's annual parallax is seconded by Mr Flamsteed's observations.

In requital of this advertisement I shall communicate to you a fancy of my own about discovering the earth's diurnal motion. In order thereto I will consider the earth's diurnal motion alone, without the annual, that having little influence on the experiment I shall here propound. Suppose then *BDG* represents the globe of the earth carried round once a day about its centre *C* from west to east according to the order of the letters *BDG;* and let *A* be a heavy body suspended in the air, and moving round with the earth so as perpetually to hang over the same point thereof *B.* Then imagine this body *A* [the MS. has *B,* which is obviously a slip] let fall, and its gravity will give it a new motion towards the centre of the earth without diminishing the old one from west to east. Whence the motion of this body from west to east, by reason that before it fell it was more distant from the centre of the earth than the parts of the earth at which it arrives in its fall, will be greater than the motion from west to east of the parts of the earth at which the body arrives in its fall; and therefore it will not descend the perpendicular *AC,* but outrunning the parts of the earth will shoot forward to the east side of the perpendicular describing in its fall a spiral line *ADEC,* quite contrary to the opinion of the vulgar who think that, if the earth moved, heavy bodies in falling would be outrun by its parts and fall on the west side of the perpendicular. The advance of the body from the perpendicular eastward will in a descent of but twenty or thirty yards be very small, and yet I am apt to think it may be enough to

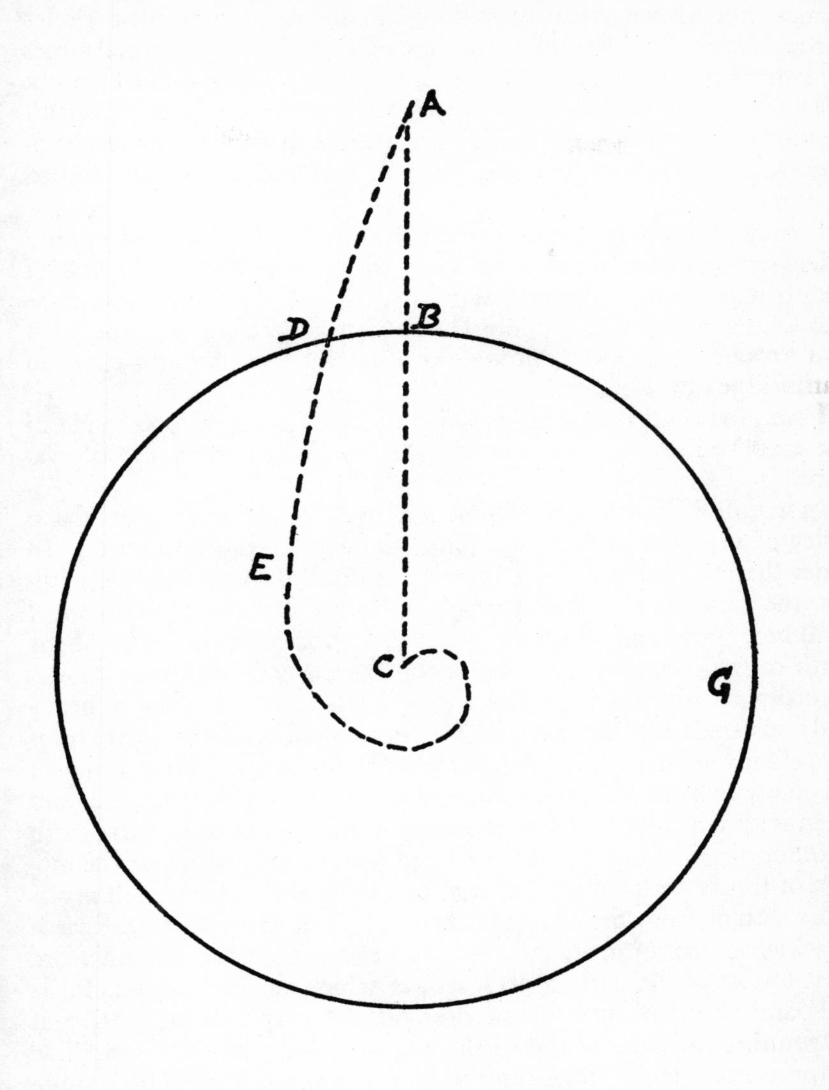
A
D
B
E
C
G

determine the matter of fact. Suppose then in a very calm day a pistol bullet were let down by a silk line from the top of a high building or well, the line going through a small hole made in a plate of brass or tin fastened to the top of the building or well, and that the bullet when let down almost to the bottom were settled in water so as to cease from swinging, and then let down further on an edge of steel lying north and south to try if the bullet in settling thereon will almost stand in aequilibrio but yet with some small propensity (the smaller the better) decline to the west side of the steel as often as it is so let down thereon. The steel being so placed underneath, suppose the bullet be then drawn up to the top and let fall by cutting, slipping, or burning, the line of silk, and if it fall constantly on the east side of the steel it will argue the diurnal motion of the earth. But what the event will be I know not, having never attempted to try it. If any body would think this worth their trial, the best way in my opinion would be to try it in a high church or wide steeple, the windows being first well stopped; for in a narrow well the bullet possibly may be apt to receive a ply from the straitened air near the sides of the well, if in its fall it come nearer to one side than to another. It would be convenient also that the water into which the bullet falls be a yard or two deep or more, partly that the bullet may fall more gently on the steel, partly that the motion which it has from west to east at its entering into the water may by means of the longer time of descent through the water, carry it on further eastward and so make the experiment more manifest.

If I were not so unhappy as to be unacquainted with your hypothesis abovementioned (as I am with almost all things which have of late been done or attempted in philosophy) I should so far comply with your desire as to send you what objections I could think of against them, if I could think of any. And on the other hand I could with pleasure hear and answer any objections made against any notions of mine in a transient discourse for a divertisement. But yet my affection to philosophy being worn out, so that I am almost as little concerned about it as one tradesman uses to be about another man's trade or a countryman about learning, I must acknowledge myself averse from spending that time in writing about it which I think I can spend otherwise more to my own content and the good of others: and I hope neither you nor any body else will blame for this averseness. To let you see that it is not out of any shyness, reservedness, or distrust that I have of late and still do decline phi[losophi]cal commerce but only out of my applying myself to other things, I have communicated to you the notion above set down (such as it is) concerning the descent of heavy bodies for proving the motion of the earth; and shall be as ready to communicate in oral discourse anything I know, if it shall ever be my happiness to have familiar converse frequently with you. And possibly if anything useful to mankind occurs to me I may sometimes impart it to you by letter. So wishing you all happiness and success in your endeavours, I rest,

Sir,

Your humble Servant

to command

Is. Newton.

P. S. Mr. Cock has cast two pieces of metal for me in order to a further attempt about the reflecting tube which I was the last year inclined to by the instigation of some of our Fellows. If I do anything you may expect to hear from me. But I doubt the tool on which they were to be ground, being in the keeping of one lately deceased who was to have wrought the metals, is lost.

Cambridge.

Novemb. 28, 1679

Endorsed. For his ever Hon^{d} Friend Mr Robert Hook at his Lodgings in Gresham College in London.[20]

This letter was read to the Royal Society at the meeting of December 4th and aroused great interest; the members were particularly enthusiastic about the experiment proposed to demonstrate the rotation of the earth. The minutes read:

"Mr. Hooke produced and read a letter of Mr. Newton to himself, dated 28th November, 1679, containing his sentiments of Mons. Mallemont's new hypothesis of the heavens; and also suggesting an experiment, whereby to try, whether the earth moves with a diurnal motion or not, viz. by the falling of a body from a considerable height, which, he alleged, must fall to the eastward of the perpendicular, if the earth moved.

"This proposal of Mr. Newton was highly approved of by the Society; and it was desired, that it might be tried as soon as could be with convenience.

20 *An Essay on Newton's Principia,* W. W. Rouse Ball, p. 141. From the original letter in Trinity College Library.

"Sir Christopher Wren supposed, that there might be something of this kind tried by shooting a bullet upwards at a certain angle from the perpendicular round every way, thereby to see whether the bullets so shot would all fall in a perfect circle round the place, where the barrel was placed. This barrel he desired might be fixed in a frame upon a plain foot, and that foot placed upon a true plain every way, and the mouth of the gun be almost in the same point over the plain, which way soever shot.

"Mr. Flamsteed hereupon alleged, that it was an observation of the gunners, that to make a ball fall into the mouth of the piece, it must be shot at eighty-seven degrees; and that he knew the reason thereof: and that it agreed with his theory: and that a ball shot perpendicularly would never fall perpendicularly: and he mentioned the recoiling of a perpendicular jet of waters. But this was conceived to arise from some mistake of the gunners, in not well taking notice of all circumstances; since a body shot perpendicularly would also descend perpendicularly; and a body shot at eight-seven degrees would fall considerably distant from the place where it was shot."[21]

It should be remembered that the Copernican theory, involving the rotation of the earth on its axis, as well as its revolution about the sun, was still a matter of doubt and dispute. One argument against the earth's rotation had been made that a body projected vertically upwards should strike the earth to the westward of its original position, as during the time of its flight the surface of the earth would have moved under it to the east. The fallacy of this objection had been shown; it is evident that the body, having originally the same horizontal velocity as the surface of the earth, would maintain this motion unaffected by its vertical flight and so would return to the same spot from which it started, if we omit the friction of the air. That the problem was not clearly understood is shown by the suggestions of Wren and Flamsteed who entirely misunderstood the fundamental principle involved in Newton's experiment. Its value will be appreciated by the following explanation. If a body be held at a considerable distance *above* the earth's surface, it will have the same angular velocity as the earth; but its linear horizontal velocity eastward will be greater than that of a point on the earth immediately beneath it, in proportion to the ratio of their distances from the centre of the earth. If, then, the body is allowed to fall freely it will preserve its initial horizontal velocity, which was greater than that

[21] Birch, Vol. III, pp. 512–513.

of the point originally beneath it, and so strike the earth to the east of that point. The experiment is theoretically a proof of the earth's rotation; but it is an exceedingly delicate one, because the distance the body can be raised above the earth is necessarily small in comparison with the earth's radius of approximately 4000 miles; the result is also greatly confused by the friction of the air.

At this point, Hooke's unfortunate vanity and jealousy again overcame his better nature. He was undoubtedly still smarting over the victory which Newton had won in the controversy about the nature of light. He could not help recognising the importance of Newton's new suggestion, but he also saw that the letter had been hastily written and contained obvious errors. Although his reply has been lost, we know that he bluntly pointed out these errors and what was worse, as it broke his agreement that their mutual criticisms should be made privately, he read his answer publicly to the Society at the same time that he sent it to Newton. At the next meeting on December 11, it was recorded in the minutes:

"Upon the mentioning of Mr. Newton's letter, and the experiment proposed in it, Mr. Hooke read his answer to him upon that subject, wherein he explained what the line described by a falling body must be supposed to be, moved circularly by the diurnal motion of the earth, and perpendicularly by the power of gravity: and he shewed, that it would not be a spiral line, as Mr. Newton seemed to suppose, but an excentrical elliptoid, supposing no resistance in the medium: but supposing a resistance, it would be an excentric ellipti-spiral, which, after many revolutions, would rest at last in the centre: that the fall of the heavy body would not be directly east, as Mr. Newton supposed; but to the south-east, and more to the south than the east. It was desired, that what was tryable in this experiment might be done with the first opportunity."[22]

Hooke was, in the main, correct in his criticism. The ball, supposing the earth to be pervious, would not fall in the spiral hastily drawn by Newton, and it would fall somewhat to the south owing to the northerly latitude of London. At the time, no one knew what the path would be after the surface of a pervious earth was reached; and what Hooke meant by "an excentrical elliptoid" can only be guessed by us, and certainly had not been calculated by him. No means could have been taken more likely to irritate Newton; he could not endure even private correction unless offered in the most tactful

[22] Birch, Vol. III, p. 516.

way; but to correct him categorically, and in public, was simply unendurable. His answer was supposed to have been destroyed, but it has fortunately been discovered just at the present writing by M. Pelseneer.[23] Its tone is dry and irritated in the extreme and, as he later wrote to Halley, "I could scarce persuade myself to answer his second letter."

Newton to Hooke

Sr

I agree with you that the body in our latitude will fall more to the south than east if the height it falls from be anything great. And also that if its gravity be supposed uniform it will not descend in a spiral to the very centre but circulate with an alternate ascent and descent made by its *vis centrifuga* and gravity alternately overbalancing one another. Yet I imagine the body will not describe an ellipsoeid but rather suit a figure as is represented [here follows a long discussion of the probable path of the body, which shows that he had not yet solved the general problem of attraction and would be of interest to mathematicians only]. . . .

Your acute letter having put me upon considering thus far the species of this curve, I might add something about its description by points *quam proxime*. But the thing being of no great moment I rather be[g] your pardon for having troubled you thus far with this second scribble wherein if you meet with anything inept or erroneous I hope you will pardon the former, and the latter I submit and leave to your correction, remaining Sr

Trin. Coll. Yor very humble Servant Is. NEWTON.
Dec 13th 1679. For Mr. Robert Hooke
at his Lodgings in
Gresham College in London.

If Hooke had a difficult temper, he at least was sincere and enthusiastic in his devotion to science, and he immediately read the letter to the Society. Its reception is given in the minutes of the meeting of December 18, 1679, together with a statement of a trial of the experiment:

23 M. Pelseneer announces his find in these words: "La lettre de Newton qu'avec la bienveillante autorisation de Mr. le Conservateur des Manuscrits du British Museum nous avons l'honneur de présenter au public est inédite. Elle fut acquise le 29 Juin 1904 à une vente chez Messrs. Sotheby & Co. et fait partie d'une collection divers catalogués sous le No. 37,021 (f. 56)." In addition to publishing the letter, M. Pelseneer gives a most careful résumé of the affair. *Cf. Isis,* Vol. XII (2), pp. 237–254, 1929.

"Mr. Hooke read his answer to Mr. Newton's former letter; as also another letter, which he had received from Mr. Newton containing his farther thoughts and examinations of what had been propounded by Mr. Hooke.

"Mr. Hooke gave also an account, that he had made three trials of the experiment propounded by Mr. Newton, and had found the ball in everyone of the said experiments fall to the south-east of the perpendicular point, found by the same ball hanging perpendicular. But the distance of it from the perpendicular point being not always the same, and the experiment having been made without doors, in the open air, nothing of certainty could be concluded from it. But he alleged, that he designed to make a trial of it within doors, where there would be less motion of the air; and he hoped to be able to do it before the next meeting of the Society."[24]

While Hooke's conduct in correcting publicly Newton's hasty suggestions was ungenerous, or at least tactless, he was apparently unconscious of the irritation he had provoked, and wrote to Newton as if all were well between them:

Hooke to Newton

Jan. 6, 1680.

Sir,

Your calculation of the curve described by a body attracted by an equal power at all distances from the centre, such as that of a ball rolling in an inverted concave cone, is right, and the two auges will not unite by about a third of a revolution; but my supposition is that the attraction always is in duplicate proportion to the distance from the centre reciprocal, and consequently that the velocity will be in a subduplicate (proportion) to the attraction, and consequently as Kepler supposes reciprocal to the distance: ....

What I mentioned in my last concerning the descent within the body of the earth was but upon the supposal of such an attraction, not that I really believe there is such an attraction to the very centre of the earth, but on the contrary I rather conceive that the more the body approaches the centre the less will it be urged by the attraction, possibly somewhat like the gravitation on a pendulum or a body moved in a concave sphere where the power continually decreases the nearer the body inclines to a horizontal motion which it hath when perpendicular under the point of suspension or in the lowest

[24] Birch, Vol. III, p. 519.

point, and there the auges are almost opposite, and the nearest approach to the centre is at about a quarter of a revolution. But in the celestial motions, the sun, earth, or central body are the cause of the attraction, and though they cannot be supposed mathematical points yet they may be conceived as physical, and the attraction at a considerable distance may be computed according to the former proportion as from the very centre....

In the mean time I must acquaint you that I have (with as much care as I could) made three trials of the experiment of the falling body, in every of which the ball fell towards the south-east of the perpendicular, and that very considerably, the least being above a quarter of an inch, but because they were not all the same I know not which was true. What the reason of the variation was I know not, whether the unequal spherical figure of the iron ball, or the motion of the air, for they were made without doors, or the insensible vibration of the ball suspended by the thread before it was cut. But it being a very noble experiment I shall not leave it before I have made a proof free from objections, of which I will send you an account. If it doth succeed there will follow several other consequences not less considerable—as, first, that all bodies will of consequence grow lighter the nearer they approach the equinoctial, the circular motion being swifter, and for the same reason the further a body is from the centre the less will be its gravitation, not only upon the account of the decrease of the attractive power which I have a long time supposed, but upon the increase of the endeavour of recess. And this gives us another way to try whether the earth has a diurnal motion though much short of what you proposed. But that I may tell you somewhat of observation, Mr Halley, when he returned from St Helena, told me that his pendulum at the top of the hill went slower than at the bottom which he was much surprised at, and could not imagine a reason. But I presently told him that he had solved me a query I had long desired to be answered but wanted opportunity, and that was to know whether the gravity did actually decrease at a greater height from the centre. To examine this decrease of attraction I have formerly made many experiments on Paul's steeple and Westminister Abbey, but none that were fully satisfactory. This will spoil the universal standard by the pendulum and the equality of pendulum clocks carried from one climate to another. And many other consequences will follow which would be too long to trouble you with at present, of which I long since gave the Society an account in writing upon the supposal of the decrease of gravity and the increase of the circular motion.

No more but that I am,

Sir, Your most humble servant,

Grm. Coll. R. H.[25]

Jan. 6, 1679/80.

Newton, by this time, was thoroughly angry and followed his usual custom of showing his displeasure by refusing to answer it and the following enthusiastic and courteous letter.

Hooke to Newton

Sir, Jan. 17, 1680.

I gave you an account by my last of the 6th instant that by the trials I had made without doors your experiment succeeded very well. I can now assure you that by two trials since made in two several places within doors it succeeded also. So that I am now persuaded the experiment is very certain, and that it will prove a demonstration of the diurnal motion of the earth as you have very happily intimated.

It now remains to know the proprieties of a curve line (not circular nor concentrical) made by a central attractive power which makes the velocities of descent from the tangent line or equal straight motion at all distances in a duplicate proportion to the distances reciprocally taken. I doubt not that by your excellent method you will easily find out what that curve must be, and its proprieties, and suggest a physical reason of this proportion. If you have had any time to consider of this matter, a word or two of your thoughts of it will be very grateful to the Society (where it has been debated) And more particularly to,

Sir,

Your very humble Servant

Gresham Coll.

Jan: 17, 1679

R. HOOKE.

For my much Honrd friend Mr Isaac Newton Lucasian Professor at his Chamber in Trinity Colledge in Cambridge.[26]

[25] The minutes of the Society are as follows: Jan. 8, 1679/80. "Mr. Hooke read another letter of his to Mr. Newton concerning some farther account of his theory of circular motion and attraction; as also several observations and deductions from that theory; as 1. That pendulum clocks must vary their velocity in several climates.

"2. That this variation must also happen at different heights in the same climate: Which last remark he confirmed by an observation of Mr. Halley at St. Helena; and 3. as a consequence of these, that a pendulum was unfit for an universal standard of measure. Hooke was desired to make his trials as soon as possible of Mr. Newton's experiment concerning the earth's diurnal motion." Birch, Vol. IV. pp. 1 and 2. This letter was copied from a rough draught in Hooke's handwriting.

[26] W. W. Rouse Ball, p. 149. From original letter in Trinity College Library.

With this letter the correspondence came to an end and there is but one more brief record of the Society[27] describing the final experiment, with the result that the ball had in its fall deviated to the east and south. The confirmation, by these experiments, of Newton's suggestion must have been purely accidental. The eastward deviation of a body from a height of twenty-seven feet, at the latitude of London, is under the most favourable circumstances only about one-fiftieth of an inch, which is entirely too small to be observed by the crude arrangements of the experiment. It has since been repeated with probable success, but, as late as the nineteenth century, Delambre, the astronomer, considered it by no means demonstrated. The southerly deviation is so small, even with the most refined methods of experimentation, that it was quite impossible for Hooke to have observed it.

One thing becomes clear from Hooke's letters; he had in some way come to the correct conclusion that the planets were held in their orbits by a force of attraction proportional to the inverse square of their distances, and also that the law of attraction apparently changed for positions within the body of the earth. But he gave no evidence of knowing that the orbit of a planet acted upon by such a force would be an ellipse, and his use of the vague term "eccentric elliptoid" indicated that he was ignorant of the true curve. An even more important fact is shown by his letters; he thought that the law of attraction must be modified if the body were near the surface of the earth as then the sizes of the attracting masses could not be neglected. Till Newton solved the general theorem, that the attraction between any two bodies is independent of their dimensions and that their masses can be concentrated at their centres, the planetary law was only approximate and could not be considered as universal.

Other men, also, had guessed the law, notably Wren and Halley; and Newton had not only guessed it, but had actually long before calculated approximately the actual force on the moon. The difference is just this; they guessed the truth but could neither prove their

27 "Mr. Hooke showed the ball, that had been let fall from the height of 27 feet, and fell into a box full of tobacco pipe-clay, sticking in the clay, upon the surface of which were made lines crossing each other: which showed the true perpendicular point indicated by the ball, when it hung suspended by a thread from the top, and how much the ball had varied from that perpendicular in its descent towards the south and east: and he explained the manner, how the same was performed in all particulars. It was desired, that this experiment might be made before a number of the society, who might be witnesses of it before the next meeting. The time appointed was the Monday following at three in the afternoon."

guess nor apply it: Newton, after his attention had been turned again to the subject, not only had the superlative merit of proving the law, but also of extending it to the whole cosmic system, and thus laid the foundation of all subsequent work in physics and chemistry.

However important this experiment and the correspondence may be in themselves, their supreme value lies rather in the fact that Newton was stirred to action by Hooke's public criticism of his blunder and began to meditate again on the law of gravitation and its applications to the whole field of mechanics. We have seen that Newton had definitely abandoned everything connected with science and had turned his attention to other affairs; these intentions should be taken at their face value as the truth. But, the problem of the falling body had turned his thoughts to the vastly greater field of celestial and terrestrial mechanics and, like a machine operating inexorably, his mind once thoroughly aroused carried him on to the end independently of his will, and contrary to his desires. It is significant of his determination to turn his life into other channels that, after he had proved rigorously the law of universal attraction and had developed a few of its essential theorems and problems, he laid his papers aside so effectually as to forget where they were, and it took all the energy and all the persuasive powers of the indefatigable Halley to induce him to repeat his calculations, and to prepare them for publication.

When the *Principia* finally appeared, its effect was astounding; first the Royal Society, and then the world, became aware that something extraordinary, something amazing, had been accomplished. So vast was the sweep of imagination, so accurate the logic, and so difficult the treatment,[28] that even the most brilliant mathematicians were unable to comprehend it; a century of comment and of verification was required before the full significance of the work was unfolded by the genius and unremitting labour of Laplace, who finally disclosed its full fruit in the absolutely mechanistic nebular hypothesis. While it was not fully understood, his contemporaries endowed Newton with god-like powers; the Marquis de l'Hôpital enquired whether he slept and ate like an ordinary mortal. Only two individuals failed to join the universal chorus: Newton, worn out and sick in mind, pled with his friends in almost abject terms to find him an administrative office, and reproached them bitterly for

[28] I found in the *Portsmouth Collection* the following note by the Rev. Dr. Derham which has not been previously published. Newton, even towards the end of his life, still "expressed himself very warmly against Hooke for claiming the discovery of the law of gravitation."

failing to satisfy his longing; and poor Hooke, when he saw the work and realised that his ambition had been thwarted again and that of all his fair dreams so few had been accomplished, made a scene in the Royal Society by claiming that he had discovered the law of gravitation and that credit for its development in the *Principia* was due to him.

When Halley reported the circumstance of Hooke's claims to Newton, he replied in two letters reviewing in detail his own side of the case and bitterly accusing Hooke of having made his life intolerable. There is little doubt of the accuracy of Newton's statement, but one would have wished that he, in the full plenitude of his fame, could have shown more tolerance and a gentler sympathy for that brave mind and spirit, housed in a suffering body. While the letters refer principally to matters connected with the preparation of the *Principia,* the portions of them which express his indignation against Hooke are given now in order to close the incident.

. . . "It is not candid," he wrote, "to require me now to confess myself, in print, then ignorant of the duplicate proportion in the heavens; for no other reason, but because he [Hooke] had told it me in the case of projectiles, and so upon mistaken grounds accused me of that ignorance. That in my answer to his first letter I refused his correspondence, told him I had laid philosophy aside, sent him only the experiment of projectiles (rather shortly hinted than carefully described), in compliment to sweeten my answer, expected to hear no further from him; could scarce persuade myself to answer his second letter; did not answer his third, was upon other things; thought no further of philosophical matters than his letters put me upon it, and therefore may be allowed not to have had my thoughts of that kind about me so well at that time. That by the same reason he concludes me then ignorant of the rest of the duplicate proportion, he may as well conclude me ignorant of the rest of that theory I had read before in his book. . . .

"Now is not this very fine? Mathematicians, that find out, settle, and do all the business, must content themselves with being nothing but dry calculators and drudges; and another, that does nothing but pretend and grasp at all things, must carry away all the invention as well of those that were to follow him, as of those that went before. Much after the same manner were his letters writ to me, telling me that gravity, in descent from hence to the centre of the earth, was reciprocally in a duplicate ratio of the altitude, that the figure described by projectiles in this region would be an ellipsis, and that all the motions of the heavens were thus to be accounted for; and this he did in such a way, as if he had found out all, and knew it most certainly. And, upon this information, I must now acknowledge, in print, I had all from him, and so did nothing myself but drudge in calculating, demonstrating, and writing, upon the inventions of this great man. And yet, after all, the first of those three things he told me of is false, and very unphilosophical; the second is as false; and the third was more than he knew, or could affirm me ignorant of by any thing that past between us in our letters.

"In short, as these things compared together show, that I was before Mr. Hooke in what he pretends to have been my master, so I learned nothing by his letters but this, that bodies fall not only to the east, but also in our latitude to the south. In the rest, his correcting and informing me was to be complain'd of. And tho' his correcting my spiral occasioned my finding the theorem, by which I afterwards examined the ellipsis, yet am I not beholden to him for any light into the business, but only for the diversion he gave me from my other studies to think on these things, and for his dogmaticalness in writing, as if he had found the motion in the ellipsis, which inclined me to try it, after I saw by what method it was to be done."[29]

These extracts will show Newton's frame of mind and his vigor of expression when he was thoroughly aroused; they are not indicative of that meekness of temper which has been carelessly ascribed to him; his apparent meekness was rather indifference to matters which smaller men would consider of importance in establishing their reputations. It is pleasant to note that he finally on December 3, 1680, wrote to Hooke: "For the trials you made of an experiment suggested by me about falling bodies, I am indebted to you thanks which I thought to have returned by word of mouth, but not having yet the opportunity must be content to do it by letter."[30]

Newton's attention having been diverted from optics and again brought back to the problem of the moon and of gravitation, he reworked more accurately his former calculations on the attraction of the earth on the moon and satisfied himself that the inverse square law would account fully for its elliptic orbit. It was mentioned be-

[29] Ball's *Essay on Newton's Principia,* pp. 157, 159, 167.

[30] Edleston, p. 264.—This passage occurs in a letter, forwarding a request of "one Dominico Casparini an Italian Doctor of Physic of the city of Lucca" who desired to dedicate a "Treatise of the Method of administering the Cortex Peruviana [quinine] in Fevers" to the Royal Society.

fore that the law he had discovered was only approximately true so long as he supposed the size of the attracting bodies affected the result. But, as a result of his blunder in describing the path of a projectile near the earth, he investigated the law of attraction of a sphere on a mass-point and solved the general theorem that the attraction of any two bodies, acted upon by a force varying inversely as the square of the distance between their centres of mass, was in all cases the same as if equal masses were concentrated at their centres. Having proved the universality of the law, he applied it to many problems of celestial and terrestrial mechanics.

It would have been possible for him to have begun at once the composition of the *Principia,* but the quarrel with Hooke had confirmed his resolution not to give any more discoveries to the world. His meditations on mechanics turned his attention to astronomy, as the field in which most of the proofs of his cosmic law were to be found. It would seem almost as if Nature heralded the birth of this great event, by announcing it with a miraculous portent for, in the latter part of the year 1680, a great and splendid comet appeared in the heavens. The seventeenth century was noteworthy for the frequency and magnificence of these Ishmaels of the solar system. The growing belief in the mechanical laws of the heavens, as portrayed by the system of Copernicus and Kepler, may have robbed these celestial visitors of much of their popular terror, and the Church may no longer have considered it obligatory to exorcise their demonic influence by prayers; but their mystery still held the public mind, and they were still believed to be a law unto themselves. Owing to the labours of two men, John Flamsteed and Newton, their waywardness came to an end, and they became subservient to the reign of mechanical law.[31]

One of the early acts of the Royal Society, after it had been granted a charter by Charles II, was to petition the King to foster the science of astronomy as a vital need for a maritime nation. According to the plan proposed, the position of Astronomer Royal was established and a grant of crown property at Greenwich was made for an observa-

[31] The great comet of 1680 is memorable for its magnificent tail which, at its greatest elongation, flamed through an arc of 70° of the heavens. It was first observed as a round nebulous mass on November 6th; it quickly developed a tail which reached a maximum on December 12th; and it faded from sight shortly after February 25th, 1681. It attained perihelion on December 8th and was then distant from the sun by the mere third of the sun's diameter, a proximity equalled by only one or two known cases. The comet was also notable because its appearance, before and after perihelion, led astronomers to believe that there had been two different comets.

tory. By a fortunate selection from amongst the amateur astronomers of the country, the Rev. John Flamsteed was given the office and directed to construct the proper buildings and instruments. He was one of the remarkable men of that great age and his genius had first been discovered by Oldenburg from an anonymous communication he had submitted to the Society. Immediately upon his appointment, he threw himself into the heart-breaking task of constructing a great observatory out of nothing, and of overcoming vexatious indifference and jealous opposition. Although he was frail in body and forced to suspend all work at frequent intervals because of persistent and excruciating headaches, he overcame all obstacles and established one of the greatest observatories in the world. The wayward King was prone to make intermittent and generous promises for the public welfare, but he was just as certain to spend the public money on his mistresses and pleasures. The building of the observatory was delayed and was not, when finished, fit for the work. As no funds were provided for instruments, Flamsteed bought a few with his own money and borrowed some from the Royal Society, against the protests of Hooke; he made with his own hands much of the equipment and would have failed even then, if he had not secured the assistance of Sir Jonas Moore. He worked prodigiously and finally produced his great catalogue of the stars in spite of lack of calculators and assistants, and in spite of a meagre salary of £100 a year which compelled him to teach pupils and to keep up his parish duties in order to live. All these he conquered by his persistence, but, at the end, he almost failed because of the determined opposition of Newton.

Flamsteed began a careful series of observations on the comet of 1680 to determine its path and came to the conclusion, contrary to the general opinion, that the two appearances were due to the same comet before and after reaching perihelion. Newton had also observed its course, and agreed with other astronomers that there had been two comets. Shortly after it disappeared he wrote to Mr. Crompton, Fellow of Jesus College, a letter to be forwarded to Flamsteed. After giving an elaborate discussion of the comet, of its appearance and path, and of the cause of the sun's action on it, he added the important sentence, "I am further suspicious that the comet of November and December which Mr. Flamsteed accounts one and the same comet were two different ones, and I find Cassini in a copy of a letter of his which Mr. Ellis showed me is of my mind." This began a long correspondence between the two men, which is a strange mixture of friendliness and hostility, and of frequency broken by long periods of silence.[32] Several letters on the subject passed between them, and Newton obstinately maintained his opinion that there had been two comets. Flamsteed felt himself to be on safe ground and that, as the recognised leading astronomer, his word should have been accepted as authoritative. He also was of a quick temper and very suspicious that others were conspiring to rob him of the fruit of his labour. His life was embittered by altercations, but much should be forgiven him because of his illness, his neglect, and his high motives. He kept careful diaries and made voluminous notes on the letters he received, so that they are a mine of information on the history of astronomy. From them, we have two accounts of his early relations with Newton and they unfortunately show the nascent jealousy which ended in a complete rupture and a public scandal. In the first account, Flamsteed wrote in the third person: "In the latter end of the year 1680 and beginning of 1681, the great comet appeared and was diligently observed by him [Flamsteed]. Before it had fully ceased to be seen, he drew all its places observed by him into a little table; which, with his thoughts concerning it, he imparted to a friend in Cambridge in a long letter, wherein he showed that the comets of November and December were probably one and the same. This being shown to Sir Isaac Newton, then only Lucasian Professor of Mathematics there, [note the touch] he wrote a letter to Mr. Flamsteed, wherein he used some arguments to prove they must be two different ones, and moreover magisterially ridiculed the contrary opinion, for which Mr. Flamsteed thought the arguments convincing and reasonable."

In his second note Flamsteed says, "Mr. Newton, who in a long letter to Mr. Crompton *for me,* argued strongly that they must be *different* comets. But (afterwards), in one to me, Sept. 19, 1685, [i.e. five years later] yielded that it was probable they were both the same. I imparted the place of the comet, deduced from my observations, by repeated calculations; and he published them in the *Principia,* 1687: but with slight acknowledgements of so laborious a work."[33]

[32] Four of the letters belong to Corpus Christi College, Oxford, and have been published in Greenstreet, pp. 35–44. The great bulk of them is included in *Flamsteed's Memoirs* by Francis Baily, London, 1835.

[33] Baily, pp. 50, 51.—Baily, who, as the vindicator of Flamsteed's reputation, was not likely to be too tender towards Newton, adds a note that he could find no foundation for

Newton, in his letter to Crompton, controverted Flamsteed's conviction that there was only one comet, although it was based on his careful observations. The introduction to the letter seems to me to be in a tone of mock modesty, and to lecture Flamsteed in a manner which was, to say the least, in bad taste: "I thank Mr. Flamsteed for this kind mention of me in his letters to Mr. Crompton, and, as I commend his wisdom in deferring to publish his hypothetical notions till they have been well considered both by his friends and himself, so I shall act the part of a friend in this paper, not objecting against it by way of opposition, but in describing what I imagine might be objected by others, and so leaving it to his consideration. If hereafter he shall please to publish his theory, and think any of the objections I propound need an answer, to prevent their being objected by others, he may describe the objections as raised by himself, or his friends in general, without taking any notice of me."[34]

The fact is, Newton was an irritating correspondent, and we have a number of complaints that he was felt to be difficult and nice to deal with. He had a habit of suddenly announcing that he did not wish to continue a subject further, and then he ceased to answer any more letters. He also was set in his opinions and, granting that he was usually right, he might have softened his statements. His eulogists were only too ready to characterise those who disagreed with his optical theories as foolish and jealous people, but they expressed no such opinion of Newton when he obstinately maintained his opinion that there had been two comets in spite of the exact observations of one of the most eminent astronomers of the time.

After Newton had reluctantly accepted Flamsteed's data and conclusions about the path of the comet, he was able in the *Principia* to establish the correct and important law, that comets were subject to the same law of gravitation as were the planets. Their waywardness and mystery were stripped from them. Their paths also were conic sections, and really ellipses which on account of their great eccentricity can be assumed to be arcs of parabolae near their perihelia. Thus comets were no longer new creations, or phenomena which disappeared, never to be observed again. Every comet, once observed, must return again with the same regularity as a planet if

Flamsteed's censure. The reader must judge whether the tone of Newton's introductory paragraph of the letter and his insistence on the existence of two comets would seem to Flamsteed as being a rebuke magisterially delivered. It would be well to recall Newton's feelings when his own work on light was criticised by those who were not well versed in that subject.

[34] Baily, *Life of Flamsteed*, p. 50.

we consider the solar system as existing alone in space. The failure to determine its orbit is due only to the difficulty of observing accurately its path during the short period of its visibility, its excessive perturbations by the planets, and the possibility of its seizure by some other star. Using Newton's idea and method, Edmond Halley plotted the orbit of the comet of 1682 with especial care. By a laborious search through the records of past appearances of comets, he found evidence that there had been a more or less regular report of a notable one at intervals of seventy-five years. He then calculated, as accurately as possible, the orbit of the comet on that assumption, and prophesied that it would appear again in August, 1757. But he cleverly concluded that it would probably be so retarded by the attraction of Jupiter that it might not be visible before the end of 1758, or the beginning of 1759. "Wherefore," says this illustrious astronomer, "if it should return according to our prediction about the year 1758, impartial posterity will not refuse to acknowledge that this was first discovered by an Englishman."[35]

The comet was actually first seen on Christmas, 1758, by an amateur astronomer, George Palitsch. It has appeared, according to schedule, twice since then, in 1835 and in 1910, the last time sadly shorn of its splendour. It is properly called Halley's comet, but behind the practical discovery lies the genius of Newton who made the discovery possible—the first dazzling prediction made from his cosmic theory. Lagrange often "asserted that Newton was the greatest genius that ever existed," and would add,—"and the most fortunate, for we can not find more than once a system of the world to establish." And I might add that the fame of many of the greatest men of science rests wholly on their verification of special problems in his synthesis.

As Newton's reputation increased, he was more and more solicited for advice and for recommendations to appointments. He was generous with both. He was very ready to recommend his friends and took trouble and time to further their interests.[36] This sympathetic side of his character is well illustrated in connection with Edward Paget's, a Fellow of Trinity College, candidacy for the mathematical mastership of Christ's Hospital. He wrote the following generous testimonial which was addressed to Flamsteed.

[35] Grant's *History of Astronomy,* p. 103.

[36] For example, I found in the Portsmouth Collection, three drafts of a letter of recommendation of a Mr. ——— as mathematical instructor in Christ's Hospital which are much interlined and corrected, and which are almost identical.

Newton to Flamsteed

Cambridge April the 3d, 1682.

These are to signify that Mr. Ellis advising with me about a person fit to be entrusted with the charge of teaching navigation to the boys of the king's late foundation, I propounded Mr. Edward Paget, Master of Arts and Fellow of Trinity College in this University, as the most promising person for this end I could think of; and that upon these considerations. He is of a temper very sober and industrious, as I am confident all that know him are ready to testify. He understands the several parts of mathematics, arithmetic, geometry, algebra, trigonometry, geography, astronomy, navigation, and which is the surest character of a true mathematical genius, learned these of his own inclination and by his own industry without a teacher: And to make him the readier in practical matters, his hand is very steady and accurate, as well as his fancy and apprehension, good; as may be seen by his writing and drawing with his pencil very well: perfections which I conceive considerable for making the boys accurate and curious in their draughts of charts, maps and prospects from sea, which joined with his knowledge in perspective and projections of the sphere will enable him to contrive and draw schemes after the best manner for the boys' apprehension, and persuades me that he will not only be dexterous and nice in the use of instruments but improve them: his long acquaintance also with variety of learning here, will help him to be methodical and clear in his teaching; which much conduces to the boys' ready and distinct apprehension of what they are taught. So that tho it may be easy to find persons valuable for some of these qualifications, yet considering him in all respect as I could not think of any other person in this University so fit in my opinion to be entrusted with a place of so great concern as that of preparing boys to make more skilful navigators than formerly, so I believe it will be difficult to meet with fitter persons abroad for that purpose. These things made me forward to propound him to the electors; but to compare him with other competitors and choose the best I leave wholly to their judgement.

Is. NEWTON, Profess. Math. Luc.[37]

Not content with this assistance, he also wrote to Collins to ask for his help. Collins naturally complied, and dwelt on the weight "the

37 Edleston, p. liv.

recommendation of the greatest mathematician of the age ought to have with the electors." With his testimonial, Newton provided the candidate with a cordial note of introduction to Flamsteed.

Newton to Flamsteed

Trin. Coll. April 3, 1682.

Sir,

The bearer hereof, Mr. Edward Paget, being competitor for the mastership over the boys of the king's foundation in Christ's Hospital for teaching navigation, and having no mathematical acquaintance in London, I conceived it might help forward his design to be introduced to such acquaintance that, by conversing with them, he might make himself known. And you being a person most eminent in your deserts, as well as by your place, I have therefore taken upon me the freedom to salute you by him: begging this favour that, as you find him by converse, so you would represent him upon occasions; or, if it be in your way, introduce him to other mathematicians, who, after conversing with him, may have occasion of representing him to the electors. I have given him a character according to my judgement of him, which he will show you: but it will be more satisfactory to know him by converse. If you please also to let him have your advice in what he is to do, you will, in all this, much oblige your affectionate and humble servant,

Is. Newton.[38]

Flamsteed noted on the back of this letter. "Mr. Paget was chosen master of the mathematical school on my recommendation: for I found an able mathematician of him to the hospital about a month after. And the hospital governors were so well pleased with the choice, that, to show their gratitude, they sent me a staff, and made me of their number the summer following.—Ebrietati deinde post annos 7 nimium addictus immemor officii, pueros neglexit, in Flandriam transiit, deposuit mimas, in Indiam tandem navigavit: faxit Deus ut sanus et sobrius redeat."

In the interval before dissipation lost him his place and drove him as far as India, his name occurs three times in connection with Newton. He is said to have carried Newton's demonstration of the law of gravitation to Halley in London, in 1684; three years later Halley sent to him one of the few presentation copies of the *Principia*

[38] Baily, p. 125.

at the author's request; and Newton mentioned that he had pointed out a few *errata* in the book. Then this friend of two great men, having acquired a certain immortality because of his contact with them, drops out of sight. We can only echo Flamsteed's pious wish that God may have restored him to a wholesome and sober life.

The next five years centre about the composition of the *Principia*. There can have been few, if any, instances in history of such profound and sustained mental effort, or of such a monumental work accomplished in so short a time. He left Cambridge only for brief and infrequent intervals. Biot states that Newton was present at a meeting of the Royal Society, in London, in June, 1682, and there learned of the accurate measurement of a degree of longitude recently executed in France, by Picard. Having noted down this length, he returned home immediately and, taking up his former calculation on the attractive force on the moon which he had made in 1665, now obtained the correct result verifying the law of gravitation.[39] It is a matter of great importance in the history of the discovery of the law of gravitation to know when Newton became acquainted with Picard's measurement, and whether he really needed to know it. The subject must be discussed fully later, but a few words should be said now. Biot is correct in saying it was discussed at the meeting of June 7, 1682.[40] But there is doubt in my mind whether he was then present. His Muniment Room record shows that he left Cambridge on May 10, but not again later in the year; unfortunately his *Redit* is not given. He certainly very rarely went to London, and then for only a few days, so that if he did go there at this time he must have remained a full month, or else have stopped there during a course of other visits, both of which were contrary to his habit. He was in Cambridge on June 20 as we know by his letter to Dr. Briggs. Also, Biot says the measurement had been made recently. The fact is, it had been published in Paris eleven years previously, in 1671,[41] and it was discussed several times in the Royal Society, notably in 1672. At that time Oldenburg was supplying Newton regularly with its *Transactions,* and an item so important for his work would have slight chance of escaping his attention.[42] It is certain that he attended the meeting of May 27, 1683, for Sir Thomas Molyneux wrote that he had been a guest then, saw Halley make some magnetical experi-

[39] Biot, p. 17.

[40] Birch, IV, p. 150.

[41] The *Biographia Britannica* erroneously gives the date as 1679.

[42] An exhaustive discussion of this point has been made by Professor Cajori, the results of which will be given in Chapter IX.

ments, and had also the opportunity of seeing several noted men, amongst whom was Newton.[43]

There seems to be little doubt that Cambridge was lagging behind Oxford and London in its cultivation of the new natural philosophy. If we omit Newton, who was a solitary worker, and his friends, the group of Platonists in Christ's College, there was little interest except in the traditional learning. We can imagine that this indifference had been lamented by the little group who met to discuss philosophy and science. The matter was brought to a focus by Paget, who tried to organise a philosophical society similar to the one at Oxford. The plan, however, fell through as the following letter explains:

Newton to Aston

[Sir,]

The design of a philosophical meeting here Mr. Paget, when last with us, pushed forward, and I concurred with him, and engaged Dr. More to be of it, and others were spoke to partly by me, partly by Mr. Charles Montague; but that, which chiefly dashed the business, was the want of persons willing to try experiments, he whom we chiefly relied on refusing to concern himself in that kind: and more what to add further on this business I know not, but only this, that I should be very ready to concur with any persons for promoting such a design, so far as I can do it without engaging the loss of my own time in those things.

I thank you for entering in your *Register* my notions about motion. I designed them for you before now, but the examining several things has taken a greater part of my time than I expected, and a great deal of it to no purpose. And now I am to go into Lincolnshire for a month or six weeks. Afterwards I intend to finish it as soon as I can conveniently, Etc.[44]

[Is. NEWTON.]

Cambridge, Feb. 23, 1684/5.

The letter is valuable as it shows who were Newton's closest friends at this time. I think we can make a shrewd guess that the person who refused to try experiments was Newton, himself, for who else was there in Cambridge to make them. It is fortunate that

[43] Weld, Vol. I, p. 293.
[44] From the copy in the Letter Book of the Royal Society (Vol. X, p. 28). The original has not been found. (Rigaud, *Essay*, App. p. 24). Aston is the early friend of Newton and was now Secretary of the Society.

he was not induced to fritter away his time on the concerns of a society as had been the fate of Hooke; we might have had a society, but we should have missed far greater things. Such societies do foster the advancement of science; they help the rank and file, but they ruin the man of original genius who becomes engrossed in their activities.

Work was now pressing so heavily on Newton that he wrote to Mr. Walker, who was schoolmaster at Grantham, to engage for him an assistant and amanuensis. A certain Humphrey Newton of that town was recommended, and acted in that capacity from 1685 to 1690.[45] Conduitt, when he was collecting materials for a life of his uncle, applied to the secretary for his reminiscences. We thus have some intimate facts of Newton's manner of living during this most important period.

Humphrey Newton to Conduitt

Sir,—Receiving yours, I return as perfect and faithful an account of my deceased friend's transactions, as possibly does at this time occur to my memory. Had I had the least thought of gratifying after this manner Sir Isaac's friends, I should have taken a much stricter view of his life and actions.

In the last year of King Charles II, Sir Isaac was pleased, through the mediation of Mr. Walker, (then schoolmaster at Grantham,) to send for me up to Cambridge, of whom I had the opportunity, as well as honour, to wait of [sic] for about five years. In such time he wrote his *Principia Mathematica,* which stupendous work, by his order, I copied out before it went to the press. After the printing, Sir Isaac was pleased to send me with several of them in presents to some of the heads of Colleges, and others of his acquaintance, some of which (particularly Dr. Babington of Trinity) said that they might study seven years before they understood any thing of it. His carriage then was very meek, sedate, and humble, never seemingly angry, of profound thought, his countenance mild, pleasant, and comely. I cannot say I ever saw him laugh but once, which was at that passage which Dr. Stukeley mentioned in his letter to your honour, which put me in mind of the Ephesian philosopher, who laughed only once in his lifetime, to see an ass eating thistles when

[45] Brewster, who quotes the letter (Vol. II, p. 90), wrongly gives these dates as 1683–1689. H. Newton, in his letter, stated that he became secretary "in the last year of King Charles II, and held the position for about five years."

plenty of grass was by. He always kept close to his studies, very rarely went a visiting, and had as few visitors, excepting two or three persons, Mr. Ellis, Mr. Laughton of Trinity, and Mr. Vigani, a chemist, in whose company he took much delight and pleasure at an evening when he came to wait upon him. I never knew him to take any recreation or pastime either in riding out to take the air, walking, bowling, or any other exercise whatever, thinking all hours lost that was [sic] not spent in his studies, to which he kept so close that he seldom left his chamber except at term time, when he read in the schools as being Lucasianus Professor, where so few went to hear him, and fewer that understood him, that ofttimes he did in a manner, for want of hearers, read to the walls. Foreigners he received with a great deal of freedom, candour, and respect. When invited to a treat, which was very seldom, he used to return it very handsomely, and with much satisfaction to himself. So intent, so serious upon his studies, that he ate very sparingly, nay, ofttimes he has forgot to eat at all, so that, going into his chamber, I have found his mess untouched, of which, when I have reminded him, he would reply—'Have I?' and then making to the table, would eat a bit or two standing, for I cannot say I ever saw him sit at table by himself. At some seldom entertainments, the Masters of Colleges were chiefly his guests. He very rarely went to bed till *two* or *three* of the clock, sometimes not until *five* or *six,* lying about *four* or *five* hours, especially at spring and fall of the leaf, at which times he used to employ about six weeks in his elaboratory, the fire scarcely going out either night or day; he sitting up one night and I another, till he had finished his chemical experiments, in the performances of which he was the most accurate, strict, exact. What his aim might be I was not able to penetrate into, but his pains, his diligence at these set times made me think he aimed at something beyond the reach of human art and industry. I cannot say I ever saw him drink either wine, ale, or beer, excepting at meals, and then but very sparingly. He very rarely went to dine in the hall, except on some public days, and then if he has not been minded, would go very carelessly, with shoes down at heels, stockings untied, surplice on, and his head scarcely combed.

As for his *Optics* being burned, I knew nothing of it but as I had heard from others, that accident happening before he writ his *Principia.* He was very curious in his garden, which was never out of order, in which he would at some seldom time take a short walk or two, not enduring to see a weed in it. On the left end of the garden was his elaboratory, near the east end of the chapel, where he at these set times employed himself in with a great deal of satisfaction and delight. Nothing extraordinary, as I can remember, happened in making his experiments; which, if there did, he was of so sedate and even temper, that I could not in the least discover it. He very seldom went to the chapel, that being the time he chiefly took his repose; and, as for the afternoon, his earnest and indefatigable studies retained him, so that he scarcely knew the house of prayer. Very frequently, on Sundays, he went to St. Mary's church, especially in the forenoon. I knew nothing of the writings which your honour sent, only that it is his own hand, I am very certain of, believing he might write them at some leisure hours, before he set upon his more serious and weighty matters. Sir Isaac at that time had no pupils nor any chamber-fellow, for that, I would presume to think, would not have been agreeable to his studies. He was only once disordered with pains at the stomach, which confined him for some days to his bed, which he bore with a great deal of patience and magnanimity, seemingly indifferent either to live or die. He seeing me much concerned at his illness, bid me not trouble myself; 'For if,' said he, 'I die, I shall leave you an estate,' which he then mentioned.

Sir, this is what I can at present recollect, hoping it may in some measure satisfy your queries.

My wife at this time is brought to bed of a son, whom I intend to nominate after my dear deceased friend. Would you please to honour me so far as to substitute Dr. Stukeley to stand as witness. I should take it as a very singular favour, and would very much oblige, Sir, your most humble and obedient servant,

HUMPHREY NEWTON.[46]

Grantham, January 17, '27/8.

Owing to the lapse of time, about forty years, he was unable to recall much of any value. After a month's delay he evidently remembered other details, and their past daily life grew to be more distinct. He consequently sent Conduitt a second letter.

Humphrey Newton to Conduitt

Sir,—I return your honour a great many thanks for the favour you have done me in deputing Dr. Stukeley to stand in your stead as

[46] *Portsmouth Collection.* Also quoted by Brewster, Vol. II, p. 91.

witness to my son. It is out of my sphere to make any grateful return, therefore doubt not but your goodness will in that point excuse my deficiency. I have bethought myself about Sir Isaac's life as much as possibly I can. About 6 weeks at spring, and 6 at the fall, the fire in the elaboratory scarcely went out, which was well furnished with chemical materials as bodies, receivers, heads, crucibles, etc., which was [sic] made very little use of, the crucibles excepted, in which he fused his metals; he would sometimes, tho' very seldom, look into an old mouldy book which lay in his elaboratory, I think it was titled *Agricola de Metallis,* the transmuting of metals being his chief design, for which purpose antimony was a great ingredient. Near his elaboratory was his garden, which was kept in order by a gardener. I scarcely ever saw him do anything as pruning, etc., at it himself. When he has sometimes taken a turn or two, has made a sudden stand, turn'd himself about, run up the stairs like another Archimedes, with an εὕρηκα fall to write on his desk standing without giving himself the leisure to drew a chair to sit down on. At some seldom times when he designed to dine in the hall, would turn to the left hand and go out into the street, when making a stop when he found his mistake, would hastily turn back, and then sometimes instead of going into the hall, would return to his chamber again. When he read in the schools he usually staid about half an hour; when he had no auditors, he commonly returned in a 4th part of that time or less. Mr. Laughton who was then the library keeper of Trin. Coll. resorted much to his chamber; if he commenced Dr. afterwards I know not. His telescope, which was at that time, as near as I could guess, was near 5 foot long, which he placed at the head of the stairs going down into the garden, butting towards the east. What observations he might make I know not, but several of his observations about comets and the planets may be found scattered here and there in a book entitled *The Elements of Astronomy,* by Dr. David Gregory. He would with great acuteness answer a question, but would very seldom start one. Dr. Boerhaave (I think it is), Prof. Lpzg., in some of his writings, speaking of Sir Is.: "That man," says he, "comprehends as much as all mankind besides." In his chamber he walked so very much that you might have thought him to be educated at Athens among the Aristotelian sect. His brick furnaces, *pro re nata,* he made and altered himself without troubling a brick-layer. He very seldom sat by the fire in his chamber excepting that long frosty winter, which made him creep to it against his will. I can't say I ever saw him wear a night gown, but his wearing clothes that he put off at night, at night do I say, yea, rather towards the morning, he put on again at his rising. He never slept in the daytime that I ever perceived; I believe he grudged the short time he spent in eating and sleeping. Ἀνέχου καὶ ἀπέχου may well and truly be said of him, he always thinking with Bishop Saunderson, temperance to be the best physic. In a morning, he seemed to be as much refreshed with his few hours' sleep as though he had taken a whole night's rest. He kept neither dog nor cat in his chamber, which made well for the old woman his bedmaker, she faring much the better for it, for in a morning she has sometimes found both dinner and supper scarcely tasted of, which the old woman has very pleasantly and mumpingly gone away with. As for his private prayers I can say nothing of them; I am apt to believe his intense studies deprived him of the better part. His behaviour was mild and meek, without anger, peevishness, or passion, so free from that, that you might take him for a stoic. I have seen a small paste-board box in his study set against the open window, no less as one might suppose than a 1000 guin. in it crowded edgeways, whether this was suspicion or carelessness I cannot say; perhaps to try the fidelity of those about him. In winter time he was a lover of apples, and sometimes at a night would eat a small roasted quince. His thoughts were his books; tho' he had a large study seldom consulted with them. When he was about 30 years of age his grey hairs was [sic] very comely, and his smiling countenance made him so much the more graceful. He was very charitable, few went empty handed from him. Mr. Pilkington, [his nephew-in-law] who lived at Market Overton, died in a mean condition, (tho' formerly he had a plentiful estate,) whose widow with 5 or 6 children Sir Is. maintained several years together. He commonly gave his poor relations, (for no family so rich but there is some poor among them,) when they apply'd themselves to him, no less than 5 guineas, as they themselves told me. He has given the porters many a shilling not for letting him [in?] at the gates at unreasonable hours, for that he abhorred, never knowing him out of his chamber at such times. No way litigious, not given to law or vexatious suits, taking patience to be the best law, and a good conscience the best divinity. Says Seneca, somebody will demonstrate which way comets wander, why they go so far from the rest of the celestial bodies, how big, and what sort of bodies they are, which had he been contemporary with Sir Is. he might have seen this prophecy of his fulfilled by the wonder of his age. Could your Honour pick somethings out of this indigested mass worthy to be inserted into the life of so great, so good, and so illustrious a person as Sir Isaac Newton, it would be of infinite satisfaction to him, Sir, who is your Honour's most humb. and most obedient servant,

H. NEWTON.[47]

Feb. 14, 1727/8, Grantham.

While these letters are not to be despised, as they give us at least a valuable first hand information of Newton, they are exasperatingly disappointing. It is almost incredible that an educated man could occupy such a position for so long and not make notes of what took place or remember many more details of Newton's life and habits. He must have known, even if not till later years, that he had been in intimate intercourse with a man whose every action would be of interest to the world. It merely confirms Dr. Johnson's conviction that "Biography is rarely well executed. They only who live with a man can write his life with any genuine exactness and discrimination; and few people who have lived with a man know what to remark about him."[48] It is one of the extraordinary and inexplicable facts of Newton's life that those who lived with him should not only have neglected to write their memoirs or remembered his conversation, but also have been surprised when their recollections were desired.

The letters omit much of the information we should like to have. The description of Newton's appearance and character is probably reliable. The statement of his ability to work incessantly with little sleep or food and his absent-mindedness is undoubtedly correct. It should be remembered, however, that the secretary knew him only during an exceptional time. The impression is rather general that this was his normal custom of life, but the evidence is pretty clear that he was, on the whole, systematic and careful in his habits. We must remember also that the work of these years broke his health, and seems to have exhausted his creative ability. The amount of time,

[47] The two letters of H. Newton are preserved in the *Portsmouth Collection*. I also found an unpublished anecdote in a letter to Conduitt written by Stukeley who had been present at the christening of the Isaac mentioned in the letters of H. Newton. "Good Sir,—Last Thursday we performed the initiation ceremony upon the young Sr Isaac Newton. The Dr. [Humphrey Newton] gave us a very handsome entertainment and your health and your Lady's were frequently remembered. I gave the midwife a guinea, the chief nurse half a guinea, and eleven shillings away among the servants."

[48] Birkbeck Hill's edition of *Boswell's Johnson,* Vol. II, p. 446.

he is said to have spent in his chemical laboratory, makes the rapidity with which he wrote the *Principia* even more extraordinary. It may be that chemical work was omitted during the eighteen months he was actually engaged in its composition.

His life was undoubtedly lonely, but he did have more associates than are mentioned, and it is odd that Masters of Colleges should have been such favoured guests. Of the friends mentioned, Mr. Ellis was afterwards Master of Caius College, Mr. Laughton was a great personal friend of Montague and was afterwards Canon of Worcester and Lichfield. Mr. Vigani was a native of Verona who drifted to Cambridge and taught chemistry there for twenty years. In 1702, he was made Professor of Chemistry and six years later Bentley, then Master of Trinity, fitted up an old lumber room as an elegant chemical laboratory and attached him to his college. But the plan for a permanent school of chemistry failed.[49] It is of this same Vigani, that this anecdote was told by Newton's niece, Catherine Barton, to show her uncle's purity of mind: "Upon Vigani's (with whom he was very intimate, and took pleasure in discoursing with him on chemistry) telling him a loose story about a nun, he broke off all acquaintance with him."[50]

Newton seems to have rivalled Lord Chesterfield in the rarity of laughing. "When Sir Isaac once laughed, 'twas upon occasion of asking a friend, to whom he had lent Euclid to read, what progress he had made in that author, and how he liked him? He answered by desiring to know what use and benefit in life that study would be to him. Upon which Sir Isaac was very merry."[51]

Like every one else who came in contact with Newton, his secretary was especially impressed with his frequent and great generosity. It must have been a notable trait. But we must put the open box, with a thousand guineas, in the class of fictions or gross exaggerations. How could Newton have collected such a great sum of gold or have carelessly left it about, when, without any subsequent increase in income, he had ten years previously been grateful for being excused from paying the dues of the Royal Society of a shilling a week? To have used it for a bait "to try the fidelity of those about him" does not consort with his frugality and business carefulness.

49 Monk's *Life of Bentley*, 2d ed., Vol. I, p. 204.
50 *Portsmouth Collection*. It is signed C. C.—Also quoted by Brewster, Vol. II, p. 93.
51 *Portsmouth Collection*. Also quoted by Brewster, Vol. II, p. 91.

CHAPTER VIII

THE MECHANISTIC HYPOTHESIS FROM DEMOCRITUS TO NEWTON

THE history of natural philosophy from the classic period down to the present time has been largely a development of the mechanistic hypothesis. In essence, this hypothesis assumes that all phenomena are due to the positions and motions of an universal substance which has an objective existence unaffected by our perceptions.[1] Its chief difficulty, and if I may say so its ultimate failure, has been to find some cause which will explain how an essentially inert substance can create in the mind those manifold and complex perceptions which are received from the external world. That is, what is the cause of motion and action, and how can they be differentiated into the various categories of phenomena?

However we may attempt to explain the cause of action of substance, the fact remains that we accept, as the fundamental expression of action, Newton's law that all bodies mutually attract each other with a force which varies inversely as a function of the distances between their centres of mass. And, in accepting that as a fact, we must give to Newton the supreme honour of creating out of the guesses of his predecessors an almost perfect theory of mechanics.

At least to the present time, the science of mechanics most nearly satisfies our needs for a science, in that it deals with sensible bodies from which have been abstracted all their attributes except the seemingly universal one of mass, or force of inertia (the *vis inertiae* of Newton); and its laws, dealing as they do with only position and motion, lend themselves readily to mathematical expression. We can, on the basis of satisfying our desire for qualitative classification and quantitative measurement, rate the sciences according to the degree

[1] There are but few treatises on scientific subjects which do not discuss the atomic and mechanistic hypotheses. Out of this vast literature, the following may be consulted with profit. Whittaker, *History of the Æther,* Dublin, 1910; Abel Rey, *Théorie de la physique,* Paris, 1923; Hannequin, *Hypothèse des atomes,* Paris, 1899; Stallo, *Concepts of Modern Physics,* London, 1900; Karl Pearson, *Grammar of Science,* London, 1911; Eddington, *Nature of the Physical World,* Cambridge, 1929; More, *Limitations of Science,* New York, 1915; lastly, that most scholarly and exhaustive *Geschichte der Atomistik,* 2 vols., by Lasswitz, Leipzig, 1890.

with which their laws are expressible in mechanical terms. According to such a classification, subjects which consider the problems of consciousness and mind are not sciences at all; and the biological sciences lag far behind physics and chemistry in their ability to predict future events with quantitative accuracy.

This does not mean that natural philosophy has advanced only along mechanistic lines, or that all men of science have been mechanists. For example, out of many which could be cited, Aristotle in classic, and Bergson in modern, times definitely opposed the mechanistic theory; while Plato restricted it to purely objective phenomena, and taught that the subjective world of ideas lay entirely outside the field of science. But I do assert that the main stream of scientific thought has flowed in the channel formed by the conflation of observation and mechanistic formulation.

The mechanistic method began with Leucippus and Democritus. It was opposed by Plato and Aristotle, although they were influenced by it. It languished during the Middle Ages; was revived at the Renaissance; and completed by Newton. In modern times, it has been so expanded that it is now the dominant factor in thought. The first explicit statement of a mechanistic universe was made by Democritus, said to be the most learned of the Greeks. In its essential ideas, his atomic theory has persisted unchanged, but its details, as he conceived them, have become entirely negligible with the increase of experimental knowledge.

Democritus first postulated that substance ultimately consisted of an indefinitely large number of indivisible atoms. Thus, all bodies differ only because of the number and relative positions and motions of their constituent atoms. As the beginning of a reign of orderliness from what may be termed chaos, which is the definition of creation, he and his disciples assumed that the atoms all had a primordial motion towards a fixed point, the common centre of the earth and of the universe, and that they differed amongst themselves only in size, shape, speed, and sequence. In addition to this downward motion, they were supposed to possess a sideways slip, which resulted in innumerable impacts between them and produced rotatory motions, the cause of variety. Thus all bodies are mere chance aggregations of atoms which in their flight come together and maintain their contiguity by a fortunate provision of hook-like antennae.[2]

[2] In giving this short statement of the atomic theory of Democritus, I am well aware that it is almost impossible to separate his own ideas from the interpretations and additions given

It was a marvelous prophecy, or guess; the modern physicist, the chemist, the biologist, and the behaviouristic psychologist still postulate the same atomic universe as did Democritus. We have vastly extended our experimental knowledge of phenomena, but the essential nature of substance and the cause of action is still a complete mystery. Our atom, or electron, is still but the name of a thing endowed with all the potential properties which it is supposed to explain and, because of our vastly increased knowledge, the inadequacy of the electron is more apparent to us than the atom of Democritus was to the Greeks. As Professor Armstrong caustically remarked, "we are told that the electron does everything but *how* it does anything we are not informed."

Reduced to its simplest terms, the atomic theory, as interpreted by the Epicureans, is the expression of the laws of probability of chance impacts. But, the absolute denial of purpose, or design, in the laws of nature is so repugnant to the mind that even its founder, whose name is a synonym for materialism and necessity, can hardly be called a pure mechanist since there are indications that he gave his atoms a tendency, or purpose, to move. At least, when he declared that the souls of men were but atoms of a finer size and of a more nimble motion, he either denied the attribute of will and purpose to the soul, or else endowed its atoms with the power of choice. And his disciple, Empedocles, certainly maintained the principle of choice, under the terms of love and hate, as guiding the creation of living beings.[3]

It was because of their search for a principle of design that the two greatest Greek thinkers, Plato and Aristotle, opposed the ideas of Democritus. The much heralded opposition of the Church to science, during the Middle Ages, was limited to the interdict of the teaching, and belief in, the atomic theory and a mechanistic universe. And the age-long conflict between science and religion narrows down

to it by his disciples, the Stoics and Epicureans. It is likely Democritus supposed his atoms to move in all directions and that the uniformly downward motion, the sideways slip, and the hook-like antennae, were later modifications.

[3] The atomic theory of Democritus has been generally characterised as synonymous with mechanistic materialism and fortuitous chance. It is well to point out that Professor Hack (*God in Greek Philosophy,* Princeton Press, 1931) takes an opposing view: "The fact that Leucippus and Democritus are habitually called 'Atomists' is responsible for the dense cloud of misunderstanding that has enveloped their doctrine" (p. 128). This false conception he lays at the door of Aristotle, who "attributed to other philosophers opinions which are obvious fabrications of his own." According to Professor Hack, Democritus believed there were, in addition to inert material atoms, also an "infinite number of indivisible Beings that possessed Spherical Form with Mind, Psyche, Fire, and God" (p. 133). He quotes passages from the classical commentators to prove that these spherical atoms animate even stones, and direct otherwise chance motions.

to the same question. There can be no doubt that the logical conclusion of this hypothesis is a denial of every form of free will; and in that sense it is atheistic. Even today there are few, and one may almost venture to say no, men of science who are willing to live in the unbreathable atmosphere of such a stultifying philosophy. In their studies and laboratories, they may theoretically subscribe to, and search for, rigorous and mechanical laws of nature, but their daily lives and actions are based on the conviction of free will and purpose.

Although Plato was singularly indifferent to experimental science, and has contributed little or nothing to its body of knowledge, he nevertheless in the *Timaeus*[4] grasped one of the fundamental principles of the scientific method and pointed out its inherent limitations. According to his philosophy, the world was created according to a plan or design by the Demiurgos or Worldbuilder; and man, being endowed with an innate knowledge of this plan, can by the right sort of education penetrate more and more deeply into a just knowledge of the Creator's design and laws. There are thus two realms, the real world of the mind and the apparent world of objective phenomena. Since our contact with the phenomenal world comes to us only through our fallible sensations the best information we can obtain of objects is limited to an opinion, or conjecture, which cannot be based on conviction, or strengthened by judgement. For example, our own observations can never be exact, nor can we be certain that our impressions closely correspond with those of others; our picture of the external world is a mere seeming one which must be modified to conform to the real, or mental, world of ideas based on the divine laws. A simple illustration will show how essentially true is this definition of the scientific method. If there be a fundamental law of science, it is that substance is conservative. Without such a conviction there is no more stability in the world than in the tricks of legerdemain where rabbits pop out of a hat. If one enquires of the average student what is the proof of this law the answer will invariably be that if one weighs a candle, enclosed in a box, before and after burning it, the weights will be the same. In brief, the claim is made that the law is not a matter of faith in the orderliness of nature

[4] There must always remain a doubt whether Plato is giving his own ideas in the *Timaeus,* or whether he is, for the most part, interpreting the philosophy of the Pythagoreans as it was understood by an educated Athenian. The appearance of Socrates in a minor rôle lends support to the belief that he did not regard the essay as an integral part of his own philosophic system. This point of view is taken by A. E. Taylor in his *Commentary on Plato's Timaeus,* Oxford, 1928.

cal system in conformity with our mental ideas. And both Plato and modern science agree that the laws of the objective world can be expressed fully only in mathematics.

So far as the physical world is concerned, Plato accepted an atomic theory in which the original Democritean atom was replaced by the four elementary substances introduced by Empedocles,—earth and fire which provide us with tangibility and visibility, and water and air which are symbolically linked to the other two by a mathematical law of mean proportion. However, these substances are but names for elementary geometrical solids built up from triangles and squares, —the cube, the tetrahedron, the octahedron, and the icosahedron. Although Plato added nothing to experimental science, yet his clearly expressed doctrine, that to the determination of things by mathematical formulæ is linked at the same time their reality and their perceptibility, was an undying service to science. Unfortunately, the neo-Platonists, instead of developing this fruitful idea, turned rather to the mysticism of the *Timaeus*; and science, till the Renaissance, looked to Aristotle as its guide.

In estimating the influence of Aristotle on science, it must be remembered that he was an almost unquestioned dictator of scientific opinion during the Middle Ages, and that he was opposed to the atomic and mechanistic theories. He was by temperament a biologist, indifferent to experimental physics, and suspicious of mathematical logic. Our discussion of his influence must be here limited to his ideas on physics in general, and on the mechanistic theory in particular. As a biologist we may well leave the estimate of his genius to the greatest of all naturalists, Darwin, who at the end of his life wrote to Dr. Ogle to acknowledge his translation of Aristotle's *De Partibus Animalium:* "From quotations which I had seen, I had a high notion of Aristotle's merits, but I had not the most remote notion what a wonderful man he was. Linnæus and Cuvier have been my two gods, though in very different ways, but they were mere schoolboys to old Aristotle."[6] But when we consider his influence as a physicist, it is more than probable that, on the whole, it was harmful in its effect on later thinkers. He has to his credit no body of experimental discoveries in physics, as he had in biology, nor does he seem to have thought them necessary. He discarded the atomic theory and mathematical formulation of quantitative measurement, and substituted a set of preconceived metaphysical principles deeply

[6] *Life of Darwin,* by Francis Darwin, Vol. II, p. 427. Appleton, 1887.

tinged with animism, such as: nature *abhors* a vacuum; matter *seeks* its own kind.[7]

When considering the natural philosophy of Aristotle, we should not forget that in the essential belief in the reality of the ideal universe he agreed with Plato. Both also regarded the universe as a manifestation of design and purpose; but Aristotle made a less distinction between the designer and the designed. While he also agreed with his teacher in postulating the existence of elementary substantial bodies, he accused Plato of assuming those elements to be mere geometric forms.

The discussion of Aristotle's scientific ideas is made more difficult because they are scattered in several books. Apparently, he pursued two main lines of thought, which are irreconcilable with each other: in the one, he viewed the universe as variations of substance; and, in the other, as a dynamic manifestation of motion. He seems to have foreseen the present cleavage between those physicists who start from the material atom, and those who build on atoms of energy.

In his first scheme, Aristotle identified substance with space, as did later Descartes, and for the same reason, since they both denied the possibility of a vacuum. The essential element of a material body is form, but the existence of bodies does not result from an act of creation out of nothing, rather it is the passage from a potentiality (*dynamis*) of substance to become form. This conception of potentiality is, perhaps, his greatest contribution to science. By it, the physicist accounts for the beginning of the downward motion of a body which has been raised to a height, and it is the essential idea in the laws of the conservation of energy, and of matter. Aristotle also accepted the four elementary forms of earth, water, air, and fire; but these were not fixed and could be changed one into another by the active agents of heat and cold, moisture and dryness. As he was a dualist, he made a definite break between the living and the inanimate worlds. To provide for life and the soul (*psyche*), he added a fifth, or quintessence. As matter is the form of physical bodies, so

[7] My use of the word metaphysical, in this sense, is frequently criticised as if I attributed to metaphysics only crude guesses. This is not at all my idea, but I know no other word to express a fundamental difference between the physical method of deduction from objective experimentation, and what I designate as metaphysical deduction from subjective experience. For example, the study of light is a physical problem and ends with the absorption of the light energy by the retina; whereas, the study of sight, I term metaphysical, as it involves sense perception and mental interpretation. Perhaps, the term psychological could be used, but psychology is generally defined as an objective and scientific study of the sensations and of the mind; and I wish to distinguish between the mental interpretation of material phenomena, and of sense perceptions.

the soul is the form of living bodies. In the plant world, the soul is limited to generative and nutritive functions; in animals, the appetitive function is added; in man, alone, there is also the rational soul.

Although Aristotle remained true to the Platonic philosophy of ideal universals and viewed the universe as the result of design, yet he was so essentially a scientist by temperament that he failed to distinguish sharply between the Designer and the designed. As the modern scientist substitutes Nature, or natural law, for God, so he constantly sought for a mechanistic scheme for the objective world; thus, he proposed motion, or change, as the efficient cause of phenomena. While he classified change in four categories,—spatial, qualitative, quantitative, and temporal,—all changes are dependent on motion in space. So far his mechanistic world of material elements, motion, and energy, is truly modern, since, for example, physicists explain light, heat, etc., as mechanical motion, and many biologists attribute life to the same cause. But, when he attempted to connect his active cause, mechanical energy, with his final cause, the Designer, he was forced to introduce the principle of animism and floundered in a morass of inconsistency.

In his mechanistic scheme, Aristotle assumed that the heavens are pure, celestial substance, the quintessence, and that, since the circle is the only invariable curve, they of necessity eternally revolve in that path. He, first, placed the stars in one outermost shell which revolves daily about the stationary earth as a fixed centre. This shell is the *Primum Mobile* whose perpetual rotation is the cause of all other motions. Next, each planet is attached to a concentric shell whose radius corresponds with its distance from the earth. The rotary motion of these secondary shells is caused by having their polar axes embedded in the substance of the circumjacent shell. That of the moon, being nearest to the earth, is the least in diameter; and all told, there are fifty-five of these shells.

Aristotle's first insuperable difficulty was to account for the motion of the *Primum Mobile*. This, he accomplished by making God the final cause of motion; for this purpose he was designated the Prime Mover, or the Unmoved Mover; and, by direct linkage, produces the rotation of the *Primum Mobile* and thus, indirectly, of all the other spheres. If we ask, how can that, which is itself unmovable, cause motion? The answer was, by love and desire. And if we again ask, how can love be a cause of motion? We find that Aristotle abandoned the mechanistic hypothesis and endowed the *Primum Mobile* with soul; and the heavenly bodies are living being. As they are necessarily perfect, they desire a life as like the everlasting and unchanging spiritual existence of the Unmoved Mover as possible. Since they cannot copy that love in kind, their desire causes them perpetually to move in circles, as the best possible substitute. Aristotle, thus, introduced an unfortunate connection between physical motion and moral principles which was to plague thought for centuries; just as the biological evolutionists of the nineteenth century are plaguing us by their unfortunate phrase of an evolution from lower to higher forms, and thus gave a moral significance to mere structural variations. Our theologians have discarded the association between motion and morals, but they still connect morals and muscles.

It has been shown that Aristotle accepted the fundamental postulates of the mechanistic hypothesis, and could escape its conclusions only by introducing the principle of animism. A discussion of the false system of science which the Schoolmen built on his dicta may be omitted; but two permanent contributions, which he gave to the scientific method, should be emphasized.

One of these contributions, the idea of potential, has already been mentioned. The other is Aristotle's discovery that science is not concerned with the problem of creation, or the beginning of substance, since natural law, to have any value, must be continuous and invariable. In conformity with this principle of law, the physicist assumes as an axiom that the nature of his substance, matter, and the laws of force and motion, have always been in the past what they are now, and what they will always be in the future. The confusion, which arises when the contrary is admitted, can be seen in the predicament of biology and psychology.

The biologists, following their acceptance of the evolution of species, have unfortunately assumed: because the earth may, at a past time, have been unfit for the existence of living bodies, therefore life itself was then non-existent. They are thus forced into the unscientific position that life, which is the biological substance, and the laws of life, were either a special creation or were evolved from mechanical matter and laws at some finite time in the past. If biological law were discontinuous in the past, then there is no certainty of its continuity in the future; or, if life and its laws are mere evolution of matter and its laws, then there is no science of biology built on the axiom that life proceeds only from life (*ovum ab ovo*). The case of psychology is still worse for it accepts a more recent time for the appearance of the self-conscious mind. And these two sciences will remain in the same unscientific condition in which they are at present, till they adopt the Aristotelian concept that substance is timeless and manifests itself in the three irreconcilable categories of matter, life, and spirit. The truth of this concept is confirmed by mathematics which has proved that the laws of matter are functions of time and space; the laws of life are not a function of space; and the laws of spirit are a function of neither time nor space.

With the collapse of the Greek and Roman civilisation, the philosophy of Plato and Aristotle was practically lost and their works were seldom read. Knowledge of Aristotelian physics was revived by the Syrian Christians[8] who translated his medical writings into Syriac. His works were first translated from Syriac into Arabic during the caliphate of Almamun (813–833). By the tenth century, his philosophy had become widely known, and its dominating authority was fixed by the two great Arabian commentators, Avicenna and Averrhoes. The western world, however, did not acquire access to his scientific writings until the latter half of the twelfth century when they and the commentaries of Avicenna, Averrhoes, and other Arabian philosophers, were translated first into Castilian and then into Latin under the direction of Archbishop Raymond of Toledo.

The rise to power of the monastic orders and the religious awakening of the twelfth and thirteenth centuries were hostile to the spread of natural philosophy on the ground that it diverted the attention from the spiritual life and, founded as it was on natural law, it substituted a mechanical world for the divinely revealed plan of God. There were sporadic attempts to forbid the teaching of natural philosophy until Gregory IX, in 1231, lifted the ban against the study of physics except for those writings which could be proved to be heretical in influence; and in 1254 the physics and metaphysics of Aristotle were officially listed in the curriculum of the University of Paris. This change of sentiment was due mainly to the influence of Albertus Magnus and Thomas Aquinas. On the one hand, as the greatest of mediæval commentators of Aristotle, and on the other, as the authors of the orthodox Catholic faith, they so fused Aristotelian philosophy and Christian ethics that the authority of the one over observation and reason became as absolute and dogmatic as the other over matters of faith.

For three centuries, the opinions of Aristotle, as interpreted by his

[8] Lasswitz, *Geschichte der Atomistik*, Vol. I, p. 85.

commentators, were the touchstone of truth; the direct evidence of experience and the deductions of the reason were confirmed, or denied, according as they agreed with his metaphysical scheme of nature. With both secular and sacred teaching entrusted to the monastic orders, the Church and the University submitted to the crushing weight of his authority. While it would be unjust to hold Aristotle accountable for the neglect of the sciences during the Middle Ages, since that was the result of the desperate need to rebuild a new social order, yet it is equally true that his philosophy led what little science there was by a false path into a barren and sterile field. It was most significant that the Renaissance of literature and art was heralded by a revival of Platonism, and that the later Renaissance of science was a determined and bitter revolt against Aristotelianism. It has commonly, and erroneously, been assumed by most historians of science that this revolt was directed against the Church but that was not the case; the opposition by the Church was for the most part forced upon it by the pressure of the teaching monastic orders, and especially of the Jesuits, who when attacked on account of their false doctrines of physical facts countered with the charge of heresy. The fault lay rather in the policy of confiding to the same persons the direction of both secular and religious instruction.

This opinion is confirmed by the great leaders of the new learning. It is noteworthy that Copernicus, Kepler, Pascal, and Newton were zealous defenders of the doctrines of their churches, and believed their scientific work to be a powerful support to the Christian religion. Of the others, Bacon, Galileo, and Descartes were at least orthodox in their public expressions of faith, and submitted to the authority of the churches in religious matters. In the published writings of all of them, whether zealous or luke-warm, I have found no trace of any hostility to the doctrines or authority of their churches, but I have found frequent and explicit statements that they were determined to break the dogmatism of the Aristotelian science.

This dogmatic and false science did not have its source in the particular beliefs of Aristotle, but resulted from the fact that his earliest commentators infused their own oriental mysticism with the metaphysical tendencies of the Greeks. In natural science Aristotle, himself, and his successor, Theophrastus, had founded a real school of the biological sciences which was smothered. Instead of developing it into an objective scientific method, his doctrine of the transmutation of the elements became the basis of mediæval alchemy with its fantastic mixture of sense and nonsense, and its supposed origin in the esoteric formulæ of the mythical Trismegistus. Still more fatal to the progress of the physical sciences were the tenets of a celestial matter which exerted a direct influence on physical phenomena and on life; of natural motions which were significant of moral attributes; and of the vitalistic conception that nature acted with purpose to avoid a vacuum, and to cause the elements to seek their natural levels. The mathematical school which flourished in Alexandria would certainly have developed into a modern science if it had been continued. The works of its five greatest leaders, Euclid (C. 300, B. C.) and Apollonius (C. 247, B. C.) in geometry, Archimedes (287–212, B. C.) in mechanics, Eratosthenes (C. 276, B. C.) in mathematics, and Hipparchus (C. 160, B. C.) in astronomy, can still be read with profit, and Copernicus closed the gap of eighteen centuries when he again picked up the lost thread of the Platonic philosophy of science. Science, with the rest of Greek culture, was lost in the collapse of classical civilisation and, when it was revived by the Arabians who had inherited the astrological beliefs of the Chaldeans, it started on its unfortunate career of alchemy and astrology. It is easy to see how those subjects acquired their fascination and power. In the Middle Ages, men saw the constant and immediate interposition of God in every act of their lives and, in the distracted and ominous state of society, feared that He had delivered the world into the power of the Devil and his satellites. It is not surprising, therefore, that they invoked the magic and prophetic arts of the astrologer and alchemist in order to get a glimpse of the future. Under the stress of so great a temptation to profit from the cupidity, the ambition, and the fear of their unlearned patrons, "the great pretenders of the Hermetic arts" developed that strange mixture of science and chicane, of serious purpose and venal deception.

In spite of its many defects, astrology kept alive an interest in science. In order to draw up satisfactory horoscopes, its votaries spent their nights in observing the planets and stars; and to locate their positions, a great variety of apparatus was constructed which far exceeded all other instruments in accuracy. Nor can we doubt that aggregations of stars served as a visible and magnified illustration of the atomic theory of matter. The unquestioned authority of astrology was the *Syntaxis* of Ptolemy, or *Almagest* as it was named by the Arabs. Although the writings of Hipparchus are lost, we are certain that he was the author of most of the observations, of the calculations, and of the catalogue, of the stars found in the *Almagest*. But, the study of the planets which enabled Ptolemy to evolve his celebrated cosmic system is his own work. However cumbersome this system with its epicycles on epicycles later became, it is the natural description of the motions and paths of the planets, satellites, and sun, as observed by a person stationed on the earth. It is superior to the heliocentric system so far as the apparent paths of the three most important bodies,—the earth, the sun, and the moon,—are concerned; it is inferior, in that the motions of the other planets and their satellites become complicated epicyclic curves. It must not be overlooked that the observed map of the heavens is still drawn with the earth as the centre and is then remade, on the basis that the sun is the fixed centre, because the calculation of the orbits is thus simplified. It is true, in a sense, that the heliocentric system is a mathematical device invented to reduce the labour of computation. There is, however, another cause which forced the abandonment of the Ptolemaic system on absolute grounds; if the earth be at rest, then the fixed stars, because of their enormous distances from it, must daily travel about the earth from east to west at simply incredible speeds; if, however, the earth revolves on its axis in the opposite direction the same result is accomplished with a reasonable velocity. The rotation of the earth is now so well established by direct evidence that there can be no question of fact as to which is the real system. Thus, the deciding factor in establishing the heliocentric system was the daily motion of the earth and not its annual revolution about the sun. The early enthusiasts for the Copernican system failed to give Ptolemy just appreciation; they overlooked the fact that their own system, while it reduced the labour of computation, did not discard the use of epicyclic paths, but merely reduced their number.

Our deepest admiration should be given to the long line of astronomers and astrologers before the Renaissance. It is little short of marvellous that they should have recorded such a mass of observations, have attained such precision of measurement without the aid of telescopes and clocks, and have performed their computations without the devices of modern mathematics. We may omit the specific record of their own achievements in elucidating the problems of astronomy, and merely mention what they accumulated for the use of their successors.

Hipparchus, besides his many contributions to a correct discussion of the perturbations of the solar system and the magnitudes involved, drew up a catalogue of the positions of 1028 fixed stars. Ptolemy made this catalogue accessible by incorporating it in the *Almagest*, and he also published his own tables of the motions of the planets which gave their positions correctly with an accuracy of a quarter of a degree. In the tenth century Albategnius corrected and enlarged the catalogue. Two centuries later Alphonso X, king of Castile, expressed his royal irritation because of the unnecessary complications introduced by God in His plan of the universe and, as he was unable to substitute his own ideas, he gathered together the most celebrated Arabian, Jewish, and Christian astronomers and set them to the task of describing more exactly the existing cosmic system. The result of their deliberations was the famous Alphonsine Tables which appeared in manuscript in 1252, but were not published at Venice until 1483. These tables, with one prepared by the Tartar prince, Ulugh-Beg provided the data for the beginning of modern astronomy and science.

By the middle of the fifteenth century, the Renaissance was in full flower so far as art, literature, and philosophy were concerned; but the new spirit of science had begun to show itself only by a certain restlessness and by a timid questioning of the dogmatic scheme of nature which had evolved from the Judaic cosmogony and the Aristotelian philosophy; the impetus to this restlessness had undoubtedly come with the revival of Platonism which followed the enthusiastic reception by the Italians of the Greek scholars who had fled from the destruction of Constantinople. With Platonic philosophy, came also a renewed interest in mathematics and mechanics. The individualism which had become so dominant in art, literature, and national life, finally penetrated religion and science, and brought about the substitution of personal responsibility both towards God and nature for the authority of divine revelation through the Church.

It is significant that the three proponents of this new attitude, Erasmus, Copernicus, and Luther, should have been almost exact contemporaries. And from their lives can be dated the struggle between religion and science which has since then been followed by a steady decline in the religious spirit, and by an equal growth of the scientific attitude of dependence on observation and reason. It would be difficult to say which of the two, Luther or Copernicus, was the more responsible for our present individualistic sectarianism and philosophic disintegration. As modern Protestantism must look to Luther for its creator so modern science is to be dated from the work of Copernicus.

Nicolaus Copernicus, or Koppernigk, was born at Thorn on the border between Prussia and Poland in 1473, and died in Fraüenburg in 1543. He first studied at Cracow and then went, as did all the eager youth, to Italy to drink in the new knowledge. This first stay was passed at Bologna and Padua, where he became proficient in mathematics; it was followed by a year at Rome, in 1500, as professor of that subject. After a short visit at home, he again returned the following year to Italy and, with the versatility then so common, he studied law and medicine at Padua and was made doctor of laws, in 1503, by the University of Ferrara. His education completed, an accomplished mathematician and an enthusiastic astronomer, he settled in Fraüenburg for the remainder of his life. His uncle, the bishop, appointed him a canon of the cathedral, and here he peacefully carried on a busy life in the church and in an observatory which he built for himself. Of a noble family, protected by the powerful influence of his uncle, well read in Greek and Latin, and distinguished in the sciences, he meditated on the insufficiency of the Ptolemaic cosmic system until he finally evolved his own planetary scheme. He tells us that he first began his great work in 1506 and pursued it with such deliberation and patience that the work was not completed until 1530. And even then, he laid it aside for thirteen more years and only published his results after his reluctance had been overborne by the entreaties of his friends. As he lay on his death-bed, his great masterpiece *De revolutionibus corporum cœlestium* was placed in his nerveless hands. His reasons for this long delay are given in his preface: "I believe that as soon as it is known what I have written in this work on the motions of the earth, a great hue and cry will be raised against me. Besides I am not so enamoured with my ideas as not to pay attention to what others will think of them; then, too, although the thoughts of a philosopher are far removed from the opinions of the vulgar, because he has set himself to seek the truth, so far as God permits to human reason, I am not disposed to reject entirely the opinions thus opposed to me. All these motives, as well as the fear of becoming, because of the novelty and the apparent absurdity, an object of derision, have made me almost renounce the project. But my friends, amongst them Cardinal Schomberg and Tidemann Gisius, bishop of Culm, have overborne my reluctance. The latter, above all others, has most insisted that

I publish this book, which I have meanwhile kept on the stocks not only nine years, but almost four times nine years."

In any astronomical system the determination of the paths of the stars is a problem of relative motion. Now, if one considers the relative positions of two moving bodies, the result is evidently the same whether one assumes both to move with respect to some other fixed point of reference, or whether one supposes either one of the bodies to be at rest and the other to perform all the motion. Thus, an observer of the stars will obtain a correct diagram of their successive positions if he plots his observations with reference to himself and the earth as a fixed point. It is in fact the only way actual observations can be made, and it is followed by astronomers today. It is thus a monument to the genius of Hipparchus, and his successor Ptolemy, that from their observations astronomers developed the well-known Ptolemaic system. Briefly, in that system, the earth was assumed to be at rest; the sun, moon, and fixed stars will then appear to revolve about it in circles, while the then five known planets describe cyclic paths which are traced out by a point on a circle rolling on another circle. Knowing the position of a planet at several points, in its orbit, its future path could be calculated from the properties of the curve. The difficulty of the system lies in the fact that such calculations are laborious because of the nature of these cycloidal curves; furthermore, every perturbation of an orbit must be accounted for by supposing a secondary epicyle until, by the time of Copernicus, the system had become embarrassingly complex.

Copernicus, early in his life, became convinced that this complicated system was contrary to the prevalent belief that the order of nature was symmetrical and simple, and that there must be some conceivable system which would be consonant with that belief. The orbits of the sun and moon agreed with the Aristotelian philosophy of the circle as the necessary and perfect celestial motion, but the paths of the planets were anything but simple and symmetrical; could not there be devised a system, he argued, which would bring them into a law of harmony? Another puzzle, in his mind, was the assumption that the fixed stars made a daily revolution about the earth. In the opinion of the classical philosophers, the universe was a small and rather intimate system. The moon, sun, and planets were each located in a solid spherical shell which rolled it about the earth, as a fixed centre, in its diurnal revolution. Just outside these was the shell which carried all the stars and thus their speed of rotation presented no special difficulty. But, as knowledge increased, astronomers began to locate the stars at increasingly greater distances from the earth till, at the beginning of the sixteenth century, the consequent speed of their motion had become an embarrassing problem.

In this state of doubtful groping he, being a student of Greek, turned, as was the custom of the day, to the classic philosophers for enlightenment. To his surprise and delight, he tells us Plutarch[9] mentioned that some of the Pythagoreans, and notably Philolaus, believed the earth to be a sphere which rotated daily on an axis, and revolved annually about the sun as a fixed centre. He also found on the authority of Martianus Capella that other philosophers supposed Mercury and Venus to revolve about the sun, and not about the earth as a centre. Copernicus seems to have grasped almost immediately the solution of the problem. He had merely to imagine himself observing from the sun as a fixed centre, and he would see the earth and the other five planets revolving about him in circles, thus avoiding the epicyclic curves observed from the earth. When he wished to calculate the path of the moon as a circle he had merely to transport himself back to the earth. Also, by supposing the earth to rotate on its axis the diurnal revolution of the sun and stars was made unnecessary. To grasp the general idea was one thing, but to support the idea by convincing proofs was a different matter, and he spent thirty years at the task before he felt that he had satisfactorily solved the problem.

Copernicus was shrewd enough to realise that his theory would meet with determined opposition and would need the most convincing proof before it would be accepted. The Ptolemaic system had the authority of centuries behind it, and the public would certainly shudder with terror at the thought of the solid earth whirling and speeding through empty space. More dangerous still might

[9] The passages discovered by Copernicus are probably as follows:

"Philolaus, the Pythagorean, believes that the earth moves in a circle about the fire, obliquely, in the same fashion as the sun and moon."

"Heraclides of Pontas and Ecphantus, the Pythagorean, make the earth move, not however in the movement of translation but in a revolving movement, like a wheel on its axle revolving about its own centre from the west to the east."

It appears that Copernicus must have confused the statement made concerning the views of Ecphantus in the second paragraph with the statement in the first paragraph by Philolaus. The passages are found in the *Collection of Opinions Adopted by the Philosophers* which was attributed to Plutarch and appears in the *Moralia,* but is now attributed to Aetius. *Cf.* Diels, *Doxographi Graeci,* p. 378.

be the opposition of the Church which would certainly regard as heterodox, and probably as blasphemous, any dislocation of the earth from its central and fixed position; even more obstinate would be the hostility of the Aristotelian philosophers who could not fail to see that such a conception of the universe meant the downfall of all the laborious structure they had erected. Copernicus could only hope that time would reconcile the people to his ideas; to ward off the opposition of the clergy, he dedicated his book to the Pope, Paul III, a man of great learning, who accepted the honour and permitted it to be published and circulated.

With the founding of the Society of Jesus in 1534 and its sanction by Paul six years later, began the great struggle between the Jesuits and the Dominicans for control over the educational system. The growth of the Jesuits had been phenomenally rapid, and into their hands had fallen the direction of the Counter-Reformation which attempted not only to suppress Protestantism but also to set the Church against the new science as heretical and contrary to the authoritative teaching of Aristotle. In spite of their opposition, the Copernican system steadily gained the adherence of astronomers and scholars. It was not until 1616 that the Jesuits were able, in the pontificate of Paul V, to place the book in the Index as heretical; and even after that it was tacitly permitted to circulate and to be read. As Kepler sadly remarked, the Copernican system had quietly spread its influence unmolested for eighty years till Galileo forced the issue by the publication, in 1632, of his *Dialogo dei due massimi sistemi*.

Important as was the work of Copernicus, he cannot be said to have established his cosmic theory. For that a mass of accurate data on the positions of the planets was needed, and he was not such an observer; indeed he could not be because of the crudeness of the instruments at his command. For this data, we are indebted to the prince of astronomical observers, Tycho Brahé. Aided by the munificent patronage of Ferdinand II, King of Denmark, he was able to build a sumptuous observatory on the island of Hven and to install there such a set of instruments as had never before been placed at the service of an astronomer; indeed, they could be superseded only by the invention of the telescope. In this observatory, and later at Prague where he secured the support of the Emperor Rudolph II, he made such accurate determinations of the positions of the stars and of the orbits of the planets, which later were embodied in the Rudolphine Tables, that he put into the hands of his assistant and successor, Johann Kepler, the material he used to develop the laws of the heliocentric system, and to remove all doubts as to its truth.

Kepler was one of the noblest and most extraordinary figures in the history of science and, at the same time one of the most opportune, since his rare combination of mysticism and passion for facts made him an ideal figure in the transition period between the mediæval and modern conceptions of science. Born, 1571, in Weil in Würtemberg, he began life as an assistant in his father's inn. Sickly and frail in health, he was exposed to such an unnatural and brutal treatment by his mother and his two elder brothers that he fled to the protection of his sister Marguerite who had a great affection for him; but here, too, he met with little favour from her hubsand who put him to hard labour in the fields. He finally escaped from this life of drudgery and was admitted to the seminary at Tübingen. Although he was a notably devout and religious man, he was expelled for heterodoxy, a fate which dogged him all his life for, in those early days of religious disturbance following the Reformation, it was difficult to adopt any views which were not heterodox somewhere in the tangled religious map of Germany. For a time, it seemed as if the adverse stars of his horoscope had relaxed their influence; he entered and made rapid progress at the University of Tübingen, and was appointed professor of mathematics in Grätz at the age of twenty-two. Here, he not only lectured but, to increase his income, he compiled an annual almanach and cast astrological horoscopes. These almanachs are a vivid example of his exuberance of imagination and accuracy for details; interspersed with his predictions of the weather, he gave free rein to his passion for the numerical harmonies of the Pythagoreans and a mystical identification of God with the sun. His good fortune, however, soon forsook him since he brought back his troubles by marrying a beautiful and noble widow who made his life a long martyrdom. Opposition to his religious views also again cropped up, and he was finally obliged to leave Grätz. This proved to be his one real piece of luck as he was appointed assistant to Tycho at Prague in the preparation of the Rudolphine star catalogue and succeeded him, two years later, as director of the observatory. It was there that he lived the rest of his life and produced his immortal work, in spite of difficulties and sorrows which would have broken the spirit of any one not devoted to the pursuit of the highest ideals. He died at Ratisbon in 1630, while on a journey made in the hope to collect his past due salary.

and of the reliability of reason, but an induction drawn from experimental evidence. One might retort that there is some faith necessary in the assumption that matter in a star, for example Betelgueuse, is identical with that on the earth; it must be admitted that our experimental evidence derived from weighing objects in Betelgueuse is slight. But we need not go so far afield to show that the general and fundamental laws of science are not formulated from the data of experience; on the contrary, our experimental data are revised and changed to conform to preconceived deductive laws. If one weighs any object ten times there will certainly be ten different numerical results, if the balance be sufficiently delicate and the experiments be done with care; and the greater the accuracy of the experimenter, the greater will be the differences of his readings. Or, if ten persons weigh the same object, the chances are that there will be ten different results, and the certainty is that they will not all agree. Which of these is the true weight, we have no means of knowing. We are driven to the dilemma of either assuming that the object has one real weight which we can obtain only approximately by taking the average of all the trials,[5] or else that it has simultaneously as many weights as there are observations; we adopt the former as the truth and tacitly admit that our opinions of the objective world must in all cases be altered to conform to preconceived subjective ideas. Let us give another illustration which does not involve measurement. The retinas of a few eyes are insensible to a difference of colour between the leaves and blossoms of a geranium. There are no objective experiments which can make these so-called red colour blind persons aware of a *colour* difference of sensation. As it happens, they form a small minority, and they submit to the opinion of the numerical majority that their eye-sight is defective, but their subjective conviction must still remain unchanged. If the contrary happened to be the case, and only rare individuals could perceive a distinction of colour between such leaves and blossoms, does any one doubt that their objective opinions would be changed to agree with the opinion of the majority? As Plato held, since objective things and their phenomena can be recognised only by observation, the most that we can derive from them is an opinion, based on belief and conjecture; and modern science follows Plato in so far that it attempts to portray not a real world but an interpretation of observed phenomena as a logi-

[5] The mathematical law of probability and chance, which governs all experimental work, is based on the axiom that errors of observation disappear only with an infinite number of trials.

Kepler's first work was his *Prodromus.*[10] He was a convinced Copernican and wrote the book to gain popular support to that system. His opening words to the reader affirm his purpose: "I propose to demonstrate to my readers in this little book what the Creator Optimus Maximus was mindful of in the creation of our *mobile* earth and in the disposition of the planets according to those five regular geometrical bodies which, ever since to our times, have been most renowned by the Pythagoreans and Plato; and how He adapted the number, the proportions, and the cause of motion, to the nature of those heavenly bodies."

One can easily recognise in this youthful book Kepler's belief in a natural law or orderliness; that is, the planets must follow, in their distances and periods, a definite sequence of numbers. Not knowing any law of force which would account for the planetary motions, and imbued with the Pythagorean and astrological belief in the mystical harmony of numbers, he incorporated their ideas in his scientific treatise. Thus, he first chose the five regular polygons and then located the orbits of the planets by an ingenious arrangement of inscribed and superscribed circles. He was the more enthusiastic over this scheme as he thought that he had disposed the planets according to the proportions of a musical harmony. His biographers express surprise, and even contempt, that Kepler should have included a disquisition on music and the harmony of numbers in an astronomical treatise; but they merely fail to sympathise with the spirit of Kepler's age, which found in musical harmony the prototype of all natural law.

In the *Prodromus,* Kepler's geometric and harmonious arrangement of the planets is briefly as follows. Locate the sun as the fixed centre of the solar system, describe about it a sphere to locate the orbit of the earth.[11] Construct a dodecahedron about the earth's sphere and on it circumscribe a sphere for the orbit of Mars. About Mars construct a tetrahedron, and its circumscribed sphere will give the orbit of Jupiter. In the same way, a cube and its circumscribed sphere locate the orbit of Saturn. Next proceeding inwardly from the earth's sphere, an inscribed icosahedron and its inscribed sphere

[10] The book was first published at Tübingen in 1596, and reissued at Frankfort in 1621, with the portentous title: Prodromus dissertationum cosmographicarum, continens mysterium cosmographicum de admirabili proportione orbium coelestium: deque causis coelorum numeri, magnitudinis, motuumque periodicorum genuinis et propriis, demonstratum per quinque regularia corpora geometrica. *Cf.* also Vol. I, *Kepleri Opera Omnia,* Ed. by Frisch, Frankfurt, 1858.

[11] For his model of the heavens see *Opera,* Vol. I, p. 215.

provide for Venus; and an octahedron and its inscribed sphere account for Mercury.

However far Kepler's fervent imagination might run away with him, in the end he settled down to the hard task of verifying his scheme by accurate calculation, and then confessed that he had fallen into error. At another time, he said: "I dared, in order that the beautiful harmony of quiescence may be maintained, to liken the sun, the fixed stars, and the intermediate heaven, to God the Father, the Son, and the Holy Ghost." However erroneous his speculations might prove to be, he took such a naïve delight in them that he invariably published them in as great detail as he did his sober scientific work. Fortunately, on the advice of Tycho, he laid aside these vagaries and applied himself to the strict business of astronomy. It was not until 1609, the year the telescope was discovered, that he finally found his master laws of the solar system and published them in his *Nova Astronomia*.[12] It was also fortunate that Tycho had made a special study of Mars, so that when Kepler became his assistant and successor he had a great collection of accurate data about that planet to digest and to analyse. Since the orbit of Mars is the most eccentric of all the planets and thus departs most from a circle, he quickly found that the discrepancies between his calculations and Tycho's observations were too great to be due to errors in observation. He finally became convinced that a circular orbit would have to be abandoned. His first guess was to assume some form of an oval[13] and with incredible patience he tried many varieties before he finally satisfied himself that the orbits of all planets were ellipses with the sun fixed at one of the foci. His second law, that the areas, swept in equal periods of time by a line drawn from the sun to the planet, were equal, followed at once from the geometrical properties of the ellipse. The number and extent of the calculations he made to prove these two laws are astonishing and he, at one place, interrupts his work to exclaim: "If you find this work difficult and wearisome to follow, take pity on me, for I have repeated these calculations seventy times, nor be surprised that I have spent five years on this theory of Mars." But Kepler was still not satisfied; obsessed with the Pythagorean doctrine of the harmony of the stars, he persisted in trying to find some proportionate relation between the planets. His joy, which he poured out in fervent thanks to God, knew no bounds

[12] Published at Prague, 1609, and reprinted as Vol. III in his *Opera*.

[13] "Orbitam planetae non esse circulum, sed figurae ovalis." *Opera*, Vol. III, p. 337.

when he at last proved his third law that the cubes of the mean distances of the planets from the sun are proportional to the squares of their annual periods.

With the establishment of the three laws for the motion of a planet, or satellite, about a fixed central body, Kepler had solved the essential, or schematic, problem of the solar system. The principle which had led both Copernicus and him to their great discoveries was the classical and purely metaphysical dogma that Nature always adopts the simplest and most nearly symmetrical course. This doctrine is unfortunately not true in fact, and it has been the source of many pernicious hypotheses. When the classification of a new set of observed phenomena is first attempted, it is inevitable that only their most salient features are considered, and the law derived from them is simple. For example, when Galileo first discovered the law that the path of a projectile is a parabola, he excluded the friction and motion of the air, variations in the force of gravity, and many other perturbations. If these so-called secondary actions are included, the actual path of any projectile is a curve so complicated that its form cannot be expressed by a soluble mathematical equation, and an approximate solution only can be obtained. As a general thesis we must admit natural phenomena are actually so complex and inextricably interwoven that we can never isolate any one set of phenomena nor attempt to picture the actual history of events. Nature, as studied by the physicist, is thus a simplified and artificial world which bears but a faint resemblance to an objective universe. No better illustration of this fact could be given than the history of the laws of the solar system. Copernicus first assumed the general law of circular orbits. The discrepancies between the calculated and observed positions of the planets soon became so apparent that Kepler substituted the less simple elliptic path. But this law presupposes that there is an action between two bodies only, the central body and its satellite; whereas the fact is, every body of the solar system attracts every other body with a constantly varying force and the problem of plotting the actual path of a planet is totally beyond our powers. Instead of an elliptical path invariably pursued, the actual course of a planet is much more like the erratic trail of a drunken man.

Great as was the achievement of establishing the heliocentric system, there still remained the question, why must a satellite revolve about its central body in an ellipse? Aristotle had assumed that the circle was the only perfect curve and that the heavenly bodies, being composed of a perfect and celestial substance, must of necessity move in circles. This teleological principle maintained its authority as an effective cause all through the middle ages and was not questioned by Copernicus, whose only contribution to the subject was that matter had a natural appetency to congregate into a spherical form and that a falling body was merely a manifestation of this inherent quality. Nor did Tycho Brahé attempt any solution of the problem of the cause of planetary motion; but his work did contribute indirectly to the discovery of a force of attraction by destroying the belief in solid celestial orbs which supported the planets in space. He proved that the comet of 1577 was at least three times farther from the earth than was the moon. Thus, these mysterious visitors were not local phenomena but bodies which freely penetrated the solar system in all directions.

One can readily understand that Kepler, with his eager and restless imagination, not only pondered over the question of planetary forces but would hazard a multitude of guesses. Having no conception of the resultant action of a force directed perpendicularly to the motion of the planet, he sought for one which would drag it, or whirl it, around the sun. In his *Mysterium cosmographicum* he assigned to the sun a sort of living principle (*animus*) which moved and regulated the planets. In the meanwhile, Gilbert had published his great treatise *De magnete,* containing an extraordinary wealth of experimental observations on electricity and magnetism, which profoundly impressed both Kepler and Galileo, drawing from the latter a rare tribute of appreciation. Gilbert not only by his experiments advanced these subjects to real sciences but, having described the earth as a great magnet, he supposed gravitation to be a magnetic force whose influence extended even as far as the moon. His hypothesis was further elaborated in a posthumous work.[14] "It is not," he says there, "so as to make the bodies unite like two magnets, but that they may go on in a continuous course." And again: "The moon does not act on the tides of the seas by its rays or its light. How then? Certainly by the common effort of the bodies, and (to explain it by something similar) by their magnetic attraction." He

[14] *De mundo nostro sublunari, Philosophia nova,* Amsterdam, 1651. The manuscript of this work was found amongst Gilbert's scattered papers and was translated and prepared for publication by his elder brother. For some reason it was not published and was found amongst Francis Bacon's manuscripts. It was finally published by Bacon's literary executor, Isaac Gruter.

thought that this cosmic magnetic force dragged the moon around the earth as the earth spins a magnetic compass needle, and also that it rotated the earth on its axis. Kepler had early become acquainted with the *De magnete* and, when he discussed the cause of planetary motion in his own *Astronomia nova,* he eagerly adopted the same hypothesis. He summarised Gilbert's views on magnetism and added: "Since the earth, as demonstrated by William Gilbert of England, is a great magnet and is rotated on its axis daily, so I believe the sun to be rotated: and for this reason, because it has magnetic fibres intersecting the direction of its motion at right angles in the same way as those fibres surround the poles of the earth in varying circles parallel to its motion: so I maintain with the best right that the moon is whirled about by this rotation of the earth and by the action of this same magnetic virtue. . . . It is therefore plausible, since the earth puts the moon in motion by its effluvium (*speciem*), and is a magnetic body, that the sun puts the planets in motion similarly by an emitted effluvium (*emissam speciem*): *Solem itaque similiter corpus esse magneticum.*"[15]

Although Galileo was not an astronomer, his invention of the telescope put into their hands so powerful an aid that we may safely ascribe to him the overthrow of mediæval astrology; and his creation of the science of dynamics substituted a correct idea and formula for force instead of those vague and useless effluvia and virtues which had been postulated as efficient causes of phenomena. As early as 1590, he had, by his spectacular experiment of dropping balls of different weights from the leaning tower of Pisa, proved that the force of gravitation was not proportional to the velocity of motion, and had thus crushed by experimental demonstration one of the fundamental doctrines of Aristotle. It is said; those who observed the experiment acknowledged that the various bodies appeared to reach the earth at the same time, but they stubbornly maintained that it must have been an optical illusion since the great Stagirite had declared a body six times as heavy as another must fall the same distance in one-sixth the time. With this incident, began his life-long controversy with the Aristotelians, a struggle to which he devoted his great power of experimentation, of logic, and of biting satire; until his adversaries, driven to desperation, finally invoked the aid of the Church with the accusation of heresy. So bitter was Galileo's satire,

[15] *Astronomia nova,* Chap. XXXIV, p. 307. Ed. Frisch. The word *species,* in scholastic epistemology, was used to express the processes leading both to sense and to intellectual knowledge. Many writers used it as the cause of action, as an effluvium or virtue.

and so biting his sarcasm that in early life he was hissed during his lectures at Pisa, and forced to resign and return to Florence. Fortunately for himself and for the world, he obtained a professorship of mathematics at Padua, where under the protection of Venice, the only state in Italy having the power and will to oppose the authority of the monastic orders and the Inquisition, he publicly experimented and lectured for twenty years, attracting by his fame young men from all Europe who came to learn the new knowledge at its source. In his first letter to Kepler, written in 1597 to acknowledge the receipt of the *Mysterium cosmographicum,* he declared that he had become a convert to the Copernican system many years before. Teaching the doctrine openly as a fact and not as an hypothesis, he created adherents and scattered them all over Europe.

The climax to his fame came with the invention of the telescope; requests for one of these magic instruments poured in on him from all parts of the world and he literally made hundreds of them with his own hands; to gaze through a telescope became the fashionable amusement of courts and society, and the serious occupation of the astronomer. Distracted by this manual labour, by the interruptions of curious visitors, and by the burden of correspondence, he found little time to pursue his scientific work. With the promise of leisure offered to him by his friend Duke Cosimo II, he forsook the protection and safety of Padua and Venice for the dangers of Florence and Pisa, where his enemies were lying in wait for him. The religious influence of his opinions was first attacked by Boscaglia, Professor of Physics at Pisa, who excited the scruples of the Dowager Duchess on the ground that a belief in the two motions of the earth was contrary to the Bible. Galileo's tactful answer was to cite Joshua's miracle as an example of puerile folly. He was also preached against by the Dominican Caccini in the Duomo of Florence and *mirabile dictu* supported by a Jesuit. But, for once the Aristotelians, Dominicans and Jesuits, united against a common enemy and gave thanks that the Lord had delivered him into their hands. No opposition to Galileo had as yet been aroused in Rome and the Pope, Paul V, was favourable to him. But the pressure from Florence finally prevailed and he was cited before the Inquisition. He was, after many delays, admonished, in 1616, by the Holy Office to renounce his heresy, and Copernicus's treatise was suspended and placed on the Index until corrected, a sentence which was not formally revoked until 1835. Galileo returned to Florence sick and despondent.

To force the issue, as Galileo had persistently done, and to inject personal attacks into a question to be ultimately decided by observation and reason, can be regarded as most unfortunate in its effect on both religion and science. Many of those who privately accepted the new science were compelled to express a public disapproval of its teachings. Kepler openly lamented the set-back which had been given to the quiet and steady spread of the doctrine. As early as 1619, John Remus wrote from Vienna to Kepler that the Copernican writings may be read by scientific men who had received special permission, and that this was common in all Italy and in Rome, itself. Besides, it was allowed to make use of the doctrine as an hypothesis. We should realise that it was then not supported by sufficient facts and that the Church was in a most awkward position; as a scientific device to simplify mathematical calculations there would be no fault to be found, but taught as a fact, the two-fold revolution of the earth was clearly contrary to those religious beliefs of the day which the authorities were bound to uphold.

It was not, however, a trait of Galileo's character to submit docilely to authority. In 1623, the Cardinal Maffeo Barberini became Pope Urban VIII; as he was most favourable to science and a personal friend, Galileo visited Rome the following year but, although he was received with favours and gifts by the Pope, he could not get the former decree revoked. Encouraged with his reception, he spent the next three years writing his *Dialogues on the two principal systems;* strangely enough, his manuscript was approved by Urban who merely required a few alterations and, after some delay, permission was given to publish. It was a rash deed and even more rashly done. In these celebrated Dialogues, Galileo not only rudely dispelled the fiction that the Copernican system was merely a mathematical hypothesis, but he subjected the Jesuits and Aristotelians to the bitterest ridicule. The spirit of malice and irony in which it was written can be judged from the opening sentence of the preface: "There was promulgated at Rome, some years ago, a salutary edict, in which to obviate the perilous scandals of the present age silence has been imposed on the Pythagorean opinion of the motion of the earth. There are some people so rash as to believe that this decree was not the result of a judicious examination but of a passion too little informed; and complaints even have been heard that Councillors totally ignorant of astronomical observations ought not, with a precipitate prohibition, to cut the wings of speculative men of intellect."

Under the form of a dialogue, the author then unfolds the new doctrine, and exposes the fallacies of the Aristotelians with bitter and scathing contempt.

The book was a great masterpiece of science and of literature, and it made an immense sensation over all Europe. But it also gave his enemies just the opportunity they needed to bring him to trial for heresy. They were able even to give credence to the rumour that Simplicio, the butt of the dialogues, was a caricature of the Pope. Spurred to action, the Congregation of the Index first ordered the sale of the book to be stopped and, in October, summoned its author to Rome. Then followed months of anxiety and terror, during which Galileo could only guess what was to be his fate. His first examination did not take place until April, and his sentence was deferred until June 22. Everyone knows the dramatic scene when finally the proud and haughty old man abjured publicly those ideas as false which he had given his life-time, and his great genius, to prove as true. He was furthermore forbidden to teach or to write, and was exiled to the villa of the Grand Duke of Tuscany. We may admit that the doctrine was heretical and that the sentence was comparatively mild; but there is no shadow of doubt that it was a colossal blunder; the trial of Galileo is still cited as an example of the bigotry and dogmatism of the Roman Church, and at the time it turned thoughtful people away from her congregations; one would be more ready to pardon her if one did not more than suspect that many of the judges secretly accepted the Copernican system as the truth.

Although Galileo was broken in health and harassed by domestic misfortunes, he heroically used his enforced leisure to collect and prepare for publication the results of his years of study on mechanics. This treatise, with the title of *Dialoghi delle nuove scienze*,[16] is undoubtedly his masterpiece and contains practically all that he had to give on the subject of physics. Since Galileo could not hope to print in either Florence or Rome, he turned to Venice for a publisher, but was blocked by the information that there was an express order

[16] It was first published by the Elzevir Press in 1638. It was translated into English by Thomas Salusbury in 1665, and not again till recently by Professors Crew and De Salvio under the title of *The Two New Sciences*, Macmillan, 1914. The authors make mention of Salusbury's translation: "It is supposed that most of the copies were destroyed in the great London fire which occurred in the year following. We are not aware of any copy in America: even that belonging to the British Museum is an imperfect one." The first complete edition of Galileo's Works was published under the editorship of Eugenio Albèri, Florence, 1842–1856, in sixteen volumes. Quite recently Professor Favaro of Padua has edited the National Edition in twenty volumes.

prohibiting the printing or reprinting of any work of Galileo, *nullo excepto*. He next turned to Germany and, although he obtained permission to publish, he still feared the long arm of the Court of Rome. Finally, availing himself of a visit from Louis Elzevir, he gave to him the manuscript to take back to Leyden, where it was published in 1638. Galileo's life, full of great achievement and bitter sorrow, came to an end on January 8, 1642; on Christmas of the same year there came into the world an even greater philosopher, Isaac Newton. We may make the history of dynamics and the mechanistic philosophy run with these two lives which spanned the century and a half, from 1564 to 1727.

On the third day of the *Dialogues on the new sciences,* Galileo discusses the laws of motion and force. The notion prevailed that force was proportional to the velocity of a body; it was therefore assumed that a constant force was required to maintain a body at a uniform speed, and also that a body, weighing twice that of another, falls twice as fast and reaches the earth in one-half the time. So far as we know, no one before Galileo had tested this latter assumption; and it was a simple matter for him to show its error by observing the free fall of two bodies of very different weights, enclosed in boxes of the same size and shape to ensure an equal resistance of the air. To test the law of gravity accurately, by measuring the time of the free fall of a body, would have been impossible with his crude timing apparatus, since the free fall is swift and the time is short. Galileo cleverly avoided this difficulty by substituting the slower motion of bodies rolling down an inclined plane. He first proved that a free, or vertical, fall is merely a special case of an inclined plane whose inclination to the horizontal is ninety degrees, and that the law of force and motion is the same for inclined planes of any angle. He next proved experimentally that bodies of all kinds, moving down an inclined plane, experienced a constant and equal acceleration, or increase of velocity per second of time, whose amount depended only on the inclination. It followed immediately that all bodies, of whatever kind and weight, fall from rest with the same acceleration and reach the earth from the same height in equal times if we neglect the friction of the air. Thus force is independent of the velocity, since it is proportional only to the change of velocity per second, and is measured by this acceleration. He had thus derived an experimental and theoretical proof of the law which he had roughly demonstrated so many years before from the tower of Pisa; that all bodies fall to the earth with the same velocity and in the same time, because the force of gravity produces the same acceleration in all bodies. Also, from his experiments and theorems on inclined planes he derived a most important deduction as follows: "Moreover it is proper to assume that any velocity observed in a moving body is, on account of its very nature, unchangeable so long as external causes of acceleration, or retardation, are taken away, a condition which obtains only on a horizontal plane: for in motion down an inclined plane there always exists a cause of acceleration, and in motion up an incline there is retardation. From which it follows in like manner that motion on a horizontal plane is everlasting and unchangeable: if it is thus constant, it will be neither weakened nor slackened and much less destroyed.[17] This is a statement, in no vague terms, of Newton's first law of motion, which he generalised to include the motion of all bodies not acted upon by forces. Also, Galileo's assumption, that the force of gravity and the upward resistance of a horizontal plane on which a body lies are equal and opposite is an anticipation of Newton's third law of the equality of action and reaction. The passage quoted shows that Galileo had defined the law of conservation of momentum; it is evident, also, that he, for the special case of gravity, anticipated Newton's second law that a force acts only in the direction of acceleration and is measured by it.

The discussion of the fourth day is devoted to the motion of projectiles, the paths of which he proved to be parabolæ. In the course of the conversation, Sagredo sums up: "It cannot be denied that the discourse is new, ingenious, and conclusive, reasoning *ex suppositione,* on the hypothesis that the horizontal motion remains always constant and that the natural motion downwards likewise preserves its tendency to increase the motion constantly in direct proportion to the time; and such motions and their velocities, when blended together, do not alter, perturb and impede each other. So that finally the path of the projectile does not in the course of its motion degenerate into another type."[18] This passage is certainly a particular case of Newton's second law of motion. Although it re-

[17] Ed. Albèri, Vol. XIII, p. 200. Also translated by Crew, p. 214.

[18] Ed. Albèri, Vol. XIII, p. 227. Professor Crew in his translation of this passage, see p. 250, renders "il naturale *deorsum* parimente mantenga il suo tenore di andarsi sempre accelerando secondo la proporzion dei tempi" as "the vertical motion continues to be accelerated downwards in proportion to the square of the time." This rendition seems to me to alter Galileo's meaning which is that the acceleration downwards is constant during the time of motion.

quired many years before it was developed by Newton into his law of universal gravitation, the intermediate steps are easily followed. If a body be moving with a uniform velocity in a circle, then there can be no force along the arc of the circle, as Galileo proved for the case of the projectile; and the only force present must be directed at right angles to the motion, or along the radius. From this deduction by Galileo, Huygens[19] derived his general law of centrifugal force, and Newton, his solution of Kepler's law some time between 1667 and 1687.

In an interesting essay[20] on the sources of Newton's ideas on the principles of mechanics, Professor Child expresses the opinion, which he frankly confesses to be a guess, that the inspiration for the preliminary matter of the *Principia* came from the work of Baliani. He states that his guess would be justified if, "after a careful search into the works that were in Newton's library, there is found a copy of a certain book, especially if it shows signs of having been much used, or if in any of his manuscripts a certain name occurs; and I will gladly acknowledge the error of my ways if such a book is not to be found. The book is *De Motu* and the author is *Baliani*." My own reading of the *De Motu* leaves me with the opinion that any connection between Baliani and Newton is extremely doubtful. His treatment of the problem of forces seems far more limited and obscure than that by Galileo. And the chance that this work by an obscure Italian was known to Newton and his contemporary English natural philosophers is far less likely than that the *Dialogues* of the most eminent man of science of the age were not familiar to them. The *Dialogues on the Two New Sciences* had been translated into English in 1665 and, although the edition may have been destroyed in the London fire of the following year, the original or some copies must have been well known and studied.[21]

If we turn to Newton, himself, for the sources of his ideas, we obtain very little information. For his discovery of the problem of the moon's force in 1666, we gather that he developed the law of in-

[19] *Cf. Horologium Oscillatorium*, published in 1673.

[20] *Cf. Isaac Newton*, 1642–1727. Ed. by Greenstreet, p. 117.

[21] For Professor Child's discussion of this point, *cf.* Greenstreet, pp. 125–129. As for Newton's manuscripts, I have found no reference in any of them to Baliani; this is not conclusive as it is certain that many of them were destroyed and others have not been discovered. As for his library, since Professor Child wrote his essay Col. de Villamil has found and published the complete catalogue of Newton's books, as inventoried at his death, and no work by Baliani is included. Professor Child makes a slight error when he states that the first book of his *De Motu* was published in 1639; it bears the imprint, Genoa, 1638. His guess, also, has not been substantiated.

verse squares from a direct study of Copernicus and Kepler with the mathematical aid of Descartes, Barrow, and Wallis. In the *Principia,* he mentions Galileo as the source from which he formulated his first and second laws of motion; and from the work of Wren, Wallis, and Huygens on the laws of impact, he obtained his third law. It is significant of his dislike for Hooke and Descartes that he omits their names. The law of attraction, as being proportional to the inverse square of the distance, he states was surmised by Wren, Hooke, and Halley and he specifically mentions that Huygens had compared the force of gravity with the centrifugal forces of revolving bodies. In his correspondence with Halley, the statement is made that Borelli had contributed something to the discovery and had written modestly about it, but Hooke had published Borelli's hypothesis as his own. He also gives credit to Bullialdus for a share in its history. While Descartes should be considered as one of the great contributors to the mechanistic hypothesis and, in fact, elaborated a vast cosmical system on that doctrine, his invention of vortices to carry the planets about the sun was the chief obstacle to the acceptance of Newtonian mechanics; and Newton took great pains to expose the failure of the vortical theory in a manner which clearly showed his satisfaction.

Although Newton stated explicitly that Borelli and Bullialdus[22] had arrived at the correct law of gravitation and also intimated that their views had been of aid to him in his own work, the various commentators on the *Principia* are quite divided in their opinions as to whether any such conclusions can be derived from the works of those two authors. It seems to me we might accept Newton's testimony rather than their opinion that those authors, whether wittingly or not, had contributed something of real importance to that great discovery. At least we can let them speak for themselves.

Bullialdus (or Bouilleaud, 1605–1694), a French astronomer, was an accurate and voluminous observer whose data on the orbits of the planets were quoted as authoritative by Newton in the *Principia.* He was an enthusiastic supporter of the Copernican system; and was so convinced, that the success of the new science was dependent on a revival of the Pythagorean and Platonic scientific conceptions, as to name his most important treatise the *Astronomia Philolaica*[23] to indicate his belief that Philolaus, the Pythagorean, was the founder

[22] It is interesting to note, in connection with Professor Child's "guess," that the works of Borelli are listed in Newton's library, but that none of Bullialdus's is mentioned.

[23] Ismaelis Bullialdi *Astronomia Philolaica.* Paris, 1645.

of the true astronomy. The work is one of the most important of the period. It contains a valuable summary of the history of astronomy and a wealth of data. While he gives proper credit to Kepler, he accuses him of advancing an erroneous hypothesis of planetary motions. The portion of the work, which discusses this hypothesis, is contained in the twelfth chapter of the first book, headed *An sol moveat planetas*. He combats Kepler's idea that the motive force of the planets resided in the sun which was endowed with a *species,* or effluvium, of a spiritual or magnetical nature, and whirled those inert bodies about him in their orbits. While he adduces four objections, the significant reasons he gives are first; if the planets are thus inert, how do they, the earth and Jupiter for example, move their own satellites and, secondly, he denies that there are any such whirling forces. In the course of his argument, he affirms that the planetary force is one which acts along the line joining the two bodies and decreases inversely as the square of the distance between them.[24]

One of the earliest attempts to explain all phenomena by means of atoms, or corpuscles, which were subject only to mechanical laws, was made by Giovanni Alfonso Borelli[25] (1608–1679), a Neapolitan, and the most distinguished member of the Accademia del Cimento. In brief, his fundamental postulate was that all natural actions are caused by a gravitational force on the corpuscles which pulls them towards the centre of the earth according to mechanical laws; but the particular forms of the corpuscles and their mutual linkages divert their downward motion into other directions. Thus, aggregations of corpuscles are like machines whose prime motive force is gravity, but whose construction is so designed as to make them operate in various ways. The dilemma which faces all mechanists is how to give an active principle to atoms which are essentially inert and passive. The problem is really insoluble and the usual method is to create an hypothetical substance which complacently does all those things which may be needed. So Borelli asserts that there are also

[24] The passage (*Cf.* p. 23) is quite explicit although the reasons are specious: "Virtus autem illa, qua Sol prehendit seu harpagat planetas, corporalis quae ipsi [Kepler] pro manibus est, lineis rectis in omnem mundi amplitudinem emissa quasi species solis cum illius corpore rotatur: cum ergo sit corporalis imminuitur, et extenuatur in majori spatio et intervallo, ratio autem hujus imminutionis eadem est, ac luminis, in ratione nempe dupla virtutem motricem in simpla tantum ratione inu (t) ervallorum contendit imminui."

[25] His most important works on physics are: Theorica mediceorum planetarum ex causis physicis deducta, Florence, 1666; De motu animalium, opus posthumum, Rome, 1681; De motionibus naturalibus, a gravitate pendentibus, Lugeluni Bataborum, 1686.

certain æthereal and living (*spirituosa et vivida*) particles which were endowed with the attribute of self-motion by God at the creation. The otherwise inert material bodies enmesh in their pores a multitude of these active æthereal corpuscles and so he accounts for the forces of gravity, magnetism, etc. This hypothesis has so many points of resemblance with Newton's speculations on an æther that he very probably was influenced by it. Borelli's contribution to Kepler's problem is found in his study of Jupiter's moons. He remarks that, when a body revolves in an orbit, it has a tendency to recede from its centre of revolution as mud from the rim of a wheel, or a stone whirled by a sling. When this force of recession is equal to a force of attraction pulling it to the centre, the body will neither approach nor recede from the centre but will continually revolve about it, and a planet will appear balanced and floating on the surface of a sphere.

This statement brings us down to the time of the active work of Newton, and may well close our summary of the growth of the mechanistic hypothesis which he completed by his discovery of an universal law of attraction. However much we may respect his predecessors, we cannot fail to recognise that their ideas were vague and that no organised scientific method could be derived from them. If we may personify Nature and give to her the attribute of choice, we may then say that out of all the human race she granted to Newton the unique destiny of disclosing her profoundest secret. All that was needed was a mathematical apparatus capable of expressing the changes of path of a body under a constantly varying motion. The classic geometry, dealing with static problems, was inadequate. But the expansion of mathematical analysis during the Renaissance was even more rapid than was that of astronomy and physics. Descartes made the first great step by his fusion of algebra and geometry. This powerful analysis was developed into the method of solving problems of curvilinear motion by expansion into infinite series; the final step was the invention of the calculus, or summation of infinitesimal variations by Newton and Leibniz.

CHAPTER IX

THE PRINCIPIA

1685–1687

When the curious in such matters, filled with a sort of awe because of the marvels of Newton's mind, enquired of him to what quality he owed a success which they characterised as superhuman, they obtained but little satisfaction. He could ascribe his success only to a patience and perseverance which he thought may have surpassed somewhat that of other men; he could discover in himself no peculiar sagacity, or especial genius. But this is no answer at all; no amount of patience and perseverance can achieve such results unless they are based on what we vaguely call genius or intuitive insight, a quality which seems mysterious because we cannot follow its logical operations. It is safe to affirm that the history of science offers no parallel to the achievement by Newton of three capital discoveries in the interval of two years; this achievement is enhanced by the fact that they were made by a youth in his second decade and without preparatory labour.

And because Newton limited his scientific work to the formulation of laws, and restrained his imagination from making hypotheses as to how nature operates, his great discoveries and laws are classic and permanent. The attraction of matter as a universal force is unquestionable, and the deductions he made from it are true so long as mathematics can express the truth. His law, that this attraction varies as the inverse square of the distance, may be an approximation; we may find that the exponent two is either a little too great or too small; and other influences may modify the effects of such attraction. But the law itself cannot be overthrown as can be an hypothesis, which attempts to explain the nature of matter or the mechanism of its action; such laws can only be made more precise.

Unlike his early work on light, which was carried on consecutively and was published currently in the *Philosophical Transactions,* Newton's first calculation of the attraction on the moon was laid aside, and the subject incubated in his mind for twenty years. When he finally published his *Principia,* the world was amazed with the realisation that the new science, begun by Copernicus, had been brought to fruition, and that a new philosophy of life had been born.

There are several reasons why the discussion of Newton's *Principia* should be treated by a biographer differently from that given in connection with his discoveries in light. In the first place, with the exception of a certain amount of spluttering by Hooke, there was no controversy. It was at once recognised that here was a work of such transcendent quality, that merely to follow its conclusions would tax the ingenuity of the best minds, and that no living persons could challenge its originality or power. Newton had become the admitted dictator of scientific thought, and there was no one able to cross swords with him. It was expedient to give in some detail the particulars of his work on light and of the controversy which resulted,—not because of the value of the facts involved, but because, out of that controversy, there came the clear enunciation of his principles of the scientific method and its limitations. It was the misconception of that work, and the inability of his opponents to distinguish between theory and hypothesis, which finally made him resolve to eliminate from his later masterpiece all discussion of *why and how* nature worked, and to announce his famous motto, *hypotheses non fingo.* And so far as I know, his *Principia* does follow more closely that precept than any other scientific treatise: and for that reason, his mechanistic theory has been developed as new knowledge has been acquired; it has been criticised, and its errors have been corrected till, in its legitimate field, mechanics is the most nearly perfect of all the sciences; it cannot be superseded, and it must remain the fixed corner-stone of all mechanistic science. If Newton's distinction between natural theory and hypothesis, between humanism and science, was made clear in that earlier discussion, it is not necessary to repeat it; to emphasize it then seemed to be opportune because of late there has been a renewed outburst of unrestrained speculation by mathematical physicists, who have forsaken the sober paths of scientific achievement in order to indulge in pure symbolism, and have invented a universe whose phenomena and laws have no correspondence with our sense perceptions.

There is also no need to discuss in detail the scientific conclusions of the *Principia* as they have been the theme of almost countless commentators. This work has been done by Lagrange, by Laplace, and by others. And those readers who have the technical equipment can readily turn to them. As for its philosophical influence on science, on pseudo-science, on society, and especially on religion, the field is too large to be incorporated in a biography and should be the subject of a special study. The *Principia* has been a great reservoir from which mechanistic philosophers have drawn their ideas and, in spite of Newton's warning, they have applied it to all sorts of problems which lie outside the field of mechanics, and even of physics.

The history of Newton's *Principia* takes us back again to the time when he spent the greater part of the years, 1665 and 1666, quietly at Woolsthorpe to escape the plague. He had just been graduated from college and had been successful enough to be appointed to a scholarship. As a boy, he had spent his days on the farm, meditating on the childish problems which interested him, and now as he comes back, a man, he takes up again his former life; but his mind is now full of profound ideas, and his meditations are to change the course of all future thought. In the long summer afternoons, he sits in the orchard which still stands near the old gray stone house; on one memorable day, an apple falls with a slight thud at his feet. It was a trifling incident which has been idly noticed thousands of times; but now, like the click of some small switch which starts a great machine in operation, it proved to be the jog which awoke his mind to action. As in a vision, he saw that if the mysterious pull of the earth can act through space as far as the top of a tree, of a mountain, and even to a bird soaring high in the air, or to the clouds, so it might even reach so far as the moon. If such were the case, then the moon would be like a stone thrown horizontally, always falling towards the earth, but never reaching the ground, because its swift motion carried it far beyond the horizon. Always falling towards the earth and always passing beyond it, the moon would follow its elliptical path if these two motions were equally balanced. How simple the idea seems to us now as we look backwards, but how difficult it was to foresee can be gathered from the fact that even a Galileo, who had solved the problem of the projectile, did not have sufficient imagination to guess that the moon was only a projectile moving swiftly enough to pass beyond the earth. Nor could Huygens, who formulated the laws of centrifugal force and motion, penetrate the secret. Perhaps even more significant of Newton's genius, was the fact that he not only guessed the law of attraction, but he immediately set himself the task of calculating what would be the law of the force which could hold the moon in her orbit.

All that we know about the initial step of this greatest of discoveries is that Newton did make a calculation to see if a force of attraction, which varied as the inverse square of the distance between the two bodies, would account for the laws of planetary motion; and, having fairly well satisfied himself of its truth, he laid the problem aside to think about other things. Nor did he make any record, at the time, of the sequence of his ideas; and he apparently was unable to tell the story accurately after some years had passed. The earliest account of his discovery was given, in 1694, by Newton to Whiston, who reported it as follows:[1]

"Upon Sir Isaac's first trial, when he took a degree of a great circle on the earth's surface, whence a degree at the distance of the moon was to be determined also, to be 60 measured miles only, according to the gross measures then in use. He was, in some degree, disappointed, and the power that restrained the moon in her orbit, measured by the versed sines of that orbit, appeared not to be quite the same that was to be expected, had it been the power of gravity alone, by which the moon was there influenc'd. Upon this disappointment, which made Sir Isaac suspect that this power was partly that of gravity, and partly that of Cartesius's vortices, he threw aside the paper of his calculation, and went to other studies. However, some time afterward, when Monsieur Picard had much more exactly measured the earth, and found that a degree of a great circle was 69½ such miles, Sir Isaac, in turning over some of his former papers, light upon this old imperfect calculation; and, correcting his former error, discover'd that this power, at the true correct distance of the moon from the earth, not only tended to the earth's centre, as did the common power of gravity with us, but was exactly of the right quantity; and that if a stone was carried up to the moon, or to 60 semidiameters of the earth, and let fall downward by its gravity, and the moon's own menstrual motion was stopt, and she was let fall by that power which before retained her in her orbit, they would exactly fall towards the same point, and with the same velocity; which was therefore no other power than that of gravity. And since that power appear'd to extend as far as the moon, at the distance of 240,000 miles, it was but natural, or rather necessary, to suppose it might reach twice, thrice, four times, etc., the same distance, with the same diminution, according to the squares of such distances per-

[1] *Memoirs of Whiston.* London, 1749, pp. 36–38. This passage is given *verbatim,* even where the author's sentence construction is certainly not all that it might be.

petually. Which noble discovery proved the happy occasion of the invention of the wonderful Newtonian philosophy."

Pemberton, who edited the third edition of the *Principia,* gives pretty much the same story of the error in the calculation, arising from having taken the wrong diameter of the earth. According to his account Newton, "being absent from books, he took the common estimate in use among geographers and our seamen, before Norwood had measured the earth, that 60 English miles were contained in one degree of latitude on the surface of the earth."

We have one other account of the discovery and later development of the law of gravitation drawn up by Newton, himself, sometime about 1714. While there are some minor mistakes, it is, on the whole, correct. This memorandum has been preserved in the *Portsmouth Collection,*[2] and is as follows:

"In the same year [1666] I began to think of gravity extending to the orb of the moon, and having found out how to estimate the force with which a globe revolving within a sphere presses the surface of the sphere, from Kepler's Rule of the periodical times of the planets being in a sesquialterate proportion of their distances from the centres of their orbs I deduced that the forces which keep the planets in their orbs must [be] reciprocally as the squares of their distances from the centres about which they revolve: and thereby compared the force requisite to keep the moon in her orb with the force of gravity at the surface of the earth, and found them answer pretty nearly. All this was in the two plague years of 1665 and 1666, for in those days I was in the prime of my age for invention, and minded mathematics and philosophy more than at any time since. What Mr. Huygens has published since about centrifugal forces I suppose he had before me. At length in the winter between the years 1676 and 1677 [probably this should be 1679 and 1680] I found the proposition that by a centrifugal force reciprocally as the square of the distance a planet must revolve in an ellipsis about the centre of the force placed in the lower umbilicus of the ellipsis and with a radius drawn to that centre describe areas proportional to the times. And in the winter between the years 1683 and 1684 [this should be the winter between 1684 and 1685] this proposition with the demonstration was entered in the Register book of the R. Society."

On the basis of Newton's conversations with Whiston and Pemberton, the tradition has thus come down to us that, having taken a

[2] *Portsmouth Collection,* sec. I, div. X, number 41.

wrong figure for the earth's diameter, his calculated acceleration of the moon towards the earth did not agree with what it should be, if the attraction varied as the inverse square of the distance from the earth. Such was his modesty and love of accuracy, so we have been taught to believe, that he put away his calculations, supposing that the force of gravity was not sufficient and that an unknown whirling force, perhaps a Cartesian vortex, must be added in order to maintain the moon in her orbit. It was also believed, on a statement of Robison, that, when he afterwards learned of Picard's more accurate measurement of the earth's diameter, he went home from London and repeated his old calculations. When he saw his ideas were likely to be confirmed, "he was so much agitated, that he was obliged to desire a friend to finish them."

In spite of the apparent straightforwardness and authority of this tradition, there are many puzzling features connected with it which make it difficult to accept. In the first place, Newton said of his work that he had found his calculations to "answer pretty nearly." Working as he did at a place where he would not have reference books, he should have been satisfied with an approximate result and, after all, his result was only one-eighth too small. He also, at the time, expected his calculation to be an approximation, as he supposed the dimensions of attracting bodies affected the result; but he thought he might, without a serious error, neglect the dimensions of the earth and moon in comparison with the very great distance between them. Finally, for simplification of the problem, he assumed the moon's orbit to be a circle instead of an ellipse. Thus, it seems that the error in taking a wrong value for the earth's diameter, an error which it will be shown could readily be corrected, is quite inadequate as a cause why Newton laid aside this work for many years.

The statement, that Newton took an incorrect value of the earth's diameter, and thus made an error in his first rough calculation of the law of gravity, is too well authenticated not to be accepted as true. It is very probable, also, that he laid aside this problem, temporarily, as he devoted himself to work on lenses and light. But, it is also generally stated that this error was not corrected, and his calculation repeated, till 1682 when he first became acquainted with Picard's new, and more accurate, measurement of the earth's diameter. It is important to discuss at length the history of one of the greatest of scientific discoveries; especially, as it can be shown that there is no likelihood that his early error delayed the publication of the *Prin-*

cipia. Realising, however, the persistence of such a legend, when once it has become established, there is little doubt that it will continue to be cited by popular writers on science, even if a more reasonable explanation be advanced.

The reason commonly given for Newton's careless adoption of an inaccurate value for the earth's diameter is that he was in the country and, having no reference books at hand, he took the "local estimate of 60 miles per degree of latitude, used by old geographers and seamen, instead of 69+ miles." Rigaud conjectures that he may have been familiar with this figure because it had been published in a text-book by Edward Wright, Fellow of Clare College. This may be ingenious, but it is certainly not conclusive.

In the first place, it will be well to consider what authorities on the measurement of the earth were available to Newton. There was undoubtedly wide divergence of opinion, but fairly reliable data were easily obtainable by him.[8] One of the most accurate determinations of the earth's diameter was made by Snell who computed 66.91 statute miles per degree of a great circle. The length of a statute mile had been defined in 1593 as equal to 5280 feet. Now Snell's estimate had been accepted by Oughtred, and by Gunter, and books by both of them were owned and read by Newton. If he used this value, his error would have been less than four per cent.

Snell's value was also mentioned in Varenius's Geography, which was a standard text, so well known that Newton edited it in 1672. But the most likely authority for him to consult was Norwood. He had published his *Trigonometry* in 1631, and his *Sea-Mans Practice* in 1636. He adopted the very convenient measure for seamen of one nautical mile for each minute of latitude, or 60 nautical miles per degree; and this practice is still in use. But he defined such a mile as being equal to 6080 feet; thus his measurement is the quite accurate one of 69.5 statute miles per degree. It would seem then, if Newton followed "the common usage of seamen" and took 60 miles instead of 69.5, he must have overlooked the difference in length be-

[8] The curious may find an elaborate discussion of the facts known at the time about the size of the earth, and the confusion in the standards of lengths, in a most valuable essay by Professor Cajori on "Newton's delay in announcing the law of gravitation" which appeared in the memorial volume, *"Sir Isaac Newton, 1727–1927"* published by the History of Science Society, Baltimore, 1928.—The writer also discusses the causes of the delay in publishing the *Principia,* and is convinced that it resulted from Newton's inability to solve the theoretical attraction of a sphere on an external point and so obtain a general solution of the problem of attraction. I think, however, that Professor Cajori neglects an even more important cause,—Newton's temperamental procrastination and distaste for developing systematically any mathematical problem.

tween nautical and statute miles, and such a mistake should not have long misled him.

Voltaire, however, stated, and he probably got the information from Mrs. Catherine Barton, that Newton was unacquainted with the work both of Snell, and of Norwood, whose measurement had been completely forgotten during the disturbances of the civil wars. But it has already been shown that Snell's value was quoted by Gunter and by Oughtred. As for Norwood, the statement is certainly wrong; the fourth edition of his *Trigonometry* was published in 1661 and the seventh edition of the *Sea-Mans Practice* in 1667, which is sufficient evidence that his work was not forgotten.

It thus seems certain that Newton could easily have found a sufficiently accurate measure of the earth's radius. Just when he recalculated his problem will probably never be known, but some erroneous statements can be corrected, and something can be done towards establishing a limit to the time which elapsed. Whiston assigns the cause of reworking the problem to an accidental turning over of his early notes, but he mentions no date. Pemberton makes two mistakes in his Preface to the *Principia.* He states that: "Some years after, a letter which he received from Dr. Hooke put him on enquiring what was the real figure, in which a body let fall from any high place descends, taking the motion of the earth round its axis into consideration." The reader will remember that this letter was the cause of Newton's solving the general theorems of the attraction of a sphere on a mass-point. This letter was written in 1679; and as it is evident, from the correspondence, that Newton was then acquainted with the law of gravitation, he must have reworked his early calculation before that time. "This gave occasion to his resuming his former thoughts concerning the moon; and Picard in France having lately measured the earth, by using his measures the moon appeared to be kept in her orbit purely by the power of gravity." This second mistake was unfortunately adopted in the *Biographia Britannica,* where it is explicitly stated that Picard's measurement was published in 1679.

Evidently Biot, in his *Life of Newton,* was misled by Pemberton's account into saying: "à ce que l'on peut conjecturer, vers le mois de Juin 1682, se trouvant à Londres à une séance de la Société Royale on vint à parler de la nouvelle mesure d'un degré terrestre, récemment exécuté en France par Picard." He thus assigns the cause to Newton's first acquaintance with Picard's work and places the date still later. Although Biot merely advanced this as a conjecture, it was published in an English translation as a positive assertion, as if it were founded on an investigation of the facts, and has been accepted as a fact by popular writers who have failed to examine the sources.

An examination of any reference book on mathematics would have shown the errors in the above statements about Picard. His very accurate measurement of the earth was made in 1669 and published in his *Mesure de la Terre* in 1671.[4] Picard's work was immediately recognised in England, and was referred to in the meeting of the Royal Society, 11 January, 1671/2, when the exact length of a degree, as he measured it, was specifically mentioned in a letter read by the Secretary. At this same meeting, Newton was elected to membership and his correspondence with Oldenburg began. The matter aroused such interest that it was read again at the next meeting. Three years later, in 1675, a detailed account was published in the *Transactions,* and it was again noticed the following year. In this same year, Newton was present at a meeting for the first time on the occasion of his being admitted a member and signing the register. But during the years Picard's work was discussed, Oldenburg had been sending him regularly the *Transactions,* and giving to him information about all matters of scientific interest. It thus seems certain that he knew the correct diameter of the earth by 1675, at the latest. Nor does it seem credible that he had not recalculated his first attempt when his attention was called to Picard's work, even if he had not done so before from the estimates of Snell, or Norwood.

It must be admitted that the argument, so far advanced, is somewhat conjectural; but there is a bit of evidence, which has been overlooked, and which should be convincing that Newton recalculated the attraction of the moon not later than 1673. In that year Huygens published his *Horologium Oscillatorium* and sent Newton a complimentary copy. In this celebrated treatise, the author developed, for the first time, the general laws for centrifugal force. That Newton read the book and recognised the bearing it had on the problem of gravitation is certain, for he wrote to Oldenburg: "I receiv'd your letters, with M. Huygens's kind present, which I viewed with great satisfaction, finding it full of very subtile and useful specu-

[4] Marie in his *Histoire des sciences* remarks that Picard's measurement "was sufficiently accurate for Newton, who awaited the results of this great operation before daring to publish his discovery of the law of universal gravitation, to find by it a full confirmation of his theory." There is no doubt that Newton used Picard's measurement in the preparation of the *Principia,* but he certainly did not await the result before daring to publish the law. In fact, Norwood's measurement was accurate enough for that purpose.

lations very worthy of the author. I am glad, that we are to expect another discourse of the Vis Centrifuga, which speculation may prove of *good use in Natural Philosophy and Astronomy,* as well as in Mechanics."[5]

Newton also must have seen that Huygens's law of centrifugal force was easily deducible from his own calculation on the attraction of the moon, and that by neglecting to follow up his work, Huygens had preceded him. This is proved from his statement in the memorandum previously quoted: "What Mr. Huygens has published since about centrifugal forces I suppose he had before me." There can be no reasonable doubt that Newton, at once, recognised that Huygens had antedated him by the publication of one of the essential deductions from his discovery of the law of gravitation, or that he would not recollect his own early work with its faulty result, and immediately recalculate it if he had not already done so? This time there would be no question of neglecting to take a reliable figure, such as Norwood's or Picard's, for the radius of the earth.

If Newton had satisfied himself fairly well in 1666 that he had found the force which would account for Kepler's planetary laws, and did not fully satisfy himself till 1673, how can we account for this delay? To suppose that it was because of taking a wrong measure for the earth, does not fit with his character, for even a very mediocre scientist could be expected to correct such a mistake. It was the opinion of Professor Adams, that the result of his first rough calculations would convince Newton that the moon was held in its orbit by gravity alone, and he strongly suspected that Newton believed then in a mutual attraction of the same sort between every two particles of matter, which was proportional to the product of their masses and inversely proportional to the square of the distance between them. Great weight should be given to this opinion of Professor Adams, not only because he was one of the greatest English

[5] The original is in the guard-book (N. 1) of the Royal Society and dated "June 23, 73." See Rigaud, p. 44.

The law of centrifugal force developed by Huygens is $f=v^2/r$, where f is the acceleration, v is the linear velocity, and r is the distance from the centre. Newton, in making his recalculation, could use either Huygens's general formula, or the special one he had derived in his earlier calculation. By Kepler's third law, T^2/r^3 is constant, where T is the periodic time of the satellite. But $v^2 = \frac{4\pi^2 r^2}{T^2}$, and by substitution, $f = \frac{4\pi^2 r^2}{T^2 r}$. Since T^2 is proportional to r^3, then f is proportional to $1/r^2$. Since the radius of the earth is approximately 4000 miles and the moon's distance 240,000 miles, the relative accelerations are as the squares of these distances. Newton's first assumption of 60 statute miles, instead of 60 nautical miles, per degree of latitude corresponds to a radius of 3400 miles, about one-eighth too small.

astronomers but he was also the active member of the Cambridge Committee which examined and catalogued Newton's manuscripts. The reason seems simple enough if we take into account his intense activity in other work during that time. In mathematics, he had made important discoveries in the solution of problems by the new method of infinite series; he had edited Kinkhuysen's *Algebra,* discovered the binomial theorem, and invented fluxional calculus. He had accomplished an astonishing amount of work in the subject of light; had prepared his course of Lucasian lectures, and had edited Varenius's *Geography*.

We may grant that Newton accomplished enough in those seven years to satisfy a life-time of work; but still the question may be asked, why did he postpone the problem of attraction which was the most important of all his work? We should remember that he had solved only an isolated problem approximately. It was contrary to his custom to publish such incomplete discoveries; he meditated on them till their full significance was revealed to him. He saw, at once, if the earth and moon attracted each other at so great a distance, then all bodies must possess a like force, and the applications of such a universal property to problems of mechanics were almost infinitely numerous.

Before such a generalisation could be made, a fundamental theorem must be proved; that is, to find the effect of the size and shape of the bodies on their attraction. Newton, in his early calculations, had assumed the distance between the earth and moon to be so great that he could neglect their own dimensions. But would the law of the inverse square of the distance hold when the bodies were close together, say for an apple on the tree, or on the ground? What was the law for bodies below the surface of the earth, and should the distance be measured from the centres, or from the surfaces of the bodies? Nor could it be assumed that the kind of material would not affect the attraction and, sometime in his life, he performed many experiments to prove that it did not. For this purpose he enclosed successively different materials in a hollow pendulum bob and found, to his great surprise, that the period of oscillation was unaffected. All this information neither Newton nor anyone else had, and he was too busy to acquire it.

In 1673, his attention was recalled to the subject by Huygens's formulation of the laws of centrifugal force, and he found that he had been forestalled in one of the most important deductions of the law of gravitation. But, even then, he was not ready for his great synthesis and, for six years more, the curtain conceals from us what he was thinking about this problem. The curtain did not rise again on this mystery drama till 1679, when Hooke wrote a civil letter to Newton, asking him to communicate to the Royal Society any philosophical results he might come upon, and, particularly, to criticise M. de Messanger's new theory of the solar system. The correspondence which ensued has been discussed in an earlier chapter. It will be remembered Newton answered, that he had just returned from Lincolnshire where he had been attending to family matters and had had no time to think about philosophy. And as a further excuse he added: "I had for some years past been endeavouring to bend myself from philosophy to other studies in so much that I have long grutched the time spent in that study unless it be perhaps at idle hours sometimes for a diversion." Then he, pleasantly, emphasized his retirement from science by confessing that he is ignorant even of Hooke's great work. He is, he sarcastically adds, highly flattered to be asked now to communicate new matters to the Royal Society when "formerly I must acknowledge I was moved by other reasons to decline, as much as Mr. Oldenburg's importunity and ways to engage me in disputes would permit, all correspondence with him about them." As to his criticising the proposed cosmic theory, that is quite impossible as there is no one in the University who makes astronomical observations, "and my own short sightedness and tenderness of health makes me something unfit."

Newton thus, with great ingenuity, relieved his feeling of resentment for past injustice, and insinuated every reason for making Hooke so angry that he would drop any further correspondence. Having got even with his enemy, his better nature induced him, as he later acknowledged to Halley, "to sweeten his answer" by adding a fancy of his own which might, by observing the free fall of a body, give a direct evidence of the earth's diurnal rotation.

It will be remembered how greatly this fancy interested the Society, and how Hooke, in his turn, took much pleasure in pointing out publicly a careless error Newton had made in supposing the path of the falling body would be a spiral. This fillip was useful and effectual, for Newton set himself seriously to the task of generalising the problem of the moon. And, in the course of this work, he solved one of the fundamental theorems of dynamics, that the attraction of a body on a mass-point situated outside, on, or inside, the surface of the body was equivalent to the attraction of an equal mass placed at its centre of gravity. The time was ripe, for other men were interested in the problem. Thus, he wrote to Halley in 1686, "I remember about nine years since Sir Christopher Wren, upon a visit Dr. Donne and I gave him at his lodgings, discoursed of this problem of determining the planetary motions upon philosophical principle." Poor Hooke had the unfortunate habit of exasperating Newton to a degree which invariably aroused him to an effort that ended in crushing his own claims to discovery. In this case Hooke's really important, although inconclusive, work was swallowed up in the masterpiece which he incited his rival to create. Newton rather bitterly acknowledged this fact: "Though his correcting my spiral occasioned my finding the theorem, by which I afterwards examined the ellipses; yet am I not beholden to him for any light into the business, but only for the diversion he gave me from my other studies to think of these things, and for his dogmaticalness in writing."[6] Pemberton[7] says that "hereupon he composed near a dozen propositions relating to the motion of the primary planets about the sun." This may be an exaggeration as Newton, in a memorandum, stated that he solved at that time only two of the important propositions later included in the *Principia.* Then this extraordinary man, apparently, dropped the subject and, except for his correspondence with Flamsteed about the comet of 1680, he seems for five years to have kept his word about giving his time to other matters he considered more interesting.

When the curtain rises for the last act of the drama, the scene discovers three men in an inn discussing grave matters. Edmond Halley, from consideration of the third law of Kepler, had come to the conclusion that the centripetal force of attraction was inversely proportional to the square of the distance. But, not being able to prove it, he went up to London from Islington in January, 1683/4, where he says:[8] "I met with Sir Christopher Wren and Mr. Hooke, and falling in discourse about it, Mr. Hooke affirmed, that upon that principle all the laws of the celestial motions were to be demonstrated, and that he himself had done it. I declared the ill success of my own attempts; and Sir Christopher, to encourage the enquiry, said, that he would give Mr. Hooke, or me, two months' time, to bring him a convincing demonstration thereof; and besides the honour, he of us, that did it, should have from him a present of a book

[6] Rigaud, App. p. 44. [7] *Cf. Preface to Princ.* 3d Ed. [8] Rigaud. App. p. 36.

of 40 shillings. Mr. Hooke then said, that he had it, but he would conceal it for some time, that others trying and failing might know how to value it, when he should make it public. However I remember, that Sir Christopher was little satisfied that he could do it; and though Mr. Hooker then promised to shew it him, I do not find, that in that particular he has been so good as his word."

Obtaining little satisfaction from his friends, the indefatigable Halley probably went back to Islington to wrestle again with the knotty problem. How much he was able to accomplish by himself we do not know; but the following August he set out for Cambridge, as he must have heard from Wren that Newton had talked about the same subject with him some years back, and might be able to offer some suggestions. Conduitt, although he is often not accurate, gives a graphic picture of the interview which bears all the ear-marks of the truth. Halley, he states, "at once indicated the object of his visit by asking Newton what would be the curve described by the planets on the supposition that gravity diminished as the square of the distance. Newton immediately answered, *an ellipse*. Struck with joy and amazement, Halley asked him how he knew it? Why, replied he, I have calculated it; and being asked for the calculation, he could not find it, but promised to send it to him."[9] After Halley left Cambridge, "Sir Isaac, in order to make good his promise, fell to work again, but he could not come to that conclusion which he thought he had before examined with care; however, he attempted a new way, which, though longer than the first, brought him again to his former conclusion. Then he examined carefully what might be the reason why the calculation he had undertaken before did not prove right, and he found that, having drawn an ellipse cursorily with his own hand, he had drawn the two axes of the curve, instead of drawing two diameters somewhat inclined to one another, whereby he might have fixed his imagination to any two conjugate diameters which was requisite he should do. That being perceived, he made both his calculations agree together."[10]

One can easily imagine the conflicting emotions that must have passed through Halley's mind when he learned, at the same moment, that Newton had solved the age-long problem of gravitation but could not find his notes,—papers which other men would have re-

[9] Conduitt's *MSS., Portsmouth Collection.*

[10] Mem. given to Conduitt by Demoivre. *Portsmouth Collection.*—This famous story of Newton, being baffled by a simple error in drawing a diagram, is also given in Conduitt's *MSS.*, but he mars it in his account.

garded as their most precious possession. I think Halley must have, then and there, penetrated the character of the man and realised the task he was about to undertake. At any rate, he left Cambridge with the hope that something large had been started; but he could not have dreamed that he had laid the foundation for the *Principia*. Newton's powers were now thoroughly aroused. He set himself to a second recalculation and found to his chagrin that he could not carry it through. That great mind had been balked by a trivial error which it pleases us to think could happen to him. He had carelessly drawn two axes of an ellipse instead of two conjugate diameters, and it was with difficulty that he found his mistake.

This last obstacle removed, Newton stayed in Cambridge the rest of the summer and, at the opening of the Michaelmas term in October, he had put into connected form enough problems on planetary motion to serve for a course of nine lectures delivered under the title *De Motu Corporum*.[11]

These lectures thus form the nucleus of the *Principia*. Mindful of his promise, Newton, in November, dispatched a copy of his demonstrations to Halley by Paget, the ill-fated protégé of Flamsteed. Halley had two characteristics in addition to his own ability, a real flair for detecting distinction in others with the patience and tact to bring out their best effort. He recognised at once the superlative character of the work submitted to him. In order to waste no time in a protracted correspondence, he, keen on the scent, travelled at once to Cambridge to confer with the author, and to urge him to send an abstract to the Royal Society so that his priority of discovery would be secured. It is probable also that the agreement was made to expand these lectures into a treatise which would embrace the applications of his discovery to the general problems of astron-

[11] The lectures of Newton from Jan. 1669/70 to 1687 inclusive, with the exception of the year 1686, have been preserved in the Cambridge University Library. They consist of four manuscript volumes. The first volume contains his lectures on light from 1669 to 1672; only the marginal notes and corrections are in his handwriting. The second volume comprises lectures on arithmetic and algebra which he gave from 1673 to 1683. The third volume contains the lectures of 1684 and 1685 *De Motu Corporum*. The lectures for the following year are either lost or were omitted. And the last volume is a series of five lectures *On the System of the World*, which he delivered in 1687, and were intended for the third book of the *Principia*. The remainder of the treatise, not divided into lectures, is bound up in the same book. Newton delivered only one lecture a week during the Michaelmas Term, making in all a course of nine or ten lectures a year. Each apparently lasted a half hour and if, as sometimes happened, no one turned up, he lingered a short while and then returned to his study. He also never repeated his lectures, but continued them the following October where he had left off the preceding December. One may surmise that his students, as Whiston confessed, understood but little of his discourses.

omy. Satisfied by a promise given to him, he returned to London and, on December 10, 1684, presented the whole matter to the Royal Society. Here, again, he succeeded: "Mr. Halley gave an account, that he had lately seen Mr. Newton at Cambridge, who had shewed him a curious treatise, *De Motu;* which, upon Mr. Halley's desire, was, he said, promised to be sent to the Society to be entered upon their register. Mr. Halley was desired to put Mr. Newton in mind of his promise for the securing his invention to himself till such time as he would be at leisure to publish it. Mr. Paget was desired to join with Mr. Halley."[12] There is considerable doubt about the contents of this "curious treatise."[13] However that may be, and it is a rather unimportant detail, we know pretty conclusively how far he had gone in his work by the end of the year.

Newton was now thoroughly committed again to publishing a scientific work, in spite of the heartburnings and vexations which that "litigious Lady" had previously imposed upon him. It is almost certain that he did not foresee the magnitude of the work which he had entered upon; at most, he expected to limit himself to the proof of a law of force which would account for Kepler's laws; to some general geometrical theorems; and to their application to planetary motions. He had resolved to expose these in the classic geometrical form and to use the newer analytical geometry, and his own method of fluxions, merely as an aid to their solution. The reason he gave for this decision was that his ideas were novel and difficult to understand in themselves, and he would have further increased the labour of comprehending them, if he had used an unfamiliar mathematical analysis. He also told his friend, the Rev. Dr. Derham, that "to avoid being baited by little smatterers in mathematics, he designedly made his *Principia* abstruse; but yet so as to be understood by able mathematicians who, he imagined, by comprehending his demon-

[12] Birch, Vol. IV, p. 347.

[13] Ball (p. 31) agrees with Rigaud (p. 15) that Halley saw in November the *Mss.* of the lectures; that the tract *De Motu* was written the following December and January, and sent to the Society as a record while the *Principia,* begun at the same time, was being written. Edleston (p. lv) believed "Rigaud's idea that the paper which he has printed from the Register of the Royal Society is different from the paper which Newton sent to Halley was an error, as the whole tenor of our information on the subject shows them to be the same." Brewster (Vol. I, p. 299, note) supposes that the demonstration sent to Halley in November was entered in the Register as part of the treatise *De Motu.*—Rigaud thoughtfully rescued this tract from the oblivion of the Register and published it in the Appendix to his *Essay.* It comprises four theorems and seven problems. He complained that the copyist who transcribed the paper into the Register had been extraordinarily careless and that he had much difficulty correcting it. Ball, since Rigaud's work had become scarce, inserted it in his own *Essay.*

strations would concur with him in his theory."[14] Already, in February, he had begun to realise the difficulty of the task and wrote to Aston that the work was requiring more time than he expected, and that he had wasted a great deal of it. Either for rest, or to attend to family affairs, he was leaving for home, but would finish the manuscript as soon as he could, after his return in a month or six weeks.[15] One might hazard the guess, that his worry and indecision were not caused by inability to solve any particular problem, such a predicament seems to have been unknown to him, but that he was seeking for a general theorem which would include the whole cosmic law. And may he not, as he did before, have found it during the hours of inspiration which so often came to him at home?

At any rate, he discovered and solved the general theorem of the attraction of a solid sphere on a small mass soon after his return to Cambridge.[16] He proved rigorously that the attraction between two solid spheres was exactly equivalent to that of the same masses concentrated at their centres, and was equal to the product of their masses divided by the square of the distance between their centres. Also, this same law holds for the attraction of a sphere on a mass point situated on its surface; and if the point lies within the sphere then the outer shell exerts no force, the resulting force being due only to the smaller solid sphere whose radius passes through the point. The significance of this theorem must have been immediately apparent to him, and we can imagine his profound satisfaction and exaltation of mind when he thus realised that to him had been given the solution of the age-long problem which had baffled the greatest minds of the past. He had found the force which would account for, and measure, the cohesion of a universe scattered through the vast distances of space; a force which would not vanish until the distance became infinite, and would not become infinite unless two bodies occupied the same point in space. All the doubts which had hitherto disturbed him were now settled. There was no longer any question as to the direction of the force between two bodies, or whether the law extended to the surface or the centre of the earth. He knew now that the path of every orbital motion is an ellipse; that even the comets submitted to this law though, when near the sun, the ellipse might be considered as approximately an hyperbola or a parabola;

[14] *Portsmouth Collection.* [15] See letter to Aston, *supra* Chapter VII, p. 245.

[16] His exits and redits for 1685 show that he was away from Cambridge from March 27 to April 11 and from June 11 to June 20. I cannot reconcile these entries with his letter to Aston.

and that the path of a projectile could be described as a parabola only because the surface of the earth was assumed to be an infinite plane instead of a sphere.

Newton now threw himself into the greater task of elaborating a cosmic system developed according to rigorous mathematical formulation, and dependent only on his general law of attraction. We learn of his profound absorption; he lived in a world of meditation. His amanuensis, Humphrey Newton, has left us the impression that he hardly seemed to be a human being, his only relaxation an occasional retreat to his chemical laboratory, and even there he may have been seeking for the principle of chemical affinity by the attraction of corpuscles. And there are legends that he was not conscious of whether he had eaten his meals or not, and that, rising in the morning, he would remain all day sitting on his bed half dressed and lost in thought. We must remember that the *Principia* was not developed from comprehensive notes and data, but was created, *de novo,* step by step. And yet by Easter, 1685, the manuscript of the first book, except for some corrections and additions, was finished; and, during the summer, the second book was composed in rough form. It is probable, also, that he worked out some of the applications of his law, which he later incorporated in the third book. At least, he turned to Flamsteed for astronomical data in four letters written between September and the following January. He stated in them that he was calculating the orbit of the comet of 1680 from three observations. He also asked for information about the tides, about the major axes of the orbits of Jupiter, Saturn, and their satellites, and expressed his thanks for the information received. When the Michaelmas term began, he gave a course of ten lectures, continuing the subject *De Motu* where he had left off the preceding year.

The whole of the year 1686 was passed in Cambridge. We may be certain that Halley kept in close touch with the progress of the work; in fact, he continued to work on the subject himself for, at the meeting of the Society on April 21, he "read a discourse of his own, designed for a *Philosophical Transaction,* concerning the cause and properties of gravity wherein he considers the several hypotheses concerning its impulses, and then mathematically deduces its consequences in the fall of heavy bodies, and the motion of projects [projectiles]."[17] At the next meeting, a week later, the memorable note was entered: "Dr. Vincent presented to the Society a manu-

[17] This discourse was published in the *Phil. Trans.* No. 179, p. 3.—Birch, Vol. IV, p. 479.

script entitled, *Philosophiae Naturalis principia mathematica,* and dedicated to the society by Mr. ISAAC NEWTON, wherein he gives a mathematical demonstration of the Copernican hypothesis as proposed by Kepler, and makes out all the phenomena of the celestial motions by the only supposition of a gravitation towards the centre of the sun decreasing as the squares of the distances therefrom reciprocally. It was ordered, that a letter of thanks be written to MR. NEWTON; and that the printing of this book be referred to the consideration of the council; and that in the meantime the book be put into the hands of Mr. Halley, to make a report thereof to the council."[18]

This Dr. Vincent, who had the honour to present the manuscript, has been erroneously identified with the husband of Newton's early fiancée, Miss Storey. It is sufficient to point out that he was a bachelor, since he was, at that time, Senior Fellow of Clare College, and continued so until his death. The following incident in his life has been recorded by Whiston[19] which sheds an interesting light on the history and the superstition of the time. He states, that he went with Dr. Nathaniel Vincent, into Norfolk, towards the end of May, 1687 or 1688, and found that the Doctor was expected to preach a sermon on the Solemnity for the Restoration, at the Cathedral of Norwich. He was known to be a great friend of King James, and Whiston thought he hoped by flattering the King to be made a Bishop at the very time when the Protestants and the University were in great dread of Popery. However, he had no suitable sermon at hand but, from some notes and with the aid of Whiston as amanuensis, he prepared one which his young assistant thought to be no better than were most of such court-sermons. Later, when the Prince of Orange came to the country's deliverance, the Cambridge mob got up and amongst other actions threatened Dr. Vincent. Frightened by this demonstration, he decided to leave college for a while. He accordingly called on Whiston, who was his Sizar, to assist him in preparing for his *Removal*. It seems that his Sizar spilled his salt that night at supper, and the learned Doctor exclaimed very solemnly: "It would be a sad completion of this omen if they should find him dead in his bed the next morning." Whiston caustically remarks that the Doctor lived a great many years after the omen.

The Council of the Royal Society did not act for some weeks,

[18] Birch, Vol. IV, p. 479.

[19] Whiston, *Memoirs*, pp. 21–24.

apparently because the president, Samuel Pepys, was in attendance on King James on affairs of the navy, and the vice-presidents were all out of town because of the fine weather. But at the meeting of May 19, Sir Joseph Williamson, vice-president in the chair, it was ordered "that Mr. Newton's *Philosophiae naturalis principia mathematica* be printed forthwith in quarto in a fair letter; and that a letter be written to him to signify the Society's resolution, and to desire his opinion as to the print, volume, cuts, etc."[20] The record, as usual, is quite colourless, but there had evidently been a somewhat acrimonious discussion during which the irrepressible Hooke again claimed that Newton had been greatly aided in the discovery of the law of gravitation by his own work, and that he expected a suitable acknowledgement to be made in the published work. How tactfully Halley managed this contretemps, and soothed the irritated author, almost as if he had been an unreasonable child, can be gathered from the correspondence which passed between them. Worried, lest an exaggerated rumour of this unfortunate incident should reach Newton's ears, Halley wrote him the following letter on May 22:

Halley to Newton

Sir,

Your incomparable treatise, entitled, *Philosophiae naturalis principia mathematica,* was by Dr. Vincent presented to the Royal Society on the 28th past; and they were so very sensible of the great honour you have done them by your dedication, that they immediately ordered you their most hearty thanks, and that the council should be summoned to consider about the printing thereof. But by reason of the president's attendance upon the king, and the absence of our vice-presidents, whom the good weather has drawn out of town, there has not since been any authentic council to resolve what to do in the matter, so that on Wednesday last the Society in their meeting judging, that so excellent a work ought not to have its publication any longer delayed, resolved to print it at their own charge in a large quarto of a fair letter; and that this their resolution should be signified to you and your opinion thereon be desired, that so it might be gone about with all speed. I am entrusted to look after the printing of it, and will take care, that it shall be performed as well as possible. Only I would first have your directions in what you shall think necessary for the embellishing thereof, and particularly whether you

[20] Birch, Vol. IV, p. 484.

think it not better, that the schemes should be enlarged, which is the opinion of some here: but what you signify as your desire shall be punctually observed.

There is one thing more, that I ought to inform you of, *viz.* that Mr. Hooke has some pretensions upon the invention of the rule of decrease of gravity being reciprocally as the squares of the distances from the centre. He says you had the notion from him, though he owns the demonstration of the curves generated thereby to be wholly your own. How much of this is so, you know best; as likewise what you have to do in this matter. Only Mr. Hooke seems to expect you should make some mention of him in the preface, which it is possible you may see reason to prefix. I must beg your pardon, that it is I, that send you this ungrateful account; but I thought it my duty to let you know it, that so you might act accordingly, being in myself full satisfied, that nothing but the greatest candour imaginable is to be expected from a person, who has of all men the least need to borrow reputation. I am, etc.[21]

Newton replied at once to Halley:

Newton to Halley

I thank you for what you write concerning Mr. Hooke, for I desire that a good understanding may be kept between us. In the papers in your hands there is not one proposition to which he can pretend, and so I had no proper occasion of mentioning him there. In those behind where I state the system of the world I mention him and others. But now we are upon this business, I desire it may be understood. The sum of what past between Mr. Hooke and me (to the best of my remembrance) was this. He soliciting me for some philosophical communications or other I sent him this notion, that a falling body ought by reason of the earth's diurnal motion to advance eastward and not fall to the west as the vulgar opinion is. And in the scheme wherein I explained this I carelessly described the descent of the fall-

[21] Birch, Vol. IV, p. 484. . . . Of the seventeen (or more) letters which passed between Halley and Newton in 1686–7, sixteen are extant. Ball has reprinted them in his *Essay* as an Appendix. I have referred to these letters and given some extracts from them in a previous chapter in order to explain the incidents of the year 1679. At the risk of being tedious, I am giving here all the parts of the letters which are of more than passing interest as they are important in revealing Newton's character. I have also in foot-notes given the reference to their first publication. If the reader desires all the details of this controversy with Hooke and minute points about the *Principia*, he may refer to Ball's *Essay*, p. 153 *et seq.*

ing body in a spiral to the centre of the earth: which is true in a resisting medium, such as our air is. Mr. Hooke replied, it would not descend to the centre but at a certain limit return upwards again. I then took the simplest case for computation, which was that of gravity uniform in a medium not resisting—imagining he had learned the limit from some computation, and for that end had considered the simplest case first. And in this case I granted what he contended for, and stated the limit as nearly as I could. He replied that gravity was not uniform but increased in descent to the centre in a reciprocal duplicate proportion of the distance from it, and thus the limit would be otherwise than I had stated it, namely, at the end of every entire revolution, and added that according to this duplicate proportion the motions of the planets might be explained and their orbs defined. This is the sum of what I remember. If there was anything more material or any thing otherwise I desire Mr. Hooke would help my memory. Further that I remember about 9 years since Sir Christopher Wren, upon a visit Dr. Donne and I gave him at his lodgings, discoursed of this problem of determining the planetary motions upon philosophical principles. This was about a year or two before I received Mr. Hooke's letters. You are acquainted with Sir Christopher. Pray know where and whence he first learnt the decrease of the force in a duplicate ratio of the distance from the centre.

Sir, I am your most affectionate and humble servant.

I. N.[22]

Halley had not only the delicate task of managing the irritability of the author, but he also found that he could not depend on the Society for funds to publish the treatise. The record of June 2 states briefly: "It was ordered, that Mr. NEWTON's book be printed, and that Mr. Halley undertake the business of looking after it, and printing it at his own charge; which he engaged to do."[23] In this emergency, when he saw his hopes about to be frustrated, Halley determined to pay the costs himself. It was no slight burden. He had been brought up to no profession as his father had been a rich man. But, on the death of his father, he found himself reduced to comparative poverty and with a wife and young children to support. In this state of his affairs, he had been glad to accept the position as assistant to the secretaries of the Society at a stipend of £50. The

[22] Ball, p. 155.

[23] Birch, Vol. IV, p. 486.

Society has been severely, and even bitterly, criticised for not securing to itself the credit of financing so great a work, but there were extenuating circumstances. The vote at the general meeting of May 19 was of no force in itself, since it required the expenditure of money and, by the statutes, no sum exceeding £5 could be paid except on order from Council. Now the Council knew that the Society was practically bankrupt, and it is difficult to see how they could legally authorise any additional obligation. In previous emergencies of this sort, they had been accustomed to depend on the generosity of individual members and, in this case, Halley evidently offered to relieve them of their embarrassment. The Society had rashly published Willughby's *De Historia Piscium* in an edition of 500 copies at a cost of £400. In addition to this large sum, Pepys had subscribed £50 towards the publication, and had provided for eighty of the plates, and other members had also contributed. The Society was also confronted with the problem of collecting unpaid dues. The situation had become so bad that the Council on July 22, 1685, ordered forty-seven names to be stricken from the roll unless they paid their arrears; amongst them, were many of the richest noblemen of the country, and also John Locke. Salaries were unpaid, and Halley and Hooke were asked to accept pay in the form of a number of copies of Willughby's book which had a very slow sale. As late as 1740, as many as 125 sets were still unsold and the Society, to meet its expenses, had to sell some of its securities in the India stock. It is reported that the generous Halley accepted this proposition; but the careful Hooke desired six months to consider it. It thus seems that criticism for this action might properly be directed against wealthy members rather than against the Society. Even so, we do not know the circumstances, and Halley may have claimed the right to be the sponsor, esteeming it an honour worth serious financial embarrassment. Somehow, opinion seems to have overlooked the duty of Newton, who was by no means poor, to contribute to part at least of the expense of the publication of his own work. His attitude is certainly a most curious one, as he seemed to take no more interest, or pride, in it than the proverbial stepfather, and was quite willing to accept the charity of one who was almost a stranger.

As soon as this agreement was reached, Halley prepared vigorously to see the work through the press. On June 7, he could write that the first book was in press.

Halley to Newton

London, June 7, 1686.

Sr,

I here send you a proof of the first sheet of your book, which we think to print on this paper, and in this character; if you have any objection, it shall be altered: and if you approve it, we will proceed; and care shall be taken that it shall not be published before the end of Michaelmas term, since you desire it. I hope you will please to bestow the second part, or what remains of this, upon us as soon as you shall have finished it, for the application of this mathematical part to the system of the world, is what will render it acceptable to all naturalists, as well as mathematicians; and much advance the sale of the book. Pray, please to revise this proof, and send it me up with your answer. I have already corrected it, but cannot say I have spied all the faults. When it has past your eye, I doubt not but it will be clear from errata. The printer begs your excuse of the diphthongs, which are of a character a little bigger, but he has some a casting of the just size. This sheet being a proof is not so clear as it ought to be; but the letter is new, and I have seen a book of a very fair character, which was the last thing printed from this set of letter; so that I hope the edition may in that particular be to your satisfaction. I am, Sr.

Your most affectionate humble servt,

E. HALLEY.[24]

The progress of the book to its completion, as well as the difficulties which Halley had to overcome, is told in the correspondence between the two. Newton was much exasperated by Hooke's new claim and, in his reply to Halley, he explained very forcibly that the claim was unjust. His letter of June 20[25] is too long to give in full, and the quarrel becomes somewhat wearisome. The following extracts, however, are important:

"The proof you sent me I like very well. I designed the whole to consist of three books; the second was finished last summer being short, and only wants transcribing, and drawing the cuts fairly. Some new propositions I have since thought on, which I can as well let alone. The third wants the theory of comets. In autumn last I spent two months in calculations to no purpose for want of a good

[24] Ball, p. 156.

[25] Ball, p. 156.

method, which made me afterwards return to the first book, and enlarge it with divers propositions, some relating to comets, others to other things, found out last winter. The third I now design to suppress. Philosophy is such an impertinently litigious Lady, that a man had as good be engaged in lawsuits, as have to do with her. I found it so formerly, and now I am no sooner come near her again, but she gives me warning. The two first books, without the third, will not so well bear the title of *Philosophiae Naturalis Principia Mathematica;* and therefore I had altered it to this, *De Motu Corporum libri duo.* But, upon second thoughts, I retain the former title. 'Twill help the sale of the book, which I ought not to diminish now 'tis yours. The articles are, with the largest, to be called by that name; if you please you may change the word to *sections,* though it be not material. . . . [Postscript] Since my writing this letter, I am told by one, who had it from another lately present at one of your meetings, how that Mr. Hooke should there make a great stir, pretending that I had all from him, and desiring they would see that he had justice done him. This carriage towards me is very strange and undeserved; so that I cannot forbear, in stating the point of justice, to tell you further, that he has published Borell's hypothesis in his own name. . . .

"Mr. Hooke has erred in the invention he pretends to, and his error is the cause of all the stir he makes. For his extending the duplicate proportion down to the centre (which I do not) made him correct me, and tell me the rest of his theory as a new thing to me, and now stand upon it, that I had all from that his letter, notwithstanding that he had told it to all the world before, and I had seen it in his printed books, all but the proportion. And why should I record a man for an invention, who founds his claim upon an error therein, and on that score gives me trouble? He imagines he obliged me by telling me his theory, but I thought myself disobliged by being, upon his own mistake, corrected magisterially, and taught a theory, which every body knew, and I had a truer notion of than himself. Should a man who thinks himself knowing, and loves to show it in correcting and instructing others, come to you, when you are busy, and notwithstanding your excuse press discourses upon you, and through his own mistakes correct you, and multiply discourses; and then make this use of it, to boast that he taught you all he spake, and oblige you to acknowledge it, and cry out injury and injustice if you do not; I believe you would think him a man of strange unsociable temper. Mr. Hooke's letters in several respects abounded too much with that humour, which Hevelius and others complain of; and therefore he may do well in time to consider, whether, after this new provocation I be much more bound (in doing him that justice he claims) to make an honourable mention of him in print, especially since this is the third time that he has given me trouble in this kind." . . .

In spite of the careful wording of Halley's report about Hooke, Newton was aroused to make a detailed repudiation of the claims; and when he learned later from some one, who had heard the news from another who had been present, that Hooke had made "a great stir," he added a scathing rebuke and a justification of his own work. No one could blame him for being thoroughly angry. But one can not excuse him for his decision—to suppress the third book simply because one man, with a mind diseased by jealousy and vanity, had foolishly made a scene. What manner of a man was Newton, who could thus contemptuously cast off his own intellectual child; there is certainly no parallel to the incident in all history. Did any other man ever show a deeper jealousy and vanity than Newton, who could let the personal criticism of another, and a slight reflection on his own character, outweigh the work of his life and the fruit of his genius? Since the book, thus mutilated, would be greatly restricted in its scope and value, he decided to change the title of *System of the World* to the colourless one of *On the Motion of Bodies.* Then it occurred to him that Halley had a financial interest in the book, however unimportant it might be to himself, so he decided to retain the catch-sale title even though it were misleading because, forsooth, " 'Twill help the sale of the book, which I ought not to diminish now 'tis yours." This incident, I confess, shocks me. It is not inspiring to see a work of genius carelessly chaffered as might be a second-hand piece of furniture, even if the advantage be ostensibly sought for a friend's purse. If gratitude had really been the motive it would have shone with a brighter lustre if he had refused to let his personal annoyance overweigh his duty to make public his work.

One can imagine what a thunderbolt such a piece of news was to Halley, for the third book was the flower of the whole work, and without it the treatise would be like Hamlet with Hamlet left out. In this frame of mind he wrote the following diplomatic letter:

Halley to Newton

Sr,

I am heartily sorry, that in this matter, wherein all mankind ought to acknowledge their obligations to you, you should meet with anything that should give you disquiet, or that any disgust should make you think of desisting in your pretensions to a Lady, whose favours you have so much reason to boast of. 'Tis not she, but your rivals envying your happiness that endeavour to disturb your quiet enjoyment, which when you consider, I hope you will see cause to alter your former resolution of suppressing your third book, there being nothing which you can have compiled therein, which the learned world will not be concerned to have concealed. Those gentlemen of the Society, to whom I have communicated it, are very much troubled at it, and that this unlucky business should have happened to give you trouble, having a just sentiment of the author thereof. According to your desire in your former, I waited upon Sr Christopher Wren, to enquire of him, if he had the first notion of the reciprocal duplicate proportion from Mr. Hooke, his answer was, that he himself very many years since had had his thoughts upon the making out the planets' motions by a composition of a descent towards the sun, and an imprest motion; but that at length he gave over, not finding the means of doing it. Since which time Mr. Hooke had frequently told him that he had done it, and attempted to make it out to him, but that he never satisfied him that his demonstrations were cogent. . . .

As to the manner of Mr. Hooke's claiming this discovery, I fear it has been represented in worse colours than it ought; for he neither made public application to the Society for justice, nor pretended you had all from him. The truth is this. Sr John Hoskins, his particular frie[n]d being in the chair, when Dr. Vincent presented your book, the Dr. gave it its just encomium, both as to the novelty and dignity of the subject. It was replied by another gentleman that you had carried the thing so far that there was no more to be added. To which the Vice-President replied, that it was so much the more to be prized, for that it was both invented and perfected at the same time. This gave Mr. Hooke offence, that Sr. John did not, at that time, make mention of what he had, as he said, discovered to him; upon which they two, who till then were the most inseparable cronies, have since scarce seen one another, and are utterly fallen out. After the breaking up of that meeting, being adjourned to the coffee-house, Mr. Hooke did there endeavour to gain belief, that he had some such thing by him, and that he gave you the first hint of this invention. But I found, that they were all of opinion, that nothing thereof appearing in print, nor on the books of the Society, you ought to be considered as the inventor. And if in truth he knew it before you, he ought not to blame any but himself, for having taken no more care to secure a discovery, which he puts so much value on. What application he has made in private, I know not, but I am sure that the Society have a very great satisfaction in the honour you do them, by your dedication of so worthy a treatise. Sr, I must now again beg you, not to let your resentments run so high, as to deprive us of your third book, wherein the application of your mathematical doctrine to the theory of comets and several curious experiments, which, as I guess by what you write, ought to compose it, will undoubtedly render it acceptable to those, that will call themselves philosophers without mathematics, which are by much the greater number. Now you approve of the character and paper, I will push on the edition vigorously. I have sometimes had thoughts of having the cuts neatly done in wood, so as to stand in the page, with the demonstrations, it will be more convenient, and not much more charge. If it please you to have it so, I will try how well it can be done; otherwise I will have them in somewhat a larger size than those you have sent up. I am, Sr,

Your most affectionate humble servt,

E. HALLEY.[26]

London, 29 June, 1686.

To Mr. Isaac Newton in Trinity Colledg. Cambridg.

On the last day of June, the President was desired to license the publication and, five days later, Pepys put his name to the imprimatur. In the meanwhile, Halley's letter had calmed the troubled waters, and had awakened the better nature of Newton. And when that occurred he usually acknowledged his fault, and apologised with sincerity and humility. Thus, he wrote to Halley:[27] "I am very sensible of the great kindness of the gentlemen of your Society to me, far beyond what I could ever expect or deserve, and know how to distinguish between their favour and another's humour. Now I

[26] Ball, pp. 162-164.—The argument of Newton and Halley, that Hooke had no just claim to the discovery because he had not published it, should be recollected when the controversy with Leibniz is discussed. Newton's case was then, what Hooke's is in this incident.

[27] Ball, p. 165.

understand he was in some respects misrepresented to me, I wish I had spared the postscript to my last." He then states what had been reported to him about Hooke, and closes the letter by agreeing to make a reference to him in the book: "And now having sincerely told you the case between Mr. Hooke and me, I hope I shall be free for the future from the prejudice of his letters. I have considered how best to compose the present dispute, and I think it may be done by the enclosed scholium to the fourth proposition." Thus, this matter was dropped, and he agreed to go on with the whole work as originally planned.

Newton spent the remainder of the summer in Cambridge, revising the manuscript of the second book, and working on the applications of his law to the motions of satellites, comets, and other cosmic problems. When College opened in the autumn, he gave his course of lectures, continuing his exposition *De Motu*. At the same time, the second book was completed and made ready for the press; but he retained the manuscript, as he thought that the printer would not be ready for it till November or December. In fact, it was not until March 1, 1686/7, that he wrote to Halley. "You'll receive the 2nd book on Thursday night or Friday by the coach. I have directed it to be left with Mr. Hunt at Gresham Coll. Pray let me beg the favour of a line or two to know of the receipt. I am obliged to you for pushing on the edition, because of the people's expectation, tho' otherwise I could be as well satisfied to let it rest a year or two longer. 'Tis a double favour, that you are pleased to double your pains about it." This is another instance which must be left to a guess; whether he found that the book had been written too hurriedly, or whether it was another case of his characteristic procrastination.

In the meanwhile, there had been trouble and delay with the printer. Six months had been wasted before even a start had been made, and Halley gave the second book to another firm in order that both books should appear at the same time. He, also, threatened to give the third book to yet another firm, but finally sent it to the original printer on his promise that it would be worked on diligently. The third book, with the title *De Systemate Mundi,* required a large amount of astronomical data, and Newton was most fortunate in being able to obtain the assistance of Flamsteed; it is also believed that Halley aided him with data and calculations. The manuscript was finally sent up to London early in April.

The satisfaction of Halley is readily understood when he finally held the complete copy in his hands and realised that his laborious task was come to an end.

Halley to Newton

London, April 5, 1687.

Honoured Sr,

I received not the last part of your divine Treatise till yesterday, though it came to town that day sennight; having had occasion to be out of town the last week. The first part will be finished within this three weeks, and considering the shortness of the third over the second, the same press that did the first will get it done so soon as the second can be finished by another press; but I find some difficulty to match the letter justly. . . .

I do not find that you have touched that notable appearance of comets' tails, and their opposition to the sun which seems rather to argue an efflux from the sun than a gravitation towards him. I doubt not but this may follow from your principles with the like ease as all the other phenomena; but a proposition or two concerning these will add much to the beauty and perfection of your theory of comets. I find I shall not get the whole completed before Trinity term, when I hope to have it published; when the world will not be more instructed by the demonstrative doctrine thereof, than it will pride itself to have a subject capable of penetrating so far into the abstrusest secrets of nature, and exalting human reason to so sublime a pitch by this utmost effort of the mind. But least my affection should make me transgress, I remain,

Your most obedient servant,

EDM. HALLEY.[28]

On the next day, he presented the manuscript to the Society: "The third book of Mr. NEWTON's treatise *De Systemate Mundi* was produced and presented to the Society. It contained the whole system of celestial motions, as well of the secondary as primary planets, with the theory of comets; which he illustrated by the example of the great comet of 1680/1, proving that, which appeared in the morning in the month of November preceding, to have been the same comet, that was observed in December and January in the eve-

28 Ball, p. 173.

ning."[29] The earlier authorities, such as Weld in his *History of the Royal Society,* state that the manuscript, "entirely written by Newton's own hand," is preserved in the museum of the Society and is esteemed its most precious treasure. Edleston, however, leaves little doubt that this manuscript is in the same hand as the first draught of the *Principia* in the University Library. Both manuscripts have corrections and additions which are undoubtedly in the author's own hand. In support of this opinion, we have the statement of Humphrey Newton, that he copied the whole manuscript, and one would suppose that as an amanuensis he had been engaged for that purpose.

The reader, when he peruses the last letter written on the publication of the *Principia,* will share the feelings of Halley and regard him as a rare spirit:

Halley to Newton

London, July 5, 1687.

Honoured Sr,

I have at length brought your book to an end, and hope it will please you. The last errata came just in time to be inserted. I will present from you the books you desire to the R. Society, Mr. Boyle, Mr. Paget, Mr. Flamsteed, and if there be any else in town that you design to gratify that way; and I have sent you to bestow on your friends in the University 20 copies, which I entreat you to accept. In the same parcel you will receive 40 more, which, having no acquaintance in Cambridge, I must entreat you to put into the hands of one or more of your ablest booksellers to dispose of them: I intend the price of them bound in calves' leather and lettered, to be 9 shillings here. Those I send you I value in quires at 6 shillings, to take my money as they are sold, or at 5^sh^ a price certain for ready, or else at some short time; for I am satisfied that there is no dealing in books without interesting the booksellers, and I am contented to let them go halves with me, rather than have your excellent work smothered by their combinations. I hope you will not repent you of the pains you have taken in so laudable a piece, so much to your own and the nation's credit, but rather, after you shall have a little diverted yourself with other studies, that you will resume those contemplations, wherein you have had so good success, and attempt the

29 Birch, IV, p. 529. It is here that Newton could gracefully have expressed his obligation to Flamsteed for pointing out his former erroneous belief about the comet.

perfection of the lunar theory, which will be of prodigious use in navigation, as well as of profound and subtile speculation. Sr. I shall be glad to hear that you have received the books, and to know what farther presents you would make in town which shall be accordingly done. You will receive a box from me on Thursday next by the wagon, that parts from hence to-morrow. I am Your most obliged humble servt,

EDM. HALLEY.[30]

To Mr. Isaac Newton,
In Trinity Colledg. Cambridg. These.

About midsummer, 1687, the *Principia* was finally published during the presidency of the Earl of Carbery. This edition was very small and sold probably for ten or twelve shillings a copy. Rather to the surprise, I think, of Halley, the edition sold quickly and, by 1691, it was very difficult to obtain a copy. Halley, in addition to all his other services, prefixed a graceful tribute to the author in a set of verses in Latin hexameters; and he also presented a copy to King James II, accompanied by a paper, explaining the purpose and accomplishment of the book, together with a flattering compliment to His Majesty. There was even a promise offered to explain the more difficult parts to the royal mind; but, I daresay, a James II would not be apt to discover the humour in such a suggestion. It seems likely that Halley did not lose a great deal financially.

So ends the history of the preparation of this remarkable book,—remarkable in its content, remarkable in that it was written in seventeen or eighteen months, and remarkable in its mode of publication. But the most inexplicable feature of the book was the attitude of the author towards his own progeny. He apparently took little interest in what he once mentioned to Halley as "your book." The text was cast in a strictly classical and geometrical form, which is not suitable to problems of motion, although he had discovered in his method of fluxions one admirably adapted to his needs. He made no concessions to his readers and he seemed to have had in mind a few, perhaps Halley and one or two others, whom he addressed personally, and to have been indifferent to all the rest of the world. In truth, few could read it then, and few have ever read it except under compulsion of the schools. For example, Demoivre, himself no mean mathematician, was by chance at the Duke of Devonshire's when Newton called to present a copy to the Duke. The young

[30] Ball, pp. 173-4.

mathematician opened the book and, misled by its apparent simplicity, thought he could master it without any difficulty. He soon found it was beyond his comprehension and that he had a long, and thorny, road to travel before he could understand it. But he bought a copy, which he tore into sheets so that he could carry a small portion in his pocket and study it in the intervals of his other work. Yet men like John Locke and Richard Bentley, who were not mathematicians, were fascinated by its philosophy. And the latter asked Newton to suggest a course of study which would prepare him to understand it. He received such a portentous list that he gave up the project lest the preparation would require the better part of his life. But he did by correspondence obtain enough insight into the author's philosophy to use it as an argument for the confutation of atheism in his famous Boyle sermons. The concluding lecture of the series was devoted to the purpose of proving the necessity of a Divine Providence, because of the orderliness in the laws of nature as demonstrated in the *Principia.*

Gregory of Scotland became an enthusiastic Newtonian, and the Universities of St. Andrews and Edinburgh were probably the first in Britain to teach his ideas. At Oxford, the displacement of the Aristotelian and Cartesian schools was slow, although David Gregory moved to that University in 1690, and Whiston laments that "he had already caused several of his scholars to keep *Acts,* as we call them, upon several branches of the Newtonian philosophy; while we at Cambridge, poor wretches, were ignominiously studying the fictitious hypotheses of the Cartesian." In the same passage, he also states that he heard Newton read one or two of his lectures though he did not then understand them. Laughton, tutor of Clare College and Senior Proctor, has the honour of having been the first in Cambridge to introduce the Newtonian philosophy, "for by choosing the *Principia* of Newton as the predominant subject both of the exercises in the schools and the mathematical examination for degrees, he enforced among the students the general attention to that immortal work, which has from his time never ceased to distinguish the University of Cambridge."[31] We must remember also that Newton, himself, lectured on the new mechanics till he left Cambridge

[31] Monk's *Life of Bentley,* Vol. I, p. 288.—The bishop gives an absurd story about Laughton who performed his proctorial duties with more zeal and rigour than discretion. On one occasion, the parliamentary representatives were entertaining a select party of their constituents at the Rose Tavern. About ten o'clock, the Proctor, preceded by a lictor, and followed by a number of undergraduates as his bodyguard, burst into the room and

although Edleston does not list his subjects or discourses. While there were individual converts, the general introduction of his philosophy was slow; it was Lord Mansfield's opinion, made during a legal argument, that the works of Milton, Locke, and Newton suffered for a considerable time before they were properly appreciated.

The appreciation of the *Principia* was even slower outside England. A few scholars, like Leibniz and Huygens, were keen to have a sight of the work, but it attracted, at first, little attention amongst continental philosophers. The introduction of the work into France was due mostly to Voltaire. During his stay in England from 1726 to 1729, he became a whole-hearted convert. While he may not have met Newton personally, he certainly became acquainted with Mrs. Catherine Barton. On his return, he wrote a number of controversial tracts on the advantages of the Newtonian system over that of Descartes, and drew the attention of his countrymen to that unknown mechanics.

The development of mechanics from the *Principia* into the most nearly exact of the sciences, during the latter part of the eighteenth century, was due to a succession of remarkable mathematicians in France and Germany. The principal cause, why the continental writers had a distinct advantage over their British contemporaries, was the overpowering influence of Newton on his countrymen; they unreservedly subjected themselves to his unquestioned authority. As a result, they persisted in using his geometrical method and made but ineffectual attempts to develop his fluxions into a useful tool. Now, the flaws in Newton's armour were an impatience of criticism, and an irritability when pressed to explain his method of thought, or to justify his assumptions. To him, a methodical exposition was unnecessary; he apparently grasped the solution of a problem as a whole, but such a faculty does not make the teacher or assist in building a new school of thought.

The continental philosophers were not subjected to such an influence; international jealousies had been aroused by the controversy which had arisen over the discovery of the calculus, and their sympathy was overwhelmingly on the side of Leibniz. The British, and Newton himself, were criticised for what was thought to have been

ordered the whole company to disperse and return to their colleges. This strange visitation was received with ridicule. Twice again he repeated the visit; nor did he stop at that, but drew a formal complaint which he presented to the Vice-Chancellor and Heads. Unfortunately for him, the ridiculous affair got into print, and his action became one of the stock stories.

an unjust attack on the character of a great and honoured man. It is not surprising that they ignored Newtonian fluxions, which was limited in its scope and deliberately obscure in its statement, and cultivated the calculus of Leibniz which had been stated clearly, and had been given an excellent nomenclature. The secretive temperament of Newton had snatched from him the fruit of his great discovery. Thus fluxions languished while the calculus was rapidly developed by the Bernoullis, and others, into the most powerful tool of modern analysis, as fundamental and universal in mathematics as the law of gravitation is in physics. The work of Euler, D'Alembert, and Lagrange, aided by others overshadowed only by such giants, created a marvellous structure out of Newtonian mechanics, with the aid of the calculus, and made it intelligible to the world.

The full significance of the *Principia* was not evident till Laplace produced his *Mécanique céleste* in which he fused into a homogeneous doctrine all the scattered work from Newton to Lagrange. In this great synthesis, he attempted to examine the results of all previous mechanicians, to correct them, and to show that the solar system is a periodic and stable configuration governed solely by the universal law of gravitation. Like Descartes, he portrayed the universe as a vast machine obedient to inexorable mechanical laws; and his famous Hypothesis is probably the utmost stretch of the human mind in portraying the origin and operation of a world machine; for whose guidance, as he haughtily informed Napoleon, there was no need of a God.

Although the title of Newton's treatise is the *Mathematical Principles of Natural Philosophy,* it was not intended to be an orderly exposition of natural phenomena; but rather to prove that the law of universal attraction of matter would account for all the motions of the planetary bodies, and for the dynamic phenomena observed on the earth. As a scientist, Newton is the successor of Galileo and, with the exception of the new law of attraction, their work is so intimately connected that it cannot be disentangled. They both sought to found a science of mechanics on a system of forces, whose sole function was to produce a measurable change of motion, in place of the mediæval science which had developed from Aristotle's metaphysics of natural positions and natural motions.

As an immediate consequence of Galileo's discovery of the laws of force, Descartes had, in his *Système du Monde,* elaborated a purely mechanistic cosmogony. To account for gravitation, and for the orbital motions of the planets, he imagined all space to be a continuum in which vast vortices drove the planets and their satellites along their orbits by the friction of the whirling motion. The cosmogony of Descartes was developed with a fascinating clarity of diction and with specious simplicity of illustration; it seized on the imagination of the world and was firmly established in the universities. To displace this explanation of the orbits of the planets, Newton had to oppose the idea that the natural motion of a planet was along a straight line, and that its curvilinear path was the result, not of forces along the path, but directed radially towards a fixed centre. He had further to prove that the Cartesian vortices were impossible as a dynamic system. And to break down this hypothesis, he chose to depend solely on rigorous geometrical theorems rather than on an appeal to the imagination; it is no wonder that even the most enlightened scientists failed to understand his purpose.

While it is true that the natural philosophers of the Renaissance, beginning with Copernicus, attempted deliberately to replace the scholastic science with a system of mechanical laws, based on experimental observation, and expressed in mathematical formulæ, yet they frequently failed to make the break complete, and fell under the influence of the old dogmatic authority. So we find Newton, who proposed to limit himself strictly to the new so-called Pythagorean school, or the Baconian inductive method as it was beginning to be called, also prefaced his work with a set of purely metaphysical definitions. But we should bear in mind that this introduction has little, or no, connection with his main discussion of physical laws.

The universe, which Newton proposes, is a very restricted and artificial one; it is a machine composed of bodies whose only attributes are position, extension, and mass, and of forces whose sole function is to cause motion and its variation. All life and its direct activities have no effect, and are banished from this universal machine, which moves and acts in obedience to rigorous mechanical law. Man is quite apart from the objective world and, as a rational being, he is limited to observing and interpreting its phenomena. His only contact with the outside world is through mechanical actions impressed on his nerves and by them transmitted to a sensorium in his brain. Man's rational soul, assumed to be an entity apart from his brain, then interprets these nerve stimuli as sight, sound, taste, etc.; interpretations which are purely subjective, and incapable of mechanical formulation. Thus, there exists, so far as physical science is concerned, an unbridgeable gap between the mechanical outer world, and the inner realm of sensations and ideas.

The fundamental postulates for such a mechanistic universe are the reality of substance (it is indifferent whether it be called matter, or electricity, or quanta) existing as bodies, formally limited in an empty and infinite space; and of force, or action, which produces variations of position and motion. Newton next accepts the classification, made by Galileo, of primary and secondary qualities. The first class are those which are inherent in bodies and inseparable from them, and without which they could not exist; the secondary qualities are those which, while distinguishing bodies, are not necessary to them; that is, if the secondary qualities were abstracted from a body it would still exist as a body. And, like Galileo and Descartes, he assigned to the first class, extension, form, position, and such other mechanical qualities as are needed to specify a body in time and space; all other qualities are subordinate and secondary to them.

Newton's empirical and inductive philosophy has, naturally, not escaped criticism. It presupposes a naïve belief in the reality of the objective world, whose attributes are not only independent of the observer, but are also concordant with his observation. The first serious attack was made by Berkeley.[32] He had studied Descartes and Newton with care, and had come to the conclusion that such a pure empiricism entirely neglected the factor of the perceiving mind. When, for example, we say that we see an object, it is not the object, but the sensation of sight perceived by the mind, which exists. If we merely close the eyes, all the visible attributes of an object vanish. And so it is with all the other sensations. The objective world, so far as we are concerned, does not exist except as the mind observes and interprets it. No one can, I think, disagree with him, that the objective world cannot be postulated as something apart from the perceiving mind, and he certainly exposed an essential weakness of the scientific method; by the empirical method, we may develop a logical system of an objective world; but, because we must interpret it as it appears to our minds, we can have no assurance that our interpretations and the facts of nature are the same, or even concordant. When, however, Berkeley passes into pure idealism, and argues that nothing exists except the perception in the mind, he then denies what he cannot prove; and the possibility, even great probability, remains that we can attain to an approximate knowledge of the real

[32] *A New Theory of Vision.* London, 1709.

nature of phenomena by the comparison of the perceptions of several persons, or by the knowledge derived from a sense organ not immediately involved, as when we record temperature changes by seeing a thermometer. The later, and acute, criticism of Hume did much to show the impossibility of a pure inductive philosophy.

As the word, science, has gradually been arrogated to almost all branches of knowledge, the assumption that the mechanical attributes of matter are to be given a peculiar necessity has been more and more criticised. Of late, for example, Professor Whitehead has attacked the distinction between primary and secondary qualities, claiming that the attributes of extension, position, and other mechanical data, are no more fundamental, nor more inseparable from matter, than are other attributes such as colour and temperature. He evidently cannot deny that those qualities are fundamental so long as we are studying mechanical problems. He is right in asserting that the phenomena of light and heat are direct perceptions and cannot be identified with, nor explained by, mechanical attributes; he is also right in asserting that the phenomena of life are not mechanical and that, therefore, the biological sciences cannot base their laws, and their method, on physical dynamics. Up to this point, one would naturally assume that Professor Whitehead was advocating a philosophy of dualism of two worlds, the vital and the material, and that each has its own laws and its own method of study. But not at all. With the reluctance of the mind to accept such an inevitable conclusion, he at once proceeds to create a new monistic philosophy. Since life cannot be explained by mechanics, let us assume that physical energy and action are manifestations of an universal life force, something akin to Bergson's *élan vital,* or self-creative evolution.

But it is not Newton, whom Professor Whitehead really criticises, nor is it his mechanistic philosophy. Newton explicitly states that he will discuss only those objective phenomena which are mechanical, and which can be demonstrated geometrically; and, if such be his purpose, no one can in justice condemn him for assuming mechanical attributes to be necessary and fundamental for his limited field. It is rather the biologists, the psychologists, and the sociologists, who have dragged the science of mechanics out of its proper limits; who have attempted to make man into a machine, and all his sensations mechanical.

Although Newton's general or philosophic definitions have little to do with his mechanics, they have been cited so constantly as the essence of his dynamics that they must be discussed. In his first definition, he identifies a body by mass, and it has been stated by all writers on mechanics, so far as I can remember, that a body is of itself inert; or, to express it vulgarly, matter is essentially dead. But, in so interpreting his idea, the remainder of this definition, and his third definition, have been disregarded. On the contrary, he makes force the essential attribute of matter, and this force is known to us by our sense perception of muscular effort, or weight. In support of this interpretation, the third definition reads: "The *vis insita,* or innate force of matter, is a power of resisting, by which every body, as much as in it lies, endeavours to persevere in its present state. . . ." And in explanation, he adds "this *vis insita,* may, by a most significant name, be called *vis inertiae,* or *force of inactivity.*" Now this force is not one which produces change, or requires the existence of another body; it is that which endeavours to preserve the identity and stability of the body in space and time.

In addition to this innate force, Newton next postulates another entity which he calls an impressed force, and "this force consists in action only." It is not an essential property of a body but acts on it from the outside and produces change and variety. It also requires the existence of two bodies to be brought into play, and it resides in neither. Thus he gives to force the double and paradoxical rôles of inactivity and activity.

There can be little doubt but that his definition of impressed force, as something detachable from matter, was based on his discovery of universal attraction. He several times insisted that he postulated its existence solely as a matter of experience, and when he speculated on its cause he invariably assigned to it an æthereal or hypothetical medium and, at times, suggested that this medium may be immaterial,—the divine power of God.[33] To make his meaning more emphatic, he distinguished, in the four following definitions, the *vis insita* from the *vis impressa* by the distinction between centrifugal force and centripetal force. To illustrate his idea, let us consider a planet revolving about the sun. In each there is an innate force of inertia (*vis insita*); the planet of itself *endeavours* to move in a straight line, which he defined later as a natural state, and the sun *endeavours* to remain at rest. But in addition, there is a centripetal force of attraction (*vis impressa*), inherent in neither, which com-

[33] In this identification of an infinite medium, or of space, with the active cause of universal force, we must recognise the influence of Henry More, and we should suspect that he depended much on Newton's scientific work.

pels both bodies to change their natural states. If this interpretation of Newton's fundamental postulates is correct, he avoided the dilemma of making bodies both inert and active, but he fell into the equal difficulty of defining force as that which produces stability and variation, and is both innate and impressed on matter. The fact is, that the subject lies outside the field of science which can discuss only phenomena, and not their ultimate causes. The same may be said of Newton's long discussion of absolute, and relative, time and space. Such questions may be proper for metaphysicians to discuss, though to the present time, the results of their discussion seem somewhat uncertain, to say the least. For the physicist, fortunately, the absolute is not significant, and his problems concern only relative, and measurable, space, and time.

After his general definitions, Newton announced three axioms, or laws of motion. The first law, that every body perseveres in its state of rest, or of uniform motion unless acted upon by an impressed force, is merely a repetition of his former definition of the *vis insita.* If we remember that a state of absolute rest is unrecognisable, and that his assumption of a mutual attraction between every pair of existing bodies precludes any body from being free from impressed forces, it is evident that the law is purely hypothetical, and not verifiable by scientific experimentation.

The third law, that action and reaction are equal and opposite, must also be regarded as purely hypothetical. This can be best shown by considering Newton's illustrations. He says that if a horse draws a stone tied to a rope, the horse will be pulled back as much as the stone is pulled forward. But a dead horse cannot initiate a pull and the previous will to move of a live horse must be excluded from a mechanistic law. Again his illustration of impact is defective. If two bodies collide, the equality of action and reaction involves the mass, or the hypothetical *vis insita,* as well as the resultant velocities. Even if we admit the explanation of impact by Hooke's law of elasticity to be satisfactory, there are cases which are not explicable even by that empirical fact. If light or heat from the sun, or any other source, falls on a reflecting body it produces an observable pressure and displacement away from the source. In this case, where the one body is acted upon there is no direct mechanical reaction on the other. For example, the light of the sun repels the tail of a comet, but there is no repulsion of the sun. Thus, to explain the laws of impact a molecular force of repulsion must be assumed; and radiant pressure requires the assumption of light corpuscles, or of an æther possessing the attribute of ponderable mass.

There thus remains only the second law and, as it defines the function of a force and expresses its measurement without involving hypothetical ideas of the nature of bodies and force, it is scientific and fundamental. It states that the measurable ratio of force to change of motion is a constant, and that this constant may be taken as the measure of the mass of a body. Such a definition of mass evidently does not involve the hypothetical concept of a *vis insita,* or the esoteric idea of effort, or the vitalistic endeavour to persevere, in material bodies; but leaves it as a mere numerical coefficient.

The laws of motion, and their corollaries, are followed by a scholium in which Newton assigned the honour of discovery of the first two laws to Galileo who by direct experimentation established the correct formula for a force. The third law follows, according to Newton, from the work of Wallis, Wren, and Huygens, on impact. To conclude our review of the preface, his metaphysical ideas have been successfully attacked, the cause of gravitation has been the subject of endless discussion and of no conclusion, and the attempts to include the phenomena of heat, light, electricity, and life in a mechanical system have invariably failed; but we should not overlook the fact that all these are foreign to the mechanics of ponderable bodies which is, in truth, the sole subject of the *Principia.*

The first book opens with the geometrical proof of a few general theorems in mechanics, and from there Newton immediately passes to the discussion of orbital motion. He first proves that, if a body moves in a conic section about a stationary body situated at its focus, a force of attraction which is inversely proportional to the square of the distance between them will be a sufficient cause of the motion. And he develops his theory of celestial mechanics on the basis that this centripetal force, or gravitation, is the only force necessary to account for the elliptic orbits of the planets and of their satellites; also, all perturbations in their motions are caused by the same force. If we further assume that a foreign body, such as a comet, enters the system with a rectilinear motion its path will be an ellipse, an hyperbola or a parabola according to the initial value given to its speed. Generalising this idea, from the principle that the action of the whole is the sum of the action of its parts, Newton assumes gravity to be the universal cause of motion. In making such a generalisation he had to rely solely on celestial motions since it was then experimentally impossible to prove the attraction of small bodies on each other. This has since been acomplished.

After the discussion of the problem of the attraction of two bodies, Newton derives an approximate solution of the problem of three bodies where one of them is so large as to be considered stationary. In this section the motion of the moon under the action of the sun and the earth is considered; also the problems of Saturn's rings, the tides, the shape of the earth, the precession of the equinoxes are dealt with mathematically for the first time. The book closes with the attempt to explain the laws of the reflection, refraction, and diffraction of light by a similar force of attraction between light corpuscles and matter.

Practically the entire second book is devoted to a discussion of the motion of fluids, and the effect of friction on the motion of solid bodies in fluids. At first sight, surprise may be felt that so large a part should have been devoted to this subject. But Newton's purpose is explained if we recall that, although he had proved gravity would account fully for planetary motion, he had the very difficult task of demonstrating not only that the hypothesis of Cartesian vortices was unnecessary, but also that they were incapable of satisfying Kepler's laws. This hypothesis reigned supreme, and it will be remembered that Newton, himself, when his first calculation indicated the insufficiency of gravity as a cause, is said to have believed a vortex to be necessary. It is evident that if space be filled with vast vortices which carry the planets in their orbits, then space must be considered to be a frictional fluid.

Newton first attacks the problem by proving that circular motion in a frictional medium would, under the action of gravity, degenerate into a spiral path ultimately causing the planet to fall on the central body. He therefore concludes, since there is no evidence of instability in planetary orbits, that space is empty and devoid of friction. Finally, in proposition 52, he attacks the problem directly and proves that a vortex will not account for Kepler's laws. This proposition states: "If a solid sphere, in an uniform and infinite fluid, revolves about an axis given in position with an uniform motion, and the fluid be forced round by only this impulse of the sphere; and every part of the fluid perseveres uniformly in its motion: I say, that the periodic times of the parts of the fluid are as the *squares of their distances* from the centre of the sphere." The proof of this proposition, with the corollaries derived from it, was really the death-blow of the Cartesian hypothesis; for, in a scholium he remarks: "I have endeavoured in this proposition to investigate the properties of vortices, that I might find whether the celestial phenomena can be explained by them; for the phenomenon is this, that the periodic times of the planets revolving about Jupiter are in the sesquiplicate ratio of their distances from Jupiter's centre;[34] and the same rule obtains also among the planets that revolve about the sun."

In addition to the principal thesis of the second book, Newton shows his marvellous power as a geometrician. There is a wealth of material on the motions of pendulums, efflux of fluids, and wave motion. Besides the mathematical demonstration of the laws of fluids, he supported his argument with elaborate series of experiments. In accuracy of measurement and ingenuity of invention, I think, Faraday alone was equal to him; and when we remember that, to this experimental power, there was also an unrivalled mathematical genius, which Faraday totally lacked, the combination justifies the awe with which his contemporaries regarded him, and still makes us regard him as the supreme natural philosopher.

Newton concludes the second book with the statement that he had accomplished the task he had set out to do: "The hypothesis of vortices is utterly irreconcilable with astronomical phenomena, and rather serves to perplex than explain the heavenly motions. How these motions are performed in free space without vortices, may be understood by the first book; and I shall now more fully treat of it in the following book." And in the prefatory opening of the third book he explains what his purpose had been. He had not tried a descriptive narrative of phenomena, but to outline a science of mechanics, founded on a few laws of motion and force known to be true from experience, and developed by mathematics. While he illustrated his conclusions by a few phenomena, he felt he could leave the applications of the theory, which he had advanced, to the work of succeeding natural philosophers. He evidently thought it would have distracted his readers from following his main argument if he had included descriptive matter. He had, of course, meditated on the vast number of cosmic phenomena which his proof of the universal attraction of matter explained. It will be remembered that he had prepared a third book in which he had set forth the applications of

[34] This is the statement of Kepler's law that the cubes of the distances of planets are proportional to the squares of their periods; thus the law of vortices which requires the squares of their distances to be proportional to their periods is erroneous.

his theory of gravity and then, at the last moment, would have suppressed it except for the earnest entreaty of Halley.

The introduction to this third book is curiously indicative of Newton's character, a strange mixture of modesty and pride. "It remains that," he wrote, "from the same principles, I now demonstrate the frame of the System of the World. Upon this subject I had, indeed, composed the third book in a popular method, that it might be read by many; but afterwards, considering that such as had not sufficiently entered into the principles could not easily discern the strength of the consequences, nor lay aside the prejudices to which they had been many years accustomed, therefore, to prevent the disputes which might be raised upon such accounts, I chose to reduce the substance of this book into the form of propositions (in the mathematical way), which should be read by those only who had first made themselves masters of the principles established in the preceding books: not that I would advise any one to the previous study of every proposition of those books; for they abound with such as might cost too much time, even to readers of good mathematical learning."

On the rare occasions when Newton discusses his own work, he does it with the calm assurance of its high value. A man of his penetrating mind could not have failed to know that he had accomplished a colossal piece of work and that he had placed science on a new and firm foundation. He knew that only a very few could understand it, and even they would probably fail to see the unlimited consequences which he had laid before them. For years, he had lived in a sort of ecstasy of meditation as the laws of the cosmos developed in his mind, and now that he had reluctantly published his thoughts, he would ward off the criticisms of those who would not exercise the same labour to understand him. And with this haughty pride there was an equal modesty when he contemplated what little he could do to solve the inexplicable mysteries of the physical universe, and there was true humility in his submission to the belief that "this most beautiful system of the sun, planets, and comets, could only proceed from the counsel and dominion of an intelligent and powerful Being."[35]

Newton's true modesty is shown most clearly in his recognition that mere activity of a vigorous mind, not only cannot arrive at useful scientific conclusions by any mathematical or verbal logic unless

[35] Gen. Schol. Book III, *Principia.*

it is based on established facts of experience; but also that such unsupported activity is pernicious in that it dazzles the minds of others and hinders true knowledge. And as proof, he cited the grandiose cosmogony of Descartes which, being founded on an inward sentiment of knowledge, "rather serves to perplex than to explain the heavenly motions." Not only did Newton believe that the first commandment of science was that theory must be based on experimental facts, but he also was ready to abandon his own without hesitation if it failed in that support. Thus, Conduitt made a note in his intended life of Newton that Molyneux, a mathematician, told him: "After he and Mr. Graham and Bradley had put up a perpendicular telescope at Kew to find out the parallax of the fixed stars, they found a certain nutation in the earth which they could not account for, and thought destroyed the Newtonian system—M. told I. N. as gently and tactfully as he could— But all I. N. said in answer was, 'It may be so, there is no arguing against facts and experiments.' "[36]

The most important applications of the theory of attraction to the explanation of phenomena, discussed in the third book, are various laws of planetary motion, the lunar theory, the precession of the equinoxes, the tides, and the planetary theory of comets. Of these his proof of the orbital paths of comets was probably the most notable prediction of Newton's theory. The treatment of the lunar theory, as given in the first edition of the *Principia,* is, as he himself expressly stated, only a specimen or fragment which outlined some of the more evident lunar inequalities due to the perturbing action of the sun. In the second edition this subject was corrected and expanded, but he frequently expressed his disappointment that he did not carry on the work to a more perfect conclusion. That he did occupy himself intermittently with the problem is known by the mass of papers on the subject which is preserved in the *Portsmouth Collection*. He often laid the blame on Flamsteed for a lack of coöperation in providing him with the data of observations; but it is more likely that his lack of interest in science after the publication of the *Principia* and his official life when he went to London, are the real reasons why the lunar theory was never completed.

The *Principia,* when it first appeared, ended as casually as if the author had grown weary of the task, and had suddenly decided to

[36] *Portsmouth Collection.*

write no more. But a General Scholium was added to the second edition in which Newton sums up the purpose and accomplishment of the work. He has, he declared, shown the Cartesian hypothesis to be untenable; and, although he has demonstrated that a universal force of gravity will account mathematically for the major phenomena of the solar system, yet he is just as convinced that no mere mechanical causes could give birth to so many regular motions, and that this most beautiful system presupposes, by the very fact of its regularity, the existence of a divine Creator. He then affirms his belief in an omniscient and omnipotent God, whose attributes we may learn to know through his laws and works. Finally, since he will frame no hypotheses, he has assigned no cause of the power of gravity, "It is enough that gravity does really exist, and act according to the laws which we have explained, and abundantly serves to account for all the motions of the celestial bodies, and of our sea." Lest, however, anyone should think he held that gravity was an occult and essential attribute of matter, he intimates that there may be an elastic and electric Spirit which pervades and lies hid in all gross bodies. "But these are things that cannot be explained in few words, nor are we furnished with that sufficiency of experiments which is required to an accurate determination and demonstration of the laws by which this electric and elastic Spirit operates." As it will be shown later, this scholium was added to the text during the preparation of the second edition, not because Newton felt that it should be an integral part of his argument, but because he had been urged to defend himself against personal attacks made on his philosophy, and on his religion.

It was instructive, in view of the pretensions of modern pseudoscience, to emphasize Newton's modest statement of what he had accomplished in the *Principia*. And, as a like example of the same spirit, the conclusion of Aristotle's *Organon* is equally significant:

"Moreover, on the subject of Rhetoric there exists much that has been said long ago, whereas on the subject of Reasoning we had nothing else of an earlier date to speak of at all, but were kept at work for a long time in experimental researches. If, then, it seems to you after inspection that, such being the situation as it existed at the start, our investigation is in a satisfactory condition compared with the other enquiries that have been developed by tradition, there must remain for all of you, or for our students, the task of extending us your pardon for the shortcomings of the enquiry, and for the discoveries thereof your warm thanks."[37]

It is a notable fact that these two works, probably the two most stupendous creations of the scientific brain, are now under attack,—the *Organon* by modern symbolists in logic, and the *Principia* by the relativists in physics. But Aristotle and Newton will be honoured and *used* when the modernists are long forgotten.

The effect of the *Principia* was revolutionary so soon as its power and scope were appreciated; due to the labours of a succession of mathematical physicists, a remarkable science of mechanics was developed. By abstracting all the qualities of bodies except their *vires insitae* concentrated at their centres of inertia, the positions and motions of these centres, and the existence of the Newtonian force of attraction along a line joining each pair of these points, the nearest approach to an ideal science was created. Given, the masses, positions, and motions of a system of bodies at any instant; then, with extraordinary precision, their future positions and motions could be calculated by a set of rigorous mathematical equations. In the meanwhile, and especially during the nineteenth century, the sciences of heat, light, and electricity made rapid strides. It was natural, and even inevitable, that theorists should turn to mechanics for a method to explain the phenomena of those sciences. As a result of these efforts, there was evolved an elaborately complex, and highly artificial, objective world of merely masses and motions which had but a faint resemblance to our sense perceptions.

Unconsciously, the physical world was divided into two almost unrelated realms, a perceptible cosmos of finite bodies, and a microcosm of the infinitesimally small. On the one hand, the actions of a drop of water, for example, were studied as if the body were a simple mechanical mass. On the other hand, the same drop was imaginatively conceived to be an enormously complex aggregation of an indefinite number of atoms, each indefinitely small, and all compacted within the superficies of the drop to form a planetary system. Having first successfully created a mechanics of the system as a unit, by abstracting from it all so-called secondary qualities, such as chemical action, heat, light, electricity, etc., each quality was then successively restored to the system and explained by endowing the atom with the attribute as a consequence of his own motion.

[37] *Cf. Translation of Aristotle's Works.* Vol. I, Ed. by Ross. Oxford.

Thus, there was elaborated a mechanical hypothesis of the atom, agreeing as nearly as possible with the principles and laws of Newtonian dynamics of ponderable bodies.

By the twentieth century, the mechanical hypothesis of the atom, or molecular physics as it was called, had become an unwieldy burden, and no imaginable atom could even satisfy the phenomena of one field of physics; while it quite failed as the *deus ex machina* of all of them. Newtonian mechanics, which was so effective an instrument in its own domain, not only began to show signs of wear, but actually cracked at every joint, when it was thus stretched to cover subjects to which it was never intended to apply. In this predicament, theorists, with the hope of preserving a unity of method, gradually made an abstraction of the concrete atom. The boldest attempt towards a philosophy of pure idealism is Professor Einstein's Generalised Theory of Relativity. By an explicit paradox, and by the use of a geometry not limited by our sense perception of only three dimensions, he has proposed a new synthesis. The world, as he pictures it, is purely idealistic, a formula expressed by mathematical equations incapable of explicit solution. The brute facts of experience are an illusion without objective existence. In one respect, we must admit that truth is formular, either verbal or mathematical. But the philosophy, which is merely a logical exercise of the active mind, and ignores the world of brute facts, may be interesting, but it ultimately evaporates into a scholasticism. And if it persists, it will cause the decadence of science as surely as the mediæval scholasticism preceded the decadence of religion.

As I have said before, it is popularly believed that modern criticism has at last broken down the classical mechanics. But Newtonian dynamics, in its own restricted field, can be superseded only by demonstrating experimentally that two bodies of sensible size, when separated by a finite distance, do not exert a mutual force of attraction: it can be corrected only by demonstrating experimentally that this force of attraction does not vary exactly as the inverse square of the distance. Till now, at least, both direct and indirect observation confirms this law. For great distances astronomy confirms it accurately; for terrestrial distances, our laboratory experiments are difficult and their accuracy is not great; for molecular distances, if the force exists, it is almost certainly proportional to a higher power than the square. The influence of other actions has been investigated. That gravity is affected by temperature, by electrical or magnetic charges, or by the material of the bodies, is extremely doubtful; the evidence is preponderantly against any appreciable influence. If the force is a function of the velocity, it is unaffected by any velocity known to be attainable by a ponderable body.

From its publication till today, the *Principia* has been the source of all theoretical physics and, so far as one can predict, it will continue indefinitely to be a model of the scientific method. We should regard it with the reverence expressed in Halley's verse:

"Nec fas est propius Mortali attingere Divos."

CHAPTER X

THE ALBAN AFFAIR AND THE REVOLUTION. CORRESPONDENCE WITH JOHN LOCKE. THE BOYLE LECTURES. SERIOUS ILLNESS

1687–1693

WHILE Newton was so deeply absorbed in the composition of the *Principia* that he was hardly aware of the ordinary functions and regimen of life, England was facing one of the gravest crises in her history. He, in the quiet and retirement of his study, was seeking to elucidate the laws of a universe so rigorous and exact that, once instituted by God, they were subject to no change and to no interruption in the uniform flow of their effects. In all the rest of England, other men were agitated by the accession of James II to the throne; even the most thoughtless viewed the future with apprehension and alarm, lest the comparative peace of the previous reign should be wrecked in a return to the turbulence and lawlessness of civil strife. It is not the least curious consequence of the events which followed, that Newton should have been drawn out of his scholarly creative life and turned into a public official and courtier.

The first solemn promises of tolerance were scarcely made by the new King before the nation realised that religious strife would again shake the foundations of the government. James not only openly professed the Roman Catholic religion, but declared it to be his dearest wish to bring the country back to that faith. It is very probable that he might have removed many of the restrictions which had been imposed on the Catholics since the time of Elizabeth, and might have obtained civil and religious freedom for them, if he had exercised tact and self-restraint, so fearful were the people that intolerance would bring a return to civil war. But, against the warning and advice of Rome to proceed cautiously, he listened to the counsel of the Jesuit coterie, who were weary of the temporising policy of his brother, and who were totally unable to judge the

English character. Urged by them, he adopted the policy of absolute rule, of intimidation, and of debauching the law courts to give his acts the specious plea of legality.

No sooner was the rebellion of the Duke of Monmouth crushed, than James gave free rein to Jeffreys to strike terror into any who might question his purpose. As Chief Justice of the Court of the King's Bench, he made the Western Circuit and sickened England with horror at his treatment of the adherents of that ill-fated cause. It is very possible that the stories of his gloating cruelty, and of his wild debauchery, have been exaggerated by his political enemies. He was undoubtedly a man of ability and, as a judge, he had the faculty of making evident the essential points of the question at issue. But, it is also certain that he paralysed with fear those who appeared in his court, and that James had found a servant after his own heart and one willing to do what he desired. To reward his service and his fidelity he was created Lord Chancellor and raised to the peerage at the extraordinarily early age of thirty-eight years.

Flushed with success, James now openly declared that he intended to use his whole power to destroy the Established Church. With this purpose in mind, he determined, in 1686, to revive the High Court of Commission. All the powerful and rigorous ecclesiastical courts of the Tudors had been abolished by the Long Parliament. After the Restoration, they had been reinstituted, although restricted in power; the High Court of Commission, however, had been expressly excepted, so there was no question but that, in reviving this court, the King's act was illegal.[1] Under the authority of this illegal court: "All colleges and grammar schools, even those which had been founded by the liberality of private benefactors, were placed under the authority of the new board. All who depended for bread on situations in the Church or in academical institutions, from the Primate down to the youngest curate, from the Vice-chancellors of Oxford and Cambridge down to the humblest pedagogue who taught Corderius, were subjected to this despotic tribunal. The Commission were

[1] *Cf. Portsmouth Collection.*—Newton made, and preserved, a copy of the legal questions involved in the dispute between the Crown and the University about the admission of papists. The following refers to the abolition of ecclesiastic courts. "By statute 16 Chas. I an act repealing of a branch of stat. 1 Elizabeth concerning Commissions for causes Ecclesiastical and said branch is repealed. It is enacted that no new Court shall be created, ordained, or appointed within this realm which shall or may have like power, jurisdiction or authority as the High Commission Court then had or pretended to have, but that all and every such Commissions and Grants and all powers and authorities granted or pretended to be granted thereby shall be void and of none effect as in and by the said statutes more fully appear."

both prosecutors and judges. The accused had no copy of the charge and could be examined and cross-examined. He could be suspended or permanently ejected and, if he were contumacious, he could be deprived of his civil rights and imprisoned for life. Over this court, the Lord Chancellor Jeffreys presided as Chief Commissioner, and even the staunchest adherents of James might well be alarmed at the consequences."[2]

The acts of the Court do not concern this biography except in its dealings with the Universities. The papist advisers of the King realised that Oxford and Cambridge were the firmest buttresses of the Church of England. The ecclesiastical dignitaries and the parish priests were among their alumni; most of the fellows were in orders; and their students would later fill the influential offices of church and state. Because of their importance, it was determined to strike at the Universities and thus cut the root of the opposition to Rome. No policy could have been rasher or more foolish. The Universities had been, and were then, consistently loyal to the Stuarts. But, they were even more jealous of their statutory rights and strongly attached to their Church; such an action was certain to arouse deep opposition and change their sentiment. Not only those then in the Universities would be aroused to a just indignation but they would have the sympathy and active support of the alumni, many holding important positions in church and state, who preserved a peculiarly deep affection for an Alma Mater where their early days had been passed and their minds trained. The Universities might have been crushed as the final step in the design; it was fatal to attack them first.

The more moderate advisers of the King proposed to establish, in each of the Universities, new colleges devoted to the teaching and promulgation of the doctrines of the Roman Church, and to make them so superior to the other colleges that the abler and more ambitious students would choose to enroll in them. This plan would, however, be slow in effect and, because of its expense, it would arouse the parsimony of the King. It was judged to be easier and cheaper to transform the existing colleges into Catholic seminaries.[3]

[2] Macaulay, History of England, Chapter VI.

[3] An interesting side-light on the cost of maintaining a college at that time is given by Burnet, *History of His Own Time*, London, 1724, Vol. I, p. 697. "Some of the more moderate among them proposed, that the King should endow a new college in both Universities, which needed not have cost above two thousand pounds a year." The following account of the struggle between the Universities and the Court relies principally on the documents and letters preserved by Newton and now in the *Portsmouth Collection*. The importance he attached to his share in the case of Cambridge before the Court of Com-

The first move was directed against Oxford, whose See was bestowed on Dr. Parker. He was a man of mediocre ability and his religious integrity can be judged from the fact that he had been a violent Independent till the time of the Restoration, and had then changed over into the highest form of the Church of England. "The Deanery of Christ-Church, the most important post in the University, was next given to Massey, one of the new converts, tho' he had neither the gravity, the learning, nor the age that was suitable to such a dignity. But all was supplied by his early conversion."[4] The most flagrant case of the King's folly was his later attempt to impose a popish president on Magdalene College. This arbitrary and illegal act was bitterly opposed by the Fellows, who, by law, were required to elect their own Head. The struggle between the college and the court so inflamed the University and the nation that, according to Burnet who was at the time in Holland, the church party and the clergy sent urgent messages to the Prince of Orange to intervene and even to resist with force the King's exercise of despotic power.

Just after the King, in 1687, began to meddle with Oxford, and before he engaged in the affair of Magdalene College, he attempted, by a seemingly insignificant act, to break down the law which excluded Roman Catholics from the University of Cambridge.[5] On Ash-wednesday, the 9th of February, 1687, the Vice-Chancellor received a letter under his Majesty's sign manual; the substance whereof was: "That hearing much in commendation of one Alban Francis, a Benedictine, the King was pleased to command the University that they should admit him to the degree of Master of Arts without administering to him any oath or oaths; whatsoever any law or statute to the contrary in any wise notwithstanding with which his Majesty was pleased graciously to dispense in behalf of the said Alban Francis."

The University authorities recognised at once the gravity of the mandate, and that the King was embarking on his plan of breaking down the restrictions against the papists. It was a more or less com-

mission is shown by the fact that he kept copies of the University statutes from the time of Elizabeth; of the full proceedings of the trial; of detailed memoranda and of several letters explaining his opinions. He rightly felt that the struggle between the King and the Universities was the direct cause of the Revolution and formed a crisis in his own life. The reader should also refer to Burnet's *History*.

[4] Burnet, Vol. I, p. 696.

[5] For the account of this incident, see: *Portsmouth Collection;* also Burnet, Vol. I, pp. 697–699; Brewster, Vol. II, pp. 106–109; and Edleston, note 90, p. lviii.

mon custom to receive, and to obey, such royal mandates to confer honorary degrees on ambassadors and foreign princes irrespective of their religion. And when the University Senate refused to obey this order, the gibe was made that they had formerly granted an honorary degree to the secretary of the Moroccan Embassy, a Mohammedan, and were now balking against a like honour to a Christian. But there was this essential difference, the recipients of honorary degrees have no vote in the Senate, while Masters of Arts, having such a vote, direct the policy of the University. There was, thus, a possible danger that the King, by continuing this policy, would be able to obtain a majority in the Senate, and so overturn the Protestant character of the University.

The mandate involved such a serious threat that the Vice-Chancellor delayed action till the Senate should obtain legal advice. At first, it was resolved to express their almost unanimous disapproval, and a Grace was drawn up to be put to the vote of the Congregation of the University in the usual way. But, since the constitution of the House was such that the Grace must first be proposed by a committee of Heads of six persons any one of whom could by his veto hinder it from being put to the House, this method was laid aside as impracticable. The reason for this unusual decision was because a Mr. Basset, one of the Heads and a declared Roman Catholic, openly espoused Fr. Francis's cause; and it was feared that, by using his veto, he would prevent the Grace from being presented. "This consideration constrained them to use another method,—to avoid a formal vote and to ask members to testify voluntarily their concurrence with the Vice-Chancellor, and advise him to refuse to admit Fr. Francis till the King had been petitioned to revoke the Mandate."

As soon as the King's letter had been received by the Vice-Chancellor, he wrote to the Chancellor, the Duke of Albemarle, to beg his intercession with the King. But the Duke replied that he had already tried without effect and recommended that a petition from the University might have more force. The Congregation, when it met, drew up such a petition setting forth their opinion that the admission of Fr. Francis, without the usual oaths, was illegal and unsafe. The petition was approved by all members, except three papists and one or two others; as it was thought that a petition signed by 150–200 persons "might look tumultuary," the more quiet, decent, and respectful way of sending it by two messengers was adopted. At the same time, a gentleman was admitted Doctor of Physic by Mandate after taking the oaths; "and the Esqre. Beedle and Register were sent to Fr. Francis to say the Senate would admit him provided he would swear as the laws appointed."

Francis insisted on the King's dispensation and, immediately upon the breaking up of the Congregation, he took horse for London to tell at White-Hall what had been done. The same afternoon the Heads sent their letter of petition to the Duke of Albemarle and a copy to the Earl of Sunderland, Secretary of State. The University messengers, Professor Smoult and Mr. Norris, could get no access to Sunderland. On February 24th, a second letter was sent from the King reiterating his Mandate and warning the University to refuse at its peril.

In the meanwhile the Senate had had very satisfactory opinions from eminent lawyers approving their action. They then composed a second letter, giving their reasons for their decision, and sent it up to London by two Fellows. These messengers were refused an audience by the King; and Sunderland, who admitted them, at the request of Albemarle, the next morning at his bed-side, merely informed them that the King was offended and would shortly give the University a further answer.

On Saturday, April 9,[6] Mr. Atterbury went to Cambridge with the following summons from the High Court of Ecclesiastical Commissioners: "Whereas complaint had been made to them against the Vice-Chancellor and Senate of the University of Cambridge for having refused to comply with his Majesty's Royal Letters in behalf of Mr. Francis they were therefore commanded to appear the Vice-Chancellor in person and the Senate by themselves and their deputies before the Lord Commissioners in the Council Chamber the 21st April to answer such things as should be objected against them in his Majesty's behalf upon the premises, etc."

Two days later, on April 11, the Senate drew up an outline of their defense which cited the statutes forbidding admission to candidates who would not take the specified oaths, setting forth the lack of jurisdiction, and also the illegality of the Court of High Commission. They then appointed the Vice-Chancellor and eight other Fellows, one of whom was Newton, to represent them with full powers under the seal of the University. Newton preserved a memorandum explaining the "reason why the delegates did not adopt the usual

[6] Newton's Mss. has the date erroneously as April 19.

custom of demurring from the Court's jurisdiction which is commonly the first and only plea in such cases. The delegates felt themselves obliged not only to defend their cause, but to satisfy the world, and they wished all persons to know the facts and reasons for their actions; wherefor they insisted on those being discussed first. If the Court's jurisdiction had come first that would, in all probability have occasioned the whole plea to be shifted and overruled."

The delegates met the Commissioners[7] in the Council Chamber on April 21. The case excited immense interest; many attended to support the University, and others to enjoy the baiting of the delegates by Jeffreys. The noise and crowd were so great that Mr. Bridgman was forced to repeat the reading of the summons. Burnet states that the defense by Pechell, Master of Magdalene and Vice-Chancellor of the University, was feebly made: "He was a very honest, but a very weak man. He made a poor defense. And it was no small reflection on that great body, that their chief magistrate was so little able to assert their privileges, or to justify their proceedings. He was treated with great contempt by Jeffreys."

Jeffreys directed all his questions to the Vice-Chancellor and soon reduced him to helpless agitation.[8] After each grilling, the embarrassed Pechell would be unable to repeat even such matters as his oath of office, and would beg to have time to put his answers into writing. When any of the delegates, shamed by the spectacle, attempted to speak, Jeffreys said insolently to one, "Nay, good Doctor, you was never Vice-Chancellor: yet when you are we may consider you"; to another, "Nay, look you that young gentleman expects to be Vice-Chancellor too, when you are Sir you may speak. Till then it will more become you to forbear."

The Commissioners were quite aware of the fact that there was no case against the University, but they tried to intimidate the delegates into submission by sentencing Pechell, for his disobedience and contempt, to be deprived of the Vice-Chancellorship and to be suspended from the Mastership of his College during his Majesty's pleasure.[9] The Court then met the delegates without Pechell. Re-

[7] The Commissioners present were Ld. Chanc. Jeffreys, Ld. Pres. Sunderland, Ld. Mulgrave, Earl of Huntington, Ld. Bishops of Durham and of Rochester, Ld. Ch. Justice Herbert.

[8] Newton preserved a verbatim report of the questions and answers.

[9] Dr. Pechell was restored to the Mastership of Magdalene in 1688. "After the Revolution he starved himself to death, in consequence of having been rebuked by Archbishop Sancroft for drunkenness and other loose habits; and after four days' abstinence, would have eaten, but could not." Note by Lord Dartmouth in Burnet's *History,* Vol. I, p. 698.

lieved of his embarrassing presence, they declared that they no longer represented the Senate as their delegation terminated with the deprivation of the Vice-Chancellor. They then drew up a statement answering the questions of Jeffreys and showing their obedience to the laws. No answer was given to this document and Jeffreys dismissed them with the warning: "Gentlemen, the best way will be a ready obedience to his Majesty's commands for the future, and by giving a good example to others to make some amends for the ill example has been given you. Therefore I shall say to you what the Scripture says, and the rather because I see most of you are divines. Go your way and sin no more lest a worse thing befall you."

Alarmed by the steadfast stand of the University and the widespread interest the case aroused, the King abandoned his attempt to coerce the Universities. But it was too late, as an influential party of the nobility opened negotiations with the Prince of Orange to assume an active part in settling the affairs of the nation. Because Newton was silent during the proceedings of the Court it has been assumed that he was a more or less negligible member of the delegation. He was not a ready speaker and was easily embarrassed in public. But two documents in the *Portsmouth Collection* prove that it was he who stiffened the delegation to resist the unlawful action of the King when the other members had agreed on a compromise. Conduitt noted for his proposed *Life* that, when the delegates were about to start to London, Stanhope, the Chancellor of Ely, drew up a paper agreeing to admit Fr. Francis to a degree provided it should not be a precedent or be repeated. All seemed ready to sign the compromise except Newton, who rose from the table and, after taking two or three turns about the room, said to the Bedell sent by the University to attend them: "This is giving up the question." "So it is," said the Bedell, "Why do you not go and speak to it?" Newton then returned to the table and told them his mind and desired them, before signing, to obtain a legal opinion. When Mr. Finch agreed with Newton, the delegation resolved to make no compromise.

The other document was the following letter by Newton which has never been published. It is important as it shows that he was active in explaining the action of the University and in trying to win support. It is also important as it is the first intimation of his deep opposition to, and dread of, Roman Catholicism which will be shown later to be one of the principal reasons for his theological writings. In this letter also, Newton makes it clear that he was opposed to the doctrine of the divine right of Kings, and placed the law of the land above obedience to Royal Mandate. Both of these settled convictions undoubtedly had their influence in electing him to the Convention Parliament. It proves, too, that Newton was a Whig by principle, and shows that the counsel he gave to the University on how to act towards King William was not dictated by others. His steadfastness against encroachments on the rights of the Church of England and of the University so impressed his colleagues that, when a greater crisis came upon the nation, they elected him to represent the University in the Convention Parliament.

Newton to ——

Sir,

Here's a strong report in the town that a Mandamus has been brought to the Vice-Chancellor to admit one F. Francis a Benedictine Monk to be a Master of Arts, and that the Vice-Chancellor sent to the Chancellor to endeavour to get the same recalled but could not prevail; which was an error in him. For all honest men are obliged by the Laws of God and Man to obey the King's lawful commands, but if his Majesty be advised to require a matter which cannot be done by law, no man can suffer for neglect of it. The Vice-Chancellor cannot by law admit one to that degree, unless he take the oaths of supremacy and allegiance which are enjoined by 3 or 4 statutes; and it is not to be said he disobeys the King's commands when he is ready to fulfil them if the party be capable to receive the act commanded which this monk cannot be, and 'tis not probable that a Convocation can be induced to give Grace for the degree to an unqualified person. And tho it should be expressed in the Mandamus that his Majesty dispenses with those oaths, yet it cannot excuse the Vice-Chancellor for he is no judge thereof, but he knows that the law of the land enjoins the taking of the oaths; and if he admits anyone without doing it he is indictable for the same, and if he modestly refuse to admit this person he can run no risk in it, and if F. Francis be acquainted with the obstacles in his way in a decent manner, and is not satisfied therewith, let him take his remedy at law, and to be sure the V. C. will hear no more of him, and by civilly standing his ground he will save the University. Let him peruse Q. Eliz. Charter for the University of Cambridge, Sat. the 26 of April in the 3d year of her reign and an act of Parliament not printed which is kept with the Statutes of the University entitled An

Act for the Incorporation of both the Universities. In the statutes you will find that all Letters Patents of the Qn's Highness or any of her progenitors or predecessors made to either of the Universities are confirmed. See of this matter Cook [Coke] 4, Institutes, page 227.

The King was advised to send a Mandamus to the Master and Governers of the Charter House requiring them to admit an old Gentleman to be a Pensioner. Now every pensioner is to take the oaths of supremacy and allegiance by the constitution of their house, but the man being a papist they refused to admit and there's no more said of it. The Master's name is Burnett, late of Christ Coll. and by the rule of elections in the giving their votes, he as the meanest man, speaks first. There were eight present. The Master and four were to lay the Mandamus aside and there were three to retain it, but the majority being against the Mandamus the Pensioner was rejected.

D. Burnett Master	Earl Rochester
Earl Danby	Earl Mulgrave
Bp. Winchester	Ld. Chancellor
Marquis Halifax	*for it*
Archbp. of Cant.	
against it	

The refusing the M. was not said to be because he is a papist but because he refused the oaths. Those that counselled his Majesty to disoblige the University cannot be his true friends for 'tis notorious that no body of men in England have been so loyal. They gave his father all their plate and infusions [?] which the gentry of England received there entrusted most of them with their lives and estates to support the crown against the wealth and strength of London and all the associated counties and the Fleet, the chiefest riches of the land. Be courageous therefore and steady to the Laws and you cannot fail and in time the King may thank you for it. If one priest be a Master you may have a hundred and they must choose Burgesses to Parliament.

I wonder that the Goodmen of Sidney do not elect their Master. An honest courage in these matters will secure all, having law on our sides.

Adieu

[Is. Newton.]

Feb. the 19th.

The prodigious strain involved in writing the *Principia* and the excitement of his experiences in London had exhausted his energy and depressed his spirits. Although he gave, as usual, a course of lectures during the Michaelmas Term of 1688 and probably continued to do so while he remained at Cambridge, we have no record of their subjects or contents. He must also have been further depressed by the death of Henry More in whose circle of friends he had been a frequent and interested associate.[10] In the spring of 1688, Montague, who had first aroused his interest in the world of affairs, permanently severed his connection with the University by vacating his fellowship. He was now in London and probably met Newton again while the latter was representing the University. If so, he would have described his own busy life and have divulged his hope of preferment from the patronage of Dorset; and, perhaps the older man envied him, and developed a certain disgust for the retired life of a scholar. Though Montague did not give up his rooms until Midsummer, he had abandoned his intention of entering the Church and, to further his political career, he married his Aunt-in-law, the Countess Dowager of Manchester. He seems to have made other unsuccessful ventures to advance his career by matrimony as the Duchess of Marlborough said of him: "He was a frightful figure, and yet pretended to be a lover; and followed several beauties who laughed at him for it."

In the meanwhile, affairs in England were going from bad to worse; and when, in June, 1688, a son was born to James, all hope of a Protestant succession was destroyed. The peers sent an invitation to William of Orange to place himself at the head of the Protestant cause; by December he had mastered the country and James had fled to France. In the interim of government, writs were issued for the election of a Convention Parliament which should settle the succession to the throne and restore the affairs of the nation after the Revolution. In this emergency Cambridge remembered the steadfast conduct of Newton against the encroachments of the late King, and elected him and Sir Robert Sawyer, also a Whig, to represent the University. At break of day on the twenty-second of January, 1688/9, he took his seat in the House of Commons, and he sat in

10 "Sept. 1, 1687. Dr. Henry More of Christ's College died; and was buried by torchlight the third day, being Sunday. His last words, as I heard, were these, or to this effect: calling his nurse he said to her, Nurse, I am going a long journey, when I shall change these for better possessions; and so presently departed. Sic Obiit Divinus ille Philosophus Cantabrigiensis: Extinctus amabitur idem." Whiston, *Memoirs*, 1st ed. p. 24.

that notable assembly till its dissolution in the following February. There were many distinguished veterans amongst the members who had returned to public life after a long seclusion; but they were thrown into the shade by two young men who took their seats for the first time. John Somers and Charles Montague speedily became the two great Whig parliamentarians of their time. They rose to the highest honours in the state, they weathered the fiercest storms, they were the munificent patrons of genius and learning, and they died within a few months of each other. While they were taking an active part, their friend, Newton, was a silent spectator of the great debates. He is supposed not to have spoken once in the House except, as was sarcastically reported, when he asked an usher to close a window. But, it does not follow that he was a useless member; he undoubtedly supported steadfastly the Whig measures, and he zealously attended to the interests of the University. Although he, later, showed pronounced administrative ability, it is doubtful if he had the readiness of mind to become a parliamentarian. At least he did not impress William III with his aptitude for affairs, if we can believe a statement of Duclos in his *Considérations sur les Mœurs*. William, who had a profound knowledge of character, was once embarrassed by a matter of politics; he was advised to consult Newton: but his reply was, Newton is merely a great philosopher.[11]

Newton's advice as to the attitude of the University is contained in thirteen letters addressed to the Vice-Chancellor, John Covel.[12] Just as the Revolution may be said to have had its inception from royal interference with the Universities, so now it was vital to its success to have their support. Newton's tactful advice was then a most important matter. Before the Parliament met, disorder had broken out amongst the students of so serious a nature that the Vice-Chancellor had addressed a general letter to the Heads of the Colleges:

Gentlemen,

Whereas, in this disorder many scholars are now in arms, and the effects thereof are to be feared as very dangerous to the whole University, as well as destructive to all good manners, I do humbly conceive our best course to reduce them would be to convene them in some public place of your Coll. to-morrow morning, if they return; and gravely, but calmly, advise them to all civil behaviour, believing

11 Quoted by Edleston, note 196, p. lxxxi.

12 Printed in 1848 in pamphlet form from the originals in his possession by Dawson Turner.

all severity at this juncture might rather tend to exasperate them more, and bring the unruly people's fury upon us all.

Your Servant,

JOH. COVEL, Procan.

December 15, 1688.

It was expedient for Newton to keep the authorities closely informed of the events as they occurred in London, and to advise them how to act so as to prevent opposition to the new reign. The day the King and Queen were proclaimed, he forwarded a copy of the proclamation and the following letter of advice.

Newton to Covel

Rev. Sir,

The King and Queen being proclaimed here yesterday, I presume you will soon receive an order for proclaiming them at Cambridge. I have enclosed the form of the Proclamation. I could wish heartily that the University would so compose themselves as to perform the solemnity with a seasonable decorum; because I take it to be their interest to set the best face upon things they can, after the example of the London divines. I am of opinion that Degrees be not given till you are authorised to administer the new Oaths. Whether that will be speedily done by authority of their Majesties and the Convention, or after the Convention is turned to a Parliament, I cannot yet resolve you. The Oath of Supremacy, as you administer it imperfectly in Latin, ought to be omitted, and both the new Oaths administered in English. You will see these Oaths in the end of the declaration. I have enclosed this post in a letter to Dr. Beaumont.

Sir, I am

Your most humble Servant,

IS. NEWTON.

London, Feb. 12, 1688/9.

As soon as the new King and Queen were proclaimed in London, the Vice-Chancellor and the Heads of the Colleges issued a proclamation of the allegiance of the University for the reason that God had vouchsafed "us a miraculous deliverance from popery and arbitrary power, and that our preservation is due, next under God, to the resolution and conduct of His Highness, the Prince of Orange, whom God hath chosen to be the glorious instrument of such an inestimable happiness to us and to our posterity." While Newton and the new Government were relieved by the news that the ceremony of the Proclamation had passed without serious disorder, there yet remained the more dangerous subscription to the oath of allegiance. Parliament had a most difficult and delicate task before it. The memory of the Civil Wars was still fresh and, however unpopular and arbitrary James had been, he had done nothing to make the throne vacant according to the widely accepted belief in the divine right of kings. His brother, Charles, had been restored on that theory and many people felt that without such allegiance continuity of government was impossible. William III, however able an administrator he might have been, was not one to arouse a popular sympathy; and the common revulsion of sympathy for the unfortunate James had turned many towards him in his exile. Nor did the exultant Whigs, now in power, help matters. They had an immense majority in Parliament, and they used all their power to crush opposition to the Revolution which they had made their party issue. In this phase of the political situation, Newton must have been of very great assistance. He was a staunch Whig and a convinced member of the Church of England: in the fashion of the day he interpreted the prophecies of the Book of Daniel as a warning against the power of the Pope and the Roman Church. He was an intimate friend of Montague and had become acquainted with Somers. In order to supplement the arguments of Covel for administering the oath, he sent him a long letter which really expounds the new Whig doctrine of limited allegiance to the King. It is an important document as it gives the principles then directing the government.

Newton to Covel

Sir,

I have had an account of the solemnity of the Proclamation; and I am glad to understand it was performed with so much decence by the wiser and more considerable part of the University, and generosity on your part. The next thing is a book of verses [sic]. If you do it at all, the sooner the better. Concerning the new oaths which you are to administer, I need not give instructions to you about their legality. But because many persons of less understanding (whom it may be difficult to persuade) will scruple at them, I will add my thoughts to yours. that you may have the fuller argument for convincing them, if I can add anything to what you have not thought of; for, seeing these oaths are the main thing that the dissatisfied part of the University scruple, I think I cannot do the University better service at present than by removing the scruples of as many as have sense enough to be convinced with reason. The argument I lay down in the following propositions:—

1. Fidelity and allegiance sworn to the King is only such a fidelity and obedience as is due to him by the law of the land; for were that faith and allegiance more than what the law requires, we should swear ourselves slaves, and the King absolute; whereas, by the law, we are free men, notwithstanding those oaths.

2. When, therefore, the obligation by the law to fidelity and allegiance ceases, that by the oath also ceases; for might allegiance be due by the oath to one person, whilst by the law it ceases to him and becomes due to another, the oath might oblige men to transgress the law and become rebel or traitors; whereas the oath is a part of the law, and therefore ought to be so interpreted as may consist with it.

3. Fidelity and allegiance are due by the law to King William, and not to King James. For the Statute of 25 Edw. 3, which defined all treasons against the king, and is the only statute to that purpose, by the king understands not only a king *de jure* and *de facto,* but also a king *de facto,* thought not *de jure,* against whom those treasons lie. Whence the Lord Chief Justice Hales, in his Pleas of the Crown, page 12, discoursing of that statute, tells us that *a king de facto and not de jure, is a king within that Act, and that treason against him is punishable, tho' the right heir get the crown.* And that this has been the constant sense of the law, Sir Robert Sawyer also, upon my asking him about it, has assured me. And accordingly, by another statute in the first of Hen. 7, 'tis declared treason to be in arms against a king *de facto,* (such as was Richard the Third,) tho' it be in behalf of a king *de jure.* So then by the law of the land all things are treason against King William which have been treason against former kings; and therefore the same fidelity, obedience, and allegiance which was due to them is due to him, and by consequence may be sworn to him by the law of the land. Allegiance and protection are always mutual; and, therefore, when K. James ceased to protect us, we ceased to owe him allegiance by the law of the land. And, when King W. began to protect us, we begun to owe allegiance to him.

These considerations are in my opinion sufficient to remove the grand scruple about the oaths. If the dissatisfied party accuse the Convention for making the P. of Orange King, 'tis not my duty to judge those above me; and therefore I shall only say that, if they have done ill, "Quod fieri non debuit, factu valet." And those at Cambridge ought not to judge and censure their superiors, but to obey and honour them according to the law and the doctrine of passive obedience.

Yesterday a bill for declaring the Convention a Parliament was read the 2^d^ time and committed. The Committee have not yet finished their amendments of it. There is no doubt but it will pass. I am in haste,

Your most humble Servant,

Is. NEWTON.

London, Feb. 21, 1688/9.

Both Brewster and De Morgan apparently considered this letter to be a personal expression of Newton's convictions. Brewster[13] commends him as conducting himself with firmness and moderation, and for upholding the principles of civil and religious liberty. And De Morgan,[14] who is engaged in combating undiscriminating hero worship, asks what had Newton and passive obedience just done to King James, that now he can claim it for King William? Then, he uses the arguments of this letter to contrast the high intellectual integrity of Newton with his social weaknesses. Both writers seem to have misjudged the whole situation. It is undoubtedly a campaign document written by Newton acting with the advice and approval of the party leaders. To me, it seems an excellent document, tactful and persuasive in its attitude towards the University and giving clearly the reasons upon which the new government could base their claims. As for the doctrine of passive obedience, it was the one in force at that time amongst those who favoured a monarchy and it had now to be twisted to apply to William and Mary, and against James. The Revolution had given the death blow in England to the doctrine of the divine right of kings, but it took many years for the fact to be recognised and admitted, and in the meanwhile reasons must be found to justify the election of William. Obedience was passing from the King to Parliament, from the Court to the Bench. Attention has been drawn to certain weaknesses in Newton's character in previous instances, and perhaps like De Morgan too much so and for the same reason; but, in this case, there

[13] Brewster, Vol. II, p. 113.

[14] De Morgan, *Essays*, p. 133.

are no moral inferences to be drawn unless one is to condemn party government. The country had taken a grave and wise step; to succeed and to bring order to a distracted country new interpretations had to be given to old and recognised formulæ. Parliament was anxious to obtain the support of the Universities, and Newton sent word that the Statutes going back to 13 Elizabeth, the Letters Patent, and Charters of both Universities had been confirmed. But Parliament also determined to prevent further meddling by the King and the Romanists. So, as a *quid pro quo,* Dr. Covel was informed that royal mandates in future would be inhibited and that a further clause would be introduced, to revise the statutes of the colleges, striking out whatever favoured Popery and substituting other precepts agreeable to the reformed religion. The University authorities feared that the greatest opposition to the new Government would be aroused when the attempt was made to administer the oath of allegiance and they suggested that it would help if mild objectors were permitted to swear by proxy. To this request Newton wrote, "I think it my duty to acquaint you that I have endeavoured much to feel the pulse of the House about such an explication of allegiance, and find such an averseness from it, that I am of opinion the petition can do no good, but may do much hurt if ill-resented by the Houses." His last letter of the series bears the date, May 15. It is easily seen that Newton, contrary to the general impression, played an important part in the Convention Parliament by acting as mediator and adviser to the University, and he, apparently, handled a difficult task with tact and success. Parliament did not rise until August; it resumed its session in October and was dissolved February 6, 1689/90. We have no record of Newton's other activity in legislation.

At this time, an event occurred which made a profound break in his life. We have noted the frequency with which he visited Woolsthorpe and the fact that he seems to have found an environment in his home which called forth his greatest powers. There is good reason to believe that his mother had been the attraction. That tie was now to be broken; his half-brother, Benjamin Smith, had been seized with a malignant fever while at Stamford. His mother, who attended him in his illness, was taken ill with the same complaint, and Newton left London to nurse her. Even when he was most engrossed in his work he would leave it to visit her; and now, when she was sick at Stamford, he sat up whole nights, using his marvelous manual dexterity to apply the blisters and so to reduce the torture which attended their dressing.[15] His efforts were, however, in vain. She is buried in the churchyard at Colsterworth with others of his family.[16] Conduitt also states that Isaac had always been deservedly favoured by his mother, and when she died she left him the much greater share of the real and personal estate. This legacy which was very considerable, together with his paternal inheritance, enabled him not only to follow his studies but also to indulge his fondness for charity and liberality.[17]

While he lived in London his address was Mr. More's house, in the broad Century, at the west end of Westminster Abbey. His health does not seem to have been good as he was once kept in his room several days by illness and again he was confined to his chamber by a "cold and bastard pleurisy." His stay in London was a turning point in his life. He had published his *Principia* and his position as a man of consummate genius was established. At Cambridge, he had been a solitary worker and academic society had not been congenial to him. What few friends he had there had either died or had left so that he was now practically alone. As a member of Parliament he had renewed his intimacy with Montague, and had come in contact with the leading men of the age. His whole outlook on life seems to have changed; he met, and was courted by, those who were prominent in the affairs of the state and the church; he mingled in society and lost all desire for the academic life and for scientific work. He probably attended some of the meetings of the Royal Society and, on June 12, he had the pleasure of meeting Huygens. The differences between the two men had long since passed away, and they had grown to measure properly each other's ability. Oddly enough each addressed the same meeting, and each chose a topic in which the other was his superior; Huygens gave an account of his theory of gravitation, and Newton made some erroneous observations on double refraction in Iceland spar.

It would be interesting to know whether Newton attended the weekly meetings of the Society regularly. The members must now

[15] Conduitt, *Intended Life, Portsmouth Collection.*

[16] Turnor, *Grantham,* p. 155. Brewster (Vol. II, p. 119) states that she was buried in the north aisle of the church.—In the parish record there is the item, "1679. Mrs. Hannah Smith was buried June 4." The date is evidently wrong.

[17] *Portsmouth Collection.*—In the Catalogue of this Collection, there is listed a letter to Newton from his mother. I was eager to read this letter as I hoped it would give some clue to her character. After a thorough search, the document was found; but, alas, it proved to be a letter to Sir John Newton, who lived in Soho, from his mother. If there was a letter from our Isaac's mother, it has disappeared.

have regarded him with the deference due one who had conferred a most signal honour on them by the dedication of his great work to the Society; and their reception of him would do much to heal the sting which he had previously felt because of what he believed to have been an unjust attitude towards his work. We may assume that he was received with flattering distinction because the smouldering jealousy of Hooke was again aroused. As early as 1674, Aubrey wrote to Anthony Wood of a complaint by Hooke that several eminent men, including himself, had been omitted in his *History and Antiquities of Oxford*. Aubrey advised him that the omission of Hooke's name had been an injustice to one of the greatest men of the age. Again in March, 1692, when Wood was about to publish his *Athenæ Oxonienses,* Aubrey wrote him two letters in which he requested a transcript should be sent to Hooke of what was to be printed concerning him.[18]

Aubrey and Hooke to Anthony Wood

Sept. 15, 1689.

Mr. Wood!

Mr. Rob. Hooke, R. S. S., did in anno 1670 write a discourse called, An Attempt to prove the Motion of the Earth, which he then read to the Royal Society; but printed it in the beginning of the year 1674 . . . . to Sir John Cutler, to whom it is dedicated, wherein he has delivered the theory of explaining the celestial motions mechanically; his words are these, pag. 27, 28, viz.

About 9 or 10 years ago Mr. Hooke writ to Mr. Isaac Newton of Trin. Coll. Cambridge, to make a demonstration of [it] *this Theory, not* telling him *at* first the proportion of the gravity to the distance, [and] *nor what was* the curved line that was thereby made.

Mr. Newton [did express], in his answer to the letter, *did express* that he had not thought of it; and in his first attempt about it, he calculated the curve by supposing the attraction to be the same at all distances: upon which Mr. Hooke told him in his next letter the whole of his Hypothesis, *scil.* that the gravitation was reciprocal to

[18] Rigaud (*Essay,* p. 41, and App. XIII and XIV) first published the above items and also the following letter in which the claims of Hooke are related. The letters were printed, in 1813, from originals in the Bodleian. Rigaud found, on examination of the original draught, that the letter, which bore the signature of Aubrey, had been written under Hooke's immediate direction; it was corrected and altered by him in many places, and the greater part is in his own hand. Following Rigaud, I have printed the original draught, with Aubrey's part in Roman type and Hooke's insertions in Italics; words erased by Hooke in order to substitute others are enclosed in brackets. *Cf.* Aubrey, *Miscellanies.*

the square of the distance, *which would make the motion in an ellipsis, in one of whose foci the sun being placed, the aphelion and perihelion of the planet would be opposite to each other in the same line, which is the whole celestial theory,*[19] *concerning which Mr. Newton hath made a demonstration,* not at all owning he received the first intimation of it from Mr. Hooke. Likewise Mr. Newton has in the same book printed some other theories and experiments of Mr. Hooke's *as that* about the oval figure of the earth and sea: without acknowledging from whom he had [it] *them,* though *he had not sent it up with the other parts of his book, till near a month after this theory was read to the society by R. H.,* [Mr. Hooke,] *when it served to help to answer Dr. Wallis his arguments produced in the R. S. against it.*

In the Attempt to prove the Motion of the Earth, &c printed 1674, *but read to the Royal Society* 1671, *pag.* 27, *lin.* 31. . . . [A long passage in Hooke's hand-writing is omitted in which he defends his discovery of the law of gravitation]. . . . Mr. Wood! This is the greatest discovery in nature, that ever was since the world's creation: it never was so much as hinted by any man before. I know you will do him right. I hope you may read his hand: I wish he had writ plainer, and afforded a little more paper.

Tuus,

J. AUBREY.

[P. S.] Before I leave this town I will get of him a catalogue of what he hath wrote, and as much of his inventions as I can; but they are many hundreds; he believes not fewer than a thousand. 'Tis such a hard matter to get people to do themselves right.

This letter shows clearly how bitterly Hooke still felt towards Newton, so bitterly that he could accuse him of plagiarism in so underhand and false a fashion. And we can readily imagine that he would continue to do all he could to destroy Newton's popularity in the Society.

With the exception of Hooke, the stay of Newton in London must have been a very pleasant episode in his life. In addition to members of the Royal Society and political associates, he also made the acquaintance of John Locke which ripened into an enduring friendship based on mutual esteem and common interests. This friendship brought him into Locke's circle which included the Earl of Pem-

19 Reference to Hooke's letter will show that he made no such accurate and detailed statement of the law of gravitation.

broke, Lord Monmouth (better known as the celebrated Earl of Peterborough), the Mashams, and also John Somers. Amongst others, he met Pepys who knew everyone in Town and would delight to introduce one whose work was now recognised as worthy of the highest respect, even if it could not be understood.

Of all these acquaintanceships, that with Locke had the most influence on Newton. In the last year of Charles II, the philosopher had fallen under the unjust suspicion that he was the author of a pamphlet which gave offence to the Government, and the King was induced to insist on his removal from his Studentship at Christ-Church.[20] The Secretary of State addressed the following letter to the Bishop of Oxford, demanding Locke's dismissal:

To the Lord Bishop of Oxford

Whitehall, Nov. 6, 1684.

My Lord,

The King being given to understand that one Mr. Locke, who belonged to the late Earl of Shaftesbury, and has upon several occasions behaved himself very factiously and undutifully to the Government, is a student of Christ-church; his Majesty commands me to signify to your Lordship, that he would have him removed from being a student, and that, in order thereunto, your Lordship would let me know the method of doing it.

I am, my Lord, &c

SUNDERLAND.[21]

The meanness of the conduct of the Dean[22] of Christ-Church would be difficult to exceed since he confessed that he had laid snares without success to destroy a member of his own College, and now dismissed him on a perfectly illegal charge. Locke left England and retired to Holland for four years. The Revolution of 1687 enabled him to return to his native country, and he arrived in the fleet that brought the Princess of Orange to England. His *Essay on Human Understanding* had been finished during his exile and was published shortly after his return to London. Such a scheme of natural law as

20 The Fellows of this College are called Students.

21 Ld. King's *Life of Locke,* 2 vols., London, 1830. Vol. I, p. 278.

22 The Dean was the Dr. Fell made notorious by the doggerel, "I do not love you, Dr. Fell."—He became Bishop of Oxford in 1676, and what was unusual, if it was not irregular, he was at the same time Dean of Christ Church *in commendam.*

Newton had portrayed was a powerful support to Locke's own philosophy. Attracted though he was to the book, he found that he could not follow the mathematical demonstrations. In this difficulty, he inquired of Huygens if the mathematics could be assumed to be sound. And, when he was assured that they might be accepted, he read the philosophical parts with care and profit to himself. Just when they met we do not know, but, in March, 1689, Newton gave him a short paper containing a proof that the planets, because of their attraction towards the sun, must move in ellipses.[23] The paper is valuable since the diagrams and demonstrations differ materially from those in the *Principia;* they are simplified and have explanatory illustrations not used elsewhere.

As the session of Parliament drew to a close it was increasingly evident that the Whigs had carried out their will with too high a hand and a general election was imminent. Public feeling had undergone a great change, in part due to the intemperate and vindictive conduct of the Whigs. Parliament, in fact, was dissolved February 6, 1689/90 and the new House of Commons contained a Tory majority. Newton could foresee that there would be no chance for his reëlection. In spite of his past efforts to retain the support of the University for his party two Tories were returned by an overwhelming majority. At the head of the poll was his former colleague Sir Robert Sawyer who had changed party; this revulsion of feeling, and Sir Robert's return were largely due to the unjust, or at least unwise, severity with which he had been treated. On a charge of malpractice, the Whigs had expelled him during the last Parliament. It is worthy of note that Newton, who has been pictured as a subservient party-man and as taking his politics on faith, cast his vote for Sawyer. The friends of Newton had evidently been impressed by his administrative ability and they influenced the King to issue a mandamus to appoint him Provost of King's College. The attempt was ill-advised as the appointment was resisted on the legal grounds that the Provost, by statute, must be in priest's orders and a Fellow of the College. "Aug. 29, 1689. Before the King and Council was heard the matter of King's College about Mr. Isaac Newton, why he or any other not of that foundation should be Provost, and after the reasons shewed and argued Mr. Newton was laid aside."[24]

His duties in Parliament finished, Newton returned to Cambridge on February 4, 1689/90. He spent the year quietly in his chambers

[23] *Life of Locke,* Vol. I, p. 389. [24] Edleston, p. lix; and Brewster, Vol. II, p. 116.

except for two short visits, and we may conjecture that he, in a rather despondent mood, busied himself correcting and making additions to the *Principia.* From now on, we have to note an increasing interest in religious subjects. His friendship with Locke had evidently led to discussions on the doctrine of the Trinity and on the prophecies. This year he put into shape, with additions from earlier notes, a very important paper on *Two Notable Corruptions of Scripture.*[25] As the following two letters show, Newton feared that his criticism of the authenticity of the two passages in the New Testament, on which the doctrine of the Trinity chiefly rests, would subject him to serious danger or, at least, involve him in a controversy. He therefore planned to send the manuscript to Holland by Locke, where it would be translated into French and published anonymously in that country or in France. Also, the position at King's College having failed, Locke and his friends were casting about to find something else which would satisfy his desires.

Newton to Locke

Sir,

I had answered your letter sooner, but that I stayed to revise and send you the papers which you desire. But the consulting of authors proving more tedious than I expected, so as to make me defer sending them till the next week, I could not forbear sending this letter alone, to let you know how extremely glad I was to hear from you; for though your letter brought me the first news of your having been so dangerously ill, yet by your undertaking a journey into Holland, I hope you are well recovered. I am extremely much obliged to my Lord and Lady Monmouth for their kind remembrance of me, and whether their design succeeded or not, must ever think myself obliged to be their humble servant. I suppose Mr. Falio [Fatio] is in Holland, for I have heard nothing from him the half year.

Sir, I am,
Your most humble servant,
Is. Newton.[26]

Cambridge, Sept. 28, 1690.

[25] *Cf.* Horsley, Vol. V, p. 493. This is his most important work on theology. I shall discuss it in a chapter devoted to that subject. It is sufficient to say now that it practically proves that he was not an orthodox Trinitarian. *Cf.* Chapter XVI.

[26] The date of this letter is incorrect as Edleston, p. lx, states that the London post-mark is Oct. 29. Mr. Falio is probably a misprint for Fatio, a young man of whom we shall hear more. The correspondence with Locke is to be found in his *Life* by Ld. King, Vol. I.

Newton to Locke

Sir, Nov. 14, 1690.

I send you now by the carrier, Martin, the papers I promised. I fear I have not only made you stay too long for them, but also made them too long by an addition. For upon the receipt of your letter reviewing what I had by me concerning the text of 1 John, v. 7, and examining authors a little farther about it, I met with something new concerning that other of 1st Tim. iii. 16, which I thought would be as acceptable to inquisitive men, and might be set down in a little room; but by searching farther into authors to find out the bottom of it, it swelled to the bigness you see. I fear the length of what I say on both texts may occasion you too much trouble, and therefore if at present you get only what concerns the first done into French, that of the other may stay till we see what success the first will have. I have no entire copy besides that I send you, and therefore would not have it lost, because I may, perhaps, after it has gone abroad long enough in French, put it forth in English. What charge you are at about it, (for I am sure it will put you to some,) you must let me know; for the trouble alone is enough for you. Pray present my most humble service and thanks to my Lord and Lady Monmouth, for their so kind remembrance of me; for their favour is such that I can never sufficiently acknowledge it. If your voyage hold, I wish you a prosperous one, and happy return. I should be glad of a line from you, to know that you have these papers, and how far you have recovered your health, for you told me nothing of that.

I am, Sir,

Your most faithful and most humble servant,

Is. NEWTON.[27]

During the latter part of the past year, Locke had had a serious illness and had made a short trip to Holland to recuperate. On his return, he had renewed his attempt to find a place for Newton. He had engaged the interest of Lord and Lady Monmouth, who were then high in the favour of King William, and also of the Mashams. With such patronage, it would seem that success was assured. But we should remember that, at this time, the Whigs were in deep disgrace, and the triumphant Tories were in no frame of mind to give honour, or place, to a member of the late Parliament. To Newton's chagrin, all the plans of his powerful friends failed. Brewster be-

[27] Ld. King's *Life of Locke*, Vol. I, p. 401.

comes almost hysterical in his denunciation of the English: "We do not envy," he laments, "the reader who peruses these simple details without a blush of shame for his country. That Locke, and Lord Monmouth, and Charles Montague, could not obtain an appointment for the author of the *Principia,* will hardly be believed in any country but our own. . . . At the age of fifty, the high priest of science found himself the inmate of a college, and, but for the generous patronage of a friend, he would have died within its walls."[28] It would seem to the simple mind, that the natural state of a "high priest of science" was to be an inmate of a college, and that it was not a shameful disgrace to die within its walls. Brewster's lament might be excused as a mere burst of sentimentality, if it were not that it marks a more serious fault which goes far to destroy our confidence in him as a biographer or historian. He shows an unfortunate ignorance of the age of which he is writing. The patronage of the men he mentions would, at the time, operate against Newton; he and they were Whigs, and the Whigs were out of power. As a matter of fact, when they returned to office an important place was soon found for him. Brewster seems quite oblivious to the state of politics. It was a period of one of the fiercest struggles of party government, and each side was engaged in strengthening its own lines, rather than in rewarding abstract merit. Nor should we assume that Newton's past life had augured especial ability as an administrator. It was significant of Montague's judgement of character that he trusted him with the delicate problem of the recoinage. To men of affairs and to the world at large, Newton was of more concern as an important office-holder and as the friend of statesmen than as a philosopher.[29]

Shortly after Locke's return to England, Newton visited him at Oates, in Essex, the estate of Sir Francis and Lady Masham.[30] Be-

[28] Brewster, Vol. II, p. 118.

[29] Two examples of this fact may be given. The first is a quotation from an old play: "Newton! Oh ay—I have heard of Sir Isaac—everybody has heard of Sir Isaac—great man—master of the Mint." The second is a quotation from Swift's burlesque compliment in his *Polite Conversations:* "Some of my enemies have industriously whispered about that one Isaac Newton, an instrument-maker, living near Leicester Fields, and afterwards a workman at the Mint in the Tower, might possibly pretend to vie with me for fame in future time."

[30] The Mashams were intimate friends of Locke, who visited them frequently. Their son, in 1707, married Abigail Hill, a cousin of Sarah, Duchess of Marlborough. As Mrs. Masham, she became the bosom friend of Queen Anne. Brewster erroneously puts this visit during the year before when Newton travelled from London to Cambridge after the dissolution of Parliament. The Buttery Book of Trinity College shows that he was away from College during part of the fortnight of Jan. 2–16, 1690/91.

sides his textual work on the Scriptures, Newton was employing his leisure to elucidate the prophecies of the Books of Daniel and of the Apocalypse, a subject on which he spent much time and ingenuity. The following letter should now be clear.

Newton to Locke

Cambridge, Feb. 7, 1690/1.

Sir,

I am sorry your journey proved to so little purpose, though it delivered you from the trouble of the company the day after. You have obliged me by mentioning me to my friends at London, and I must thank both you and my Lady Masham for your civilities at Oates, and for not thinking that I made a long stay there. I hope we shall meet again in due time, and then I should be glad to have your judgement upon some of my mystical fancies. The Son of man, Dan. vii. I take to be the same with the Word of God upon the White Horse in Heaven, Apoc. xix. and him to be the same with the Man Child, Apoc. xii. for both are to rule the nations with a rod of iron; but whence are you certain that the Ancient of Days is Christ? Does Christ any where sit upon the throne? If Sir Francis Masham be at Oates, present, I pray, my service to him with his lady, Mrs. Cudworth, and Mrs. Masham. Dr. Covel is not in Cambridge.

I am

Your affectionate and humble servant,

Is. Newton.

P. S. Know you the meaning of Dan. x.21: *There is none that holdeth with me in these things but Mich. your Prince?*[31]

The next letter we have addressed to Locke shows that Newton hoped a letter of recommendation might secure for him the comptrollership of the Mint, and also that Locke was wrestling with the *Principia.* The incident of the effect of strong light on the eyes was very interesting to me as I, in my early boyhood, had been fascinated by the same phenomenon. I used frequently to stare at the reddish disc of the early morning sun until from fatigue it first became dark. Then gradually a coloured disc would form, grow bright and seem to slip downward; only to be followed by another coloured outline until there would be a succession of these discs forming and slipping

[31] Ld. King's *Life of Locke,* Vol. I, p. 402.

down like a string of balloons. Fortunately, I performed this dangerous experiment before the brilliance of the sun had made it serious.

Newton to Locke

Cambridge, June 30th, 1691.

Sir,

Your deferring to answer my letter is what you needed not make an apology for, because I use to be guilty of the same fault as often as I have nothing of moment to write, and therefore cannot in justice complain. If the scheme you have laid of managing the controller's place of the M., will not give you the trouble of too large a letter, you will oblige me by it. I thank you heartily for your being so mindful of me, and ready to assist me with your interest. Concerning the *Ancient of Days,* Dan. vii. there seems to be a mistake either in my last letter, or in yours, because you write in your former letter, that the Ancient of Days is Christ; and in my last, I either did, or should have asked, how you knew that. But these discourses may be done with more freedom at our next meeting. I am indebted to my solicitor, Mr. Starkey. If you please to let me have your opinion what I should send him, I will send it with a letter by the carrier. My Lady Masham and you have done me much honour in looking into my book, and I am very glad to have the approbation of such judicious persons. The observation you mention in Mr. Boyle's book of Colours, I once made upon myself with the hazard of my eyes. The manner was this: I looked a very little while upon the sun in the looking-glass with my right eye, and then turned my eyes into a dark corner of my chamber, and winked, to observe the impression made, and the circles of colours which encompassed it, and how they decayed by degrees, and at last vanished. This I repeated a second and a third time. At the third time, when the phantasm of light and colours about it were almost vanished, intending my fancy upon them to see their last appearance, I found to my amazement, that they began to return, and by little and little to become as lively and vivid as when I had newly looked upon the sun. But when I ceased to intend my fancy upon them, they vanished again. After this, I found that as often as I went into the dark, and intended my mind upon them, as when a man looks earnestly to see any thing which is difficult to be seen, I could make the phantasm return without looking any more upon the sun; and the oftener I made it return, the more easily I could make it return again. And at length, by repeating this without looking any more upon the sun, I made such an impression on my eye, that if I looked upon the clouds, or a book, or any bright object, I saw upon it a round bright spot of light like the sun; and, which is still stranger, though I looked upon the sun with my right eye only, and not with my left, yet my fancy began to make the impression upon my left eye, as well as upon my right. For if I shut my right eye, and looked upon a book or the clouds with my left eye, I could see the spectrum of the sun almost as plain as with my right eye, if I did but intend my fancy a little while upon it; for at first, if I shut my right eye, and looked with my left, the spectrum of the sun did not appear till I intended my fancy upon it; but by repeating, this appeared every time more easily. And now, in a few hours' time, I had brought my eyes to such a pass, that I could look upon no bright object with either eye, but I saw the sun before me, so that I durst neither write nor read: but to recover the use of my eyes, shut myself up in my chamber made dark, for three days together, and used all means to divert my imagination from the sun. For if I thought upon him, I presently saw his picture, though I was in the dark. But by keeping in the dark, and employing my mind about other things, I began in three or four days to have some use of my eyes again; and by forbearing a few days longer to look upon bright objects, recovered them pretty well, though not so well, but that for some months after the spectrum of the sun began to return as often as I began to meditate upon the phenomenon, even though I lay in bed at midnight with my curtains drawn; but now I have been very well for many years, though I am apt to think, that if I durst venture my eyes, I could still make the phantasm return by the power of my fancy. This story I tell you, to let you understand, that in the observation related by Mr. Boyle, the man's fancy probably concurred with the impression made by the sun's light, to produce that phantasm of the sun which he constantly saw in bright objects: and so your question about the cause of this phantasm, involves another about the power of fancy, which I must confess is too hard a knot for me to untie. To place this effect in a constant motion is hard, because the sun ought then to appear perpetually. It seems rather to consist in a disposition of the sensorium to move the imagination strongly, and to be easily moved both by the imagination and by the light, as often as bright objects are looked upon.

If the papers you mention come not out, I will tell you at our next meeting what shall be done with them.

My humble service to Sir Francis, my lady, and Mrs. Cudworth.

I am

Your most humble servant,

Is. NEWTON.[32]

In addition to Locke and his friends, the brilliant young scholar, Bentley was drawn to the mechanistic philosophy of the *Principia* as an illustration of the wisdom of a Divine Creator. He, too, was appalled by its mathematical difficulties and decided to accept the geometric demonstrations on faith after he received from John Craigie, a mathematician, a list of preparatory works to study.[33] The *Principia* was also beginning to attract the attention of the younger mathematicians. One of the most important of these disciples was David Gregory of Edinburgh, whom we have noticed before. He was elected Savilian Professor of Astronomy at Oxford this year, largely by the influence of Newton, and introduced the new mechanics to his students. Newton was always most generous in aiding his followers and not only wrote him a testimonial[34] but also gave him the following personal letter of introduction to Flamsteed.

Newton to Flamsteed

London, August 10, 1691.

Sir,

'Tis almost a fortnight since I intended, with Mr. Paget and another friend or two, to have given you a visit at Greenwich; but, sending to the Temple Coffee-house, I understood you had not been in London for two or three weeks before: which made me think you were retired to your living for a time. The bearer hereof, Mr. Gregory, Mathematic Professor of Edinburgh College in Scotland, intended to have given you a visit with us. You will find him a very ingenious person, and good mathematician, worth your acquaintance. I hope it will not be long before you publish your catalogue of the fixed stars. In my opinion, it will be better to publish those of the first six magnitudes observed by others, and afterwards, by way of an appendix, to publish the new ones observed by yourself

32 Ld. King's *Life of Locke,* Vol. I, p. 404. 33 Edleston, p. 273.

34 To be found in the *Portsmouth Collection,* Cf. Baily's *Flamsteed,* p. 670.

alone, than to let the former stay too long for the latter. I would willingly have your observations of Jupiter and Saturn for the 4 or 5 next years at least, before I think further of their theory: but I had rather have them for the next 12 or 15 years. If you and I live not long enough, Mr. Gregory and Mr. Halley are young men. When you observe the eclipses of Jupiter's satellites, I should be glad to know if in long telescopes the light of the satellite, immediately before it disappears, incline either to red or blue, or become more ruddy or more pale than before.

Sir, I am your most humble servant,

Is. Newton.[35]

The reference to the eclipses of satellites is an excellent illustration of Newton's acuteness of mind. He was evidently interested in the question whether the separate colours of the spectrum travel with different velocities. The satellites of Jupiter are so small that they are almost instantly blotted out when an eclipse takes place. If the red and blue rays of their white light travel with even slightly different velocities *in vacuo* then, during so long a path, the final appearance of the light should be tinged with the colour which travels slowest; and when the satellite emerges from the eclipse its appearance should be tinged with the colour which travels fastest and gradually turn to white when they all reach the eye. It may be added that no such effect occurs, and it is even now held to be the best evidence that all rays travel at the same speed *in vacuo*. Newton's casual remark, that Halley would be able to complete their work, if they should not live long enough, was not tactful nor likely to help Gregory's chances; Flamsteed had a veritable obsession against Halley, as his answer to this letter and other letters prove.

Flamsteed to Newton

The Observatory, February 24, 1691/2.

Sir,

Though I have long delayed to return an answer to yours of the 10th of August last, yet I have always had it in my mind; and having now got a fit opportunity, I shall not longer decline it, lest you think me unmindful of our former friendship, or as unwilling, or unprepared to answer it, as I am represented to you. I did Mr. Gregory, who brought it, all the kindness I could, without prejudice to an

[35] Baily's *Flamsteed*, p. 129.

ingenious old friend who was much solicited by the University to put in for the vacant Professorship, but was prevailed with to decline, by the management of a person, [Halley] who is always putting the question to my friends, why I do not print my observations? He might have satisfied you, and all others with whom he converses, if he pleases, of the reason; but I perceive, by yours, he is not desirous: but rather to gain me the ill opinion of my friends, from whom I have ever desired to deserve the best, and am confident I have ever endeavoured to serve very heartily. You advise me (and I am sure it is upon his suggestions and misrepresentations) to publish first a catalogue of the correct places of such fixed stars of the first six magnitudes as have been observed by others; and afterwards, by way of an appendix, to publish those new ones, observed by myself alone.

I take your advice very kindly, because I know you are sincere in it, and wish me all the success I can desire in my labours, and all the reputation they can deserve from them: and I shall give you very substantial reasons why I cannot do this at present, and show you what you may expect from me, and in what time hereafter; nor shall I forget to give such an answer as it deserves to our *friend's* question and calumny, in the close of my letter.

It would be needless, as well as a tedious task, to give you the history of my observations; since I believe you are acquainted with it sufficiently, by what discourse I have had with you formerly: otherwise it would be requisite to give it, to vindicate myself in every particular of my conduct. . . . .

It only remains that I give you the answer I would make to our suggesting *friend,* when he asks me why I do not print my observations? 'Tis first I do not find myself under any obligations to receive instructions what to do, or be governed by him and his associates, the *Muss's* [?]. Secondly, I would not thrust such an incomplete catalogue on the world as he has done from St. Helena:[36] nor be obliged to compliment the best reputed astronomers of our time (as he has done all of them) by telling them that, had their catalogues been extant, he would have called his a supplement to theirs, as he has done (for want of them) of Tycho's. Nor will I give any one occasion to tell the world I have erred a 60th part of what La Hire has published he does in a star of the Crosiers and one of the Centaur:

[36] Halley had recently returned from an expedition to St. Helena where he had made magnetical and astronomical observations.

that I understand what I have to do, much better than he; and when, and how, it will be best for me to publish my own labors; that I will not be beholden to him for his assistance or advice: that if he wants employment for his time, he may go on with his sea projects, or square the superficies of cylindric ungulas: find reasons for the change of the variation, or give us a true account of all his St. Helena exploits; and that he had better do it, than buffoon those to the Society, to whom he has been more obliged than he dares acknowledge: that he has more of mine in his hands already, than he will either own or restore; and that I have no esteem of a man who has lost his reputation, both for skill, candour, and ingenuity, by silly tricks, ingratitude, and foolish prate: and that I value not all, or any of the same of him and his infidel companions; being very well satisfied that if Christ and his apostles were to walk again upon earth, they should not escape free from the calumnies of their venomous tongues. But I hate his ill manners, not the man: were he either honest, or but civil, there is none in whose company I could rather desire to be.

But my letter makes you now do penance. I beg your pardon for a just indignation, to which some very foolish behaviour of his very lately has moved me: and desire you to assure yourself, that no one is more sincerely your servant, than your affectionate friend and brother,

JOHN FLAMSTEED.[37]

In December of this year, another of Newton's admirers amongst the younger scholars of the day makes his first appearance. Fatio (or Facio) de Duillier, a young Swiss refugee, had come to London and, according to his own account, had studied the *Principia* more intensely and more understandingly than had any one else. Fatio, later, played a prominent, and not very creditable, part in the Leibniz controversy and a more extended notice will be given about him in

[37] The letter is much too long to quote in full. The parts omitted are purely technical. The person so bitterly referred to is Halley. The cause seems to have been partly jealousy, partly Halley's rather importunate eagerness and vivacity, and partly what Flamsteed and Newton termed his atheism. Flamsteed was a clergyman without toleration for any tinge of even latitudinarianism; Newton rebuked Halley severely for his religious views but preserved his admiration and friendship. Flamsteed's abuse of Halley is a real blot on his own character but we should not judge him by our own standard of propriety as it was an age notorious for extravagant epithets. The advice which Newton offers about the publication of the catalogue of stars, and Flamsteed's determination to follow his own plans, are important as they give the cause for the later controversy between the two men. For the complete letter, see Baily, p. 129.

that connection. At present, we learn from him that copies of the *Principia* had become scarce, and that he had importuned Newton to publish a revised edition. Finding it impossible to succeed by that method, he proposed to undertake the editorship himself and, by inserting his own notes and explanations, improve the treatment and expand the work into a folio. Fortunately nothing came from the project. But the young man's attentions flattered and pleased Newton, and admitted him into the inner circle of his followers. Fatio visited him in Cambridge the following year. He was depressed both physically and spiritually and was much encouraged by the kind reception and wholesome advice which he received. On returning to London, he became much alarmed by a severe cold which affected his lungs and he wrote to Newton, "I thank God that my soul is extremely quiet, in which you have had the chief hand" and then expressed the wish that, in case of his death, the same kind friendship should be extended to his eldest brother. The letter was, at once, answered, assuring Fatio that he was dear to him and would be remembered in his prayers. Newton's intercourse with young men is one of the most attractive sides to his character. He was quick to recognise ability in them, and to foster it with advice and with concrete evidences of his interest. He treated them with a certain grave courtesy which must have appealed greatly to their aspiring ambitions. It was, perhaps, their difference in age and accomplishment, which put the older man at his ease and precluded the possibility of arousing the sensitiveness and jealousy that marred so frequently his relations with those more apt to oppose or to criticise him. A striking illustration of his interest in young men is shown by his tactful and delicate plan to aid Fatio with a gift of money and even to provide him with accommodations at Cambridge by making him an allowance. "I have now received," he wrote, "the box of rulers, with your receipt of £14. I sent you that money because I thought it was just; and therefore you compliment me, if you reckon it an obligation. The chamber next me is disposed of; but that which I was contriving was . . . . to make you such an allowance, etc."[38]

We shall rely on the correspondence of Locke for most of the events of the year 1692. Newton's anxiety to obtain an official position had grown to such a degree that his repeated failures bred in him a feeling of humiliation and disgrace. Others were obtaining rewards for their services in behalf of the Revolution, but he, who had loyally

[38] *Cf.* Edleston, p. lx. Quoted from the *Gentleman's Magazine,* LXXXIV, 3.

supported the new Monarch in Parliament and had given lustre to the age by his scientific work, could not obtain even a humble position. The latest attempt to make him Master of the Charter House did not appeal to him and he despondently gave up all hope. In this frame of mind, aggravated by the nervous reaction from his excessive intellectual labour, he began to brood over his condition and, by a not uncommon twist of the mind, he became obsessed with the idea that the failures were owing to the hostility of some of his friends and to the inertness of others. He imagined that Montague, absorbed in his own schemes and rapidly rising to power, had raked up an old and forgotten grudge against him in order to rid himself of such a dead-weight on his shoulders. He lamented that Locke would not care to visit such an unsuccessful place-hunter as himself, and if the Monmouths now forsook him, there would be no hope left; and he must reconcile himself to end his days in the obscurity of an academic life. Lest he may have hurt this last chance, he apologised with almost abject humility for what may have seemed to be an intrusion upon the nobleman's society. He had tried to solace his enforced solitude with an enquiry into religious subjects; but, here again, his fears intervened, and he desired to have his manuscript on the validity of the doctrine of the Trinity returned to him, since its authorship might become known and add to his other troubles. The following four letters justify this introduction.

Newton to Locke

Sir, Cambridge, Dec. 13, 1691.

When I received your former letter, I was engaged here by the term, and could not stir. I thank you for putting me in mind of Charter-house, but I see nothing in it worth making a bustle for: besides a coach, which I consider not, it is but £200 per annum, with a confinement to the London air, and to such a way of living as I am not in love with; neither do I think it advisable to enter into such a competition as that would be for a better place. Dr. Spencer, the Dean of Ely, has perused the specimen of Le Clerc's Latin Version of the Old Testament, and likes the design very well, but gives me no remarks upon it. Pray return my most humble service and hearty thanks to my Lady Masham, for her Ladyship's kind invitation; and accept of mine to yourself for so frankly offering the assistance of your friends, if there should be occasion. Mr. Green called on me last Tuesday, and I designed to have answered your letter sooner, but beg your pardon that I did not.

I am
Your most humble servant,
IS. NEWTON.[39]

Newton to Locke

Cambridge, Jan. 26th, 1691/2.

Sir,

Being fully convinced that Mr. Montague, upon an old grudge which I thought had been worn out, is false to me, I have done with him, and intend to sit still, unless my Lord Monmouth be still my friend. I have now no prospect of seeing you any more, unless you will be so kind as to repay that visit I made you the last year. If I may hope for this favour, I pray bring my papers with you. Otherwise I desire you would send them by some convenient messenger, when opportunity shall serve. My humble service to my Lady Masham, and to Sir Francis if at Oates.

I am
Your most humble servant,
IS. NEWTON.

[P. S.] I understand Mr. Boyle communicated his process about the red earth and Mercury to you as well as to me, and before his death, procured some of that earth for his friends.[40]

Newton to Locke

Cambridge, Feb. 16th, 1691/2.

Sir,

Your former letters came not to my hand, but this I have. I was of opinion my papers [his Tract on the Corrupt Passages in the New Testament] had lain still, and am sorry to hear there is news about them. Let me entreat you to stop their translation and impression so soon as you can, for I design to suppress them. If your friend hath been at any pains and charge, I will repay it, and gratify him. I am very glad my Lord Monmouth is still my friend, but intend not to give his Lordship and you any farther trouble. My inclinations are to sit still. I am to beg his Lordship's pardon, for pressing into his company the last time I saw him. I had not done it, but that Mr. Pawling pressed me into the room. Miracles of good credit con-

[39] Ld. King's *Life of Locke*, Vol. I, p. 414. [40] *Ibid.*, Vol. I, p. 408.

tinued in the Church for about two or three hundred years. Gregorius Thaumaturgus had his name from thence, and was one of the latest who was eminent for that gift; but of their number and frequency, I am not able to give you a just account. The history of those ages is very imperfect. Mr. Pawling told me, you had writ for some of Mr. Boyle's red earth, and by that I knew you had the receipt. Your most affectionate and humble servant,

Is. Newton.[41]

Newton to Locke

Sir, Cambridge, May 3rd, 1692.

Now the churlish weather is almost over, I was thinking, within a post or two, to put you in mind of my desire to see you here, where you shall be as welcome as I can make you. I am glad you have prevented me, because I hope now to see you the sooner. You may lodge conveniently either at the Rose tavern, or Queen's Arms inn. I am glad the edition is stopped, but do not perceive that you had mine, and therefore have sent you a transcript of what concerned miracles, if it come not now too late. For it happens that I have a copy of it by me. Concerning miracles, there is a notable passage or two in Irenaeus I. 22, c. 56, recited by Eusebius, 1.5 c. 17. The miraculous refection of the Roman army by rain, at the prayers of a Christian legion, (thence called fulminatrix) is mentioned by Ziphilina apud Dionam. in Marco Imp. and by Tertullian Apolog. c. 5, and ad Scap. c. 4, and by Eusebius 1.5, c. 5. Hist. Eccl., and in Chronico, and acknowledged by the Emperor Marcus in a letter, as Tertullian mentions. The same Tertullian somewhere challenges the heathens to produce a demoniac, and he will produce a man who shall cast out the demon. For this was the language of the ancients for curing lunatics. I am told that Sir Henry Yelverton, in a book about the truth of Christianity, has writ well of the ancient miracles, but the book I never saw. Concerning Gregory Thaumaturgus, see Gregory Nystra in ejus vita, and Basil de Spiritu Sancto, c. 29.

My humble service to Sir Francis and his lady.

I am

Your most humble servant,

Is. Newton.

P.S. I know of nothing that will call me from home this month.[42]

[41] Ld. King's *Life of Locke,* Vol. I, p. 409. [42] Ld. King's *Life of Locke,* Vol. I, p. 415.

We, unfortunately, have not Locke's replies, but he evidently assured Newton that his friends had not deserted him; to prove his own steadfast regard, he had arranged to pay a visit to Cambridge. The reference to Boyle and alchemy in these, and the following letters, requires some explanation.

Robert Boyle had died December 30, 1691. His death had removed the most distinguished philosopher of the day. He was not only a great chemist and physicist to whom we owe a profound study of the nature and properties of gases but, rich and allied with a powerful family, he was also a most generous patron of learning and was regarded as an example of the highest integrity and nobility of character. The great Dutch chemist Boerhave has given us this splendid tribute to his genius. "Mr. Boyle, the ornament of his age and country, succeeded to the genius and enquiries of the great Chancellor Verulam. Which of Mr. Boyle's writings shall I recommend? All of them. To him we owe the secrets of fire, air, water, animals, vegetables, fossils; so that from his works may be deduced the whole system of natural knowledge."[43] He was not only eminent as a man of science but could have been equally so in literature and in theology. Dr. Johnson affirmed that "The attempt to employ the ornaments of romance in the decoration of religion, was, I think, first made by Mr. Boyle's *Martyrdom of Theodora;* but Boyle's philosophical studies did not allow him time for the cultivation of style; and the completion of the great design was reserved for Mrs. Rowe."[44] He also quoted a famous aphorism of Boyle's: "Testimony is like the shot of a long-bow, which owes its efficacy to the force of the shooter; argument is like the shot of the cross-bow, equally forcible whether discharged by a giant or a dwarf."[45]

Boyle, like Newton, was an ardent alchemist, and he had convinced himself that he had found a recipe for multiplying gold by the agency of mercury and a certain red earth. At his death, he left the inspection of his papers to three friends, of whom Locke was one. Now Locke enquired of Newton what he thought of its promise. Newton had, evidently, become somewhat sceptical, not of the principles of alchemy, but of our ability to transmute the metals. Although he is still tempted to try the process, he counsels caution, and expresses his doubt that Boyle had succeeded. His doubt arose from the fact that Boyle had first told him of the discovery years before and

[43] Weld's *Hist. R. S.,* Vol. I, p. 328.
[44] Hill's *Ed. of Boswell,* Vol. I, p. 312.
[45] *Ibid.,* Vol. IV, p. 281.

yet nothing had come of it; and also because a company, which had been formed to exploit the recipe, had gone to pieces. But the most suspicious fact was that Boyle, while professing to give him the complete recipe, had withheld one important step in the process as he, himself, had discovered. We get an interesting side-light on Newton's own attitude towards alchemy from the following letters which show that the subject fascinated him, as it did so many others, and that he could not give up all hope of its truth. One would give much to know what was the "one argument against it, which I could never find an answer to."

Newton to Locke

Sir,

. . . .

You have sent much more earth then I expected. For I desired only a specimen, having no inclination to prosecute the process. For in good earnest I have no opinion of it. But since you have a mind to prosecute it I should be glad to assist you all I can, having a liberty of communication allowed me by Mr. B. in one case which reaches to you if it be done under the same conditions in which I stand obliged to Mr. B., for I presume you are already under the same obligations to him. But I fear I have lost the first and third part out of my pocket. I thank you for what you communicated to me out of your own notes about it. Sir I am

Your most humble servant

Is. NEWTON.

Cambridge July 7th
1692.

[P. S.] When the hot weather is over I intend to try the beginning tho' the success seem improbable.

For John Locke, Esq. at Mr. Paulen's in Dorset Court in Chennel Row in Westminster.

Newton to Locke

Sir, August 2d, 1692.

I beg your pardon that I sent not your papers last week; the carrier went out a quarter of an hour sooner than I was aware of. I am glad you have all the three parts of the recipe entire; but before you go to work about it, I desire you would consider these things, for it may perhaps save you time and expense. This recipe I take to be the thing for the sake of which Mr. Boyle procured the repeal of the Act of Parliament against Multipliers, [i.e., alchemists] and therefore he had it then in his hands. In the margin of the recipe was noted, that the mercury of the first work would grow hot with gold, and thence I gather that this recipe was the foundation of what he published many years ago, about such mercuries as would grow hot with gold, and therefore was then known to him, that is, sixteen or twenty years ago, at least; and yet, in all this time, I cannot find that he has either tried it himself, or got it tried with success by any body else: for, when I spoke doubtingly about it, he confessed that he had not seen it tried; but added, that a certain gentleman was now about it, and it succeeded very well so far as he had gone, and that all the signs appeared, so that I needed not doubt of it. This satisfied me that mercury, by this recipe, may be brought to change its colours and properties, but not that gold may be multiplied thereby; and I doubt it the more, because I heard some years ago of a company, who were upon this work in London, and after Mr. Boyle had communicated his recipe to me, so that I knew it was the same with theirs. I enquired after them, and learnt that two of them were since forced to other means of living; and a third, who was the chief artist, was run so far into debt that he had much ado to live; and by these circumstances, I understood that these gentlemen could not make the thing succeed. When I told Mr. Boyle of these gentlemen, he acknowledged that the recipe was gone about among several chemists, and therefore I intend to stay till I hear that it succeeds with some of them.

But, besides, if I would try this recipe, I am satisfied that I could not, for Mr. Boyle has reserved a part of it from my knowledge. I know more of it than he has told me; and by that, and an expression or two which dropped from him, I know that what he has told me is imperfect and useless without knowing more than I do: and, therefore, I intend only to try whether I know enough to make a mercury which will grow hot with gold, if perhaps I shall try that. For Mr. Boyle to offer his secret upon conditions, and after I had consented, not to perform his part, looks oddly; and that the rather because I was averse from meddling with his recipe, till he persuaded me to it; and by not performing his part, he has voided the obligation to the conditions on mine, so that I may reckon myself at my own discretion to say or do what I will about this matter, though perhaps I shall be tender of using my liberty. But that I may understand the reason of his reservedness, pray will you be so free as to let me know the conditions which he obliged you to, in communicating this recipe; and whether he communicated to you any thing more than is written down in the three parts of the recipe. I do not desire to know what he has communicated, but rather that you would keep the particulars from me, (at least in the second and third part of the recipe,) because I have no mind to be concerned with this recipe any farther than just to know the entrance. I suspect his reservedness might proceed from mine; for when I communicated a certain experiment to him, he presently, by way of requital, subjoined two others, but cumbered them with such circumstances as startled me, and made me afraid of any more: for he expressed that I should presently go to work upon them, and desired I would publish them after his death. I have not yet tried either of them, nor intend to try them; but since you have the inspection of his papers, if you design to publish any of his remains, you will do me a great favour to let these two be published among the rest. But then I desire that it may not be known that they come through my hands. One of them seems to be a considerable experiment, and may prove of good use in medicine for analysing bodies; the other is only a knack. In dissuading you from too hasty a trial of this recipe, I have forborne to say any thing against multiplication in general, because you seem persuaded of it; though there is one argument against it, which I could never find an answer to, and which, if you will let me have your opinion about it, I will send you in my next.[46]

[Is. Newton.]

Boyle's death had an important, although indirect, influence in spreading the philosophical and religious tendencies of the *Principia.* He, himself, belonged to that group of English men of science who saw in the discovery of natural laws the best evidence of a Divine Providence. They were convinced with Milton that:

> "The world was all before them, where to choose
> Their place of rest, and Providence their guide."

To further the idea that science should be the expositor of the Christian religion, Boyle bequeathed by his will the sum of fifty pounds a year to establish a lectureship for the defense of religion against infidels. By the terms of the bequest, eight sermons a year

[46] Ld. King's *Life of Locke,* Vol. I, p. 410.

were to be delivered in one of the London churches by a lecturer chosen annually by four trustees. The distinguished honour of being nominated as the first of these lecturers fell to Richard Bentley, principally by the influence of Bishop Tenison, one of the trustees. Bentley was, at that time, barely thirty years old; he was chaplain to Dr. Stillingfleet, Bishop of Worcester, and had leaped to sudden fame the year before by the publication of his *Epistle to Dr. Mills.* This essay exhibited such erudition and critical acumen, that it established the author's reputation in the highest rank of scholarship; and from that moment the eyes of every scholar in Europe were directed towards his work.[47]

Bentley chose the general title of *A Confutation of Atheism* for the subject of his lectures, delivered in the spring of 1692 in Tenison's former church of St. Martin's in the Fields. The fame of the founder was so great as to excite the deepest interest in this lectureship, and it was an extraordinary honour to inaugurate them with so young a man. Bentley surpassed even the expectations of his patrons. His attack on atheism was directed specifically against the doctrines of Hobbes and Spinoza which had seriously affected the ideas of the higher classes of society. He deliberately led up to the conclusion, discussed in the seventh and eighth lectures, of the demonstration of a divine Providence as proved by evidence of design which followed from Newton's discoveries of the laws of the physical universe. The *Principia* had been published five years previously, but it was still a closed book to most persons because of the difficulty of the mathematical proofs. Bishop Monk informs us that, "to Bentley belongs the undoubted merit of having been the first to lay open these discoveries in a popular form, and to explain their irresistible force in the proof of a Deity";[48] and also we are assured rather too confidently by him, that the effect of these discourses was such, that atheism was deserted as untenable ground; or, to use his own expression, "the atheists were silent since that time, and sheltered themselves under deism."

Bentley's lectures were published the following year. Before they

[47] *Cf.* Monk's *Life of Bentley,* Vol. I, pp. 33–46.

[48] Edleston, p. 273, states that Bentley, in the summer of 1691, solicited the aid of Craig and Newton to help him master the *Principia.* Brewster, Vol. II, p. 125, makes a curious mistake in this connection. He states that Bentley made the enquiries in order to prepare for these lectures. He evidently forgot that Boyle, their founder, did not die until December 30, 1691, or five months later. Bentley could hardly have foreseen this future use he would find in studying the *Principia.* Bishop Monk thinks Bentley had attended some of Newton's lectures, and that he mastered the mathematics of the treatise. As to the first point it was only a surmise, and I seriously doubt the second.

were issued from the press, he took the precaution to consult Newton as to the correctness of the use of his ideas. An important correspondence followed, and Newton's four letters are a most valuable contribution to our knowledge of his ideas on the nature of gravity and the cosmic system.[49]

Bentley, in his introductory letter to Newton, tells him that his mind would be at ease if he were sure that he had kept his argument conformable to a correct exposition of the hypothesis found in the *Principia*. He desires Newton's criticism on the following points. First, he proved in the sixth sermon that the present system of the world cannot have been eternal. Therefore atheists are in error because they, denying the existence of a Divine Creator, must assume that matter was uncreated and eternal. Thus, according to them, all was once chaos; or what is the same thing, in the beginning all matter was evenly, or nearly evenly, diffused throughout all space. Secondly, in his seventh sermon, he proceeded to show that matter, in such an initial state of chaos, could never by natural laws convene into our actual universe, or into any like system. He, lastly, accepted the universal law of gravitation of all matter as a natural cause of phenomena, as a matter of fact and not of hypothesis. That Newton may see if he is tender enough how he engaged his name in this matter, he quotes the following passage from the sermon: "Indeed as to the cause and origin of this gravity Newton was pleased to determine nothing. But you will perceive in the sequel of this discourse that it is above all mechanism or power of inanimate matter, and must proceed from a higher principle and a divine energy and impression." Bentley's conclusion is obvious: Since the universe was created and is now governed by a divine Providence, the operating force of gravity cannot be an inherent property of matter acting through a distance, but it is the power of the divine will exerted upon matter.

Apparently, Newton had not thought much upon the philosophical foundation of his ideas nor had he gone deeply into the conclusions which others would derive from his cosmic system. He seems to have been quite content to consider the universe as a divinely created machine composed of certain mechanical parts, and

[49] The original letters are in Trinity College Library. They were published as a separate pamphlet in 1756, when they were reviewed by Dr. Johnson in the *Literary Magazine*. They have since been published by Horsley, *Op. Newtoni*, Vol. IV, pp. 429–442. The understanding of these letters has been much aided by the publication of Bentley's letter of enquiry to Newton by Brewster. *Cf.* Vol. II, p. 463.

operating according to prescribed laws. The sole business of the natural philosopher was to discover by observation and experimentation the construction and principles of this machine; and, from the data so obtained, derive mathematically their consequences. He thus limited science to the investigation of a mechanical world from which had been abstracted all phenomena of life, of will, and of consciousness. So he answered Bentley with that baffling tone of detached diffidence, which he often exhibited when some of his work was criticised or questioned, and which fastened on him the opinion that he was exceedingly modest. But, it should be remembered, that he was unbendingly firm in his convictions and indifferent to criticism on questions he had deeply meditated. He expressed this diffidence in the opening passage of his third letter: "The hypothesis of deriving the frame of the world, by mechanical principles, from matter evenly spread through the heavens, being inconsistent with my system, I had considered it very little before your letters put me upon it." The tentative groping for an answer to Bentley's questions is so apparent that Dr. Johnson's remark is sound, when he said that, "The principal question of these letters gives occasion to observe how even the mind of Newton gains ground gradually upon darkness."

Newton began his series of three letters to Bentley with a statement of his purpose when he wrote his *Principia,* which will certainly sound strangely to modern ears that have come to regard science as an end in itself,—a discipline able to displace religion rather than to uphold it. "When I wrote my treatise about our system, I had an eye upon such principles as might work with considering men, for the belief of a Deity; and nothing can rejoice me more than to find it useful for that purpose. But, if I have done the public any service this way, it is due to nothing but industry and patient thought."

After stating his purpose, Newton then answers Bentley's questions. He first postulates matter, throughout all space, to be uniformly distributed in the beginning, and every particle to have an innate force of gravity towards all the rest. He then considers two cases. If space were finite then the mutual forces of gravity would cause all the matter to drift down to a centre and there form one great spherical mass which is contrary to fact. If space, however, were infinite, there would be no central point, and matter could not concentrate into one mass; but some matter would fall towards one point and some towards another, so as to make an infinite number of great masses, scattered at great distances from one another throughout infinite space, such as is exhibited by the positions of the stars. But, whatever primary arrangement of matter might have existed, it was his settled conviction that the motions, the orderly arrangement, and the orbits of the planets could not spring from any natural cause, but must have been impressed upon them by an intelligent agent. Dr. Johnson made the comment that matter distributed through infinite space either must have been created or be eternal. If it was created, then it infers a creator; if eternal, it must have remained evenly spread from eternity, and so would not ever begin to coalesce except by a cause beginning to act as it never had before. This objection to a uniform distribution of matter, he continued, Sir Isaac seems by degrees to have understood since in a second letter, he changes his hypothesis to the extent of admitting that to begin to move, matter would originally have to be unevenly distributed in order to create a multitude of bodies. But as Dr. Johnson again pointed out; if matter were ever unevenly spread, its motion towards centres would be coincident with its existence. Newton's dilemma is obvious. If space be finite, the imagination insists on a boundary and enquires of what it consists and what is beyond. If space be infinite, then we cannot postulate an even distribution of matter for space and matter would be identical. In his last two letters, Newton, apparently, clearly recognised the futility of speculating on an initial state of the universe, or on the causes of its development. The function of science should be limited to an investigation of those natural phenomena which exist now and can be perceived objectively by our senses.

There seems to be much ignorance about his conception of gravity as an inherent property of matter, or as an occult force. I shall give two quotations from these letters which should make his attitude clear and explicit. "I would now add," he wrote, "that the hypothesis of matter being at first evenly spread through the heavens is, in my opinion, inconsistent with the hypothesis of innate gravity, without a supernatural power to reconcile them; and therefore it infers a Deity." This is the postulate assumed by both Kant and Laplace in their nebular hypotheses as the primordial state of a universe which was to be dependent only on natural causes. It was Newton's deeper insight which made him recognise that matter evenly distributed throughout space and acted upon only by gravity must remain in that state forever unless the balanced force of gravity was disturbed by some supernatural cause. Again: "It is inconceivable, that inanimate brute matter should, without the mediation of something else, which is not material, operate upon, and affect other matter without mutual contact; as it must do, if gravitation, in the sense of Epicurus, be essential and inherent in it. And this is one reason, why I desired you would not ascribe innate gravity to me. That gravity should be innate, inherent and essential to matter, so that one body may act upon another at a distance through a *vacuum,* without the mediation of any thing else, by and through which their action and force may be conveyed from one to another, is to me so great an absurdity, that I believe no man who has in philosophical matters a competent faculty of thinking, can ever fall into it. Gravity must be caused by an agent acting constantly according to certain laws; but whether this agent be material or immaterial, I have left to the consideration of my readers."

When men of science attempt to explain the nature of space, time, and substance, to picture an initial state of the universe, or even to deal with the universe as a whole, they are so far outside the field of science that their conclusions are mere empty words, without significance. Science is, by its very nature, restricted to problems based on our sense perceptions and capable of experimental observation. Space, time, and substance are postulates, accepted as true, on which science is built and by which phenomena are explained; to derive their properties, in turn, from the conclusions derived from them is but a vicious argument in a circle which gets us nowhere and has no end. To assert the contrary, is to subscribe to the belief that we can attain an absolute knowledge of phenomena. It is the most striking evidence of the sanity of Newton's genius that, while he speculated on such problems because of the natural curiosity of the mind, he saw they could not be included in the scientific method. The conclusion of such speculations always ended with him in the acceptance of a divine Providence, of whose design we have an intuitive knowledge sufficient for us to predict with considerable accuracy a limited order of events. True science to him, and ultimately the idea must be accepted by all of us, is restricted to the world of the finite in space, time, and substance; both the infinitely large and the infinitely small are inaccessible to discovery through our sense perceptions and by science.

The greatest minds have speculated on the cosmic problems. Descartes's world of pure extension is an abstraction which could never start its operation of grinding the cosmic dust and creating planetary vortices except by the initial jog of an outside power. And his glittering edifice has dissolved in a mist of meaningless words. The nebular hypotheses of Kant and Laplace, independently evolved from Newtonian dynamics and so like each other as to be one of the striking coincidences of chance, fail to give any clear and exact ideas, and crumble at the test of an enquiring mind. It would have been jejune to have discussed Bentley's and Newton's confutation of atheism by scientific empiricism if there were not still existent the lingering hope that science has the key to unlock those impenetrable mysteries. It is a matter of the deepest regret that Professor Einstein, after his efficient service in extending Newton's ideas of the relativity of our knowledge, should, with his followers, have then plunged into a peculiarly aggravated case of propounding a positive and absolute system of space, time, and energy. They have, in essence, thrown science, which had emerged from the Renaissance into a sane and powerful method, back into the spirit of the Middle Ages. If they succeed, our conception of the objective world will be as dogmatic, and as foreign, to our common sense perceptions as were the cosmic ideas of the monks. They created a world founded on a pre-supposed divine revelation, and we are creating another with no more substantiality than mathematical symbols and formulæ.

It is necessary to return to Newton's personal affairs. There is evidence that his health had not been good for some years and towards the end of 1693, his condition assumed an alarming and sinister aspect, as he showed signs of serious mental disturbance. This illness has been clouded by mystery and conflicting reports; some have tried to pass it off lightly, and others have so exaggerated it that they regarded it as the dominant influence in all his later life. We have now sufficient material from which to present an accurate and reasonable statement of its character and effects.

This illness has been laid to many causes,—to an intense desire to obtain office, social position and wealth, followed by a morbid chagrin because of repeated failures to satisfy this ambition; to mental shock due to a mysterious fire which destroyed a mass of cherished manuscript; to religious excitement; to depression of spirit because his scientific work had not received a sympathetic and proper appreciation. But, these supposed causes are not in accordance with his character and temperament, either before, or after, this period of his life. At no other time, did he show any solicitude for wealth or popular approval, rather the contrary; and his disposition was equable and serene except in rare cases; even during his personal controversies his conduct gave no evidence of unrestrained passion. Why, then, should we suppose that passionate emotions so intense as to cause physical and mental derangement were created by desires which did not exist at any other period of his life? Is it not altogether simpler, and more probable, to regard them as symptoms and results of his illness, and to seek for its cause elsewhere,—especially so since, when he recovered his health, these morbid symptoms disappeared and never again returned? Nor, does the cause of his illness seem difficult to find.

If the reader will examine carefully the account which Humphrey Newton gave of Newton's manner of life during the strenuous years devoted to the composition of the *Principia,*[50] a feeling of wonder will arise that he survived such a total neglect of the fundamental rules of health. It is an extraordinary chronicle of absolute carelessness about food, lack of sleep, total absorption in profound thought during long hours broken by feverish activity in his laboratory. His nervous state is graphically pictured by his incessant restlessness, and interminable pacing up and down his room. Is it surprising that relief from this pressure was followed by an attack of what is now familiarly known as nervous prostration? In the autumn of 1692, he complained of sleeplessness and loss of appetite. His letters clearly show signs of his despondency and loneliness; he began to have the *idée fixe* of a conspiracy against him and that his dearest friends were deserting him or treacherously trying to thwart his desires. At the same time, his work showed no confusion of mind; his philosophical letters to Bentley, his theological writings, his mathematical and chemical work are as sane and clear as usual; his perturbation exists only in an uncontrollable exaggeration of his naturally jealous and suspicious temperament.

Newton's condition finally aroused the apprehension of his friends who had, evidently for some time, been puzzled by his conduct. The first definite news came from Pepys. They had become acquainted during Newton's term in Parliament, and although Pepys was now out of office, he was still a man of influence, and maintained his eager desire to associate with learned men. Shortly after Boyle's

[50] *Cf.* Chap. VII, pp. 246, 249.

death, he wrote to Evelyn: "Pray let Dr. Gale, Mr. Newton, and myself, have the honour of your company to-day, forasmuch as Mr. Boyle being gone, we shall want your help in thinking of a man in England fit to be set up after him for our Peireskius, besides Mr. Evelyn."[51] That Newton was suffering from a pronounced attack of nervous prostration, and that he was a victim of mental delusion in so far as to believe in a conspiracy against him, is only too certain from a letter he wrote to Pepys with no apparent cause as there is no evidence of his being in trouble or embroilment.

Newton to Pepys

September 13, 1693.

Sir,—Some time after Mr. Millington had delivered your message, he pressed me to see you the next time I went to London. I was averse; but upon his pressing consented, before I considered what I did, for I am extremely troubled at the embroilment I am in, and have neither ate nor slept well this twelve-month, nor have my former consistency of mind. I never designed to get any thing by your interest, nor by King James's favour, but am now sensible that I must withdraw from your acquaintance, and see neither you nor the rest of my friends any more, if I may but leave them quietly. I beg your pardon for saying I would see you again, and rest your most humble and most obedient servant,

Is. Newton.[52]

Pepys was dumfounded by such a letter and, not knowing how to answer it, he wrote first to Millington to enquire casually whether Newton was ill. After he received an equally vague answer, his fears were increased, and he then wrote the following letter that he might have explicit news.

Pepys to Millington

September 26, 1693.

Sir,—After acknowledging your many old favours, give me leave to do it a little more particularly upon occasion of the new one con-

[51] Pepys *Diary and Correspondence,* ed. Braybrooke. Dr. Gale was one of the Sec. R. S., and Nicholas Peiresc was held to be the type of what a learned and accomplished man ought to be.

[52] *Cf.* Brewster, Vol. II, pp. 142–146, for this and the succeeding letters which were in Lord Braybrooke's collection. Millington was a Fellow of Magdalene College, Cambridge, Pepys's Alma Mater. Brewster gives the erroneous impression that Pepys was then Secretary to the Admiralty. He, of course, lost his position when James lost his throne. The error is of some importance as it makes Newton's disclaimer of seeking Pepys's and King James's favour a stronger evidence of his mental perturbation.

veyed to me by my nephew Jackson. Though, at the same time, I must acknowledge myself not at the ease I would be glad to be at in reference to the excellent Mr. Newton; concerning whom (methinks) your answer labours under the same kind of restraint which (to tell you the truth) my asking did. For I was loth at first dash to tell you that I had lately received a letter from him so surprising to me for the inconsistency of every part of it, as to be put into great disorder by it, from the concernment I have for him, lest it should arise from that which of all mankind I should least dread from him and most lament for,—I mean a discomposure in head, or mind, or both. Let me, therefore, beg you, Sir, having now told you the true ground of the trouble I lately gave you, to let me know the very truth of the matter, as far at least as comes within your knowledge. For I own too great an esteem for Mr. Newton, as for a public good, to be able to let any doubt in me of this kind concerning him lie a moment uncleared, where I can have any hopes of helping it.—I am, with great truth and respect, dear Sir, your most humble and most affectionate servant, S. PEPYS.[53]

Millington to Pepys

Coll. Magd. Camb., Sept. the 30, 1693.

Honor'd Sir,—Coming home from a journey on the 28th instance at night, I met with your letter which you were pleased to honour me with of the 26th. I am much troubled I was not at home in time for the post, that I might as soon as possible put you out of your generous pain that you are in for the worthy Mr. Newton. I was, I must confess, very much surprised at the enquiry you were pleased to make by your nephew about the message that Mr. Newton made the ground of his letter to you, for I was very sure I never either received from you or delivered to him any such; and therefore I went immediately to wait upon him, with a design to discourse him about the matter, but he was out of town, and since I have not seen him, till upon the 28th I met him at Huntingdon, where, upon his own accord, and before I had time to ask him any question, he told me that he had writ to you a very odd letter, at which he was much concerned; added, that it was in a distemper that much seized his head, and that kept him awake for above five nights together, which upon occasion he desired I would represent to you, and beg your pardon,

[53] Brewster II, p. 143.

he being very much ashamed he should be so rude to a person from whom he hath so great an honour. He is now very well, and, though I fear he is under some small degree of melancholy, yet I think there is no reason to suspect it hath at all touched his understanding, and I hope never will; and so I am sure all ought to wish that love learning or the honour of our nation, *which it is a sign how much it is looked after, when such a person as Mr. Newton lies so neglected by those in power.* And thus, honoured Sir, I have made you acquainted with all I know of the cause of such inconsistencies in the letter of so excellent a person; and I hope it will remove the doubts and fears you are, with so much compassion and publicness of spirit, pleased to entertain about Mr. Newton; but if I should have been wanting in any thing tending to the more full satisfaction, I shall, upon the least notice, endeavour to amend it with all gratitude and truth. Honoured Sir, your most faithful and most obedient servant,

JOH. MILLINGTON.[54]

Pepys to Millington

October 3d, 1693.

Sir,—You have delivered me from a fear that indeed gave me much trouble, and from my very heart I thank you for it, an evil to Mr. Newton being what every good man must feel for his own sake as well as his. God grant it may stop here. And for the kind reflection he has since made upon his letter to me, I dare not take upon me to judge what answer I should make him to it, or whether any or no; and therefore pray that you will be pleased either to bestow on me what directions you see fit for my own guidance towards him in it, or to say to him in my name, but your own pleasure, whatever you think may be most welcome to him upon it, and most expressive of my regard and affectionate esteem of him, and concernment for him. I have a debt to acknowledge to you, (but was prevented in my last, by the thoughts I was then overborne with in this matter,) from the great satisfaction you was pleased to give me by your pupil (on whose behalf I have lasting thanks also to pay you) to my enquiries about Mr. Pyets, beseeching you to make the same scrupleless use of me in whatever relation you can think me capable of rendering you any service, for I would do it with great pleasure, remaining, dear Sir, your most humble and most faithful servant,

S. PEPYS.[55]

[54] Brewster II, p. 144.

[55] *Ibid.*, II, p. 145.

It is quite clear from these letters that Newton, in his ordinary conversation with strangers, appeared quite rational, it was only when certain subjects were in his mind that his aberration was noticeable. Pepys was apparently reassured and, two months later, he wrote to Newton, wisely ignoring his incoherent letter and his health, and merely expressing a continued friendship and good-will towards him. At the time, the town was much interested in the mathematical chances of the Groom-Porter's lottery, and he took the liberty of asking Newton to give a solution to a problem of dice throwing. Newton's answer is quite clear and calm, and he is anxious to assist his friends upon all occasions.[56]

But Newton was far from well. One can imagine the consternation that Locke felt when, without warning, he received such a letter as is given below. The letter to Pepys and the two following letters to Locke can leave no doubt that he was on the verge of a total mental collapse which, if not checked, would have led to insanity. Nor can we doubt that the judicious and truly amiable replies of Pepys and Locke had great influence in dissipating the hallucinations which were seizing him.

Newton to Locke

Sir,

Being of opinion that you endeavoured to embroil me with women and by other means, I was so much affected with it, as that when one told me you were sickly and would not live, I answered, 'twere better if you were dead. I desire you to forgive me this uncharitableness. For I am now satisfied that what you have done is just, and I beg your pardon for my having hard thoughts of you for it, and for representing that you struck at the root of morality, in a principle you laid down in your book of ideas, and designed to pursue in another book, and that I took you for a Hobbist. I beg your pardon also for saying or thinking that there was a design to sell me an office, or to embroil me.

I am your most humble

And unfortunate servant,

IS. NEWTON.

At the Bull, in Shoreditch,
London, Sept. 16th, 1693.[57]

[56] There are four of these letters; three are published in Braybrooke's *Diary and Correspondence of Pepys* and the fourth by Brewster, Vol. II, p. 471.

[57] This and the two subsequent letters are printed in King's *Life of Locke,* Vol. I, pp. 416–420.

Locke to Newton

Oates, Oct. 5th, 93.

Sir,

I have been ever since I first knew you, so entirely and sincerely your friend, and thought you so much mine, that I could not have believed what you tell me of yourself, had I had it from any body else. And though I cannot but be mightily troubled that you should have had so many wrong and unjust thoughts of me, yet next to the return of good offices, such as from a sincere good will I have ever done you, I receive your acknowledgement of the contrary as the kindest thing you could have done me, since it gives me hopes that I have not lost a friend I so much valued. After what your letter expresses, I shall not need to say any thing to justify myself to you. I shall always think your own reflection on my carriage both to you and all mankind, will sufficiently do that. Instead of that, give me leave to assure you, that I am more ready to forgive you than you can be to desire it; and I do it so freely and fully, that I wish for nothing more than the opportunity to convince you that I truly love and esteem you; and that I have still the same good will for you as if nothing of this had happened. To confirm this to you more fully, I should be glad to meet you any where, and the rather, because the conclusion of your letter makes me apprehend it would not be wholly useless to you. But whether you think it fit or not, I leave wholly to you. I shall always be ready to serve you to my utmost, in any way you shall like, and shall only need your commands or permission to do it.

My book is going to the press for a second edition; and though I can answer for the design with which I writ it, yet since you have so opportunely given me notice of what you have said of it, I should take it as a favour, if you would point out to me the places that gave occasion to that censure, that by explaining myself better, I may avoid being mistaken by others, or unawares doing the least prejudice to truth or virtue. I am sure you are so much a friend to them both, that were you none to me, I could expect this from you. But I cannot doubt but you would do a great deal more than this for my sake, who after all have all the concern of a friend for you, wish you extremely well, and am without compliment.

[The draught of the letter is endorsed: " J. L. to Is. Newton."]

Newton to Locke

Sir,

The last winter, by sleeping too often by my fire, I got an ill habit of sleeping; and a distemper, which this summer has been epidemical, put me farther out of order, so that when I wrote to you, I had not slept an hour a night for a fortnight together, and for five nights together not a wink. I remember I wrote to you, but what I said of your book I remember not. If you please to send me a transcript of that passage, I will give you an account of it if I can.

I am your most humble servant,

Is. Newton.

Cambridge, Oct. 5th, 1693.

I believe that Newton recovered entirely his health by the end of the year; the last letters to Pepys and to Locke show that he had realised his condition, and his apologies express a pathetic humility for his unwarranted attacks on them. We hear of no more trouble, and the only permanent effect of his illness was a certain lassitude of mind and unwillingness to engage in creative work. The Scotch philosopher, Dugald Stewart, has left a beautiful tribute to Locke's character, in a comment on his letter, which deserves quoting: "For the preservation of this precious memorial of Mr. Locke, the public is indebted to the descendants of his friend and relation, the Lord Chancellor King," and he adds, speaking of Locke's reply, "it is written with the magnanimity of a philosopher, and with the good-humoured forbearance of a man of the world; and it breathes throughout, so tender and so unaffected a veneration for the good, as well as great, qualities of the excellent person to whom it is addressed, as demonstrates at once the conscious integrity of the writer, and the superiority of his mind to the irritation of little passions": he concludes, "I know nothing from Locke's pen which does more honour to his temper and character.[58]

Academic circles are not entirely free from gossip, and we can not doubt that rumours of the mental condition of so conspicuous a member, as Newton, must have spread through the Common Rooms of the Colleges. There is even some cause for believing that the advisability of at least investigating his sanity was discussed officially,

[58] Ld. King's *Life of Locke,* Vol. I, p. 416.

and that the Chancellor placed him under the supervision of his friends. At least, some persons believed that he had been confined, for a time, in his rooms. There is, however, no certain evidence that Newton was temporarily insane or that he was confined to his rooms; but such rumours were certainly carried to the Continent, and must have been more or less current in England. Biot, who was an ardent admirer of Newton and who wrote a most appreciative life of him in the *Biographie Universelle,* published there a letter from a Mr. Vanswinden which is certainly authentic, and which has caused endless discussion. In this letter, the following passage occurred: "There is among the manuscripts of the celebrated Huygens, a small journal in folio, in which he used to note down different occurences; it is side Z., No. 8, page 112, in the catalogue of the library at Leyden: the following extract is written by Huygens himself, with whose hand-writing I am well acquainted, having had occasion to peruse several of his manuscripts and autograph letters. *On the 29th May, 1694, a Scotchman of the name of Colin, informed me, that Isaac Newton, the celebrated mathematician, eighteen months previously, had become deranged in his mind, either from too great application to his studies, or from excessive grief at having lost, by fire, his chemical laboratory and some papers. Having made observations before the Chancellor of Cambridge, which indicated the alienation of his intellect, he was taken care of by his friends, and being confined to his house, remedies were applied, by means of which he has lately so far recovered his health as to begin to again understand his own Principia.* Huygens [Biot continues] mentioned this circumstance to Leibniz, in a letter, dated the 8th of the following June, to which the latter replied on the twenty-third: 'I am very happy that I received information of the cure of Mr. Newton, at the same time that I first heard of his illness, which, without doubt, must have been most alarming. It is to men like Newton and yourself, Sir, that I desire health and a long life.' "[59]

This anecdote bears the ear-marks of what, at least, was commonly believed at the time to be Newton's state of mind and health.

[59] Biot's Life of Newton, Eng. Trans. p. 25.—The original as written by Huygens is: "1694, die 29 Maii, narravit mihi D. Colin, Scotus, celeberrimum ac rarum geometram, Ism. Newtonum, incidisse in phrenitin abhinc anno ac sex mensibus. An ex nimia studii assiduitate, an dolore infortunii, quod in incendio laboratorium chemicum et scripta quaedam amiserat. Cum ad archiepiscopum Cant. [Chan. Cantab.?] venisset, ea locutum, quae alienationem mentis indicarent; deinde ab amicis cura ejus suscepta, domoque clausâ, remedia volenti nolenti adhibita, quibus jam sanitatem recuperavit, ut jam nunc librum suum Principiorum intelligere incipiat."

The mysterious fire here referred to has become one of the stock legends about him, and is assigned by various writers to very different periods of his life. The most popular and false account places the incident in London during his latter years, and should have a place here in order to try to suppress it. The story is given in Maude's *Wensleydale* as follows: "His temper was so mild and equal, that scarce any accidents disturbed it. One instance in particular, which is authenticated by a person now living, (1780) brings this assertion to a proof. Sir Isaac being called out of his study to a contiguous room a little dog, called Diamond, the constant but incurious attendant of his master's researches, happened to be left among the papers, and by a fatality not to be retrieved, as it was in the latter part of Sir Isaac's days, threw down a lighted candle, which consumed the almost finished labours of some years. Sir Isaac returning too late, but to behold the dreadful wreck, rebuked the author of it with an exclamation (ad sidera palmas) 'Oh Diamond! Diamond! thou little knowest the mischief done!'—without adding a single stripe." This famous little dog, Diamond, is a mythological beast which I have ventured to believe was created in the undergraduate mind to relieve the solitude of a lonely scholar. I am quite willing to believe that Newton did suffer the loss of some manuscripts by a fire, but I am certain that such a loss would not unhinge the mind of such a man as Newton. Dr. Stukeley, whose reminiscences are trustworthy, stated that Newton, "wrote a piece of chemistry, explaining the principles of that mysterious art upon experimental and mathematical proof, and he valued it much; but it was unluckily burned in his laboratory, which casually took fire. He would never undertake that work again,—a loss much to be regretted. Mr. Newton [i.e. Humphrey Newton] of this town, tells me likewise, that several sheets of his *Optics* were burnt by a candle in his room, but I suppose he could recover them again."[60] But, Humphrey Newton, in his letter to Conduitt, stated that he knew nothing of the *Optics* being burned except by report as it happened before the *Principia* was written; that is, before 1685. There is another account, which is perhaps the most trustworthy of any, and it is important especially for the reason that it was written in 1692 by an undergraduate. The story he tells shows pretty clearly that rumours were current in the University, and had even percolated down to the undergraduates, of something mentally wrong with Newton. The anecdote, as I give it,

[60] *Portsmouth Collection.* Also quoted by Brewster, Vol. II, p. 94.

is in a manuscript diary of Abraham de la Pryme, a student then in his second year of residence in St. John's College. It is as follows:

"1692. Feb. 3d. What I heard to-day I must relate. There is one Mr. Newton (whom I have very oft seen) Fellow of Trinity College, that is mighty famous for his learning, being a most excellent Mathematician, Philosopher, Divine, etc. He has been fellow of the Royal Society these many years, and amongst other very learned books and tracts he's written one upon the mathematical principles of Philosophy, which has got him a mighty name, he having received especially from Scotland abundance of congratulatory letters for the same: but of all the books that he ever wrote there was one of colours and light established upon thousands of experiments which he had been 20 years of making, and which had cost him many hundred of pounds. This book which he valued so much, and which was so much talked of, had the ill luck to perish, and be utterly lost just when the learned author was almost at putting a conclusion at the same, after this manner:—

"In a winter's morning leaving it amongst his other papers, on his study table whilst he went to Chapel, the candle which he had unfortunately left burning there too, catched hold by some means of other papers and they fired the aforesaid book, and utterly consumed it, and several other valuable writings, and which is most wonderful did no further mischief.

"But when Mr. Newton came from Chapel and had seen what was done, every one thought he would have run mad, he was so troubled thereat that he was not himself for a month after. A long account of this his system of light and colours you may find in the Transactions of the Royal Society which he had sent up to them long before this sad mischance happened unto him."[61]

There can be little doubt, from the evidence which has been presented, that Newton had suffered a serious mental break-down and it is very probable that, for a short time, he was subjected to some form of oversight and restraint. If the latter be true, he soon recovered from the attack, and was to all appearances his normal self. His friends in London and Cambridge stifled, as far as possible, the rumour which had spread to the continent. Wallis, for example wrote to Waller, Secretary of the Royal Society, as late as 1695: "I

[61] Edleston, p. lxi.

have, since, a letter from Sturmius [a Professor of Mathematics in Altdorf] which signifies that he had, some weeks before, received the book I sent him. He sends me word of a rumor amongst them concerning Mr. Newton as if his house and books and all his goods were burnt, and himself so disturbed in mind thereupon, as to be reduced to very ill circumstances. Which being all false, I thought fit presently to rectify that groundless mistake."

Opinions as to the permanent effect of Newton's illness range from that of Brewster to Biot's. Brewster marshals his evidence, to prove that his mind was not even temporarily affected, by citing his letters to Bentley and other intellectual work. It needs no proof to show that Newton was capable of clear and sustained philosophical thought; but he may at the same time have been so obsessed with the idea that his friends had forsaken him or were conspiring against him as to have suffered from a mania of persecution and melancholy. On the other hand, Biot regarded this illness as a critical turning point in his life and the cause why "Newton, though only forty-five [50] years old, never more gave to the world a *new* work in any branch of science."

If one examines Newton's life with critical detachment he will be forced to the conclusion that the regrettable traits of his character were permanently intensified during the later half of his life. He became steadily more dictatorial, more suspicious, and more worldly. His treatment of Flamsteed, of Leibniz, and of uncomplaisant members of the Royal Society, is hard to reconcile with his character as a young man. When an obsession of persecution once seizes on a mind so delicately adjusted, it is difficult to shake off and, in his case, he found relief in the flattery which a new set of admirers was only too ready to lavish upon him. Biot also thought his interest in religion and theology was greatly intensified by his illness and, to support that opinion, his theological works are assigned to a late period of his life. But his correspondence with Locke proves quite the contrary. His most important works, the *Two Corrupt Passages in the New Testament,* his *Interpretation of Prophesy,* and his *Chronology,* were begun much earlier than 1691. His scientific work, which resulted from his manual dexterity and his logical imagination, has been so emphasized that we are apt to forget an equally strong trait of imagination which caused him to meditate on the mystery of the cosmos, the mystical doctrine of the Trinity and of the Prophecies.

To assign the cause of his interest in religion either to fear, or to mental debility, is to judge his character quite erroneously. It was the natural outlet of a true piety and humility, and it aroused the highest effort of his intellect and industry. The comparative value of his scientific and theological work is not involved in the question.

CHAPTER XI

RELUCTANCE TO PUBLISH. THE LUNAR THEORY AND CORRESPONDENCE WITH FLAMSTEED. APPOINTMENT TO THE MINT

1693–1696

THE friends of Newton were, at this time, deeply concerned not only about his health and disquietude of mind, but also lest his dilatoriness and reluctance to publish would rob him and England of the glory of his discoveries. His work on light had brought him fame, but he persistently refused to publish anything further in that subject so long as Hooke was alive. It was known that he had a mass of notes and manuscripts which recorded new experiments on light, but the rumour was abroad that they, and others on chemistry, had been burned, and that he refused to re-write them. And, in the meanwhile, other men were profiting by his silence. His *Principia* had been accessible to scholars for four or five years but it was now out of print. A second revised and enlarged edition was badly needed. In many places it was obscure; there were many errors of print; but above all the theory of the moon's motion, its most striking application, had been merely sketched and needed to be developed. Two young mathematicians, David Gregory and Fatio de Duillier, had prepared voluminous notes on the text and were eager to assist him in the editing. Duillier's hopes in this direction have been mentioned; Gregory's commentary on the *Principia* extended to 213 closely written folio pages and, in May, 1694, he visited in Cambridge for the purpose "of consulting the divine author [consulendi divini autoris gratia.]"[1] His friends, however, could not arouse him; he was sick, weary, and depressed; and the realisation of the sort of letters he had written to Pepys and Locke must have added to his depression.

In the fields of light and mechanics, his reputation was established; but Wallis saw clearly the trouble he was laying up for himself by his neglect in explaining and completing his discovery of the fluxions. Leibniz had published his differential calculus in the *Acta Eruditorum* of Leipzig for 1684, in a form quite similar to that which he

[1] Rigaud, p. 100.

had described in his private letters to Newton. This calculus, cultivated by himself and the brothers, Bernoulli, had by 1695 become a powerful tool, vivifying the whole field of mathematics and physics. And, a year later, de l'Hôpital published a treatise on the calculus so systematic and so modern in treatment that it could be used today. All Newton had done was to establish his priority of discovery by writing to Leibniz that he had found some years previously a general method of finding curves and areas; but he had refused to explain his method and had concealed it in a jumbled sentence. He had, according to the opinion of most mathematicians, used his fluxions to solve some of the problems in the *Principia,* but he had translated them into Euclidean form and had omitted the analytic solution. So in England, no progress was being made with fluxions, and Wallis was anxious that the credit should be given to Newton and his country.

Newton, to all appearances, seemed quite indifferent to the progress of Leibniz's work; he may even have been ignorant of it, but, in the *Principia,* he had certainly acknowledged that Leibniz had discovered the calculus independently of any aid from himself. In a Scholium to Proposition VII, Book II, he stated: "In a correspondence which took place about ten years ago, between that very celebrated mathematician G. Leibniz and myself, I mentioned to him that I possessed a method (which I concealed in an anagram) for determining maxima and minima, for drawing tangents, and for similar operations, which was equally applicable both to rational and irrational quantities: that illustrious man replied that he also had fallen on a method of the same kind [se quoque in ejusmodi methodum incidisse], and communicated to me his method, which scarcely differed from mine, except in the notation and the idea of the generation of quantities."

This statement seems perfectly clear in its acknowledgement of Leibniz's independent discovery of the calculus, except for the possibly ambiguous phrase *he also had fallen on a method of the same kind;* this might be construed to mean that Leibniz had solved the jumbled sentence and so had received a hint which was sufficient to start the mind of so able a mathematician on the same road to discovery. If the reader, however, will refer back to what Newton here calls his anagram he will grant that such a supposition is an absolute impossibility. Biot[2] is quite justified in stating: "The above passage

[2] Biot, *Life of Newton,* p. 30.

in the *Principia* is in truth a formal recognition of Leibniz's claims. It was so considered by every one when it appeared, and during twenty years Leibniz was allowed, without any dispute, to develop all the parts of the differential calculus, and to deduce from it an immense number of brilliant applications, which seemed to extend the power of mathematical analysis far beyond any preconceived limits." Unfortunately, when the later controversy arose, Newton, either on his own initiative or swayed by the influence of others, took advantage of his ambiguous phrase and repudiated, in his third edition, this honourable acknowledgement.

Wallis was, at this time, preparing his collected works for the press and determined to include in them an account of Newton's fluxions in order to remedy as far as possible the unfortunate situation which had arisen. At his urgent request, Newton wrote two letters, dated 27 August and 17 September, 1692, in which he gave the two Latin sentences that he had so far successfully concealed. He also explained briefly his method of fluxions and illustrated its power by solving two problems. These letters, which Wallis included in his own works, are thus the first information the public received of Newton's fluxions.[3]

While Wallis's works were still in the press, Leibniz, 7/17 March, 1693, wrote a most friendly and appreciative letter to Newton in which, for the purpose of trying to renew their former correspondence, he expressed the hope to have something great from him on tangents and quadratures.[4] Leibniz's conduct towards Newton in this whole matter had been above reproach. After explaining fully his own method to Newton and giving him ample opportunity to publish his discovery, there can be no question that he was fully justified in making public his own calculus. Nor can we find any fault with him for not mentioning in the *Leipzig Acts* the earlier discovery of the fluxions by Newton, who might resent a reference

[3] Wallis, *Opera,* Vol. II, p. 391. The second volume was published in 1693, the first in 1695; but false title-pages make them appear as of 1699, when the third volume was published. When the controversy between Newton and Leibniz broke out, the question of the dates of this publication became important. De Morgan (*Essay,* p. 92, foot-note), comments on this matter of dates: "A person who reads Wallis's collected works under the date of 1699 easily convicts the author, as honest a man as ever lived, of the grossest unfairness, upon his own testimony." He, also, in the preface to the first volume, excuses himself from mentioning the differential calculus since he considered it merely a form of the fluxions which Leibniz had grasped from the celebrated Oldenburg letters. Such a statement goes to show that Wallis knew these letters from hearsay only and had, from that national pride which seems to have animated all those who engaged in this unhappy controversy, blindly neglected or misconstrued the plain facts of the case.

[4] Raphson, *Historia Fluxionum,* London, 1715, pp. 119, 120.

to what he, himself, had so persistently concealed. There is a fine ring of sincerity to the statement Leibniz made some ten years later when he gave his reason for publishing his first account of the calculus: "I made known the elements of the new analysis some years ago; at the time, I was more concerned with its general use than with my own fame, which I, perhaps, could have furthered better if I had held back the method. But it is pleasant to me to see in the gardens of others the fruit grown from seeds then scattered by me."[5]

This final appeal by Leibniz succeeded in drawing an answer from Newton which should be read with careful attention. It has been neglected by those who have tried to unravel their complicated controversy, yet it throws a clear light on Newton's earlier attitude of mind. Only the first portion need be quoted; the latter part gives an elegant solution, by his method of fluxions, of what Euler afterwards called a "celebrated problem much agitated amongst Geometers," and a critique of Huygens's theory of gravitation which are now of no importance except to students of the history of mathematics. The letter, which was written in Latin, is as follows.

Newton to Leibniz

Celeberrimo Viro
Godefrido Gulielmo Leibnitio
Isaacus Newton S. P. D.

I did not reply to your letter immediately upon its receipt,—because it escaped my attention from having been lost a long time amongst my papers; it was not until yesterday that I came upon it unexpectedly. This has greatly vexed me since I hold your friendship in the highest regard, and have considered you for many years past to be one of the most eminent Geometers of this age, as I have testified on every proper occasion. For, although I shun philosophical and mathematical correspondence as much as I possibly can, yet I feared lest our friendship might suffer some detriment if I remained silent and that, the more, since Wallis is about to publish again his *History of Algebra* and will insert some new matter from the letters which I sent to you formerly by Mr. Oldenburg, and thus gave to me the occasion for writing to you concerning that fact. For, he requested me to reveal a certain twofold method which I had concealed till then by transposed letters. Thus I was constrained to explain, as briefly as I could, my method of fluxions which I had

[5] Guhrauer, *Biog. Liebniz,* Breslau, 1846, p. 290.

concealed in this sentence. *Data æquatione quantitates quotcunque fluentes involvente invenire fluxiones, et vice versa.* I trust, also, that I have written nothing which may displease you, and if there be anything which you find worthy of blame that you will point it out to me by letter, because I value friends more than mathematical inventions. . . . . Vale.[6]
Dabam Cantabrigiae, Octob. 16/26, 1693.

We must not forget that this letter was written nine years after Leibniz had published his calculus and during that time it had come to be recognised on the continent as one of the fundamental discoveries in mathematics. Now, he writes this letter which no one can read without the conviction that its author was sincere in his warm expression of esteem, and in his mortification that his negligence might be construed as a discourtesy. Would anyone go out of his way to testify to the distinction and genius of another if there were even a suspicion in his mind that the man had been guilty of gross plagiarism or had even received assistance from himself? The idea is absurd. Note also, that Newton was deeply apologetic because he had been persuaded to give Wallis the explanation of his method and of his concealed sentences before he had imparted this information to Leibniz. It is clearly an open acknowledgement that the first information of his fluxions was due to Leibniz as a reciprocal courtesy for the full and candid disclosure of the calculus which had been made to him years before. And now, even though he had forsaken mathematics and so, by inference, would develop his method no further, he wished to give his friend the meaning of his jumble of letters and an illustration of how problems could be solved by fluxions before they became public property. In the hope that he has done the honourable thing, he calls their friendship to witness, and begs for criticism if his statement of the case is not entirely satisfactory.

How keen Wallis had become to conquer Newton's reluctance to publish is seen from the following letter:

Wallis to Newton

Sir, Oxford, Apr. 10, 1695.

I was in hopes of seeing you in Oxford last summer; which made me neglect sending you (by the carrier) two cuts which belonged

[6] Edleston, p. 276.

to the volume you had before. They were not wrought off at the rolling-press when you had the rest; but are easy to be inserted in their proper places. I send them now, with the other volume; which I desire you to accept. [Vols. I and II of his Collected Works.]

I understand (from Mr. Caswell) you have finished a treatise about light, refraction and colours; which I should be glad to see abroad. 'Tis pity it was not out long since. If it be in English (as I hear it is) let it, however, come out as it is; and let those who desire to read it, learn English. I wish you would also print the two large letters of June and August [October] 1676. I had intimation from Holland, as desired there by your friends, that somewhat of that kind were done; because your notions [of *Fluxions*] pass there with great applause, by the name of *Leibniz's Calculus Differentialis.* I had this intimation when all but (part of) the preface to this volume was printed-off; so that I could only insert (while the press stay'd) that short intimation thereof which you there find. You are not so kind to your reputation (and that of the nation) as you might be, when you let things of worth lie by you so long, till others carry away the reputation that is due to you. I have endeavoured to do you justice in that point; and am now sorry that I did not print those two letters *verbatim*.

I understand you are now about adjusting the moon's motions; and, amongst the rest, take notice of that of the *common centre of gravity* of the earth and moon as a conjunct body; (a notion which, I think, was first started by me, in my discourse of the flux and reflux of the sea.) And it must needs be of a like consideration in that of Jupiter with his satellites, and of Saturn with his. (And I wonder we have not yet heard of any about moon.) But Saturn and Jupiter being so far off, the effects thereof are less observable by us than that of the moon. My advice upon the whole, is, that you would not be too slow in publishing what you do.

I am Sir
Your very humble Servant,
JOHN WALLIS.[7]

For Mr. Isaac Newton
Fellow of Trinity College and
Professor of Mathematics,
in Cambridge.

Nor was he content with a personal appeal to Newton, as he in the same year enlisted the aid of others. He wrote to Waller, Secre-

[7] Edleston, *Newton's Correspondence with Cotes*, p. 300.

tary of the Royal Society, to ask him to help and also to use his influence with Halley. In answer, Waller wrote that, "Mr. Halley has promised to write to Mr. Newton concerning those letters [those written to Leibniz in 1676] you mention. I hope they may be procured from him and thank you for the intimation thereof." The Royal Society, also, had aroused itself and on July 4, 1694, entered in the *Journal Book:* "Ordered that a letter be written to Mr. Isaac Newton praying that he will please to communicate to the Society in order to be published his treatise of light and colours and what other mathematical or physical treatises he has ready by him." In view of the fact that this action was taken in order to counteract the fame of Leibniz, it is worth mentioning that he also wrote to the Society urging them to persuade Newton to publish his further thoughts and improvements on the *Principia,* and his other physical and mathematical discoveries, lest his death should rob the world of such valuable work.

The last appeal I shall cite is an extract from a letter of Wallis to Halley: "I have written several letters to Mr. Newton about it [i .e. printing the two letters] pressing with some importunity the printing of them, and of his treatise about light and colours (as being neither just to himself nor kind to the public to delay it so long.) As to the letters, I sent him a fair transcript ready for the press,[8] which if he would print, it might best be done here, (and I would take the care of it). . . . But he did not seem forward for either. . . . As to that about light and colours (for which I am more solicitous) your interest may possibly prevail with him better than mine to get it published."[9] While the ostensible purpose of this pressure on Newton to publish was to protect his rights of discovery of the calculus, there seems to me to have been a wide-spread fear that his recent illness might result in mental incapacity, or death, and so prevent his unfinished work from ever being completed.

The relations between Newton and Leibniz, at this time, can be summarised as follows:

1. Newton had secured proof of the priority of his discovery of the calculus by sending, as was frequently done at that time a concealed sentence, to Leibniz whose activity in the subject was to be feared. He was satisfied with this proof of priority; but he did not

[8] Newton's copies of them may have perished in the fire which destroyed a mass of other papers, and, as Wallis supposed, Leibniz's answers among them; see Wallis's *Works,* III, 654, or *Commerc. Epistol.* 2d ed., pp. 110 and 211.

[9] Edleston, *Newton's Correspondence with Cotes,* p. 301.

wish to publish his method because of the criticism his work on light had aroused.

2. He admitted Leibniz's subsequent and independent discovery of a method similar to his own, and was indifferent to the public reputation and use which followed from its publication.

3. After repeated solicitation, he permitted Wallis to publish in his collected works the concealed sentences and just enough of the method to show the world what it was; but he had lost interest in natural philosophy, and was unconcerned whether or not it was developed by others into a method for general use.

4. He was satisfied so long as Leibniz and a chosen few were aware of his priority of discovery. This is in agreement with his peculiar views on the question of rights of discovery. To him, a new invention was the exclusive property of its discoverer whether he published it or not; as he, himself, declared, no credit is due to a second discovery even if done independently. It is needless to say that it is the established custom to give the credit to the one who first publishes a discovery.

5. He did not change this attitude until some of Leibniz's partisans insinuated that he had received assistance from Leibniz. Then he grew bitter; but he forgot that his own partisans had also accused Leibniz of plagiarism. The sequel to the controversy will be told in its proper place.

An incident occurred in May of the year, 1694, which gives an interesting side-light on the prevalent belief in ghosts amongst even sedate and learned university dons, and the scornful disbelief in them of Newton. A house opposite St. John's College, occupied by a Mr. Valentine Austin, was thought to be haunted. A crowd of curious people had gathered at the door and were watching three of the Fellows, and a Fellow-commoner, of the college, who had rushed in armed with pistols. It chanced that Newton passed by and seeing several of the scholars gaping at the door, "Oh ye fools!" says he, "will you never have any wit? Know you not that all such things are mere cheats and impostures? Fie! Fie! go home for shame." And so he left them, scorning to go in.[10]

It is to be expected that a man, who had developed his own ideas so carefully as did Newton and who had passed his life in a university, would have very definite opinions on education. It is fortunate that we have two letters written by him at this time which give

[10] Edleston, note 113, p. lxiv.

quite fully his reflections on the subject. They show very clearly that, however detached from the ordinary currents of life he may have seemed to be, he had the gift of knowing how the minds of the young should be disciplined. He might have been an excellent school-master if his fate had placed him in that position. Edward Paget had been appointed, as mentioned before, mathematical master at Christ's Hospital on the recommendation of Newton and Flamsteed. He found the scheme of study in mathematics for the boys to be unsatisfactory and drew up a new one. Before accepting his plan, the directors of the school sent the Treasurer, Mr. Hawes, to Cambridge to advise with the Lucasian Professor, and other mathematicians, and to get their opinions in writing as to the advisability of adopting the proposed changes. Newton, with his usual care and thoroughness, sent an elaborate report and critique in a letter to Hawes, enclosed in another to Paget. The letter is too long to give in full and some of the particular recommendations are not of general value, but certain portions are well-worth reading as they are the only examples we have of his ideas on education and show a generally unsuspected side of his character.[11] So much attention has been concentrated on Newton's transcendant scientific genius that we are apt to overlook the fact that his meditations covered the most diverse subjects and that his judgement was eminently sound on both theoretical and practical matters. He would have attained eminence in almost any profession in which he had engaged.

He first gave seven reasons for condemning the old scheme. "In general," he concluded, "the whole scheme is so confused and immethodical, as makes me think that they who drew it up, had no regard to the order of the things, but set them down by chance as they first thought upon them, without giving themselves the trouble to digest and methodise the heap of things they had collected together; which makes me of opinion, that it will not be for the reputation of the foundation to continue this scheme any longer without putting it at least into a new form.

"But then for the things it contains I account it but mean and of small extent. It seems to comprehend little more then the use of instruments, and the bare practice of seamen in their beaten road, which a child may easily learn by imitation, as a parrot does to speak, without understanding in many cases the reason of what he does; and which an industrious blockhead, who can but remember what he

[11] The letters and Newton's own scheme are published in Edleston, pp. 279–299.

has seen done, may attain to almost as soon as a child of parts, and he that knows it is not assisted thereby in inventing new things and practices, and correcting old ones, or in judging of what comes before him: Whereas the mathematical children, being the flower of the Hospital, are capable of much better learning, and when well instructed and bound out to skillful masters, may in time furnish the nation with a more skillful sort of sailors, builders of ships, architects, engineers and mathematical artists of all sorts, both by sea and land, than France can at present boast of."

He was quite certain in his own mind of the advantage to be obtained by a theoretical discipline for even the most practical of professions. "'Tis true that by good natural parts some men have a much better knack at mechanical things then others, and on that account are sometimes reputed good mechanics, but yet without the learning of this article, they are so far from being so, as a man of a good geometrical head who never learnt the principles of geometry, is from being a good geometer. For whilst mechanics consist in the doctrine of force and motion, and geometry in that of magnitude and figure: he that can't reason about force and motion, is far from being a true mechanic, as he that can't reason about magnitude and figure from being a geometer. A vulgar mechanic can practise what he has been taught or seen done, but if he is in an error he knows not how to find it out and correct it, and if you put him out of his road, he is at a stand; Whereas he that is able to reason nimbly and judiciously about figure, force and motion, is never at rest till he gets over every rub. Experience is necessary, but yet there is the same difference between a mere practical mechanic and a rational one, as between a mere practical surveyor or gauger and a good geometer, or between an empiric in physic and a learned and a rational physician."

He also enclosed his own outline of the mathematical course best suited to boys who are preparing themselves to be engineers. It followed Paget's plan in the main in proposing a graded course beginning with arithmetic, followed by geometry, trigonometry and navigation. His own contribution was to supplement the mathematical work by a study of the physical laws of force and motion. It seems to me that, beginning with the correspondence with Locke, his letters became more human and lose some of the dry formality and constraint which mark his earlier style. This is shown in his letter to Hawes, especially in its conclusion which is almost genial:

"I will add, that if instead of sending the observations of seamen to able mathematicians at land, the land would send able mathematicians to sea, it would signify much more to the improvement of navigation and safety of men's lives and estates on that element. I hope Sirs you will all interpret my freedom in this letter candidly and pardon what you may think amiss, because I have written it with a good will to your Foundation, and now I have spoke my thoughts I leave the whole business to the wisdom of yourself and the Governors." Not content with this counsel, he fortified it by a second letter to Hawes in which he recommended the Governors to investigate an outline of mathematical courses of instruction drawn up by Sir Jonas Moore some fifteen or sixteen years previously. He, himself, had examined this proposal and had found it excellent; and, in addition, the support of a man of such wealth and influence would be a great assistance to their Foundation. Sir Jonas was an influential Fellow of the Royal Society and a most liberal patron of science; amongst his other public benefactions, his gifts of money and instruments to the Royal Observatory had enabled Flamsteed to carry on the work when no funds were forthcoming from the public Treasury.

The proposed scheme of Paget, with Newton's comments, was then sent to Wallis and Gregory, at Oxford, who gave their opinion and advice in a joint paper. It is significant of the importance which education held in the minds of the Governors that it was only after the approval of three such eminent men had been received that they decided to make the change. In the meanwhile, the ill-fated Paget had lost his position because of his drunkenness and loose morals, and a Mr. Samuel Newton had succeeded him, largely on the recommendation of his name-sake. Not content with securing him the place, Newton in the following year wrote Hawes to explain his reasons for his recommendation. "As for Mr. Newton, I never took him for a deep mathematician, but recommended him as one who had mathematics enough for your business, with such other qualifications as fitted him for a Master in respect of temper and conduct as well as learning. . . . I thank you for your concern and pains in behalf of Mr. Newton, and am very glad to understand that he behaves himself so well. For tho' I was almost a stranger to him when I recommended him, yet since he was elected, I reckon myself concerned that he should answer my recommendation. The ill-will you may have got by your acting for him I perceive is but of little extent and cannot hurt you. Mr. Caswell's friends at Oxford blame his friend near London, and some of them think the place would not have suited with his humour, so that I am satisfied you made the best choice."[12] The friend near London, who had recommended Caswell for the position, was Flamsteed. The failure to defeat Newton's candidate and the blame for the appointment of Paget, which seems to have been laid on Flamsteed, may have exasperated his jealous and suspicious nature, and may account in part for the pique which later appeared in his correspondence with Newton on the subject of the moon's motion. Newton's interest in the Hospital did not end with the adoption of the new curriculum. In 1696, when he was in London in connection with his appointment to the Mint, he visited the Hospital, examined its library, and gave his advice on the purchase of books. Again, in the following year, he examined five of the boys and found them perfected in their work, except for a few particulars, and well qualified to be placed at sea as apprentices. For this help he received the unanimous thanks of the Committee. In the same year he was present at two of the Hospital meetings and served on a committee to determine how a gift of £100 might best be spent on the mathematical library.

While Newton, apparently, turned a deaf ear to the solicitations of others to publish, he had quietly taken up the work of correcting errors in the *Principia* and of extending the law of gravitation to various cosmic problems; the most difficult and the most interesting of these was the theory of the moon's motion. Next to the attraction of the sun, it is readily seen that the moon exerts a greater effect on the earth's motion than any other of the heavenly bodies. Before his discovery of the universal attractive force which determines the paths of the planets, there could be no method of attacking the problem except the roughly empirical one of plotting the successive positions of the moon during a long period of time, and of attempting to find from them such variations in its motion as could be shown to be periodic in nature. The cause of such variations was entirely unknown. As soon as Newton had discovered that there was an actual force of attraction between every two bodies which depended only on their masses and the geometrical distance between them, it was at once seen that the attraction of the sun, and of the planets, must constantly alter the speed and the course of the moon's primary elliptical orbit about the earth.

[12] Edleston, p. 296.

Could, then, a formula be derived from the law of gravitation, and from the mutual distances of the bodies composing the solar system, which would permit us to calculate with accuracy the future positions of the moon? He had shown that if the earth and moon could be discussed as two bodies alone in space then its orbit would be a true ellipse, drawn with the earth as a focus. But such a supposition is entirely academic; and the actual path of our satellite, pulled simultaneously by many bodies, is rather like the course of a drunken man trying to follow a prescribed path, alternately hurrying and lingering, and staggering from side to side. Owing to the small size of the moon, the attraction of the sun and planets has a first order effect on its path. The problem of calculating the position of the moon under the combined pulls of the earth and the sun is the celebrated problem of the three bodies and no general solution is attainable; if we add to this problem the attraction of a fourth body, say Jupiter, we are faced with one which has not even a particular solution.

Besides the influence of the sun and planets there are many other causes of perturbation; for example, the common centre of gravity of the earth and moon does not coincide with the centre of the earth because of the relatively large mass of the moon; the equatorial belt of the earth, the tides, the precession of the equinoxes, and all irregularities in the earth's motion, have their effect. It is no wonder that the cosmic system failed to account for even the major perturbations of the moon. Before the time of Ptolemy only one was known, he found a second, and Tycho Brahé discovered two others; these were all that could then be discovered from observation. The first real improvement in the lunar problem was made in 1638 by Jeremiah Horrox, a most brilliant English astronomer who announced his theory at the age of nineteen and died at the premature age of twenty-two years. Newton, who followed the method of Horrox, merely indicated the general principles of the moon's motion in the first edition of the *Principia;* it was not until the second edition appeared in 1713 that he developed, but still incompletely, those ideas which have enabled his successors to perfect to such an extraordinary degree the lunar theory. The great treatise of Professor Ernest Brown distinguishes some thirty, or more, perturbations and calculates them with more or less accuracy.

Newton, to succeed in his attempt to develop the lunar theory, was absolutely dependent on the most accurate observations of the successive positions of the moon available at the time. He seems to have been influenced to make a try at the general solution of the problem by having accidentally seen a catalogue of 150 places of the moon during a visit to the Royal Observatory. Flamsteed had noted them, with the errors between the observed and computed positions indicated, for his own use and as a check on Horrox's theory. With Flamsteed's assistance in furnishing observations, he worked on the problem persistently during the latter part of the year, 1694, and all the year following, and more or less intermittently after that till some time between 1698 and 1700. The results of this work were given in the second edition of the *Principia* in 1713; but, while he there correctly expounded the two principal perturbations of the moon and had discussed four new ones, it would be erroneous to suppose that the true positions of that satellite could be calculated with accuracy from his work. As Flamsteed, with the bias for accuracy natural to the foremost practical astronomer then living, pointed out to Newton's deep chagrin, the calculated and observed positions were not in sufficient agreement for astronomical purposes, and it required the labour of later men to bring them into harmony and to demonstrate the reliability of the theory.

The alliance of two such men, if they could work together in intellectual amity and mutual good-will, would have been an ideal combination. Unfortunately, they were temperamentally incompatible and, although the work was done, it was accompanied by a certain amount of ruffled spirits and rather petty bickering which was magnified in importance by a bitter controversy which arose between them at a later date. Both were what Locke termed men *nice* to deal with. Flamsteed was carrying on his great catalogue of the stars under heart-breaking difficulties. He was, it is true, the Astronomer Royal and was supposedly supported by the state; he had been given the title and a building, but there royal patronage ceased. Almost no instruments had been provided, and he had been forced to equip his observatory by borrowing what apparatus he could, by begging funds from private benefactors such as Sir Jonas Moore, and by making many with his own hands. He was wretchedly paid and had to use his valuable time in giving private lessons and carrying on the duties of a parish priest to eke out his income. But, perhaps, his greatest distraction came from the lack of assistants and calculators so that he had to spend much of his precious time in purely mechanical work and to pay, out of his pocket, what help he did procure. Add to all these difficulties the fact that he was frequently incapacitated for work by attacks of headache and indigestion, and we can easily account for, and excuse, his irritability, his intolerance of religious scepticism, and his jealous insistence that his conquest of such difficulties should be recognised. If we neglect these minor frailties, we find him to be a man of great integrity, of high character, and of a deep and sincere piety. Nor should we overlook the fact that Flamsteed held the high position of Astronomer Royal and was the most distinguished observer of the age; it was, in itself, a generous act to subordinate his own work to assist another to prove a theory which could not be, at the time, certain of success. Neither Newton, nor he, to say the least, was fitted for team-work.

The reputation and character of Flamsteed suffered deeply for nearly a century and a half. It was generally believed, and quite unjustifiably, that he had wilfully and jealously withheld data in his possession and necessary for Newton, and so had prevented the accomplishment of this great achievement. This slur on Flamsteed's character was not only widely current in England, where it was fostered by a concerted action to exalt Newton by detracting from the reputation of anyone who ventured to oppose him, or was involved in the unfortunate controversies which marred his life; but, it also spread to the continent and was believed there, as a letter of Leibniz to the astronomer, Roemer, convincingly shows: "Flamsteed withheld his observations of the moon from Newton. On that account, they say he has as yet been unable to complete his work on the lunar motion."[13] And even now, when the material to disprove this unjust charge is accessible, a sinister reputation clings to Flamsteed as well as to Leibniz, so hard is it to dispel the illusion of the unhuman perfection of Newton's character.

The facts concerning the relations between Newton and Flamsteed, both during this period and during their later and final rupture, were not known till Francis Baily, who was himself an able astronomer, published the *Life of Flamsteed*.[14] He was led into undertaking this work by accidentally learning that a neighbour had in his possession a large collection of original manuscript letters of Flamsteed written to his former assistant, Abraham Sharp. On examination, he found that they contained much new matter, connected with

[13] Quoted by Edleston, p. lxvii.

[14] The full title of the book is: *An Account of the Revd John Flamsteed,* The First Astronomer Royal; compiled from his own manuscripts, and other authentic documents, never before published. To which is added his British Catalogue of the Stars, corrected and enlarged. By Francis Baily, Esq., Vice-President R. A. S. Printed by order of the Lords Commissioners of the Admiralty. London, 1835.

the astronomer's labours, not generally known. Spurred on by this find, Baily, with the assistance of the then Astronomer Royal, discovered a vast mass of manuscript books, papers, and letters, belonging to Flamsteed which had been lying, unnoticed and neglected, on the library shelves of the Observatory for sixty years. After arranging and minutely examining the manuscripts, he soon found that the character of Flamsteed had not been properly presented by his biographers and that, in justice to him, they should be published.[15] Baily's proposal to undertake the work of publication was made in a letter addressed to the Duke of Somerset, President of the Board of Visitors of the Royal Observatory, and by him it was ordered to be transmitted to the Lords Commissioners of the Admiralty, with a recommendation that it should be carried into effect. With the compliance of the Commissioners, the work was printed at the public expense. Because of the criticism directed against Baily for publishing a book which was held to disparage Newton, it should be noted that a large majority of the Board of Visitors who recommended the publication were men of science holding important positions, and its chairman was *ex officio* the President of the Royal Society. The propriety of issuing a work dealing with the life of an eminent man of science and supported by such a recommendation should hardly be a subject for discussion. The only life of Flamsteed available, at the time was the one given in the *General Dictionary,* and his character as there portrayed is so at variance with the facts accessible in the documents and letters deposited in the Observatory that Baily accused the editors of deliberately suppressing this information because they considered it imprudent to risk an article reflecting so seriously on the characters of two such men as Newton and Halley. As he justly says: "These personal motives however have long passed away, and now cease to exist: and however unpleasant and painful it may be to an enlightened mind, to find two such eminent characters as Newton and Halley mixed up with subjects of the kind to which I shall presently allude, and pursuing a line of conduct towards Flamsteed, which tends to make them appear less amiable in our eyes, yet a proper regard for truth and justice prevents any suppression, at the present day, of the many curious and important (though often at the same time lamentable) facts which these manu-

[15] Baily (*cf.* p. xvi, note) particularly notes, "Sir David Brewster, in his recent life of Newton, has (by a singular error, to which I have alluded more at length, in page xxxiii) exhibited Flamsteed also in a character which he by no means deserves, and which indeed is totally at variance with Flamsteed's whole history."

scripts have, for the first time, now brought to light." He adds that he had tried to find documents which would explain and extenuate the conduct of Newton and Halley but, to his regret, without success; for this purpose, he searched the British Museum, the libraries of Oxford and Cambridge, and the *Portsmouth Collection*.

Of Flamsteed, he says, that his dominating characteristic was his interest in religion and that he would have followed whole-heartedly the life of a clergyman if his bodily weakness had not prevented an active career. Towards Newton, Flamsteed felt a high esteem and, till their final rupture, always spoke of him with the greatest respect: "Mr. Newton's approbation is more to me (exclaimed Flamsteed) than the cry of all the ignorant in the world." And even after their total breach of friendship, he wrote in a letter: "I believe him to be a good man at the bottom; but, through his natural temper, suspicious."[16] This opinion is in agreement with that of others who came in close contact with him. We must remember also that all through their first intercourse their relations were friendly and courteous, except for occasional bickering; and the coolness, which afterwards developed into active hostility, did not show itself till Newton moved to London. Even then, Flamsteed says that he sometimes visited him in Jermyn Street; that they were civil towards each other, but that Newton was not as friendly as formerly.[17]

The first hundred pages of Baily's book contain Flamsteed's diary of his life written principally to vindicate his own conduct towards Newton and Halley, and to preserve a record of the difficulties he encountered in carrying on his work and in equipping the Observatory. This historical account is followed by all of Flamsteed's correspondence which the editor could find. Of the 281 letters published, the correspondence with Newton consists of nineteen letters written between October 7, 1694 and September 14, 1695,[18] together with two before that date which have been previously referred to, and eighteen later ones which will be considered in their proper time. The second part comprises the corrected and enlarged British Catalogue of Stars,[19] followed by voluminous notes and comments of the editor.[20] The book concludes with a supplement, printed two years later, in which Baily reviews his earlier opinions, and justifies his action in publishing the book in spite of the virulent attacks which had been directed against him.

16 Baily, pp. xx–xxii.
17 *Ibid.*, p. xxxii.
18 *Ibid.*, pp. 133–160.
19 *Ibid.*, pp. 365–505.
20 *Ibid.*, pp. 506–672.

We can hardly understand the excitement and indignation with which the book was received, nor the contempt which was directed against its author for making public a matter which reflected on the character of Newton. We can ascribe these attacks only to the idolatry which had grown up about his character as well as about his intellectual genius, and the determination to suppress all facts which in any way ran counter to this ideal. In adopting this method of suppression, two important considerations were forgot; rumours had always been current that Newton had unfortunate temperamental weaknesses and, like all rumours, they exaggerated his failings and imputed them to malice. In the second place, simple justice required that other men, of high attainments and character, should be vindicated; there are few things more contemptible than to whiten the character of one man by blackening that of another. The truth was bound to come out at some time and it was fortunate that the ungrateful task was undertaken by such a man as Francis Baily. He was a man of sterling character, an astronomer of repute, and he was actuated by no mean nor scandalmongering motives. He presented all the documents he could find with verbal accuracy; he rendered a fine service to science by making accessible a most valuable astronomical work of his country's first Astronomer-royal; his prefatory comment was moderate and restrained, and expressed his deep regret that Newton and Halley appeared in an unamiable light. Even after his own motives were assailed, and he felt it necessary to justify himself, he refrained from bitterness.

It is expedient to consider Baily's defense and Brewster's attitude towards the book at some length; if for no other reason than that Brewster's *Life of Newton* is still the standard work from which most persons' knowledge and estimate of Newton are derived. As I have said before, I have been forced to the conviction that the book is a singularly unreliable work. The facts as given are correct but, as the author himself confesses, he felt it to be his duty as a biographer not to publish facts, which were not generally known and which he had discovered from documents privately owned, if they detracted from the personal character of his hero. A second serious defect is that it depicted Newton as an independent genius; it thus fails to give his predecessors and contemporaries due credit for their work; nor does it trace their influence on his ideas. The third fault is that a historical background to Newton is almost totally missing. Brewster seems, at least, to have been but very slightly acquainted with the life and thought of the seventeenth and eighteenth centuries. Now, the political, religious, and even literary ideas of the time had a profound effect on Newton's ideas and life. Brewster hardly considers them and, when he does, his apparent ignorance of the philosophy of life in its general sense, and his unfamiliarity with the mode of expression and even of the language of the period, make him incapable of giving an accurate or useful critique. But the gravest defect of the book lies in the fact that Brewster adopts the rôle of the advocate instead of the historian. He was too honourable to suppress the truth, or at least to give false evidence, but having convinced himself that Newton was perfect in character he so presents each event in his life that Newton's conduct appears to be quite justified. We get no lights and shadows, and, as a result, the reader is left to wonder what really was his character, what were his motives, why was his life so marred by quarrels, and even whether he was a human being at all. We owe to Brewster a great debt of gratitude for the immense amount of new material which he discovered, but he failed to give us a philosophical and critical life of Newton because he failed to penetrate his character. Like most historians of science, his narrow and specialised training unfitted him to treat his subject historically or critically. Students of science learn only the theories and experimental discipline fashionable in their day and are lamentably ignorant of the historical background of their subject.

Baily, in the supplement to his book[21] discusses the charges made against Flamsteed under two heads:

"1. That Flamsteed did not understand, and therefore could not justly appreciate, Newton's theory of gravitation, and more especially his new theory of the moon; consequently, he was not fully aware of the great assistance that could be afforded, by his observations, in the formation and verification of that theory."

"2. That Flamsteed showed an unwillingness, and even an objection, to furnish Newton with the requisite lunar observations to enable him to perfect that theory; a reluctance which consequently endangered the completion of that important work."

Baily treats the first of these charges at length. He proves that Newton's lunar theory was based on the work of Horrox, and that Flamsteed had known and studied the theory for thirty years. In fact the observations on the moon, which gave Newton the incentive to undertake the problem and enabled him to succeed, were collected

21 Baily, p. 677.

for the purpose of comparing the calculated with the observed positions of the moon. But, such a detailed discussion of this first charge should have been unnecessary. It is absurd, on the face of it, to suppose that one of the ablest living astronomers did not understand, and appreciate, the value of the lunar theory; or that he did not know accurate observations were essential to its development and verification. He may have been in doubt whether Newton could satisfactorily apply his law of gravitation to its solution, but he certainly showed a willingness, and even eagerness, to aid him to put it to the test.

As for the second charge, Baily points out that Flamsteed at once sent, on Newton's first request, 150 observations of the moon's positions and shortly added thirteen more. On examination of the second volume of Flamsteed's *Historia Cœlestis,* Baily found that they comprised all of the lunar observations made by him up to that time.[22] He then examined each letter of their correspondence and shows, as the reader may verify, that at each future request made by Newton for more observations, Flamsteed sent, as promptly as possible, all the additional observations which he had been able to make and compute in the interval. There was, at times, some delay which was shown to be due to unpropitious weather, illness, or necessary attention to his parochial duties. Newton, on the other hand, who seemed in a feverish haste at times to finish the work, did not hesitate to delay it on account of short journeys home, or for other business. Towards the close of the correspondence, although Newton had written to him an almost insulting rebuke,[23] Flamsteed returned good for evil by offering to transcribe and to send all his approximate observations with the sextant which he had made from 1679 to 1690. The friendly correspondence was then renewed, and Newton's last letter proves that it was he, and not Flamsteed, who stopped the work, since he wrote: "I am newly returned from a journey I lately took into Lincolnshire, and am going on another journey: so that I have not yet got any time to think of the theory of the moon; nor shall I have leisure for it this month or above: which I thought fit to give you notice of, that you may not wonder at my silence." On the back of this letter, Flamsteed noted his answer as follows: "My distemper abates; the pains of my head are not greater, but I am rarely free from them but when I am travelling. I am setting on that work that was interrupted by them in the spring. My exercise will

[22] Baily, p. 711.

[23] *Cf. infra.* the letter of June 29, 1695.

devour no small part of my time, and therefore I shall desire my friends to excuse me if I answer not their letters so fully nor readily as formerly; however, when you want more of my lunar observations I shall cause them to be transcribed, and it will be no trouble."

Flamsteed's only stipulations, before he gave to Newton his invaluable personal observations, were that he would not communicate the data to anyone, and would not impart the theoretical results obtained from them to anyone else, without his consent. The request that his work should be protected, lest anyone else should use it for his own benefit, was directed specifically against Halley whom he hated and feared. But, as a general stipulation, it was a perfectly proper one to make, and Newton promised categorically to respect it. Flamsteed records in his autobiography:[24] "Nevertheless he imparted what he derived from them, both to Dr. Gregory and Mr. Halley, *contra datam fidem*. The first of these conditions I was not much concerned whether he kept or not: but he has, I believe, kept it. The latter (which was the most material) he has forgot or broke." In confirmation of Newton's breach of promise, Baily[25] states that, when Gregory published his *Astronomiae Elementa* in 1702, he introduced as a Scholium, in page 332, what he designated as Newton's lunar theory and claimed it to be given in the very words of its author,—"*ipsis auctoris verbis expressam.*" Brewster, even, admits the grave charge, but excuses it in these extraordinary words: "His connexion with Flamsteed had ceased for many years, and therefore the brief notice of the lunar theory which he communicated to Gregory in June, 1702 [rather quick work as Gregory's book was published the same year,] could not be considered as a breach of the condition under which Flamsteed brought him."[26] Then he quotes an unpleasant incident quite foreign to the subject and given only by Rigaud, "that the reader may be sufficiently aware of the *rash charges* which Flamsteed never scrupled to make against those who displeased him," and so he raised a smoke-cloud to conceal his own admissions.

It is an extraordinary commentary on Brewster's historical method that, after railing against Baily for publishing the correspondence,

24 Baily, p. 62. 25 *Ibid.*, p. 688.

26 Brewster, Vol. II, p. 167, foot-note. It should be remembered that Newton and Flamsteed were both living in London after 1696, that they visited each other, and that letters passed between them in 1698 about the lunar theory and again in 1700, so that Brewster's "many years" was at most four and probably only two. Also Flamsteed, being near at hand, could with less effort be given the results than Gregory who was in Oxford.

after being unmercifully severe on Flamsteed's character, and after categorically stating that, "In consequence of the delay in getting Flamsteed's observations, he [Newton] was not able to proceed any farther with the lunar theory,"[27] he calmly concludes his discussion, a few pages later, by admitting that Baily had completely exonerated Flamsteed of the charges made against him: "We have no hesitation in saying, that the two charges against Flamsteed of ignorance of the importance of the theory of gravity, and of unwillingness to supply Newton with the observations he required for his lunar theory, have no sufficient foundation. With the exception of those occasional bursts of spleen against Halley, which must have been annoying to his friend, his letters to Newton, though sometimes of an irritating tendency, are yet respectful, and even affectionate, and exhibit not only a willingness, but an anxious desire to supply him with every observation he possessed and even to make and to reduce new observations expressly for his use."[28]

Not even Baily would claim more. The historian, who sets out to write the life of a man with the intention of not permitting himself to admit any faults, or weaknesses, in him, is driven into desperate straits and subjects himself to grave criticism. Brewster, because he was an honourable man, does admit the truth when he cannot avoid it, but he does so only after he has first made a vicious attack on those who force him to acknowledge the faults of his hero. While he admitted that Baily had cleared Flamsteed of a serious blot on his character and on his scientific reputation, he is outraged because the admission has reflected on Newton's character. He will therefore paint Flamsteed in as unpleasant colours as possible and ascribe to Francis Baily the most contemptible motives. As I have said before, Brewster is the authoritative source of Newton's life and his lack of responsibility should be demonstrated. He, in this instance, first created a false impression of facts by stating in his Preface, page xi, "It was reserved for two English astronomers [Flamsteed and Baily,] one a contemporary and the other a disciple, to misrepresent and calumniate their illustrious countryman." He knew this was false about Baily at least, who was his own friend and who was esteemed as a man of the highest honour; and he sinned the more deeply in that he waited to slander his friend until he was dead and could not defend himself.

And, although he admitted in the body of his work that Baily's

[27] Brewster, II, p. 167, note. [28] Brewster, II, p. 183.

exoneration of Flamsteed was complete, Brewster clouds the issue by first attacking the publication of the book in the preface where he states: "In 1835 the scientific world was startled by the publication of Baily's *Life of Flamsteed,* a huge volume, deeply affecting the character of Newton, and, strange to say, printed, and circulated throughout the world, at the expense of the Board of Admiralty. The friends of the great philosopher were thus summoned to a painful controversy, which, had it been raised in his lifetime, would have been summarily extinguished." We should be quite willing to overlook the slur implied by the reference to the size of the volume and the manner of its publication, if it had not been made to give the impression that the world, including himself, was startled because the author had secretly prepared his book and obtained authority, by improper methods, to publish it at the public expense for fear it would be suppressed if its contents had been known. Now the fact is, Baily took the precaution to read a paper to the Astronomical Society in which he outlined his defense of Flamsteed two years before his book was published. This paper was printed in the Society's *Monthly Notice* which Brewster would receive as a Fellow. The nature of Baily's forthcoming book was a common topic of conversation in scientific circles, and Brewster must have been familiar with it.

The propriety of the savage attack on Baily because his publication of Flamsteed's diary and correspondence provoked a controversy which "deeply affected the character of Newton" is a question of Brewster's good taste and judgement, whose answer must be left to the reader. When, however, he expressed his astonishment and disgust, in his *Memoirs of Newton,* because Baily had published a life of Flamsteed, and had included the differences between him and Newton, it is not a question of taste, but one of veracity. Some twenty years earlier he had written to Bailey: "If you have not already resolved upon it, I would venture to urge you to prefix a life of Flamsteed to your edition of the *British Catalogue,* and this would afford you an excellent opportunity of giving an account of the differences between him and Newton."[29] But, after all, Flamsteed's fits of irritability towards Newton, which were matched by an equal pettishness of Newton, and his outbursts of hatred and suspicion against Halley, which Newton bore with sufficient equanimity to make no protest, are of minor importance; the signifi-

[29] De Morgan, *Newton: his Friend: and his Niece,* London, 1885, p. 106.

cant thing is that Brewster finally agreed with Baily in absolutely clearing Flamsteed from the charge of preventing the completion of the lunar theory.

The fact is, too much has been made of the question of the *prompt* assistance of Flamsteed. The failure to complete the lunar theory must rest on Newton alone. He was singularly independent of the aid of others in all his work, and jealously concealed from everyone what he was meditating. He allowed the *Principia* to germinate for twenty years, and then completed it because of the persistent prodding of Halley; he could not be aroused to prepare for its second edition until twenty-six more years had elapsed, and the third edition came out just before his death. So notorious was his reluctance to complete any of his work in a form for publication that it has been seriously claimed we should have had no published results of his work except for the solicitations of others. Why then should we be surprised that his lunar theory was completed only to a point which satisfied its author and then was abandoned? Newton gave a sketch of the theory in the *Principia* as an illustration of the law of gravitation and he worked on it intensively and fairly persistently during the years 1694 and 1695. Then he went to London and absorbed himself so deeply in his new duties that he rebuked Flamsteed severely for suggesting any interruption of the King's business in order to continue his scientific work; there are, however, reasons for believing that he worked intermittently on the problem till 1698, or possibly till 1700. But he lived for twenty-seven years afterwards in the full possession of his faculties, and there is no evidence that he showed any active interest in scientific production. It is absurd to suppose Newton, during all that time the most honoured man in the scientific world, could not for the mere asking have obtained from astronomers, including Flamsteed, all the observations available. In addition to his constitutional procrastination, we should accept at face value his statement to Leibniz that he had definitely forsaken philosophical and mathematical work for other business; and a total break in his interests was made feasible by his appointment to the Mint. How far his illness contributed to this languor in creative work, we can not judge with assurance, but it does seem to have been a plausible cause. His letters to Flamsteed show an irritability of mind and periods of unwonted haste to finish the task, followed by intervals of despondency during which it was laid aside for trifling reasons. Nor did his mind operate with its customary machinelike precision and untiring regularity. It is the only work which wrung from him any expression of distress. When he was complimented on his success, he answered that it was the only subject which caused his head to ache; and when Halley frequently urged him to complete his lunar theory, he replied that he would think of it no more as it made his head ache, and kept him awake so often. That this was a real excuse and not indifference is more than probable from a remark he made later to Conduitt; if he lived till Halley made six years' observations, "he would have another stroke at the moon."[30]

After this long discussion, I shall give excerpts from the correspondence of Flamsteed and Newton with little comment.[31]

Flamsteed notes in his biography for the date, Saturday, September 1st, 1694. "Mr. Newton came to visit me. Esteeming him an obliged friend, I showed him about 150 places of the moon, derived from my observations and tables by myself, and servants hired at my own expense; with the differences or errors, in three synopses written on large sheets of paper, in order to correct the theory of her motions. On his earnest request I lent them to him, and allowed him to take copies of them (as I did not doubt but that by their help he would be able to correct the lunar theory)."[32]

A week later Flamsteed wrote to Newton, who had been unwell at the time of his visit to the Observatory, to send him a medical recipe and assured him of his cooperation: "What I gather from my observations shall be freely imparted to you, and I shall never refuse to impart either the observations themselves, or my deductions from them, to any persons that will receive them with the same candour that you do. If I desire to have them withheld from others who make it their business to prick faults in them, to censure them, and asperse me no less unjustly than ingratefully, you will not blame me for so doing. When Mr. H[alley] shows himself as candid as other men,

[30] Brewster, Vol. II, pp. 157, 158.

[31] Baily, pp. 133–160. This section gives all of their correspondence he could find. He states that he examined the *Portsmouth Collection* but did not find Flamsteed's letters to Newton. He was therefore limited to publishing the memoranda and comments which it was the custom of Flamsteed to write on the backs of letters he received to preserve a rough draught of his answers. Brewster, however, remarks (Vol. II, p. 161) that he found nearly forty of these letters which complete the correspondence, while Mr. Baily was able to publish only eleven of Flamsteed's letters. Brewster claims that he has thus been able to form a more correct judgement on those delicate questions to which this controversy gave rise. But the fact is the differences which Brewster instances between the letters and the memoranda are so slight as not to affect the main issue. I have read carefully the thirty-six letters of Flamsteed to Newton in the *Portsmouth Collection* and have included longer extracts from them as they give interesting information about both men.

[32] Baily, p. 61.

I shall be as free to him as I was the first seven years of our acquaintance, when I refused him nothing that he desired."

Newton to Flamsteed

Cambridge, October 7, 1694.

Sir,

Since my return hither, I have been comparing your observations with my theory, and now I have satisfied myself that, by both together, the moon's theory may be reduced to a good degree of exactness: perhaps to the exactness of 2 or 3 minutes. I forbore writing to you a few days, till I had considered your observations, that I might be able to acquaint what further observations are requisite. And besides those 50, which you tell me you have, ready calculated, and those I have already, your observations of this winter will be very material: and therefore I am very glad you have ordered your servant to calculate them. . . .

I thank you heartily for your receipt. At present I beg your observations of Jupiter and Saturn: and what you send by penny post direct for Mr. William Martin, a Cambridge carrier at the Bull in Bishopsgate-street; and order it to be delivered there before 2 of the clock on Monday, lest he be gone: for he goes every Monday, at 2 o'clock, from London to Cambridge. I am yours to serve you,

Is. NEWTON.[33]

Flamsteed to Newton

Observatory, October 11, 1694.

Sir,

I have yours of the 7th instant: before it arrived I had prepared a letter to you, which I sent not: because I was too late for the post. I shall give you the contents of it; and then answer that I received last night.

After you were gone hence, Mr. Halley applied himself to me, and desired I would allow him to see the lunar observations I had imparted to you. I told him that I should not be unwilling, provided that he in like manner would impart what he had talked so much of to the Society; his amendments of the lunar theory. We had some discourse of it: and he told me that there was an equation of about 9′ necessary in the quadrature: that this was begun and ended in the

[33] Baily, p. 133.

line of the syzygies; and occasioned the variation in the octants to be 7′ or 8′ greater or less than the tables made it. This I perceived was your equation; and told him so. He was silent.

Soon after, he came to Greenwich with one friend only in his company. I was surprised at it; and took the occasion of minding him of his disingenuous behaviour in several particulars; which he bore because he could not excuse it. . . .

Sir, I am yours to serve you,

JOHN FLAMSTEED.

P. S. I shall write to you again, as soon as I can get another synopsis transcribed. At present I am very busy about some other papers I am to send to a philosophical friend. J. F.

To Mr. Isaak Newton, at Trinity
College, in Cambridge.[34]

Newton to Flamsteed

Trin. Coll., October 24, 1694.

Sir,

I return my hearty thanks to you for the communications in your last; and particularly for your table of refractions near the horizon. The reason of the different refractions, near the horizon, in the same altitude, I take to be the different heat of the air in the lower region. For, when the air is rarefied by heat, it refracts less: when condensed by cold, it refracts more. And this difference must be most sensible when the rays run along in the lower region of the air for a great many miles together; because 'tis this region only which is rarefied and condensed by heat and cold: the middle and upper regions of the air being always cold. I am of opinion also that the refraction in all greater altitudes is varied a little by the different weight of the air discovered by the baroscope. For, when the air is heavier, and by consequence denser, it must refract something more than when 'tis lighter and rarer. I could wish therefore that in all your observations, where the refraction is to be allowed for, you would set down the weight of the baroscope, and heat of the air; that the variation of the refraction by the weight and heat of the air may be hereafter allowed for, when the proportion of the variation by those causes shall be known.

A day or two before I left London, I dined with Mr. Halley, and

[34] *Ports. Coll.*—Baily (p. 134) omits the postscript and gives one slight variation.

had much discourse with him about the moon. . . . He told me, some years ago, his correction of the moon's eccentricity, and repeated it when I was with him last in London: and this made me free in communicating my things with him. By your observations I find it to be a very good correction. I reckoned it a secret which he had intrusted with me; and therefore never spake of it till now. Upon my saying that I hoped to mend the moon's theory by some observations you had communicated to me, and that those observations made the parallactic equation in the quadratures between 8′ and 10′, he was desirous to view them. But, I told him he must not take it ill if I refused him that, because I stood engaged to communicate them to nobody without your consent. I am very glad that there is like to be a new correspondence between you; and hope it will end in friendship. . . .[35]

On October 25, Flamsteed wrote that he had had a conversation, the day before in London, with Halley who had said much about the moon's motion. On being told that what he disclosed about the moon "smelled of Newton's theory;" he answered, "in truth you helped him with that." Later in the letter, he mentioned: "Mr. Paget I hear is ill of a fever. I am heartily sorry for it. If he should die I know no person to succeed him but Mr. Caswell who wants his talent of drawing and writing neatly. In others is much his superior. But I hope he may recover though he has buried three of his pupils of this distemper."[36] And on the 29th, he sent the synopsis of the lunar observations and refractions which had been promised.

On November 1st, Newton wrote that he "desired only such observations as tend to perfecting the theory of the planets, in order to a second edition of my book [the *Principia*]: and would not give you the trouble of superfluous communications." He then softened this hint not to be burdened with too many suggestions by giving him the explanation of the menstrual parallax of the sun. Flamsteed, November 3d, answered that he understood Newton was as yet only comparing his observations with the emendations resulting from the new theory; but he hoped when the theory was complete the results would be sent to him as freely as he had supplied the data which confirmed it.

[35] Baily, p. 137.—This is the first reference to Newton's important correction of atmospheric refraction when measuring altitudes of stars.

[36] *Ports. Coll.*—It should be recalled that Caswell was defeated by Samuel Newton because of Newton's recommendation.

Newton to Flamsteed

Cambridge, Novem. 17, 1694.

Sir,

. . . .

I believe you have a wrong notion of my method in determining the moon's motions[37]: for I have not been about making such corrections as you seem to suppose, but about getting a general notion of all the equations on which her motions depend; and considering how afterwards I shall go to work, with least labor and most exactness, to determine them. For the vulgar way of approaching by degrees is bungling and tedious. The method which I propose to myself, is, first to get a general notion of the equations to be determined, and then by accurate observations to determine them. If I can compass the first part of my design, I do not doubt but to compass the second: and that made me write to you, that I hoped to determine her theory to the exactness of two or three minutes. But I am not yet master of the first work; nor can be, till I have seen something of the moon's motions when her apogee is in the summer signs: and to go about the second work, till I am master of the first, would be injudicious; there being a complication of small equations which can never be determined till one sees the way of distinguishing them, and attributing to each their proper phenomena. Sir, if you can have but a little patience with me till I have satisfied myself about these things,[38] and make the theory fit to be communicated without danger of error, I do intend that you shall be the first man to whom I will communicate it.[39]

And because I would give you as little trouble as may be, if you please to communicate to me the right ascensions and apparent meridional altitudes of the moon, as you have found them in your observations, without allowing for the refraction and parallax, I will take care of all the rest, and return your synopsis of her longitudes and latitudes, etc. But I desire her right ascensions by the correct places of the fixed stars: for otherwise, your observations will not reach to distinguish and determine those small equations which remain to be found out: and I would not have the work to do over a second time. This may give you a little trouble at present, but it will

[37] Flamsteed's note: "I had; and he of me: and still has."

[38] Flamsteed's note: "As much as he pleases: I have waited 5 years for them."

[39] This statement establishes the fact that he had agreed to Flamsteed's stipulation not to give the results to anyone else.

save you ten times the trouble which you must otherwise undergo hereafter; and that perhaps without bringing the moon's theory to half that perfection which I think I have a prospect of. If you please to do me this favour, then I desire that you would send the right ascensions and meridional altitudes of the moon, in your observations of the last six months. . . .

And for the trouble you are at in this business, besides the pains you will save of calculating (and that upon an erroneous hypothesis as I must do) the observations you communicate to me, and the satisfaction you will have to see the theory you have ushered into the world brought (as I hope) to competent perfection, and received by astronomers, I do intend to gratify you to your satisfaction: though at present I return you only thanks; as I do heartily for what you have already communicated.

I am, your affectionate and humble servant,

Is. Newton.

P. S. I sent your papers back by the carrier yesterday, and this letter should have been sent by the post before.[40]

In the above letter, Newton enclosed his promised table of the apparent displacement of a star due to the bending of the rays of light by refraction as they passed through the atmosphere. He had used the time, when the moon's theory was at a stand-still, to compute this correction for each degree of altitude from 0° to 90° for the summer, spring, autumn, and winter. It was a most valuable aid to astronomers and was a graceful return for Flamsteed's assistance to him. But Newton's tactless offer to pay Flamsteed for his coöperation deeply hurt his pride and did much to counterbalance any feeling of gratitude. One should not offer a fee to an Astronomer Royal for scientific coöperation, and Newton several times adopted the tone that he was engaging the help of an assistant rather than enjoying the benefit of a collaborator.

Flamsteed to Newton (Extract)

27 November, 1694—I have been very ill of a cold ever since I wrote to you last and have had great pains in my head, nor am I yet free of them, but I hope to get to London this week on the election day [of the Royal Society], not having been there this month before. I shall there acquaint Mr. Halley that I have a new table of refrac-

40 Baily. p. 139.

tions from you that answers my observations, but I hold it advisable not to let it go abroad as yet, for they seem bigger ascending towards the vertex than you make them, which causes me to think you make the height of the air less than it ought to be. . . . Mr. Halley, I am told, is for printing what he has to say concerning the moon and 'tis thought we shall have it in some *Transaction*.

Newton wrote to him on December 4th to express a hope that he was again well, and then urged him to apply himself to make all the observations he could, "A little diligence in making frequent observations this month and another month or two hereafter, will signify more towards setting right the moon's theory than the scattered observations of many years." Newton's offer to pay Flamsteed for his services and his somewhat pedantic request to be diligent "this month" were, I am sure, made quite innocently, but they touched two of the astronomer's most sensitive points, his poverty and his pride. In the following letter he complains of Newton's treatment and justifies himself. He evidently knew his failing of a quick temper since he kept a first draught on his desk for four days before he posted his letter. We know this because Baily printed the first draught, dated December 6, which he found in Flamsteed's papers; this draught differs considerably from the posted letter, dated December 10, which is preserved in the *Portsmouth Collection* and which I read. The whole tone of the letter is milder, and what Brewster terms "the four obnoxious paragraphs" in Baily's draught are omitted.[41]

Flamsteed to Newton

The Observatory, December 10, 1694.

Sir,

I am glad I did not impart your table of refractions to any body (since I find you have better considered and think of altering it) since you were not pleased to impart the foundations on which you calculated it to me. I have been seeking of them and at last found a way of answering them, admitting 2 spheres of vapors, one the usual height about 2½ miles, the other much less, with two hori-

[41] Brewster (Vol. II, p. 172) has a long and, what seems to me, an obtuse foot-note about this letter. He asserts that we can place no confidence in Baily's abstracts of the letters to Newton although he, himself, admits elsewhere these differences from the letters as sent are unessential. He says of this case they are entirely different, which is not true; and he intimates that Flamsteed deceitfully kept draughts which were milder in tone than the letters actually sent; whereas when there are variations the opposite is true. One wonders

zontal refractions; and with little labor have answered those under 5 degrees within half a minute, those above much nearer. . . .

I know very well the equations of the moon's motion are the highest this month and the next, than they can be again this 9 years: and had therefore determined to let slip no opportunity of observing her. My indisposition has not hindered me; but the fogs and clouds have kept her from my view since the first quadrature of the last month till now the clouds seem to break, and if it proves frost I promise myself fair weather, and frequent opportunities of determining her place in the meridian, which you need not doubt but will be imparted to you. But, I must entreat you to be patient and bear with me for a little time: for I must visit my cure at Christmas, and prepare before for my journey to it, which will employ me some days: so that I cannot give you the places of the moon you desire, till after the holidays. But then you shall have them, if God spare me life and health; and without any consideration or recompense but such communications as are usually made betwixt persons conversant in the same sort of studies.

But I am displeased with you not a little for offering to gratify me for my pains; either you know me not so well as I hoped, or you have suffered yourself to be possest with that character which the malice and envy of a person, from whom I have deserved much better things, has endeavoured to fix on me and which I have disputed because I know he used me no other ways than he has done the best men of the Ancients, nay our Saviour, his Apostles. Permit me to give a truer character of myself and which you shall always find me answer. I can boldly say I was never tempted with covetousness. God always blest me with more money than I know well how to dispose of, and those that know me, even those who calumniate me, know how free I have been of it on good occasions. . . .

All the return I can allow, or even expected from such persons with whom I corresponded, is only to have the results of their studies imparted as freely as I afford them the effect of mine or my pains[?]. I have told you my disposition plainly, and, if hereafter you offer me any other than this just reward, I shall think as meanly of you as I

whether Brewster had never written preliminary draughts and then softened some of their expressions.—In this letter Flamsteed also accuses Halley of deceitfulness in regard to a book by Viviani which he heard had been given to Newton. It offered Flamsteed a new cause of complaint. The incident is obscure and trifling, and merely shows that he sought every occasion to justify his hatred against Halley. As it has no bearing on Newton I have omitted it.—Brewster wrongly dates the letter, December 16.

fear you have been persuaded to think of me by false and malicious suggestions. . . . Your sincerely affectionate friend and
humble servant
JOHN FLAMSTEED.[42]

Just as Newton's tendency to sudden gusts of ill-temper and unfounded criticism of his friends was one of his worst faults, so one of his finest qualities was his sincere repentance. And, now, when he saw that he had deeply offended Flamsteed, he was quick to apologise. In his letter of December 20th, he assured him that he had not intended to conceal the method of calculating the table of refractions but had omitted it because of the haste in which the letter was written. Then he gave a full demonstration of the beautiful theorem from which he had calculated his table of refractions and which Biot regarded as one of the finest efforts of his genius. The note closes with this apology: "What you say about my having a mean opinion of you is a great mistake. I have defended you when there has been occasion, but never gave way to any insinuations against you. And what I wrote to you, proceeded only from hence, that you seemed to suspect me of an ungrateful reservedness, which made me begin to be uneasy. But if you please to let all this pass, and concur with me in promoting astronomy, I'll concur with you, being your faithful friend to serve you."

Newton's letters of January 15 and January 26, 1694/5, are devoted to requests for more observations on the moon, and a further discussion of atmospheric refraction. From now on his correspondence shows an increasing nervous irritability as if the pressure of the work were beginning to weigh on his mind and to make him impatient to finish it at the earliest possible moment. He would be done with it at all costs. He wrongly imagines that Flamsteed is dilatory and does not appreciate the value of the theory; and he adopts a magisterial tone, warning Flamsteed that his reputation will rest on his unquestioning assistance rather than on his own independent work. He also complains to others, certainly to Bentley and probably to Halley, that Flamsteed was preventing the successful completion of the lunar theory. It was these complaints which made Edleston stick

[42] The extracts from this letter, as I give them, are copied verbatim from the original in the *Portsmouth Collection*. If the reader will compare them with the preliminary draught published by Baily, p. 143, he will be convinced that my criticism of Brewster in my preceding foot-note is justified.

to his opinion that Flamsteed had withheld his observations after January, 1694/5, and so had robbed us of the lunar theory.[43]

There is certainly no justification for this opinion. On January 18, 1694/5, Flamsteed wrote that he was busily engaged on the work of preparing the necessary tables for shortening his work of calculation. Again, on January 29, he promises to send nine places of the moon observed and calculated from his tables in the summer of the year, 1692. There follows a long account of his work and of his desire to help. This letter ends with a postscript, which perhaps accounts for Newton's silence and his growing suspicion that Flamsteed was not aiding him; "I am sorry for the indisposity and pray God send you your health again, etc." On February 7, Flamsteed wrote again to express a bitter disapproval of Halley whom he accuses of having boasted of certain of his lunar observations which were really Flamsteed's. He works himself up into a great fury and promises that Newton "shall hear no more of him [Halley] from me till we meet when I shall tell you his history which is too foul and large for a letter." There seems to be little doubt that Newton had again suffered from a serious break-down or, at least, such a rumour was current, for Flamsteed finishing by writing: "The day after I received your last, Mr. Hanway brought me news from London that you were dead, but I showed him the letter which proved the contrary. He had it from Sir C. Wren to whom he wrote immediately to satisfy him of the falsehood of that report. I bless God for the [sic] life and pray for your perfect health."[44]

Newton to Flamsteed

Sir, Cambridge, Feb. 16, 1694/5.

. . . .

As for your observations, you know I cannot communicate them to any body, and much less publish them, without your consent. But if I should perfect the moon's theory, and you should think fit to give me leave to publish your observations with it, you may rest assured that I should make a faithful and honorable acknowledgement of their author.[45] . . .

On March 15th, Newton wrote to Flamsteed in regard to the ap-

[43] Edleston, note No. 118, pp. lxiv and lxvii.
[44] From the original letters in the *Portsmouth Collection*.
[45] Baily, p. 151.

pointment of the successor to Paget as mathematical master of Christ's Hospital and gave his reasons for having proposed three persons for the place. His next letter, of date April 23rd, contains the following passage which is significant of his alternate periods of haste and delay, and his weariness of the task: "When I set myself wholly to calculations (as I did for a time last autumn and again since Christmas in making the table of refractions) I can endure them and go through them well enough. But when I am about other things (as at present) I can neither fix to them with patience nor do them without errors; which makes me let the moon's theory alone at present, with a design to set to it again and go through it at once. When I have your materials I reckon it will prove a work of about three or four months: and when I have done it once I would have done with it for ever."[46]

On the 25th of April, Newton wrote a short letter which can be omitted. He then waited for two months before writing again; apparently, he became impatient because additional observations were not forthcoming and, on June 29, he brusquely urged Flamsteed to send observations as he found them and not to bother about calculating the positions of the moon as he could attend to that work more expeditiously himself.

Newton to Flamsteed

Cambridge, June 29, 1695.

Sir,

I received your solar tables, and thank you for them. But these, and almost all your communications will be useless to me, unless you can propose some practicable way or other of supplying me with observations. For as your health and other business will not permit you to calculate the moon's places from your observations, so it never was my inclination to put you upon such a task, knowing that the tediousness of such a design will make me as weary with expectation as you with drudgery. I want not your calculations, but your observations only. For, besides myself and my servant, Sr. Collins (whom I can employ for a little money, which I value not) tells me that he can calculate an eclipse, and work truly. I will therefore once more propose it to you, to send me your naked observations of the moon's right ascensions and meridional altitudes; and leave it to me to get her places calculated from them. If you like this proposal, then pray

[46] Baily, p. 153.

send me first your observations for the year 1692, and I will get them calculated, and send you a copy of the calculated places. But if you like it not, then I desire you would propose some other practicable method of supplying me with observations; or else let me know plainly that I must be content to lose all the time and pains I have hitherto taken about the moon's theory, and about the table of refractions.

I am glad you betake yourself to riding for your health, rather than to physic. It is certainly the best and safest remedy for an ill habit of body, arising from bad blood in most cases; and therefore you may do well to continue it.

I am your humble servant,

Is. NEWTON.[47]

Newton's blunt statement, that all he wanted from Flamsteed was the service of an observer and not the assistance of a colleague in deriving the lunar theory, may have suited his own convenience but it was not a courteous return for the essential help of a distinguished astronomer. Flamsteed justified himself by making a memorandum on the back of the letter to which was added a detailed list of all the observations he had furnished: "Let the world judge whether Mr. Newton had any cause to complain of want of observations, when all these were imparted to him. I was ill of the headache all the summer, which ended in a fit of the stone: yet I forbore not, as I was able, to serve him without reward or the prospect of any. I contend it."[48] His list of observations adds up to the impressive number of 201 observed and calculated positions of the moon and 243 rougher ones which had not been calculated.

But, Newton had fallen into what can only be described as an uncontrollable fit of nervous irritation and, out of a clear sky, wrote the following letter which was almost as incoherent and insulting as those he formerly sent to Pepys and Locke.

Newton to Flamsteed

Sir, Cambridge, July 9, 1695.

After I had helped you where you had stuck in your three great works, that of the *theory of Jupiter's satellites,* that of your *catalogue*

[47] Baily, p. 157. [48] Baily, p. 142.

of the fixed stars, and that of calculating *the moon's places from observations,* and in all these things freely communicated to you what was perfect in its kinds (so far as I could make it), and *of more value than many observations,* and what (in one of them) cost me above two months' hard labor, which I should never have undertaken but upon your account, and which I told you I undertook that I might have something to return you for the observations you then gave me hopes of, and yet, when I had done, saw no *prospect of obtaining them,* or of getting your *synopses rectified.* I despaired of compassing the moon's theory, and had thoughts of giving it over as a thing impracticable, and occasionally told a friend so who then made me a visit. But now you offer me those observations which you made before the year 1690, I thankfully accept of your offer, and will get as many of them computed as are sufficient for my purpose. . . .

I am your most humble servant,
Is. NEWTON."[49]

Flamsteed noted on the back of the letter, "I was ill all this summer, and could not furnish him as I had done formerly. He mistook my illness for design, and wrote this hasty, artificial, unkind, arrogant letter. Answered it July 13th."[50] In this answer Flamsteed ignored the attack on him but warns Newton that "a report is industriously spread in town that I have refused to impart any more observations to you. I heard that he [Halley] who spreads it intends you a visit ere long. I hope you will take notice of his disingenuity in this particular, since 'tis only my violent distemper and your own silence that were the cause of mine. I shall answer yours more fully next week." And then, on July 18th, he delivered a rebuke so dignified and so charitable that it should have made Newton blush: "I have just cause to complain of the style and expression of your last letter. They are not friendly, but that you may know me not to be of that quarrelsome humour I am represented by the Clerk of the Society, [Halley,] I shall waive all save this expression, *that what you*

[49] Baily, p. 157.—The only cause, which I can find for this sudden outburst is a passage in Flamsteed's letter of a week previous (*Cf. Portsmouth Collection*) in which he confesses: "I had unwarily given Mr. Caswell of it [Newton's Table of Refractions] when first sent me but, on the information of your desire not to have it pass abroad, I acquainted him with it. 'Tis as safe as in your own desk. Of the second [Table] no one has yet any copy from me, nor shall have it without your leave." In view of Newton's idiosyncrasy for secrecy about his work, this seems to me a sufficient cause of his anger.

[50] *Ibid.*, p. 158.

communicated to me was of more value than many observations. I grant it—as the wire is of more worth than the gold from which it was drawn. I gathered the gold matter, and fined and presented it to you sometimes washed. I hope you value not my pains the less because they became yours so easily. I allow you to value your own as high as you please, and require no other reward for what assistance I sometimes afford you, but that I may now and then see some of the workmanship; and if that be not ready when I desire it, or if you think it not fit to favour me with it, I can easily be contented. Nor do I take it amiss that you often take no notice of some small particulars whereon I have desired to know what you have determined. Since I know very well that in things of their nature it is difficult to determine, and we often change what at first we thought would need no alteration or towards none. I have altered my solar numbers five times, and would not be ashamed to change again if I saw reason for it. If you answer me that you have not determined whether any other than the usual equations are to be used in the syzygies, if you are not resolved how the moon's mean motion is to be corrected, you may say it. I shall urge you no farther, and nevertheless whenever you let me know that it lies in my power to serve you, I shall do it freely. But you will not complain of me to others without cause, and thereby add to the affliction I suffer from my obstinate distempers, and the calumnies of disingenuous and impudent people, if you have any value for your friend and humble servant."[51]

July 18, 1695. [JOHN FLAMSTEED.]

Newton's answer, while it tacitly admits his rudeness, does not seem adequate to have made peace between them as it evidently did; Flamsteed's ready acceptance of what was only an implied apology puts his character in a very favourable light.

Newton to Flamsteed

Sir, Cambridge, July 20, 1695.

The report you mention[52] was much against my mind, and I have written to put a stop to it. I thank you for your communications of

[51] *Portsmouth Collection.*—This rebuke evidently cut Newton deeply. Many years afterwards he referred to it in this ungracious manner. "Machin told me that Flamsteed said 'Sir Isaac worked with the ore he dug,' to which Sir Isaac replied, 'if he dug the ore, I made the gold ring.'"—Conduitt's MSS.

[52] Flamsteed's withholding observations. Newton's denial of the report should be emphasized.

the table of fixed stars and your lunar observations. So soon as I have got some business off my hands, I intend to get such of them calculated as I have need of, and send you the places. The moon's mean motion is not much amiss, and may be retained as you printed it till I can determine it more exactly. I believe there is an equation requisite in your syzygies, but I am not yet master of it. Such niceties I have not yet determined, and you must have patience with me till I can compass them, otherwise I must desist; as your impatience had once made me resolve to do. The Horroxian Theory, by the table of eccentricities and equations of the apogee which I sent you, never errs above 10 or 12 minutes; and so is twice as exact as your printed tables, which err sometimes 20 or 21 minutes: but I would not advise you to spend your time in calculating by it till I have compassed the small equations, which I cannot do till I have observations for a sufficient number of cases. Such expostulations or expressions, in your last and some other letters as tend to a difference, I pass by. Pray take care of your health. Dr. Battely (chaplain to Archbishop Sancroft) was much troubled with violent headaches, and found it a certain cure to bind his head straight with a garter till the crown of his head was numbed: for thereby his head was cooled by retarding the circulation of the blood. 'Tis an easy remedy, if your pain be of the same kind.

I am your humble servant,

Is. NEWTON.[53]

Flamsteed to Newton

23 July, 1695.

Yours of the 20th instant I have received this morning. It sets all right betwixt us. I have as great a stock of patience, and as good an one as I have of observations, and 'tis all ways drawn out on every occasion to serve my friends. My indisposition hindered me from serving you as I desired. You mistook the reason of my silence. I hope you will have the patience on my account that you demand of me on yours. . . . The next week I am going to my parsonage, but I shall take care to have you furnished with another sheet of observations before. If you would rather have any other than the remains of 1677, let me know it. I shall fit you according to your desires. . . . By frequent trials and alterations of his contrivances, Kepler found out the true theory of the planetary motions. You must not be ashamed to own that you follow his example. When the inequali-

[53] Baily, p. 159.

ties are found, you will more easily find the reason of them than he could do when but little of the doctrine of gravity was known.

[JOHN FLAMSTEED.][54]

In answer to this letter, Newton patches up the incipient quarrel, but he rather tactlessly starts it again by offering to pay Flamsteed's assistant a fee.

Newton to Flamsteed

Cambridge, July 27, 1695.

Sir,

The other day I had an excuse sent me for what was said at London about your not communicating [observations], and that the report should proceed no further. I am glad all misunderstandings are composed. I thank you for your nonagesimal table: I designed to make such a table, and it saves me the labor. You may continue your observations if you please till Octob. 10th, 1677. But I had rather you would send me those from Aug. 24th, 1685, to July 5th, 1686, when the aphelium was in the same position as in the year 1677. For when I see all your observations together in this position of the aphelium, I can tell better what to select for this case. The transcribing of these things gives your servant trouble: and for encouraging him I shall order Will Martin, the Cambridge carrier, (who lodges every week, from 9 in the morning on Saturday till 3 in the afternoon on Monday, at the Bull in Bishopsgate-street,) to pay him; [two guineas if you please to let him call for it, or to pay it to his or your order in London, if you please to let me know where.[55]] I shall not have time to go through all your observations, but will send you the times, for which I would have them, when I have done with these for this position of the aphelium.

I am your thankful, humble servant,

IS. NEWTON.[56]

I shall add two short extracts from Flamsteed's replies to Newton's letter:

(August 4, 1695) "I take it very kindly that you acquainted me with your intent to gratify him for his pains before you did it, but I

[54] *Portsmouth Collection.*

[55] This passage was crossed out in the manuscript and the word "guineas" altered into "shillings," apparently by Flamsteed for no known reason.

[56] Baily, p. 159.

must entreat you to forbear. He is paid all ready. A superfluity of moneys, I find, is all ways injurious to my servants. It makes them run into company, and waste their time idly, or worse. I take care he wants nothing. If you send him verbal acknowledgement of his pains, and commendations for his care and fidelity in copying, it will be a reward for him, and encouragement the best you can give him, and further I cannot allow. . . . Pray say nothing to anybody of your proposal."

(August 6, 1695) "I write this purposely to you, because I know a spark [Halley] is with you, that complains much I have lived here twenty years and printed nothing. I do not intend to print a St. Helena catalogue, and for that reason I defer the printing of anything thus long, that when I do print it may be perfect, as by the grace of God it shall. . . . Yesterday and this day, I bless God for it, I have only had some small grudgeings of my headache so that I hope now in a little time to be clear and able to follow my studies as formerly . . . which have been interrupted by the most uncomfortable kind of distemper that I have ever had; for, during the stone and in a consumption, I had the satisfaction of enjoying the pleasures of my thoughts, but this would not permit me that."[57]

Newton finally broke a silence of two months by writing the following letter which closes this correspondence on the lunar theory.

Newton to Flamsteed

Cambridge, Sept. 14, 1695.

Sir,

When I received your last, Mr. Halley was with me about a design of determining the orbs of some comets for me. He has since determined the orb of the comet of 1683 by my theory;[58] and finds, by an exact calculus, that it answers all your observations and his own to a minute. I am newly returned from a journey I lately took into Lincolnshire, and am going another journey: so that I have not yet got any time to think of the theory of the moon, nor shall have leisure for it this month or above: which I thought fit to give you

57 *Portsmouth Collection.*

58 This is evidently the first record of Halley's determination of the orbit of what is now known as Halley's Comet and it is also the first great astronomical discovery derived directly from Newton's gravitational dynamics.

notice of, that you may not wonder at my silence. I hope you get ground of your distemper, and that I shall ere long hear that you are well recovered.

I am your humble servant,
Is. NEWTON.[59]

This letter was written on the day Newton started on a second journey of a fortnight. It is a question whether he now abandoned his work on the lunar theory because he had solved the problem in its general form to his own satisfaction and, as in other cases, had lost his desire to complete it in detail; or whether his two journeys were taken in connection with his coming appointment to the Mint. Whichever may have been the cause, he abruptly broke off his correspondence with Flamsteed just as he previously had refused to write to Leibniz in regard to fluxions. The charge that Newton was handicapped in his work by the dilatoriness and lack of coöperation of Flamsteed, has been proved to be without foundation. If any further proof were needed that its abandonment was due to Newton alone, it can be found in the fact that Flamsteed was eager to continue. Puzzled by the silence of Newton, after waiting four months for an answer to his last letter, he again wrote to enquire why the work had stopped but could extract no reply. He offered to provide further observations, and then went on to say: "But if what I hear be true, you will have little need of them, for I have been told, ever since I came out of Surrey, that you have finished the theory of the moon *on incontestable principles;* that you have determined six general inequalities not formerly known; and that nevertheless the calculations will not be much more troublesome or difficult than formerly. I am heartily glad to hear this, and should be more so to have it from yourself, for in truth I suspect you are scarce so forward; and I flatter myself with the opinion, that if you were, you would have acquainted me with it, as you promised both when I imparted the three synopses of lunar calculations, and observed places to you, and in your letters since. Pray let me know how far you are proceeded, you will oblige me, and, if you please, the true reason *why I have had no letters from you this four months.*"[60]

The chief source of trouble between the two men was undoubtedly Halley. On the one side, Newton had a feeling of gratitude towards

[59] Baily, p. 159.
[60] Quoted from a letter dated January 11, 1695/6. Brewster, Vol. II, p. 182.

him and was influenced by his advice. On the other side, Flamsteed hated him; no other feeling can account for the bitterness of his language. In judging his intemperate accusations we must discount the language in which they were clothed, as it was a time when trifling disapproval was expressed with bitter invective. If one accepted at face value the statements of the leading writers of the day, one would conclude that England contained only unmitigated scoundrels. We do know that he shocked both of them by what they believed to be his atheism and immoral ideas: to Flamsteed, they were utterly abhorrent; by Newton, they were judged with tolerant disapproval. Today, he would probably be accused of neither. When he learned that Newton was actually engaged on the lunar theory, he expected Flamsteed to subordinate his own work, and to supply data without delay. He exaggerated Newton's casual and irritable complaints and spread reports, that Flamsteed was wilfully withholding necessary and precious observations, when it would have been easy for him to learn the facts. Also knowing Newton's procrastinating habits, he disapproved of the agreement not to publish the results till Flamsteed permitted the inclusion of his observations. In order to get the lunar theory before the public he, with David Gregory, persuaded Newton to break his promise and to permit Gregory to use the results in his Astronomy. Whatever Halley's motives may have been, he must bear a large part of the blame for an unpleasant episode in the lives of two very eminent men.

While Newton was trying to distract his mind from dwelling on his disappointment in not securing an appointment to a public office, great changes had occurred in the political situation; the Whigs had returned to power in a new Parliament, and Somers and Montague had begun those careers which were to dominate the Government for so many critical years. Montague had not forgotten his friend, and with rare good judgement he had determined to enlist the services of the scientific philosopher in his new and drastic financial policy. In the autumn the rumour was current that Newton had been appointed Master of the Mint.[61] It seems probable that the expectation of the coming change in his life was the true reason for his sudden lack of interest in the moon; but, made cautious by

[61] Wallis wrote to Halley, Nov. 26, 1695: "We are told here [Oxford] that he is made Master of the Mint, which if so, I do congratulate to him." Edleston, note 126, p. lxviii and p. 302.

past disappointments, he took pains to contradict the report. Even as late as the following spring, when the matter was undoubtedly settled, he wrote to Halley to deny the rumour.

Newton to Halley

Cambridge, March 14, 1695/6.

Sir,

I understand that a report has been some time spreading among the Fellows of the Royal Society, as if I was about the longitude at sea. For putting a stop to that report, pray do me the favour to acquaint them, (as you have occasion,) that I am not about it. And if the rumour of preferment for me in the Mint should hereafter, upon the death of Mr. Hoar, or any other occasion, be revived, I pray that you would endeavour to obviate it by acquainting your friends that I neither put in for any place in the Mint nor would meddle with Mr. Hoar's place, were it offered me. You will thereby oblige

your most humble and most obedient servant,

Is. Newton.[62]

Five days after this letter was written, Newton received the official notice of his appointment to the Mint.

Montague to Newton

19th March, 1695/6.

Sir,

I am very glad that at last I can give you a good proof of my friendship, and the esteem the king has of your merits. Mr. Overton, the Warden of the Mint, is made one of the Commissioners of the Customs, and the king has promised me to make Mr. Newton, Warden of the Mint. The office is the most proper for you. 'Tis the chief officer in the Mint. 'Tis worth five or six hundred pounds per annum, and has not too much business to require more attendance than you may spare. I desire you will come up as soon as you can, and I will take care of your warrant in the meantime. Pray give my humble services to John Lawton. I am sorry I have not been able to assist him hitherto, but I hope he will be provided for ere long, and tell him that the session is near ending, and I expect to have his company when I am able to enjoy it. Let me see you as soon as you

[62] Macclesfield *Corr.*, Vol. II, p. 419.

come to town, that I may carry you to kiss the king's hand. I believe you may have a lodging near me. I am, Sir, your most obedient servant,

CHAS. MONTAGUE.[63]

There have been few cases of such an abrupt change in the life and work of an eminent scientist as now fell to Newton's lot. He had, after a series of humiliating supplications, obtained his wish; a record which makes an anecdote due to Conduitt seem ludicrous. He stated that Montague, when asked why he "gave Newton employment *before he wanted it or asked it,*" replied, "that he would not suffer the lamp which gave so much light to want oil." Although Newton never expressed the least regret that his creative work stopped so abruptly in the flower of his age, and however useful his new life may have been, the world can never cease to regret that either temperament or a permanent lassitude from ill-health robbed it of the services of one of the greatest geniuses of all time. Before we narrate the second half of Newton's life, we must pause for a moment to consider the political and financial condition of England.

[63] Brewster, Vol. II, p. 191.

CHAPTER XII

REVISION OF THE COINAGE. LIFE IN LONDON

1696–1703

Before the new life of Newton in London can be narrated, we must consider the political and social condition of England and, especially, the lives of two men, John Somers and Charles Montague, with whom his career and fortunes were intimately bound. The theory of the divine right of kings, which had been so obstinately held by the Stuarts, had been shattered by the Commonweath, patched up at the Restoration, and finally destroyed by the election of William and Mary to the throne. Although Mary, at least, was a Stuart, they could claim no birth-right to the throne so long as James and his son were alive. The leaders of the Whig party, who staged the Revolution, were committed to a constitutional monarchy and placed William on the throne in agreement with that principle of government. For example, Somers wrote a tract on the right of James II to the throne in which he contended for the absolute authority of parliament to limit, restrain, or qualify the right to the succession. Again, six years before the Revolution, he defended the principle of a limited monarchy in no uncertain terms: "If they mean by those *lovers of commonwealth principles* men passionately devoted to the public good, and to the common service of their country,—who believe that Kings were instituted for the good of the people, and the government ordained for the sake of those that are to be governed, and therefor complain or grieve when it is used to contrary ends, every humane and honest man will be proud to be ranked in that number."[1] How sympathetic Newton was with these views of Somers was strikingly shown by his letter on allegiance to King William which he wrote to Vice-Chancellor Covel.[2] His statement there that "Fidelity and allegiance sworn to the King is only such a fidelity and obedience as is due to him by the law of the land," is typical of the new principles of government

[1] Campbell, *Lives of the Chancellors*, Vol. IV, p. 76.

[2] *Cf.* Chapter X, p. 348.

which were guiding Somers and the Whig party in their transformation of England into a limited monarchy. For the first time, we note the existence of party government; the people had split upon a great question. On the one side, were the Tories who were loyal to James; in its ranks were the conservatives, the Roman Catholics, and the strong Churchmen. Opposed to them were the Whigs who had engineered the Monmouth Rebellion, had now seated William safely on the throne, and were determined to govern through the agency of the House of Commons. The rise of power of the Commons was facilitated by the personal qualities of the new King. He was an alien who never really mastered the English language and, in spite of his undoubted ability as an administrator and soldier, his cold and restrained temperament made no personal appeal to loyalty or affection. His heart was in the Netherlands, and his intimate friends, with whom he could relax from his austerity, were his Dutch associates who had followed his fortunes, and whom he now loaded with favours. His one absorbing desire was to humble the ambition of Louis XIV, and he looked upon England as the reservoir from which to draw the power to form and maintain a European coalition against a common enemy. Under his guidance, England threw off her subserviency to France, and became the dominant influence in continental affairs. The frequent absences of the King required him to delegate his power to the leaders of the Whig party who were quick to take advantage of their opportunity.

It is easy to see that William was absolutely dependent on the loyal support of the Whigs; without it, the repeated attempts to bring back the Stuarts might have succeeded, and the dream of his life would have been thwarted. The Whigs came to power hungry for position after a long abstinence. Elated by their triumph, they quickly caused a revulsion of sentiment by their rash obstinacy and vindictive measures. To prevent the wrecking of his plans, the King was forced to dissolve Parliament frequently, and to dilute his Cabinet and Privy Council with a mixture of Tories. Although party government rapidly established itself in the reigns of William and of Anne, the policy of a Cabinet composed of members only of the dominant party had not been developed; thus government, more or less divided in its ideas and sympathies, was distracted and a prey to the personal ambitions of its members. Such a period of confusion offered a rare opportunity to young men of strong will and keen intellect who rose to great positions with startling rapidity, and fell as quickly. The Whigs were consolidated and kept absolutely under control, while in power during the reign of William, by a small clique which under the famous name of the Junto was directed by Somers, Montague, Wharton, and Russell. Although the Junto fell into disgrace during the reign of Anne, it still retained its control of the party without interruption, in office or out of it, till the Hanoverian succession.

The ideas of the nation in the three great fields of law, finance, and religion, underwent profound changes. The responsibility of leadership in all three fell to the Whigs, and in two of them the influence of Newton was direct and powerful. In government, the nation had changed from an absolute, to a constitutional, monarchy and the legal questions involved were decided during the chancellorship of Somers. The financial system of England had staggered through the disturbances of the Civil War and had grown worse during the inefficiency and corruption of the Stuarts. There was no banking organisation to stabilise business such as had been developed in Florence and Holland, and the current money had deteriorated to a state of desperate confusion. Meanwhile, cost of government had increased enormously; the country was at war, and the prospect that it would be protracted pointed to a steadily growing budget. The reform of the finances which carried England through this crisis and made it the richest country in Europe is a monument to the genius of Montague. The most difficult and hazardous part of this task was the recoinage of the money and according to Montague, himself, its success was largely due to the administrative work of Newton. Lastly, the long and bitter struggle between Roman Catholicism and the extreme forms of Protestantism had ended in the precarious supremacy of the Church of England. It is frequently asserted that the Anglican Church is a mere compromise between the absolute authority of Romanism and the logical anarchy of Sectarianism; but such an opinion does little justice to the English theologians of the sixteenth and seventeenth centuries who developed a positive doctrine which aimed to reconcile a revealed religion with the new scientific discoveries. In a later chapter, I shall show the influence of Newton in this field, and trace the effect of the *Principia* on modern religious thought.

Newton's life and opinions were so bound up with the fortunes of the Whigs that, although the direct influence of Somers consisted only in a recommendation for his appointment to the Mint, a brief survey of his life is advisable. John Somers,[3] the son of a prosperous country attorney, after a brilliant career in Parliament was appointed Lord Chancellor; and during the seven years he presided over the Court of Chancery only one of his decrees has been discovered to have been reversed. He possessed the rare combination of a great mind, a modest and noble character, and the "most exquisite taste of politeness." There have been few, if any, men in public life who have commanded such universal respect, admiration, and affection. Lord Campbell says of him that he was a "a ripe and good scholar as well as lawyer; and, regard being had to his acquaintance with modern languages and literature, perhaps the most accomplished man that ever rose to high eminence in the profession of the law of England." He was a favourite of the King and Parliament; the High Church party coveted him; the merchants respected his knowledge of trade and finance; the lawyers were proud of him; and as a discriminating patron "all works of any merit in verse or prose were inscribed to him." In spite of his popularity and accomplishments, he could not weather the storm which overwhelmed his party. During the Parliament of 1698, feeling in the country ran high against the Whigs. The Commons threw off the guidance of Somers and Montague; in this the members were influenced by the Tory supporters of Anne, who saw in the ill-health of William the prospect of future power. They used certain unpopular clauses of the Treaty of Ryswick with such effect that the exasperated King threatened to abdicate; dissuaded from this rash move, he yielded to popular clamour and deprived Somers of the Great Seal. Flushed with this success, the Tories impeached him in 1701 but he was acquitted in the most honourable terms. He, by his charm of manner, even partially overcame Anne's prejudice, and would have been restored to his high offices, at the accession of George I, if his health had permitted. In 1698, he succeeded Montague as President of the Royal Society and gracefully resigned five years later in order that Newton might be elected to that high office.

Valuable to Newton as the support of Somers may have been, he owed far more to the steadfast friendship and influence of Montague, who introduced him to society and the Court, and who brought his friends to the house of the philosopher, enlivened by the attractions of his young and charming niece, Catherine Barton. We have al-

[3] Campbell's *Lives of the Chancellors;* Macaulay's *History of England;* Weld's *History of the Royal Society.*

ready described the early life of Montague and shall now continue it from the time he had won the town by his parody of *The Country Mouse and the Town Mouse*. Lord Dorset presented his young protégé to the King shortly after his coronation with the whimsical introduction: "'May it please your Majesty, I have brought a Mouse to have the honour of kissing your hand'; at which the King smiled, and being told the reason of his being so called, replied with an air of gayety, 'You will do well to put me in a way of making a Man of him,' and ordered him an immediate pension of £500 per annum, out of the privy purse, till an opportunity should offer."[4] Such was the pleasant and easy beginning of the young man's brilliant career. While opportunity, through patronage, was often a most delightful method, it was somewhat erratic in its choice, and the other Mouse, Matthew Prior, saw with chagrin his companion's luck, and his own neglect. Some time later he called Lord Dorset's attention to his own needs in a metrical epistle to which he added as a postscript:

> My friend Charles Montague's preferred;
> Nor would I have it long observed,
> That one Mouse eats, while t'other's starved.

But his reward did not come till later and then from Montague, who, after many years of neglect, gave him the temporary position of secretary to the Commission to negotiate the Treaty of Ryswick.[5]

In the Convention Parliament, Montague had not taken a prominent part in the debates. Now, certain of royal favour and having acquired an income with some social standing from his marriage, he directed his energies to a political career. His opportunity came in 1691 when he was appointed Chairman of a Committee to prepare a Bill for regulating trials in cases of high treason. He gained such applause in the management of the Bill, and showed such eloquence in debate that, with the support of Dorset, he was immediately made a Commissioner of the Treasury and Privy Councillor. For nearly seven years, he was the undisputed master of Parliament; by his

[4] *Works and Life of Halifax*, Anonymous, p. 17.

[5] The share of Montague in the composition of the parody is contemptuously referred to in Spence's *Anecdotes*, p. 102, by Lord Peterborough: "'Did not he write the Country Mouse with Mr. Pryor?' 'Yes, just as if I was in a chaise with Mr. Cheselden here, drawn by his fine horse, and should say,—Lord how finely we draw this chaise!'"—Montague's neglect of Prior and his lion's share of the rewards of their work were also held up against him. Mrs. de la Rivière Manley, one of the society gossips and scandal-mongers of the day, thus accuses Montague: "Pryor whose easy natural Muse and early friendship, has made both of 'em immortal! Where is gratitude? Where is honour, in neglecting the first step upon which he mounted from obscurity, etc.?"

eloquence and by his power in the Junto, he controlled a majority of votes; his genius revolutionised the finances of the country and was rewarded by his appointment, in 1694, as Chancellor of the Exchequer. Macaulay says of him that every one of those years had been made memorable by great parliamentary victories, and by great public services. His career had been more splendidly and uninterruptedly successful than that of any member of the House of Commons, since the House of Commons had begun to exist. But when the Parliament of 1698 met, his good fortune forsook him; he had long been hated by the Tories for his rapid rise to fame, and his extraordinary good luck had excited the envy and secret hostility of many of the Whigs. While his enemies could not attack him on the side of his ability, they found his personal traits an easy mark. The faults of his character were glaring and such as to make him unpopular; his intoxicating rise to success and fame had made him proud and haughty even to insolence; he shunned his old companions who had consorted with him in his days of obscurity. It was said that admiration of himself, and contempt of others, were indicated by all his gestures and written in all the lines of his face. The very way the little jackanapes, as the hostile pamphleteers loved to call him, strutted through the lobby, making the most of his small figure, rising on his toes, and perking up his chin, filled his enemies with rage. He was described as living in riotous extravagance and debauchery in his great estate on the Thames, where, surrounded by a crowd of toadies, he eagerly listened to the gross flattery they poured into his ears. Boundless rapacity and corruption were charged against him to account for his great fortune. In spite of his genuine love of literature, and of his munificent patronage of literary merit, he was greedy and undiscriminating in his taste which Pope said was fed on dedications. And Grub Street could devise no fable so absurd about Montague that it was not certain to find credence in more than half the manor houses and vicarages of England. As a reward for his services, he was more savagely reviled and lampooned in prose and verse than almost any other politician in English history. The best evidence that his real character was maligned are his relations with persons who would not have tolerated intimacy with so contemptible a man. He helped to make the fortune, and retained the affectionate esteem of Addison and of Newton. Even after Swift had turned in bitterness against his old associates, he still declared that he loved Montague better than any other Whig. And no man, with a character such as has been painted by his enemies, could have won the love of Catherine Barton and retained it until his death in spite of the rumours which were circulated about their relations.

The record of Montague's achievements in Parliament is an impressive catalogue. He raised the first general mortgage of £1,000,000 to provide funds for the wars and was thus the founder of the national debt; taking advantage of a plan of Paterson, he instituted the Bank of England and established its modern financial system; he revised the charter of the East India Company and gave it a new life; and he also restored the currency, the greatest of his services, meeting its great expense by the substitution of the far more popular window tax[6] for the customary and obnoxious hearth tax. In spite of such services, he had hardly taken his seat in the Parliament of 1698 when he realised the bitterest mortification which a successful politician can experience: he had lost his influence; and his eloquence, which formerly swayed his listeners, now fell on deaf ears.

Whatever Montague's character might have been, he was doomed to failure as can be seen from the fate of Somers. A step, however, which he had taken a few weeks before Parliament met had made his downfall more certain and ignominious. He had hedged, and prepared a shelter for himself in fear of approaching trouble, by securing for his brother Christopher the Auditorship of the Exchequer with reversion to himself. The Auditorship was a life position with a large salary, and the duties were formal and easy; it is evident that he could not, himself, with decency, or probably even legally, audit his own accounts. Although he carried through this bold stroke and made certain for himself an ample income, secure from the hazards of political changes; yet he increased the animosity of his enemies and cooled the zeal of his adherents. When the members learned of this trick, their rage was unbounded. He was nicknamed the Filcher and was baited to such an indecent extent in the House of Commons that on one occasion he was irritated into uttering an oath and, on another, he burst into tears of rage and vexation which only increased the mockery of his foes. Montague, unable to bear the mortification of his position, resigned his places and took the Auditorship; the King, although their relations had never been

[6] This tax was the cause of blocking up unnecessary windows. Newton's house is an example.

personally intimate, rewarded his services and relieved his embarrassment, by raising him to the peerage with the title of Baron Halifax. He, like Somers, was impeached and acquitted.

The difference in attitude towards public principles, then and now, could not be better illustrated than by an incident which occurred at the death of King William. It is included in the *Life of Halifax* by his panegyrist, who evidently saw nothing unusual in it. So keen was Montague for place that: "when her late Majesty, Queen Anne, to whom the malice of his enemies had rendered him obnoxious, ascended the Throne, and to whom, notwithstanding, his supposed aversion to the measures some persons about her had taken, he paid the first compliments of condolence and congratulation, that were made her, by taking coach from Kensington to St. James's Palace, as soon as the breath was out of the deceased King's body."[7] His friends saw no impropriety in this indecent haste; but his enemies, who were guilty of the same eagerness to welcome the new and rising star, added it to their budget of calumny. One of their writers, in a poem called the *Golden Age,* referred to the incident,

> "Dissembling States-men shall before thee stand,
> And Halifax, he first shall kiss thy hand."

Montague, now Halifax, remained in more or less obscurity during her reign; but his persistent anti-Romanism together with his steady advocacy of the Hanoverian succession brought their reward; he was appointed one of Regents at the accession of George I. He was shortly after permitted to transfer the Auditorship to his nephew and heir, George Montague; and he was then made First Commissioner of the Treasury, Earl of Halifax, and invested with the Order of the Garter. He did not enjoy his new honours long, as he was taken ill suddenly on May 15th, 1715, with an inflammation of the lungs, and died four days later.

Montague's greatest service to the nation lay in the field of finance, and of all this work none compared in importance with his successful recoinage of the currency. Money is now so stabilised, and so accurately minted, that counterfeiting and adulterating the coin are infrequent crimes; then, they were so general that a piece of full value was a rarity. The penalty for both crimes was hanging; but

[7] *Life of Halifax,* Anon., p. 75.

in spite of a constant procession of these unfortunate wretches to the gallows, the evil was in no way checked. The general debasement of the currency had become a national calamity, but the individual act of removing a minute portion of metal from a few coins seemed an insignificant crime for so drastic a punishment. The sympathy of the people extended to the malefactors; juries would not convict except in flagrant and wholesale cases, and judges would not sentence; while the evil effect of the practice spread its poisonous influence throughout the trade and life of the nation. Macaulay gives a vivid, but not overdrawn, account of the desperate state into which the money had fallen; and he rightly estimates the importance of the work of Montague and Newton in rehabilitating the coinage far above the more spectacular reforms of bad government. During even a most disturbed and evil rule, the common people manage to pursue their personal affairs, but such a state of the money as then existed affected every moment and every transaction in their lives.

The standard currency of the country was silver; and till the reign of Charles the Second the minting of the coin had been carried on by the process introduced by Edward the First in the thirteenth century. The metal was cut with shears and then shaped and stamped by the hammer. Coins made thus by hand were not exactly round nor true in weight and, as they were neither milled nor inscribed on their rims, they were easy to clip, or file, without detection. Clipping thus became one of the most profitable kinds of fraud. The custom had become so detrimental that, in the reign of Elizabeth, it was treated as high treason. At the time of the Restoration, a large proportion of the coins had been more or less mutilated. To remedy this condition, a mill worked by horses was set up in the Tower which stamped the coins accurately and inscribed their edges with a legend; as, however, the old money was kept in circulation, the remedy was useless. The new coins were either hoarded, or melted down and shipped abroad; the old coins persisted as the medium of business, and they continued to shrink in weight and value.

In the autumn of 1695, it was found by actual and careful test that the average value of a shilling coin had been reduced to six pence. Every transaction was accompanied by a bitter altercation between the buyer and the seller; the former insisting on estimating the coins by tale, and the latter by weight. Every Saturday night, all over the country, was a period of riot and bad feeling between employer and employé. The labourer and the clerk might receive the stipulated number of shillings, but for their purchases they acted like sixpences or less. We have, as a startling witness of these troubles, the complaints of Dryden that his publisher, Tonson, on one occasion included forty brass shillings in a payment of clipped money, and at another time the money was so bad that all of it was returned. If the foremost writer of the day was so treated, we can easily imagine the distress of the common people. The question had become so serious that King William, in his address to Parliament, in 1695, included a recommendation that the coinage should be completely reformed. As a result Montague, the Chancellor of the Exchequer, was empowered to prepare a Bill to provide for the recoinage of all the money.[8]

It was a bold decision of Montague to risk so serious a disturbance in the affairs of the nation during a time of war. The greatest apprehension was aroused; the Jacobites used every effort to discredit the government, and many of the Whigs counselled timorous and half measures. By the most skillful management, Montague carried his Bill for the recoinage through the House which, on the twenty-first of January, 1695/6, was signed by the King. The more important measures of this Bill were that the money of the kingdom should be recoined according to the old standard of weight and fineness; that the new pieces should be milled; that the loss on the clipped pieces should be borne by the public exchequer; that a time should be fixed after which no clipped coin should pass except in payments to the government; and that a final date, May 4, 1696, should be set when mutilated money could not pass at all.

The loss to the government involved in the redemption of the mutilated money could not be estimated, but Montague prepared for the emergency by obtaining a loan from the Bank of England, secured by a new tax levied on the number of windows of the houses, excepting only the inhabitants of cottages who had been cruelly

[8] Macaulay, Chapter XXI, states that "the world had never seen . . . an alliance so close, so harmonious, and so honourable as that which bound Somers and Montague to Locke and Newton." This statement, which has also been accepted by Brewster as applicable to Newton, is misleading. Somers and Locke were of the greatest assistance to Montague in preparing the Bill and securing its adoption. It is easy to prove by the known dates, that the Bill was passed, its provisions were in operation, and the actual recoinage was begun by February 1695/6. Newton did not receive his appointment as Warden of the Mint till the following month and it must have taken some time for him to assume active charge of the work. We have no evidence that he was ever consulted during the preliminary portion of the work and, from his letters, there is reason to believe that he took no share in it. His service is memorable only by his efficient management during the later months of the coinage, and of the Mint till his death.

harassed by the assessors of the former hearth tax. By February, 1695/6, the recoinage was begun. Ten furnaces were built in the gardens behind the Treasury; huge heaps of mutilated coins were melted and cast into ingots, and then were immediately transported to the Tower to be minted. From that time till the fourth of May, the first panic subsided, and the scarcity of money was not severely felt. In March, Newton assumed charge of the work, and branch mints were established in several towns; notably, Chester, where Halley was installed as his representative. The real agony began in May when the clipped coins were no longer received by the government in payment of taxes. There was little of the old money which would pass the test and the new money was just beginning to trickle from the Mint; but, by means of barter, of promissory notes given by merchants, and of negotiable paper issued by the Exchequer, the summer slowly wore away. It was not till August that the first faint signs of returning ease in the money situation appeared, and there is no doubt that the able administration and indefatigable industry of Newton shortened this period of distress. He wrote peremptorily to Flamsteed that he would not be teased about mathematical things nor trifle away his time while he was about the King's business. The Wardens of the Mint had previously been fine gentlemen who drew their salaries and rarely condescended to do any work. It had been considered a great feat to coin silver to the amount of fifteen thousand pounds weight a week; but under the energetic management of Montague and Newton, the weekly coinage soon rose to sixty thousand pounds, and finally to a hundred and twenty thousand pounds. But even this rate was inadequate, and normal conditions were not restored till the following spring.

The history of Newton's connection with the Mint can be told briefly. He retained the position of Warden, which gave to him the actual management of the work, till 1699 when the great undertaking of the recoinage was completed. When this was safely out of the way, and the Mint had settled down to normal conditions, he was promoted to be Master of the Mint and held the position for life; as soon as his income was ample, he resigned all connection with Cambridge. On the authority of Conduitt, who was in a position to know, Newton's income as Master of the Mint has been generally stated to be between £1200 and £1500 a year. But Colonel de Villamil, who recently discovered the complete inventory of Newton's estate, has proved that Conduitt spoke carelessly; in that document he testified on oath the true figure of his uncle's income was as follows:

Salary as Master of the Mint, per annum	£600— 0—0
Salary as Assay Master, per annum	60— 0—0
Perquisite of one shilling tenpence per pound weight of gold minted from Jan. 1 to March 20, 1726/7, the day of his death	303—17—6
Perquisite of threepence farthing per pound weight of silver minted from Jan. 1 to March 20, 1726/7	3— 5—9¾

As there is no reason to suppose that more metal was coined during the seventy-nine days from January first to his death, his income from the Mint was, at least, £2078 per annum.[9] Thus, for twenty-eight years, Newton received a more than generous salary; those were pleasant times for an official who was fortunate enough to possess the proper influence.

His position, during the first three years, was a most difficult one; not only must the employés be spurred to the greatest loyalty and effort but, also, political troubles had to be counteracted. The Jacobites and Tories seized the chance to use the crisis to discredit the government and to foment discord in the workmen and officers of the Mint. Serious disturbances broke out first at Chester; friction arose between Clark, the Master-worker, Lewis and other clerks at Chester, on one side, and Halley and Weddell, friends of Newton, on the other. Clark challenged Weddell to a duel which ludicrously ended in words, and Lewis threw a standish at him. Halley, alarmed at these dissensions, finally wrote to Newton to use the potent influence of Montague, Chancellor of the Exchequer, should it be necessary, and to exercise great prudence in trying to compose the quarrel. He accused Clark of being the source of the dissensions and wrote that the troubles would cease if the "proud, insolent fellow" were removed. He "has been at London this two months, and left all business (which has for this month past kept us all fully employed) to our care, though we know not why we should charge ourselves with, he not desiring it. But we have been willing to serve the public by giving a constant attendance and animating all parts of the mint so that, at this time, we have closed of[f] all that was imported above five weeks since; and have issued about fifty thou-

[9] *Cf.* de Villamil, *Newton: the Man*, p. 33.

sand pounds of new money."[10] He offered to resign but thought he should continue in order to further the work. Newton, with friendly consideration, undertook to relieve him of his embarrassment by finding for him another position although it would have removed a devoted and valuable ally from the work.

Newton to Halley

London, Feb. 11, 1696–7.

Sir,

This morning Colonel Blunt, the King's first Engineer, was with me, and acquainted me with the design the King has to allow ten shillings per diem for two masters to teaching Engineering (I mean the mathematical grounds of it) two hours each day, to those of the army who will come to hear them publicly, Engineers, and Officers, and others, who shall have the curiosity and capacity. I proposed you as a fit person to be one of the two, if you should think fit to accept of the thing. By bringing you acquainted with the Officers and making you known to the King, it may be a means of making way for something better. The Colonel will call on me seven or eight days hence for an answer. I am

Your faithful friend to serve you,

Is. Newton.

P. S. I wrote to you the last post for an Engineer's place. I question you can have both.[11]

But Halley stuck to his post till the Chester branch was closed, and then he received an appointment as observer on the first scientific expedition to be undertaken by England, which had for its object to aid navigation by studying the variation of the compass in different parts of the earth.

In addition to the troubles created at Chester, Newton had to meet a serious attack on his own administration. A certain William Chaloner claimed to have discovered gross irregularities in the conduct of the Mint. He was ordered to disclose his information to a special Committee of the House of Commons under a guarantee of personal protection against threats which he asserted had been made on his life. Chaloner's story was that the officers of the Mint had

[10] The account of the troubles at the Chester Mint is taken from letters of Halley to Newton, dated from November, 1696, to August, 1697. *Portsmouth Collection.*

[11] Macclesfield, Vol. II, p. 420.

trumped up charges against himself, had committed him to Newgate Prison, and had kept him in irons for seven weeks. When they failed to secure evidence against him, they then laid a plot to involve him in coining false money in the hope of undermining any testimony he might bring against their own criminal acts. At this point, the affair seems to have faded out; the Committee sat several times, but no action was taken and no report of its proceedings has been found. As Newton's character was deeply involved, Brewster,[12] with the assistance of Lord Brougham, made a diligent search for evidence of the truth of the charge, and found in the British Museum documents which completely exonerated him. Amongst other papers, a short tract was unearthed giving an account of the life and execution for high treason of Chaloner. According to this account, he was undoubtedly a man of great talents, but of an evil character, who devised the plot in order to conceal his own criminal actions. His biographer says: "He scorned to fly at low matters. He pretended his commitment to be malicious, and accused that worthy gentleman, Isaac Newton, Esq., Warden of his Majesty's Mint, with several other officers thereof, as connivers (at least) at many abuses and cheats there committed. This accusation he impudently put into Parliament, and a committee was appointed to examine the same who, upon a full hearing of the matter, dismissed the same gentleman with the honour due his merit, and Chaloner with the character he deserved."

Direct attempts were also made to oust Newton from his position. He was offered other places and bribes of money for favours and patronage. Such attempts might have one of two motives; either to provide a lucrative place for a political henchman, or to impair the efficiency of the Mint in order to embarrass Montague. One remarkable instance of his integrity of character, and of his determination to stick to what he believed to be his duty, is preserved in a letter to Conduitt from the Rev. Dr. Derham, an intimate acquaintance of Newton.[13] "The last thing, Sir, that I shall trouble you with, shall be a passage relating to the coinage of the copper money some years ago, which pleased me much in setting forth the integrity of my friend Sir Isaac. The occasion of our discourse was, the great inconveniences which many underwent by the delay of the coinage of this sort of money. The occasion of which delay, Sir Isaac told me, was from the numerous petitions that were presented to them, in

[12] Brewster, Vol. II, p. 201.

[13] *Portsmouth Collection.*

most of which some person or other of quality was concerned. Amongst others, he told me that an agent of one had made him an offer of above £6000, which Sir Isaac refusing on account of its being a bribe, the agent said he saw no dishonesty in the acceptance of the offer, and that Sir Isaac understood not his own interest. To which Sir Isaac replied, that he knew well enough what was his duty, and that no bribes should corrupt him. The agent then told him, that he came from a great Duchess, and pleaded her quality and interest. To which Sir Isaac roughly answered, 'I desire you to tell the lady, that if she was here herself, and had made me this offer, I would have desired her to go out of my house; and so I desire you, or you shall be turned out.' Afterwards he learned who the Duchess was."

During his administration of the Mint, Newton was several times offered large gifts and pensions, but he always declined them. The astronomer Cassini, during a visit to England shortly after the treaty of Ryswick, was authorised by Louis XIV to ask him to accept such a pension as a recognition of his discoveries. Also, towards the close of Queen Anne's reign, Bolingbroke sent Dean Swift to his intimate friend, Catherine Barton, asking her to let her uncle know "the Government thought it a sin that his thoughts should be diverted by his place at the Mint, and that the Queen would settle upon him a pension of £2000 a year." The proposal was dropped when Newton briefly replied, "My place is at their disposal, but I will have no p[ension]."[14] This incident is always cited as an attempt to bribe Newton in order that his lucrative place might be given to a Tory henchman. While it is true that party was then using every means to strengthen their lines and prevent the approaching Hanoverian succession, I doubt if such a method would have been necessary to obtain his resignation. The Tories had permitted him to keep his place undisturbed during years of bitter party strife, and they had honoured him with knighthood; to remove a political opponent would have been looked upon as a matter of course. Both Bolingbroke and Swift were distinguished men of letters and there is no reason to assume that they were not offering a graceful tribute to the most illustrious scholar of the age.

The record of Newton's official life is meagre but, such as it is, it confirms the accepted opinion that he performed his duties faithfully and well in an age of general coruption; in fact, he set a standard of

[14] Conduitt MSS. *Portsmouth Collection.*

public service. Edleston has collected a few items worth preserving. In 1717 and 1718, he presented in person to the House of Lords elaborate reports on the comparative values of domestic and foreign coins, and on the amount of coinage accomplished during those years. These reports were afterwards laid before the House of Commons in pursuance of an address to the King. The value of the gold guinea had been steadily falling after the silver money had been standardised in purity and weight, and one effect of his statistics was to fix the guinea at twenty-one shillings, the ratio which it still maintained when the standard was changed to gold. In 1724, he presented an adverse report on the circulation of Wood's brass half-pence. This action won him the bitter opposition of Swift who was deeply interested in providing the Irish with an abundant medium of small value. In his *Voyage of Gulliver to Laputa* he retaliated by caricaturing the activities of the Royal Society, and it is generally supposed that Newton, the President, was the prototype of those philosophers who dreamed preposterous undertakings, and were aroused from their foggy abstraction by taps of a bladder administered by a watchful attendant. Newton's ideas on criminal punishment are known from a letter written to Lord Townshend.

Newton to Lord Townshend

My Lord,

I know nothing of Edmund Metcalf convicted at Derby assizes of counterfeiting the coin; but since he is very evidently convicted, I am humbly of opinion that it's better to let him suffer, than to venture his going on to counterfeit the coin and teach others to do so until he can be convicted again, for these people very seldom leave off. And it's difficult to detect them. I say this with most humble submission to his Majesty's pleasure and remain

My Lord

your Lordship's most humble and obedient Servant

Is. NEWTON.[15]

Mint Office Aug. 25, 1724.

During the last years of Newton's life, he rarely went to the Mint and desired to resign in favour of Conduitt who was satisfactorily carrying on the duties of the office as his deputy. After his death, Conduitt succeeded him as Master. There is a story connected with

15 Edleston, p. 316

Conduitt's appointment which sheds a light on a practice common enough at the time but offensive to our sense of propriety. It is related by Whiston in his *Memoirs of Dr. Samuel Clarke,* and his reference to Bishop Hoadly is strong evidence of its truth.[16]

"A. D. 1727, upon the death of Sir Isaac Newton, Dr. Clarke was offered by the Court the place he possessed of Master of the Mint, worth, *communibus annis,* £1200 to £1500 a year. Upon this offer the doctor advised with his friends, and particularly with Mr. Emlyn and myself, about accepting or refusing it. We were both heartily against his acceptance, as what he wanted not, as what was entirely remote from his profession, and would hinder the success of his ministry. Whereupon, after no small consideration, he absolutely refused it. Nor do I give credit to those surmises, as if Mr. Conduitt, who succeeded, was obliged to give the Doctor, privately, an annual share of his profits, or what was equivalent thereto; with this only abatement, that Mr. Conduitt did actually give £1000 to void a place among the king's writers, which place was freely bestowed on a son of the Doctor's, who could not otherwise be so well provided for, after himself had refused the former much greater place. . . . And as for the Doctor's refusal of the former improper preferment, though entirely omitted by Dr. Sykes, and almost entirely by Bishop Hoadly, I take it to be one of the most glorious actions of his life. . . ."[17]

The estimation of the value of Newton's public service to the nation has varied widely; even the propriety of a man of such genius devoting so large a portion of his life to a more or less routine office has been questioned. It would be absurd to subscribe to Brewster's sentimental effusion that Newton, the High Priest of Science, had been ignored by a callous nation and doomed to the obscure life of a scholar immured in academic cloisters until a tardy recognition of his services placed him in a position of affluence and honour as Master of the Mint. Newton had always had an income sufficient for the needs of a scholar and bachelor. As for the comparative honour of the two positions, that to be paid to him as a Master of the Mint can hardly match with that as a scholar and philosopher. Nor was

[16] Whiston's *Memoirs* have been discredited by Newton's partisans and unjustly. Because a man was a somewhat fanatical Arian and tried to revive primitive Christianity, and because he unfortunately had a grievance against Newton, are not reasons for discrediting his direct statements. His life is a witness to his willingness to suffer for what he believed to be the truth. Dr. Samuel Clarke was a prominent divine and philosopher; as a staunch supporter of Newton, he defended the Newtonian philosophy against Leibniz in a series of letters published in the *Des Maizeaux Collection.*

[17] De Morgan—*Newton: His Friend: and His Niece,* p. 153.

he neglected during his life time; there have been few scientists who have enjoyed so deep a respect and admiration by their contemporaries as did he. Again the statement of Brewster[18] that: "Elevated to the Chair of the Royal Society, and enjoying the confidence of the Prince Consort, Sir Isaac had it in his power to do *something* for the promotion of science." What an extraordinary statement to be made by an author, himself a distinguished scientist! What could Newton do for science, through the patronage of a Prince Consort or even of a learned society, to compare with the discoveries he might have made? Even thus to address him invariably as Sir Isaac is irritating, as if his fame and memory had been certified by the complaisance of a stupid Queen Anne.

But, the more one studies the vital importance of the recoinage, the more one is convinced that it needed the united effort of four such men as Montague, Somers, Locke, and Newton. If he had temporarily laid aside his philosophical studies to assist in such an emergency, he would have deserved the honour due to a benefactor of the nation; but one cannot regard his position in the Mint for thirty years except as a sinecure. He was fifty years of age at the time of his appointment and, apparently, at the height of his powers. He had given to the world inestimable fruits of his genius. If he preferred to give no more, and to change his manner of life, it would be churlish even to question his motives; but no one can take satisfaction in his choice. There is no doubt that he desired social distinction and contact with men of affairs; that he enjoyed his intimacy at Court, or that he found satisfaction as a dispenser of patronage; but none of these causes accounts for his abrupt cessation from scientific work. To find a reason for it, we are driven to the conjecture that he never had been deeply interested in science for itself, and that he wished to have the opportunity to follow his stronger inclination towards theology and history; or we must accept the opinion that the excessive strain incident to the composition of the *Principia,* and his subsequent illness, had permanently debilitated his will power, or had disturbed the delicate adjustment of his marvellous brain. Newton, only, could answer the question, and he has left no word to tell us of his motives. All we can say is: in the first half of his life, his inventive power excelled that of other men; and in the latter half, it ceased.

It is altogether probable that Newton, when he first moved to

[18] Brewster, Vol. II, p. 219.

London, accepted Montague's invitation to lodge near him. The recoinage had already been begun, and he would find little leisure to look about for permanent quarters; also it would be convenient to be with his friend while learning his new duties. At any rate, it was not till autumn that he moved into his own house in Jermyn Street, where he was to live for the next twelve years. The house stood just behind St. James's Church, Piccadilly, and its site, which is now occupied by Jules's Hotel, is marked by a commemorative tablet. While there were living quarters in the Tower for the Warden, he does not ever seem to have occupied them, although both Swift and Voltaire supposed he did. The choice of a residence so far from the Mint may, at first sight, seem surprising, but his work was probably mostly conducted at the Exchequer which was nearby in Whitehall. It was there that the old coins were received, valued, and cast into bullion, and where the principal duties of the Warden would be performed. In fact he seems, at least after the first rush of work was over, to have spent only one day a week at the Tower. When he became President of the Royal Society he had its weekly meeting changed from Wednesday to Thursday so as not to interfere with his duties at the Mint. And it was well known by his friends that he was engaged there on Wednesdays as is proved by a letter of Locke who requested his cousin, Lord King, to call on Newton, but to avoid Wednesday as that was his day at the Tower.

Jermyn Street, lying as it does in Westminster, was beginning to be a fashionable neighbourhood, but we must suppose that Newton's income for some years would require him to maintain a modest housekeeping. Shortly after he set up for himself, he installed a favourite niece, Catherine Barton, as manager of his establishment, and she by her wit and beauty soon made it a centre of young and gay life. Even when he enjoyed a much larger salary as Master of the Mint, his biographers found it difficult to understand how he managed to live in an ample fashion, and yet to leave so large a fortune, unless he were a shrewd investor of his savings. Fortunately, the researches of Colonel de Villamil have proved that his income was much greater, and his establishment more frugal, than they were supposed to have been. That, in the later years of his life, he lived well is recorded by Conduitt, who was himself a man of means and who, after his marriage with Mrs. Catherine Barton in 1717, lived with Newton for ten years. He stated in a letter to

Fontenelle[19] that Newton lived alone except for his niece who was with him nearly twenty years before and after her marriage. They lived in a handsome and hospitable manner, without ostentation or vanity. There he received visits from many distinguished foreigners attracted to him by his fame, and to them he gave, on occasion, splendid entertainments. "All the time he had to spare from business and the civilities of life, in which he was scrupulously exact and complaisant, was employed in the same way on history, chronology, divinity, and chemistry, and he was hardly ever alone without a pen in his hand and a book before him. All the studies he undertook, he had a perseverance and patience equal to his sagacity and invention."

Newton has given so many proofs of generosity and had so equable a disposition that we can readily believe he was an affectionate and indulgent guardian to his niece and provided her with the means to preside worthily over the society attracted by her charming personality. There is only one adverse account of his hospitality which may be given now, although it relates to his last years when he was ill. It bears all the marks of personal pique and rather cheap wit at the expense of a man, crowned with a great age and honour. In 1725, the Abbé Alari, former tutor of Louis XV and a friend of Bolingbroke, spent two months in London: "He visited the University of Cambridge and the great Newton, who enjoyed, at that time, in the capital of England, the general esteem of Europe, and 50,000 livres of salary as Master of the Mint. The Abbé having gone to his house at nine o'clock in the morning, Newton began by telling him that he was eighty-three years of age. There was in his chamber the portrait of his patron, Lord Halifax, and one of the Abbé Varignon, of whose geometrical writings he had a high opinion. 'Varignon,' he said, 'and Father Sebastien, the Carmelite, are those who have understood best my system of colours.' The conversation at last turned on ancient history, with which Newton was then occupied. The Abbé, who was deeply read in Greek and Latin authors, having made himself very agreeable, was asked to dinner. The repast was detestable. Newton was stingy, and gave his guests wines of Palma and Madeira, which he had received in presents. After dinner he took the Abbé to the Royal Society, of which he was the President, and made him sit at his right hand. The business began, and Newton fell asleep. When it was over, every body signed the register, and the

[19] Turnor, p. 163. *Portsmouth Collection.*

Abbé among the rest. Newton took him to his house, and kept him till nine o'clock in the evening."[20]

We may be sure that Montague was an important factor in the new household. And however much he may have alienated others by his arrogance, ostentation, and libertinism, he must have shown there his better side as Newton was not a person to tolerate such traits. Newton's circle must have been drawn from many and diverse sources; in it could be found the political associates of Montague; serious men of letters and science attracted by Newton, and the "Wits" who made the niece one of the toasts of the famous Kit-Cat Club.[21]

Although Newton was a silent man and often abstracted in general society, he was sought after by the leaders of thought even in his early and busy years at the Mint. For example, Bentley, who then occupied the position of the Keeper of the King's Library housed in St. James's Palace, formed a club of a few friends who for their intellectual powers could hardly be matched at that, or any other, time. In a letter to Evelyn, written in the autumn of 1697, he mentions his intention of founding such evening meetings: "I think I have at last obtained of the Treasury, to repair and augment the King's Library here. Sir Christopher Wren, Mr. Locke, Mr. Newton, etc., (and I hope when in Town Mr. Evelyn) are to meet here once or twice a week in the evening."[22] Evelyn's diary and Bentley's letters, which give so much information about the life of their time, are strangely silent about the discussions which took place in such a unique gath-

[20] *Essais Hist. sur Bolingbroke.* Compiled by Gen. Grimoard. Vol. I, p. 155, Paris, 1808. Quoted by Brewster, Vol. II, p. 388.—Newton's inventory shows that he was frugal and simple in his tastes. He spent little on his service, his wardrobe, or his furniture.

[21] Both Somers and Montague were original members of this famous Whig Club. It is said to have been founded by Jacob Tonson, the bookseller. Its name was taken from its meeting at the house of Christopher Cat, in Shire Lane, near Temple Bar. It was famous for its mutton pies:

"Immortal made as Kit-Cat by his pies."

Or as some say, the name was derived from the sign of his house, the "Cat and Fiddle." During the summer the members met at "The Upper Flask" on Hampstead Heath. Dinner began at the late hour of three o'clock and often lasted until six. The meetings were noted for their wit and, by rumour, for heavy drinking. One custom was to choose the most popular lady of the town as a toast, and to inscribe her charms on a wine glass with a diamond. The following feeble verses to Catherine Barton are ascribed to Montague:

"Beauty and wit strove each in vain
To vanquish Bacchus and his train;
But Barton, with successful charms,
From both their quivers drew her arms:
The roving god his sway resigns,
And cheerfully submits his vines."

[22] Bentley's *Correspondence,* Vol. I, p. 152.

ering. We could dispense willingly with many other anecdotes to have had a first hand report of some of those intimate conversations.

Newton had no sooner forsaken the life of the scholar, and embarked on his new career, than he made a diligent search into his family connection in order to establish his status as a gentleman. He was in the embarrassing position of being a lord of a manor, but the manor was a pitifully small one, his immediate family were palpably yeomen farmers, and he evidently could not trace his ancestry further back than his grandfather. As mentioned before, he testified on oath to the Herald's College that he had reason to believe that he was descended from the Newton family of Lincolnshire but could not trace the connection. That he was not satisfied with the proof of this relationship is shown by a conversation reported to have been held between Newton and James Gregory: "Sir Isaac said, 'Gregory, I believe you don't know that I am a Scotchman?—'Pray, how is that?' said Gregory. Sir Isaac said he was informed that his grandfather (or great-grandfather) was a gentleman of East (or West) Lothian: that he went to London with King James I at his accession to the crown of England: and that he attended the Court, in expectation, as many others did, until he spent his fortune, by which means his family was reduced to low circumstances." We might suppose that Gregory would have been proud to welcome a Newton into his family, but his Scotch pride of race interfered. To Newton's insinuation, Gregory bluntly replied, "Newton a gentleman of East Lothian? I never heard of a gentleman of East Lothian of that name." Newton, thereupon, said he had it only by tradition, and immediately turned the conversation to another subject.[23]

Those who look upon Newton as a philosopher, dwelling in the clouds, have an erroneous picture of the man. He was observant and interested in small things, and was careful in his dealings with others lest they should overcome him in a bargain. He was generous in helping the affairs of his village community but he retained throughout life the country boy's attitude towards little affairs. It is amusing to note how attentive he was to have his instructions carried out and how minutely he watched his neighbours. When he was an old man, the most famous in the world, he took time to settle just how many

[23] It was a common practice of the time to bolster up a shaky pedigree by attaching it to one of the impecunious but haughty Scotch *lairds* who swarmed to London with James I to mend their fortunes. It is wiser to consider the advent of Newton as one of the unaccountable appearances of a great genius rather than to seek for the source of his qualities in a mediocre county family. Those who are curious about his pedigree should consult Brewster, Vol. II, pp. 537–545.

sheep and cattle he was entitled to have graze on the common. And when he was thought to be so immersed in the composition of the *Principia* as to be oblivious to the most important things of his life and of the world, we are astounded by the fact that he interrupted his meditations to write a long letter, going into minute details about repairing a house and barn, and threatening his tenants with a lawsuit if they did not mend their ways. While the following letter is long, it will give the reader a totally new and unexpected idea of Newton as a human being. It is also one of the very few of his personal letters which has been preserved.

Newton to a Friend

Sir,

Before I received yours I had an account from Mr. Parish of the arbitration, and thereupon wrote to Mr. Parkins to know how the indentures run, and to Mr. Storer, to know distinctly what it is that his son Oliver deposes. I had a speedy answer from Mr. Parkins, whereby I understand that Mr. Storer is bound to leave all things in a tenantable repair, by a clause which you do not mention; but from Mr. Storer I have not yet received an answer, and therefore cannot write to you what I designed for putting an end to these differences.

When I met Mr. Storer and his sons at Wolstrope, that is at Lady-day last, I was satisfied with the removal of the wheat hovel and with the thatch of the houses in view, as I went up the yard to the house. I do not say that there was no faults, for I am shortsighted, and did not (that I remember) go close to the barn, not being then minded to call Mr. Storer to a strict account for repairs. Thence we went into the orchard, and I was pleased with the repairs of the slated house, but told Mr. Storer's sons that he was an ill husband with the drain below, and he promised it should be scoured. Then turning to Robin's house I pointed to two very faulty places in the thatch, and Mr. Storer's sons confessed it rained in, and promised it should be mended. Thence I went into the dwelling-house to receive Mr. Storer's rent, and when he was going to pay it he told me that his son found boards for the gutters of the Lucome windows, which I was to pay for, but the bill was lost, and so desired that I would allow 30s for these boards. After some words, I put it to him whether he could honestly affirm that the boards were worth so much. He answered he could not, but he hoped I would not stand with him for a small matter. To which I presently answered that I would not stand with him, and so remitted 30s. of his rent on account of the bill which he said was lost. About a fortnight after coming to Colsterworth, I was three or four times at Wolstrope, and one of those times going into the garden I found the walls ruinous, and in going through the pales between the garden and the house, I observed that they, and the great gates, were much out of order. At the time also the pales were wanting to the swine-coat and some of the long pales plucked off from the cow-house. At that time I heard also that they had carried away the fence from the new quick in the clay-field,[24] and made money of it. Mr. Storer represents that the hedge was decayed and grown useless before; but this is to excuse one fault with another, for Mr. Storer was to keep it in repair, I paying for the wood. After I understood these things, I was called out of the country before I could speak with Mr. Storer, and afterwards, in hay time, I had notice that the linghouse was ruinous, for want of repair, and that Mr. Storer's son refused to repair it. Soon after a friend viewed the tenements, and sent me an account of those things out of repair which I had observed, and some other things also which I had not noted. And at that time, or some time after, I understood that Mr. Storer's son refused absolutely to do any repairs, and had treated Will. Cottam with ill language about it. Whereupon, considering that they had not repaired Robin's house, and left divers other things out of repair, and that Mr. Storer's son, living with his father, and being his father's agent, could not persist in a refusal of repairs, without his father's knowledge and encouragement, I resolved to call the father to a general account for repairs, which could not be done but by suit, and because the son was concerned in the aforesaid hedge, I resolved to sue them both, and this the rather because his son had disparaged the living at Lady-day in my hearing, I being of opinion that he did it as well behind my back as before my face, to hinder me of tenants who might put me upon calling them to account for repairs. This was the occasion of the suit which I tell you, that you may understand I was not rash in beginning it, as Mr. Storer endeavours to persuade his friends.

I hear 'tis represented I should be well pleased with repairs at Lady-day, and allow Mr. Storer 30s. on that account, and say that things were better in repair than when Mr. Burch left them. But I have told you that the 30s. was in discharge of a bill, and respected only the slating of the house, which was done at my charges, and if I

24 This clay-field is still used. Quick was the familiar name for a hedge.

was pleased with what I had repaired, what is that to Mr. Storer? Because I eased [him] of repairs of the side of the house, there is the more reason that he should leave other things in good repair. He was indeed at the charge of carriages, but that was a bargain, and I have, on the other hand, allowed him 30s. for boards, which perhaps were not worth half the money. And if I was kind to him in that, he is very disingenuous to turn it to my disadvantage. For this is to snap me by the fingers for giving him bread.

Whether I said that things were left better in repair by Mr. Storer than by Mr. Burch I do not remember, and if it be understood generally, it's manifestly false. For I could not say so of Robin's house, because I complained of its being out of repair, nor of the garden walls, because I had not then viewed them, nor of the gates and pales, because I did not see any repairs of late done to them, nor could I say so of the repairs of anything for which I now sue. But of the slated house, and, if you please, of all the houses taken one with another, I might, and do now say, that they were better in repair when Mr. Storer left than when he entered. But then I add, that this is nothing to Mr. Storer's purpose, for 'tis my charge of £11—10s. in slating, which makes amends for all the rest. And if I have repaired the main building substantially, that must not excuse Mr. Storer from repairing what belongs to his own share. So you see that what Mr. Storer alleges himself amounts to nothing. In short, as I did not begin this suit without just occasion, so now I have begun it I do not intend to end it without satisfaction. If Mr. Storer will send me a satisfactory answer to my last, I'll endeavour to make a final end in my next, but if he goes on to misrepresent things, I'll solicit Mr. Parish to give you another meeting. I thank you for undertaking the office of an arbitrator, and that you may inherit the blessing promised to peace-makers, is the hearty wish of. . . .

[Is. Newton.]

Cambridge, Jan. 11th, '87/8.[25]

In 1698, Montague's wife died and, whether or not he regarded that loss as a great affliction, it made a profound change in his life. It was also the year when he fell from power, and there can be no doubt that he was a prey to the deepest anxiety. Newton, too, must have regarded the future with alarm; it was only too probable that he would share in the downfall of the statesman. Their consultations

[25] Brewster, Vol. II, pp. 546–548.

must have been frequent and prolonged. But Montague had made a still stronger attachment in the house of his friend in the person of his niece. We do not know just when Catherine Barton came to London but the probability is that she had been her uncle's housekeeper for some years. Montague early developed a deep affection for her, and proved his love with a devotion which was perhaps the most disinterested relationship in his chequered life.

We know little about Newton's immediate family, but we do know that he was unfailingly generous towards his relatives and that his affection for his mother and his niece, Catherine, was wholehearted and steadfast. I have been unable to find any references about his half-sisters, and their brother; and the few about their children lead one to believe that they were a rather worthless lot. De Morgan has discovered an unsavoury anecdote of Newton's half-nephew, Benjamin Smith. He is reported to have been one of the most profligate clergymen of the day and that is to admit a great deal. He was ordained by Newton's friend, Dr. Stukeley, an act which Bishop Warburton termed a "furious scandal."[26] We learn something of the attitude of the time towards the office of the clergy from the apology of Stukeley that he had refused to give him a testimonial of character, and had only given him a title of office which had reference to his livelihood and not to his morals. This extraordinary version of the affair caused Warburton to congratulate Stukeley on the excellence of his justification. When this nephew was a youth, Newton wrote him scorching letters of rebuke, describing his actions and his character in terms which were as blunt and descriptive as the conduct was indecent. These letters fell into the hands of a clergyman after Smith's death and were destroyed, for fear Newton's reputation might suffer if it were known that he was acquainted with such coarse language. Such was the colourless character that his worshipers were determined to invest him with, and have us forget that he had passed his childhood amongst the roughest of country boys where he would become quite familiar with the rudest language, and would use it on occasion without being himself indecent. His sister Hannah married a clergyman named Barton and had several children. One of these was the Catherine Barton who has already been mentioned. A son entered the army and was killed in Hill's ill-fated expedition against Quebec. Swift refers to

[26] The "scandal," in the Bishop's opinion, may have been due to Smith's character, or to the fact that he was not ordained by a bishop.

this Colonel Barton in his *Journal to Stella* as Catherine's good-for-nothing brother for whom she could mourn only as a matter of form, and adds that his manner of death was the most praiseworthy act of his life. There is also the startling statement in the life of the "famous witty divine Sidney Smith," by his daughter Lady Holland, that he was the grandson of the famous witty Catherine Barton, which is obviously an error. In the fourth edition of the book, the name of this ancestress was changed to Maria Barton and, possibly, she may have been a daughter or granddaughter of Colonel Barton.

With the exception of his mother, Catherine Barton, born in 1680, was the only one of Newton's relatives who was in any way distinguished, or who exerted any real influence on his life. While her father was probably poor, his ancestors had possessed estates in Northamptonshire for several hundred years and were related to a number of the honourable families of that neighbourhood. Newton was early attracted to her and singled her out to give her the best of educations. Shortly after he moved to London, he practically adopted her and placed her in charge of his establishment.

In August, 1717, she married John Conduitt, M. P., who was Newton's deputy in the Mint during the latter years of his life, and succeeded him, at his death. The Conduitts lived with him from their marriage until his death; their only child, Catherine, married John Wallop, Lord Lymington, and their son succeeded to the title of Earl of Portsmouth, and from this connection Newton's papers came into the possession of that family. She must have been a charming and beautiful girl whose picture has come down to us as the famous, witty, and virtuous Mrs. Barton.[27]

In spite of the general and emphatic belief in the rectitude of both Newton and his niece, there has persisted a smothered rumour that she lived for years with Montague as his mistress, and that Newton not only connived at the illicit connection, but obtained his public post because of it. It is simply incredible to us now that a man of Newton's integrity and strict principles could have tolerated such a relationship or that he could have been ignorant of it, if it existed. The question, and it is one of interest to settle if possible, is, did Mrs. Barton live in Montague's house or not? Was she his friend, his mistress, or his unacknowledged, but legitimate, wife? The unqualified answer to these questions has been made almost impossible

[27] In the eighteenth century the title of *Miss* was restricted to young girls. The title of *Mrs.*, with the addition of the Christian name, was used for unmarried ladies. While I have adopted the title of *Mrs.* I have thought it unnecessary to add the Christian name.

because no one, at the time, deemed it advisable to publish the facts of the case. Neither Newton's family, nor his friends, gave any public explanation of the connection. Even Montague's biographer, who published his life immediately after his death, mentioned the affair in such an ambiguous manner as to increase suspicion and to add to the obscurity. We must conclude that the secret was for some adequate reason jealously guarded, or else that the rumour of a liaison with so great a nobleman was not a serious blot on a woman's reputation.

Fortunately, De Morgan became interested in the problem and, with his keen interest in intricate historical questions, he collected all the evidence he could find. As a result of his investigation, he has proved that the scandal, while publicly suppressed, was privately widespread during Newton's life; he has shown it to be almost certain that she lived in Montague's house; and, as an illicit connection was unbelievable to him, both on Newton's and her account, he concluded that they were privately married and that, while the marriage was known to their circle of friends, it was for some reason never publicly acknowledged.[28] Brewster also discusses the problem at length.[29] He takes the stand that, because of Newton's high moral character, Catherine Barton could not have lived in Montague's house in any capacity except as his publicly acknowledged wife; therefore their relationship was one merely of Platonic friendship. He states categorically that there was no rumour of a scandal during Montague's life-time, and that Newton and Conduitt would have been compelled to acknowledge the marriage, or to explain the connection, when the great legacy he left to her in his will aroused the "censure of the world," if there had been any doubt of her virtue. Although Brewster thus unqualifiedly declares in his *Memoirs of Newton* that she had never been an inmate in Montague's house, he wrote while the work was in preparation several letters to De Morgan, who had published an essay giving his argument for a private marriage; in these letters he showed only too clearly that he privately believed, or almost believed, just the contrary. De Morgan later published portions of these letters, and a few extracts from them will show his grounds for criticising Brewster's reliability as a biographer. In one letter Brewster wrote: "I am trying to put together a

[28] De Morgan, *Newton: His Friend: His Niece*. Published posthumously by his wife, London, 1885.—In addition to an acute analysis of this problem, the book contains many interesting comments on Newton's life and his times.

[29] Brewster, Vol. II, pp. 270–281.

few pages *re* Halifax, and the wife you have given him. It is the most disagreeable portion of Newton's history. Newton's character is not protected, even if a private marriage could be proved, I have come to the conclusion, on grounds which I fear will not satisfy you, that Mrs. Barton *never lived* in Halifax's house." Having assumed this stand, he declared that: "Every means of defense, therefore, against such an hypothesis becomes obligatory on me as his biographer." If the function of a biographer is thus purely one of defense we should not be surprised that he could admit: "In writing the first volume of his life, I have been led to think Newton more *human* than I had formerly believed; and I must confess that I entertain very nearly, if not wholly, the views which you have published."[30] However the reader may decide from the evidence which will now be presented, Brewster's conclusions must be discounted as he, himself, acknowledged that he presented the case as counsel for the defense, and not as a dispassionate biographer.

When Montague, whom we shall now call Halifax, died he left Mrs. Barton a large legacy which aroused gossip and even scandal. Brewster sums up his opinion as to the motives of this legacy, as follows: "When the contents of this will became known after the death of Halifax, Mrs. Barton did not escape the censure of the world, though she was regarded by all who knew her as a woman of strict honour and virtue. During his lordship's life, and when a frequent visitor at the house of Newton, his affection for Mrs. Barton and his delight in her society, *never once excited the criticism of his contemporaries;* and there is not the slightest reason to believe that it exceeded that love and admiration which married men, and men of all ages, ever feel in the presence of physical and intellectual beauty. Halifax was not a libertine, and the very terms of affection in which he accounts for his liberality to Miss Barton are the most satisfactory proof that his love was virtuous and her conduct pure."[31] In the first place, the terms of affection which Halifax used towards Mrs. Barton would be natural and appropriate to a wife, but such terms of affection, addressed to an unmarried friend, thirty years of age, and accompanied with a rich legacy, are anything but a convincing proof that his love was virtuous, and her conduct pure; there were even persons so sceptical as to think they strengthened the contrary opin-

[30] These extracts are taken from De Morgan, pp. 109, 111.—It is needless to say that no such doubts are expressed in Brewster's volume where the incident is treated, and Newton is shown to be more *human* than in the first volume.

[31] Brewster, Vol. II, p. 271.

ion. If a marriage had been known then, or earlier, there would have been no censure or comment. In the next place, Halifax was a widower and not a married man, as his wife died in 1698, only two years after Newton moved to London. Brewster must have been profoundly ignorant of the history of the time if he did not know that the statesman was admired for his ability, but was almost universally characterised as a shameless libertine. There would have been no surprise in the popular mind if he were accused of a liaison with any woman; a contrary belief in this case would result from a conviction of the character of Newton and of his niece, and not from the virtue of Montague. The statement that she was a virtuous woman is quoted from Halifax's biography, but Brewster throws discredit on that evidence by later attacking the reliability of the work, —except when he agrees with it. As to the last point, that the criticism of Newton's contemporaries was not excited; the decision must rest on the evidence now to be given.

Voltaire, while he was in England during the years 1725 to 1728, and while both Newton and his niece were alive, became a fervent admirer of the Newtonian philosophy; and, in fact introduced it into France. In 1765, he published his *Lettres Philosophiques* to explain that philosophy and, with his customary malicious habit, he inserted this gibe as an illustration of the selfishness and low motives which actuate politicians even when they ostensibly reward merit. "I thought in my youth," he says, that Newton made his fortune by his extreme merit. I had supposed that the Court and the city of London named him Master of the Mint by acclamation. Not at all. Isaac Newton had a most charming niece, Madame Conduitt; she greatly pleased the Chancellor of the Exchequer, Halifax. The infinitesimal calculus and gravitation would have been of no assistance to him without a pretty niece."[32] Brewster's comment is that Voltaire's sneer scarcely deserves our notice; but a sneer by Voltaire was sure to influence public opinion; it usually was based on fact, and it certainly deserves serious attention. To prove that Newton did not owe his appointment to his niece is an easy matter of dates; when he was selected for his position, his niece was only fifteen years old and

[32] *Lettres Philosophiques,* number 21. "J'avais cru, dans ma jeunesse, que Newton avait fait sa fortune par son extrême mérite. Je m'étais imaginé que la cour et la ville de Londres l'avaient nommé par acclamation grand maître des monnaies du royaume. Point du tout. Isaac Newton avait une nièce assez aimable, nommée Madame Conduit; elle plut beaucoup au grand trésorier, Halifax. Le calcul infinitésimal et la gravitation ne lui auraient servi de rien sans une jolie nièce."

had not met Halifax, nor probably been in London. But as evidence that there was a widespread and contemporaneous opinion as to the relations of Halifax and Mrs. Catherine Barton, it is very significant. Voltaire may have got his facts mixed, but he must have got the scandal from conversation with the many persons he met in London, and it must have been pretty widely known, or his hit would have had no effect. To suppose that it insinuated a reward for a virtuous affection is not to know Voltaire, or the age.

The most circumstantial evidence that the rumour was widespread in London, is to be found in a book of fashionable gossip and scandal published in 1710 by Mrs. de la Rivière Manley.[33] In the book, Eginardus visits London, disguised as Constantinople and supposedly in the eighth century, and chronicles the eighteenth century gossip and scandal about its principal personages, also thinly disguised under Roman names. Halifax figures as *Julius Sergius* and Mrs. Barton as *Bartica.* The work was undoubtedly scandalous, and often indecent, but it had a great run and was reprinted several times. Now, such books may be notorious for not telling the truth, but they must serve up stories, highly spiced, which are widely whispered, or else they fail to attract attention.[34]

Eginardus visits Halifax in his palace on the Thames and describes its lavish luxury and its wanton debaucheries in terms appropriate to the Roman Emperors. Mrs. Manley knew his history intimately, and cynically recounts all the scandals of his life. In particular, Eginardus asks, "What is become of the charming *Bartica?*" And Sergius answers sobbing: "She's a traitress, an inconsistent proud baggage, yet I love her dearly, and have lavish'd myriads upon her, besides getting her worthy ancient parent a good post for connivance. But would you think it? She has other things in her head, and is grown so fantastic and so high, she wants me to marry her, or else I shall have no more of her truly; 'twas ever a proud slut." Again Eginardus: "He presented me the wine, and continued his indigna-

[33] *Memoirs of Europe, towards the close of the eighth century. Written by Eginardus, Secretary and Favourite to Charlemagne; and done into English by the translator of the New Atlantis.* London: Printed for John Morphew, near Stationers Hall, 1710.—As I could obtain no copy of this rare work, I am deeply indebted to Mr. F. E. Brasch, of the Library of Congress, who furnished me with a photostatic copy of the pages which refer to Halifax.

[34] Mrs. Manley was sufficiently important and decent to be a friend of Swift. He sent her "hints" for a sixpenny narrative of the stabbing of Harley by Guiscard; he tried to get her a pension; and he dined with her at least once apparently in the company of Mrs. Van Homrigh. De Morgan, *Newton,* etc. p. 34.

tion against *Bartica.* He told me, if he pined himself to death, he was resolved not to marry her whilst she was so saucy."[35]

And lastly as contemporary evidence, we have a statement of Halifax's biographer. In 1715, the year of his death, *The Works and Life of Halifax* was published anonymously. It contains the poetical works of Halifax and follows them with a eulogistic life of the statesman. The facts of his life are but lightly touched upon, the emphasis being placed on his parliamentary career with long reports of his speeches. The work is supposed to have been written by William Pittis and, as it is dedicated to Halifax's nephew and heir, we should regard it as an official record, sponsored by the family. "I am likewise," he writes, "to account for another omission in the course of this history, which is that of the death of the Lord Halifax's Lady; upon whose decease, his Lordship took a resolution of living single thence forward, and cast his eye upon the widow of one Colonel Barton, and niece to the famous Sir Isaac Newton, to be superintendant of his domestic affairs. But as this lady was young, beautiful, and gay, so those that were given to censure, passed a judgement upon her which she no ways merited, since she was a woman of strict honour and virtue; and though she might be agreeable to his Lordship in every particular, that noble peer's complaisance to her, proceeded wholly from the great esteem he had for her wit and most exquisite understanding, as will appear from what relates to her in his will at the close of these Memoirs."[36] Unless we throw out this evidence as entirely false, and there are no grounds for doing so and many for not doing so the meaning is obvious. Sometime after Halifax became a widower in 1698, Catherine Barton, mentioned as the widow instead of the sister of Colonel Barton, lived with him as his housekeeper. To refute the gossip that she was his mistress, the biographer states emphatically that her position was one of strict honour and virtue. No one will credit the idea that she left her uncle, who had shown her such tender affection and who certainly needed a housekeeper more than her friend, to be the hired superintendant of a fashionable widower's house. But, if she were married to him, the statement of the biographer is perfectly clear. The custom of maintaining marriages secret was far from uncommon at that time and if, for an unknown reason, they determined on that course, it

[35] *Memoirs of Europe*, pp. 294 and 295. The word *parent* refers to Newton as a relative in the French sense.

[36] *Life of Halifax*, p. 195.

would be expedient to establish her at the head of his table as a widow.[37] If she was not his wife we should have to accept what Nichols says of her in his edition of Swift:[38] "This lady, the widow of Colonel Barton, and niece to Sir Isaac Newton, was a distinguished beauty and is celebrated in three different poems in the fifth volume of Dryden's *Miscellanies*. In her widowhood she was entertained by Lord Halifax, who was very liberal to her at his death."[39]

It thus seems practically certain that Catherine Barton lived with Halifax in some capacity for several years, and the evidence is greatly strengthened by the provisions of his will which will be given later. We can also, with less certainty, fix the period during which this relationship existed. The date when she came to London to live with Newton is indicated as being some time before 1700 by a letter to her, from him.

Newton to Catherine Barton

To Mrs. Catherine Barton
At Mr. Gyre's at Pudlicot,
near Woodstock, in Oxfordshire.

London, Aug. 5, 1700.

Dear Niece,—I had your two letters, and am glad the air agrees with you; and though the fever is loth to leave you, yet I hope it abates, and that the remains of the small-pox are dropping off apace. Sir Joseph Tilley is leaving Mr. Toll's house, and it's probable I may succeed him. I intend to send you some wine by the next carrier, which I beg the favour of Mr. Gyre and lady to accept. My Lady Norris thinks you forget your promise to write her, and wants a letter from you. Pray let me know by the next how your face is, and

[37] Brewster says that this biography cannot be regarded as a work of any authority as it was written by some literary hack connected with the disreputable house of Curll.—Curll may have been a disreputable man but he published many respectable books. But this is of small consequence, since Brewster quotes the above passage and follows with the comment, "with the exception of the mistake that the lady was the widow of Colonel Barton, we may admit the truth of the preceding passage." In the *Memoirs of Newton,* Brewster admits the truth of the passage and explains it as meaning that she did not live in Montague's house. In one of his letters to De Morgan there is this passage: "I fear I shall make a poor story about Mrs. Conduitt. You have exhausted the subject. I find it distinctly stated by Conduitt that his wife *lived with Sir Isaac twenty years.* How then could she have been housekeeper to Lord Halifax? *I think his Lordship's biographer does not speak the truth.*

[38] *Cf. Works of Dr. Jonathan Swift.* Ed. by Bowyer, Nichols, et al, London, 1765–1779. The passage is one of Nichols's notes (Vol. XVI, p. 135) on a letter of Swift to Lady Worsley—April 19, 1730. In the letter Swift enquires, "How is our old friend Mrs. Barton? (I forget her new name.) I saw her three years ago, at Court, almost dwindled to an echo, and hardly knew her."

[39] The word entertained was then regularly used in the sense of *entretenu,* or kept.

if the fever be going. Perhaps warm milk from the cow may help to abate it.—I am your very loving uncle,

Is. NEWTON.[40]

While there is no explicit statement that she was then living with him, its whole tone is that of a letter written to one who had left home for a visit. If she had not been in London, and in her uncle's house, the reference to Mr. Toll's house and to Lady Norris would not be matters that would have been mentioned. As Newton set up housekeeping in Jermyn Street in the autumn of 1696 when his niece was sixteen years old and had probably finished her education, it is natural to assume that she became an inmate of the house at that time, or shortly afterwards. The time of her coming to London has been confused by a memorandum of Conduitt which states, "that nobody ever lived with him [Newton] but my wife, who was with him near twenty years, before and after her marriage [to Conduitt]." As Newton lived in London thirty-one years, it leaves about ten years unaccounted for. Brewster interprets this statement to mean not only that no one except Mrs. Barton lived with Newton, but also that she lived with no one else during his life. He then fixes the date of her going to London in 1701, in spite of the evidence of the letter just quoted. Thus, she lived with her uncle, by his reckoning, sixteen years before her marriage to Conduitt in 1717, and four years after it. As Newton did not die till six years later, Brewster assumes, without any evidence, that the Conduitts spent them separated from him, and mostly at their country estate.[41] Such a supposition seems most unlikely as those were just the years when the advanced age and infirmities of Newton required the companionship of his niece, and also they were years when Conduitt assisted at the Mint. To make my estimate agree chronologically with Conduitt's statement of "near twenty years," I should say that she lived with her uncle from about 1698 till his death, except for nine years when she lived with Halifax.[42] The chief reason for assigning the year 1706 as the date of her removal to Halifax's house, is because in that year he

40 Brewster, Vol. II, p. 213. *Cf. Portsmouth Collection.*

41 Mrs. Conduitt owned the country estate bequeathed to her by Halifax, but there is no record that they lived in it. In Newton's inventory, there appears the item of "Manuscripts in a box sealed up at the house of John Conduitt, Esq." This inventory is dated May 5, 1727, nearly two months after Newton's death. This house was in Hanover Square.

42 The dates for the above reckoning are as follows: from 1698 [?] to 1706 with Newton; from 1706 to 1715, with Halifax as "superintendent of his domestic affairs"; after Halifax's death, from 1715 to 1717, with Newton; from 1717 to 1727 with Newton, as wife of Conduitt.

made a codicil to his will in which he bequeathed his jewels and three thousand pounds to Mrs. Catherine Barton and, in the same year, an annuity of two hundred pounds was purchased in the name of Newton to be held in trust for her by Halifax.[43]

It is proper now to discuss the provisions of Halifax's will which gave the fuel to the smouldering fire of gossip and scandal about Newton. His will was drawn up and witnessed on the 10th of April, 1706.[44] By it, he left his entire estate to his relatives, with small bequests to his friends and servants; neither Newton nor his niece is mentioned. But, two days later, he added a codicil to "give and bequeath to Mrs. Catherine Barton, all the jewels I have at the time of my death; and likewise three thousand pounds as a small token of the great love and affection I have long had for her."

On the first of February, 1712/3, Halifax revoked his first codicil, and wrote a new one in which he gave to Newton one hundred pounds, "as a mark of the great honour and esteem I have for so great a man." He then gave to Mrs. Catherine Barton five thousand pounds, the rangership and lodge of Bushy Park with all its furnishings for her life, and the rents from his manor of Apscourt to keep the estate in repair and good order. "These gifts and legacies, I leave to her as a token of the sincere love, affection, and esteem I have long had for her person, and as a small recompense for the pleasure and happiness I have had in her conversation."[45]

[43] Brewster argues that since it was bought in Newton's name, it must have been bought by him,—a conclusion which does not necessarily follow. If Newton did pay for the annuity I should regard it as a generous gift to provide for her marriage to Halifax. I certainly cannot agree with Brewster who calls it "a debt due to his favourite niece whom he had educated and who had for twenty years kept his house." In the first place, when the annuity was made she had kept his house for only five or six years; and, in the next place, most persons would assume that Newton, by supporting her in comparative luxury and by introducing her to the best intellectual and fashionable society of the country, had laid a heavy obligation on her. It is difficult, too, to believe that he could buy such an annuity. According to all accounts, he had saved little, or nothing, when he went to London. It is most improbable that he could maintain his establishment on his income and within ten years invest from £2000 to £2400 in an annuity for the benefit of even a favourite niece. If Newton were not the purchaser, it must have been Halifax.

[44] The will and its codicils are given verbatim in the *Life of Halifax* as an appendix.

[45] Attention should again be called to the fact that *conversation* then meant the general social intercourse of persons living together. It was also commonly used to express sexual intercourse. Brewster here, as in several other important cases, falls into the confusion which results from ignorance of eighteenth century usage. He justifies his interpretation of their Platonic friendship by this statement: "Miss Barton presided at her uncle's table, and by her 'excellent conversation' [i. e., table-talk], excited the love and affection even of some of her married friends." I fear if Brewster had made the same statement to her contemporaries, he would have been horrified by the interpretation which would have been put upon it. Flamsteed gave point to the common interpretation of Halifax's gift by quoting it, and simply italicising the words *excellent conversation*.

To close this long discussion, I shall quote a letter, which De Morgan considered to be a proof of the marriage.

Newton to a Relative

Leicester Fields, May 23, 1715.

Sir John,

I am concerned that I must send an excuse for not waiting upon you before your journey into Lincolnshire. The concern I am in for the loss of my Lord Halifax, and the *circumstances in which I stand related to his family,* will not suffer me to go abroad till his funeral is over. And therefore I can only send this letter to wish you and your lady and family a good journey into Lincolnshire, and all health and happiness during your stay there. And upon your first return to London I will wait upon you, and endeavour by frequenter visits to make amends for the defect of them at present.

I am, Sir,

Your most humble and most obedient servant,

ISAAC NEWTON.[46]

The Sir John of Lincolnshire can only be the Sir John Newton who was reputed to be a kinsman and the head of the family. De Morgan considers that the phrase he has italicised is a formal statement of Newton's relationship by marriage to Halifax, made four days after his death.

There is little more to be said about this puzzling incident in Newton's life. The evidence is convincing to me that Mrs. Catherine Barton lived in Montague's house in some capacity for several years. It is also equally convincing to me that neither Newton's, nor Montague's, family, nor their intimate associates regarded the connection as in any degree questionable. Newton's letter to Sir John, whom he considered as the head of the family, establishes a recognised relationship with Montague and the form of his reference puts it in the class of a proper one. Also, Montague's biographer goes

[46] De Morgan, *Newton,* p. 49—This letter was sold by Christie and Manson in 1856 as part of a quantity of Newtoniana owned by Thomas Rodd, and bought by De Morgan's friend, Mr. Libri, who showed it to him. The handwriting was declared to be Newton's. The letter was unknown to Brewster. But, he would probably have claimed it to be a forgery on the evidence of the signature. In the *Athenæum,* he asserted, in connection with some other letters, that the full name *Isaac* occurring in a signature was a strong presumption of forgery as he recollected only one instance in which the signature was written with the full name. This is a palpable error. In the correspondence published by Edleston there are five letters in English and one in Latin signed *Isaac;* in Flamsteed's correspondence, one; in the Macclesfield Collection, four; and in Brewster's own *Life,* where very few letters are quoted in full, there are two in English and one in Latin.

out of his way to testify to her strict honour and virtue as if he were answering rumours to the contrary. Again, much dependence can be placed on Swift's admiration for her, as he was critical in regard to the reputation of his female friends. Lastly, Newton's life was passed in the strong light of publicity and, while the prevailing attitude towards female virtue was easy, he could not have escaped censure. On the other hand, it is incredible that she, a member of a fashionable set, and enjoying an ample income, should have accepted the position of hired superintendent of Montague's household. We are thus driven to the conclusion that they were married. Why it was kept secret will probably never be known. The only plausible reason is that Montague had suffered once from the stings of the wits because of his first marriage. And he, a great but parvenu nobleman, may have feared to reawaken further gibes if he allied himself with a plebeian family. No help can be obtained from Newton's papers. I found only two or three memoranda which bore on the subject and they merely referred to the transfer of the annuity and of the estate from the heir of Halifax to Mrs. Catherine Barton. If there was a marriage, it may come to light some day from the examination of parish registers; otherwise the question seems likely never to be answered satisfactorily.

Newton may have found in his new occupation a full and satisfactory life, and have persisted in his resolve to be done with scientific investigations; but his phenomenal mastery of mathematics persisted to the end of his life, and only needed a spur to call it forth. A remarkable instance of this is shown in his famous solution of the brachistochrone. In June, 1696, John Bernoulli challenged the mathematicians of the world, as was a frequent custom, to solve the two problems: 1. To find the curve connecting two points, at different heights and not in the same vertical line, along which a body acted upon only by gravity will fall in the shortest time. 2. To find the curve, having this same property (the brachistochrone), such that the two segments of a straight line, drawn through the curve from any given point, will, when raised to any given power and added together, make the same sum. Bernoulli allowed six months for the solutions, but, at the request of Leibniz who had solved one of them, he extended the time for a year longer in order that all contestants should have an equal chance. On the 29th of January, 1696/7, the challenge was received by Newton from France and, *on the next day,* he sent to Montague, who was then President of the Royal Society, solutions of both problems. They were published anonymously in the January number of the *Transactions,* and were read before the Society in February. It is said that Bernoulli recognised the author from the sheer power and originality of the work; "*tanquam ex ungue leonem.*"[47]

Another instance of Newton's ability to solve mathematical problems "at sight" is well-known. In 1716, Leibniz, who was smarting under the accusation by the friends of Newton of plagiary, and of mathematical inferiority, sent a problem as a postscript in a letter to the Abbé Conti "for the purpose of feeling the pulse of the English analysts."[48] The problem proposed was to determine the equation of a curve which will intersect at right angles an infinite number of curves of a given nature, expressible by a general method. It is credibly reported that Newton received this problem about five o'clock, while returning home from the Mint weary with the day's business, and that he solved it the same night before going to bed.

To the examples previously given of Newton's courtesy towards young men, and his interest in their ideas, the following may be added. While he was in the thick of his work on the recoinage, he received a letter from John Harington, an undergraduate of Oxford, explaining a method of representing harmonic musical ratios by additions to the sides of a right-angled triangle, and alluding to the bearing the subject had upon the principles of architectural beauty. The artistic side of music does not seem to have interested Newton. At least, he never went to the opera but once and afterwards criticised it in this pithy manner: "There was too much of a good thing, 'twas like a surfeit of dinner. The first act, I heard with pleasure; the second stretched my patience; at the third, I ran away."[49] On the other hand, he was profoundly affected by the significance of the constant and unaccountable occurrence of simple geometrical ratios in physical phenomena. He found in musical harmony the principle of law and order in the cosmos, and believed that the Creator revealed Himself to us through our appreciation of those mathematical ratios. Indeed, we can assign the cause of his predilection and ad-

[47] Catherine Barton is the authority for this anecdote. A short note signed with her initials C. C. states: "1697. Bernoulli sent problem.—I. N. home at 4 P.M.—finished it by 4 A.M." *Cf. Portsmouth Collection.* As both of these problems have an important bearing on the Leibniz controversy they will be referred to in that connection.

[48] *Des Maizeaux Collection,* 2d. Ed., Tome II, *p.* 10.

[49] Letter of Stukeley to Mead, *Portsmouth Collection.*

miration for the classical geometers to their use of the pure geometrical method. In his discovery of the law of universal gravitation and his elucidation of its effects by the classical method, his greatest satisfaction was that he had finished the beautiful edifice which they had so well begun and had established forever,—

"Harmonisch all das All durchklingen."

In this advocacy of the Pythagorean-Platonic philosophy, he was following the ideas of his great predecessors, Copernicus, Kepler, and Galileo. But he went even further than they: "He thought Pythagoras's music of the spheres was intended to typify gravity and, as he makes the sounds and notes depend on the size of the strings, so gravity depends on the density of matter."[50] So he laid aside his own work to write to a young man a letter, too long to give in full, but which is cited as a model of wise and courteous encouragement.

Newton to Harington

Sir,

By the hands of your friend, Mr. Conset, I was favoured with your demonstration of the harmonic ratios, from the ordinances of the 47th of Euclid. I think it very explicit and more perfect than the *Helicon* of Ptolemy, as given by the learned Doctor Wallis. Your observations hereon are very just, and afford me some hints which, when time allows, I would pursue, and gladly assist you with any thing I can, to encourage your curiosity and labours in these matters. I see you have reduced, from this wonderful proposition, the inharmonic as well as the coincidences of agreement, all resulting from the given lines three, four, and five. You observe that the multiples hereof furnish those ratios that afford pleasure to the eye in architectural designs: I have, in former considerations, examined these things, and wish my other employments would permit my further noticing thereon, as it deserves much our strict scrutiny, and tends to exemplify the simplicity in all the works of the Creator; however, I shall not cease to give my thoughts towards this subject at my leisure. I beg you to pursue these ingenious speculations, as your genius seems to incline you to mathematical researches.

. . . .

In fine, I am inclined to believe some general laws of the Creator prevailed with respect to the agreeable or unpleasing affections of all our senses; at least the supposition does not derogate from the

[50] Conduitt's MSS. *Portsmouth Collection*.

wisdom or power of God, and seems highly consonant to the macrocosm in general. Whatever else your ingenious labours may produce I shall attentively consider, but have such matters on my mind, that I am unable to give you more satisfaction at this time; however, I beg your modesty will not be a means of preventing my hearing from you, as you proceed in these curious researches; and be assured of the best services in the power of

Your humble Servant,

Is. NEWTON.[51]

[Jermyn Street] May 30, 1698.

It is pleasant to keep this charming letter of Newton in mind for it will be necessary to narrate a series of exceedingly regrettable quarrels which marred these later years of his life.

Flamsteed notes that he sometimes visited Newton at the Mint, or at his house in Jermyn Street. "We continued civil: but he was not so friendly as formerly, because I could not [confirm] Mr. Halley's and Dr. Gregory's assertions concerning his corrections of the Horroxian lunar theory." However that may be, Newton paid a visit to the Observatory, on December 4, 1698, at the time of evening service, in order to obtain twelve more computed places of the moon which he needed for the work he was then doing on the lunar theory. The importance of these favours must be borne constantly in mind, for, as Baily remarks, there was no other person, either in England or on the continent, who could supply this essential material for developing the theory.

In the autumn of 1698, Wallis had written several letters to the Astronomer to say that he was publishing the third volume of his *Collected Works* and was printing in an appendix some Latin letters, written by other men, amongst which he would be glad to include Flamsteed's discovery of the parallax of the pole-star.[52] It will not, he adds, be to your disadvantage to publish it there; it will be

[51] Edleston, p. 302—While Newton did not follow Kepler in his whole-hearted acceptance of the Pythagorean cult of numerical harmony, he was profoundly influenced by that astronomer's belief that the purpose and plan of the Creator was revealed to us by a search for such ratios. In the curious treatise, *Harmon. Mundi,* Kepler seeks for the rules of this divine principle and, as usual, mixes much acute observation with his mystical hypotheses. Newton outgrew the mysticism of Kepler, but he advised Harington to study such acute suggestions of Kepler as the following, quoted by Edleston: "Wheresoever, in architecture, we examine accurately the proportions of lengths, to breadths, and depths, they are found, even by observers unskilled in mathematics, to be very closely in harmonic ratios." The truth of this dictum is appreciated by anyone who seeks to understand the supreme beauty of the Parthenon.

[52] Flamsteed was the first to discover an apparent motion of the fixed stars. He assigned the cause to a parallax, or displacement of a star, produced by the orbital motion of the

an honour to you, and to our nation, to have it thus announced that you were the first to discover a stellar parallax.

During this correspondence with Wallis, Flamsteed wrote to his friend Colson to inquire about a malicious report which had been reported to him by his servant. According to this story, Colson and a Colonel Bruce "had told him that Mr. Newton had perfected the theory of the moon *from Mr. Halley's observations,* and imparted it to him, with leave to publish it; and that Mr. Halley would publish it in a short time." Flamsteed, remembering Newton's solemn promises not to divulge his observations to anyone, and not to publish this theory before it had first been shown to him, wished to have the report verified as he thought it must have been a mistake of his servant's, and might injure Halley with Newton or Colonel Bruce. He concluded his letter with this simple statement of a fact: "Mr. Newton's theory, when perfected, must needs agree with my observations, since it is built, as he freely owns, upon them and his doctrine of gravitation: and the one without the other will not do the business; but both together will, as he says himself. Mr. Halley's could be of no use to him." It should also be remembered that Flamsteed's suspicion was justified as Newton did, let us hope thoughtlessly, break his promise and give the information both to Gregory and Halley.

Flamsteed complied with Wallis's request and, either to protect himself from Halley and Gregory, whom he profoundly distrusted, or from the pardonable vanity of wishing to have his aid to Newton publicly expressed, he inserted a paragraph to be published with his discovery of the parallax, which brought down on him the wrath of that sensitive person, Newton.

His reference was as follows: "Contraxeram etiam cum Do. Newtono, doctissimo, tunc temporis in academia Cantabrigiensi Professore, necessitudinem, cui lunae loca ab observationibus meis ante habitis deducta 150 dederam, cum locis simul è tabulis meis ad earum tempora supputatis tum similia in posterum prout assequerer promiseram cum elementis calculi mei in ordine ad emendationem theoriae lunaris Horroccianae qua in re spero eum successus consecuturum expectationi suae pares."[53]

Earth. In this, he was wrong as that parallax is too small to have been observed with his instruments. The true cause of his seeming parallax was later proved by Bradley to be due to the aberration, or bending, of the rays of light.

[53] *Portsmouth Collection.*—It may be translated as follows: "I had contracted a friendship with Mr. Newton, then the most learned professor of the time in Cambridge University. To

The history of the breach in the friendship of Newton and Flamsteed, caused by this paragraph, is easy to follow from extant documents;[54] and however irritable in temper Flamsteed may often have been, he acted throughout this episode with dignity and moderation. Wallis wrote to him again in December that the letter on parallax had been translated into Latin and he found it to be quite proper for publication. He had sent the sheets to Flamsteed by Dr. Gregory, who was on his way to London and would deliver them to him in person. He also advised that an English version should be published in the Royal Society *Transactions.* It seems that Gregory was accustomed to meet his friends in Hindmarsh's Shop in Cornhill and, either on his initiative or on their advice, he acquainted Newton with the proposed reference to his lunar theory. Newton, evidently, objected violently to any published statement being made about his work as if he had needed help; for Wallis, at the end of the month, wrote to Flamsteed that a friend of his, and of Newton, had requested him not to print the paragraph, "which speaks of your giving Mr. Newton observations of the moon."

As soon as Flamsteed heard this news, he, at once, wrote to Newton on 2 January, 1698/9, to explain the circumstances of his obnoxious paragraph. He began his letter by saying he had been in the neighbourhood of Jermyn Street on that day but had not called as he had nothing to offer except his respects and best wishes on Newton's birthday. Nor would he write now if he had not had a letter from Wallis. He then reviewed the history of the affair and quoted the obnoxious paragraph. He gave as his sole reason for agreeing to publish his discovery of the parallax that, by thus announcing the results of his work at the Observatory, he could "silence some busy people who are always asking *why I did not print.*"

The letter concludes as follows:

Flamsteed to Newton

. . . .

Sir, this is the paragraph, [as quoted; cf. *supra*] and *all of it.* I think there is not near so much in it as I acknowledge to myself, and (I have heard from other worthy gentlemen) you have acknowledged

him I had given 150 positions of the moon deduced from observations which I had made previously, and I promised to supply him with additional observations as I should make them together with my principles of calculation. This I did, in order to correct the lunar theory of Horrox, and I trust that he may have a success equal to his expectations."

[54] See Baily, pp. 160–169, Brewster, Vol. II, pp. 476–479, and the *Portsmouth Collection.*

to them, and therefore cannot think it was from any intimation of yours, (tho' he says it would be *displeasing to you if it were printed,*) but out of a design to ingratiate with you that he put an arrest upon this paragraph. I think the word *Horroccianae* may be omitted, tho' I put it in because you allow that theory as far as it goes; you found the faults of it by the differences from my observation. He was a countryman, and tho' your theory will be new in that, (tho' you give us the reasons, and derive it from natural cause,) yet he gave the groundplot, and it will be an honour both to you and me to do him justice.

Sir, My observations lie the king and nation in at least 5000 lb. I have spent above 1000 lb. out of my own pocket in building, instruments, and hiring a servant to assist me now near 24 years. 'Tis time for me (and I am now ready for it) to let the world see I have done something that may answer this expense, and I therefore hope you will not deny me the honour of having said that I have been useful to you in your attempts to restore the theory of the moon. I might have added the observations of the comets, places given you formerly of the superior planets, and observations at the same time with the moon's, but this I thought would look like boasting, and therefore I forbore it.

I desire you would please to let me know by a line whether Dr. Gregory ever shewed you my letter, I mean Dr. Wallis his translation of it, which I think I have altered in the paragraph above from what it was, but cannot say in what words, because I returned the Doctor his copy, with my transcript of it enlarged and altered, together; but whenever 'tis printed, you will find it agree with the copy above exactly.

Sir, I am told Dr. Gregory is to be tutor in mathematics to the Duke of Gloucester, *which place, I was told some months ago* (when the settling of his household was first discourst of) *was designed for me.* To make a variance betwixt you and me and Dr. Wallis, and to engage you to procure him the favour of Mr. Montague, I am apt to believe he recommends himself in this business. He thinks, perhaps, it will depreciate me, and keep me from being his competitor. Let him not trouble himself. I have an interest much beyond his whenever I please to move that way, but I do not think the Duke yet fit for a mathematical tutor, or that he will be this four or five years. I hate flattery, and shall not go to Court on this account till I am sent for, or have notice that I am desired. That place might, indeed, afford me the opportunity of procuring help for my assistance, or I could defray the charges out of pay; but I fear it would be as prejudicial to me otherwise, and therefore shall not move to traverse the Doctor's designs, except he force me to it by his *treacherous behaviour*.

Sir, I beg an answer to this letter speedily, and you need tell me no more but that you have seen the paragraph before, or not seen it; that you gave such orders to Dr. Gregory or not, that I may return an answer to Dr. Wallis; and hereafter, if any such flatterers as he come to say any thing to you that may tend to make a difference betwixt us, pray tell them you will inform me, and you will forthwith be rid of them. I shall always use the same course towards you, whereby a friendship that began early may continue long and be happy to both of us, which, through God's blessing, I hope it may, at least I shall always endeavour it, being ever, Sir,

Your most affectionate friend and humble servant,

JOHN FLAMSTEED, M. R.

[P. S.] Pray enquire what company Dr. Gregory keeps, that you may not be deceived in his character. The Scotch think to carry all before them by the Bishop of Salisbury, whom I esteem, (next the Bishop of Wester above the rest of the clergy,) but I cannot think him wise in placing his countrymen about the young Duke.

To Mr. Isaak Newton
Warden of the Mint,
at his house in German Street, near
St. James's, London.—These present.[55]

When Newton ignored this explanation, Flamsteed wrote to him again to know whether the interdiction was his own or merely an officiousness of Dr. Gregory. And he also wrote to Wallis: "I expected an answer [from Newton] on Thursday: and none coming, wrote to him then again to desire him to let me know whether what Dr. Gregory had wrote to you was by his direction or not; and having no return conclude he thinks not fit to take notice of it, or that he is not in town. I think it concerns not Dr. Gregory to have been thus busy, and that neither you nor I ought to take any more notice of it than Mr. Newton does; and, therefore, you may please to let that paragraph, and the next, stand as it is, without alteration."

But Flamsteed had not long to wait to learn Newton's true feel-

[55] *Portsmouth Collection.*

ing, his second letter had loosed all the pent-up hostility which had been for a long time suppressed with difficulty, and he was overwhelmed to receive what Baily moderately terms that most extraordinary reply, and what most persons would name that most unwarranted insult.

Newton to Flamsteed

Jermyn Street, Jan. 6, 1698/9.

Sir,

Upon hearing occasionally that you had sent a letter to Dr. Wallis about the parallax of the fixed stars to be printed, and that you had mentioned therein with respect to the theory of the moon, I was concerned to be publicly brought upon the stage about what, perhaps, will never be fitted for the public, and thereby the world put into an expectation of what, perhaps, they are never like to have. I do not love to be printed upon every occasion, much less to be dunned and teased by foreigners about mathematical things, or to be thought by our own people to be *trifling* away my time about them, when I should be about the King's business. And, therefore, I desired Dr. Gregory to write to Dr. Wallis against printing that clause which related to that theory, and mentioned me about it. You may let the world know, if you please, how well you are stored with observations of all sorts, and what calculations you have made towards rectifying the theories of the heavenly motions. But there may be cases wherein your friends should not be published without their leave; and therefore I hope you will so order the matter that I may not on this occasion, be brought upon the stage. I am your humble servant,

Is. Newton.[56]

However irritable Flamsteed's temper may have been, he kept it in admirable control through this whole trying incident. He contented himself with the following dignified rebuke.

[56] We could have no more glaring instance of Brewster's bias and prejudiced opinions against all those who came into contact with Newton than his views on this letter. In his first and small *Life of Newton* published in 1831, he made the singular mistake of quoting it as a letter *from Flamsteed to Newton* (v. p. 243) and says that it is "characteristic of Flamsteed" to whom he assigns a vicious temper. And he draws the conclusion that "Flamsteed, not sufficiently aware of the importance of the lunar theory, received Newton's requests [for observations] as if they were idle intrusions [on the King's business at the Observatory], in which the interests of science were but slightly concerned."—But, when he wrote his later and larger *Memoirs of Newton*, published in 1855, he had learned his mistake and correctly cited Newton as the author; and, although he there reluctantly admitted that Flamsteed had

Flamsteed to Newton

January 10, 1698/9.

Sir,

Yours dated Jermyn-street, January 6th, arrived here last night, the 9th, with the general post mark and charge upon it, as if it had come from some place less than 80 miles remote from London. I waited for it from the 2nd to the 7th instant, Saturday night; and then wrote to Dr. Wallis, that I thought he needed not take any notice of Dr. Gregory's letter to him, to forbear printing that clause in mine wherein I had mentioned you, since you took no notice of two of mine I had wrote to you that week, concerning it, which made me think, you thought it not worth your while to concern yourself about it. Now I find you did desire Dr. Gregory to write so to him, I shall write to him myself to alter that passage, so as he was advised, and so as I believe you will find no just cause of offence in it: my letter goes to him this night, the altered paragraph you have at the foot of this letter.

I did not think I could have disobliged you, by letting the world know that the King's Observatory had furnished you with 150 places of the moon, derived from observations here made, and compared with tables; in order to correct her theory: since (not to seem to boast) I said nothing of what more it has furnished you freely with. As I had leisure, and Mr. Halley has not stuck to tell it abroad, both at the Society and elsewhere, that you had completed her theory, and given it to him as a secret, I could not think you would be unwilling our nation should have the honor of furnishing you with so many and good observations for this work, as were not (I speak it without boasting) to be had elsewhere: or that it should be said you were about a new work, which others said you had perfected. I thought not it could be any diminution to you, since you pretend not

freely and fully supplied his observations, and had recognised the importance of the lunar theory, he still insisted on Flamsteed's indecency of language and envious ill-temper. Since he must now admit that the letter was *from Newton to Flamsteed,* he softened his criticism of it to these gentle terms (Vol. II, p. 204 *seq.*): "If Newton had written this letter as a simple expression of his feelings . . . we should have regarded it as unseemly"; however, Newton may have been offended at the tone of Flamsteed's letters. "But independently of these circumstances, Newton was *entitled to express his feelings* at being 'brought upon the stage,' and thus exposed to being dunned and teased by foreigners." He merely wished to stifle any rumour that he was occupied with anything but "the King's business."—Brewster is also wrong when he attributes the reference "to the King's business" to Flamsteed; I shall prove later that it was pointed at Bernoulli who had tried by his problem of the brachistocrone to expose Newton's ignorance of the calculus.

to be an observer yourself. I thought it might give some people a better notion of what was doing here, than had been impressed upon them by others, whom God forgive. You will pardon me this freedom, and excuse me when I tell you, if foreigners come and trouble you it is not my fault, but those who think to recommend themselves to you, by advancing the fame of your works as much as they possibly can. I have sometimes told some ingenious men, that more time and observations are required to perfect the theory; but I found it was represented as a little piece of detraction, which I hate, and therefore was forced to be silent. I wonder that hints should drop from your pen, as if you looked on my business as *trifling;* you thought it not so, surely, when you resided at Cambridge: its property is not altered: I think it has produced something considerable already, and may do more, if I can but procure help to work up the observations I have under my hands, which it was one of the designs of my *Letter to Dr. Wallis* to move for. I doubt not but it will be of some use to our ingenious travellers and sailors; and other persons that come after me, will think their time as little misspent in these studies, as those did that have gone before me. The works of the Eternal Providence I hope will be a little better understood through your labours and mine, than they were formerly. Think me not proud for this expression; I look on pride as the worst of sins: humility as the greatest virtue. This makes me excuse small faults in all mankind, bear great injuries without resentment, and resolve to maintain a real friendship with ingenious men: to assist them what lies in my power, without the regard of any interest, but that of doing good by obliging them.

To Mr. Newton.[57] [JOHN FLAMSTEED.]

It is claimed that Newton was justified in objecting to Flamsteed's published notice because it would distract him from the King's business, but he permitted himself other distractions, he could find time to write to Harington on harmony and could carry on his work on the lunar theory; it is also claimed that the notice was itself objectionable, but it is difficult to see on what grounds.[58] I fear that

[57] Baily, p. 168.

[58] As contemporary evidence that Wallis found nothing objectionable in Flamsteed's conduct, I may quote a postscript of a letter from him to Newton: "I don't apprehend any prejudice to you in printing it, being merely true matter of fact: and it seems of concernment to him [Flamsteed] to satisfy the world (from this and other things mentioned) that he is not idle; though he be not yet in readiness to publish the whole of his observations (for which he is frequently called upon), it being a great work."

those, who admire him most, will the most regret that such a man as Newton could display such petulance and ill-temper. We must agree with Flamsteed that he was misled by flattery, and that he became increasingly autocratic and difficult to deal with as he grew older. But we should bear in mind the temptations to which he was subjected. It would be difficult for any one to maintain a modest and just attitude who was publicly compared to a god. He was much influenced by Halley and Gregory, both of whom were intensely jealous of his reputation and resented the idea that anyone aided him in his divine inventions. They had the selfish, but pardonable, enthusiasm of the discoverers of genius; one of them could look upon the *Principia* as due to his initiative and persistence, and the other as the first teacher of its philosophy; and they both wished to keep him to themselves. Nor should we be surprised that self-interest influenced them, as Flamsteed so bitterly insisted. Newton was now an important personage with the influence of the all-powerful Montague at his command. Halley had obtained his position at the Mint, and Gregory his professorship at Oxford through the influence of Newton. And one was shortly to be offered two teaching positions and a post on a scientific expedition, while the other looked to be given the lucrative tutorship to the Duke of Gloucester if Flamsteed was correctly informed. Nor can we doubt that they resented deeply Flamsteed's continual diatribes against their characters. In my own mind, I can find some little excuse for Newton's outburst; I believe that Flamsteed was intensely irritating to him personally and, by the repeated warning not to be deceived by those who professed to be his friends, finally broke down his self-control.

It is extraordinary that those who suffered from Newton's suspicious and difficult temperament,—Flamsteed, Locke, Leibniz, Pepys, Whiston, Montague,—preserved a profound respect for him. Either they recognised his essential rectitude and nobility of character and forgave this one weakness, or else they were overawed by the sheer majesty of his genius, "that divinity which doth hedge a King," and submitted to what in another would be deemed a personal affront.

The friendship between Newton and Flamsteed was ended by this episode, but they continued to meet occasionally. Flamsteed satisfied his wounded feelings by a retort which was ingeniously contrived to sting Newton in his tenderest spot by the insinuation of a reproof drawn from the Bible. In a letter to a friend, Mr. Lowthorp, he first warns him to be careful in his behaviour to Newton. He tells him that he had been three times to call during which they had discussed the publication of his own catalogue of stars and the old complaint of the pernicious interference of friends. He then narrates this incident during his last visit: "I believe him to be a good man at bottom, but, through his natural temper, suspicious, and too easy to be possessed with calumnies, especially such as are impressed with raillery. To cure him of it, finding a Bible in his room where I waited his rising (for I got to his house before he was up, and spent a part of the time I waited in reading,) meeting with a sheet of paper I wrote upon it this distich, which I remembered from a late satire—

'A bantering spirit has our men possessed,
And wisdom is become a standing jest.'
Read Jeremiah, ch. ix to the 10th verse.

I do not know whether he has seen it, but I think he cannot take it amiss if he has; and if he reflects a little on it, he will find I have given him a seasonable caution against his credulity, and showed him the way of the world much better than his politics or a play could do."[59]

There was some excuse for Newton's irritability and dislike to having attention directed towards any activity except his duties at the Mint. He, a scholar inexperienced in executive work, had been brought to London for the responsible work of the recoinage, and his position was a target for the complaints and fears that arose from the desperate financial straits in which the recoinage had temporarily involved the nation. As he evidently desired to retain his office, he may well have feared lest any attention drawn to his scientific work might arouse the criticism that he was neglecting his duties, and so give the enemies of Montague the excuse to displace him. In fact, he had every reason to be worried about the future. It might have been thought necessary to enlist temporarily the services of such a man as he to meet an emergency; but the recoinage was now finished, and the office would, under normal conditions, return to its

[59] Baily, pp. 174–176.—The passage of Jeremiah, referred to, is a tremendous indictment of deceit and slander. Its spirit may be judged from this verse: "They will deceive every one his neighbour, and will not speak the truth: they have taught their tongue to speak lies, and weary themselves to commit iniquity. Thine habitation is in the midst of deceit." One would like to know what was Newton's reaction; whether he repented, or stiffened his pride.

previous condition of being a sinecure to be held by a needy gentleman or a political henchman; also, at this time, the Whigs were in desperate straits, and Montague was fighting the final battle which ended in his downfall. Under these circumstances, it was only too probable that he would share the misfortunes of his party and of his patron. That he considered his position to be precarious and temporary, is suggested by the fact that he had retained his fellowship and professorship at Cambridge. It was a great tribute to his work that he was not only kept in office, but was promoted to be Master and Worker of the Mint at a much larger salary. From now on, since the duties of his position were not onerous and he could regard it as permanent, we find him engaged in many outside interests, and enjoying the honours which came to him.

The French Academy of Sciences had been remodelled and, in 1699, Newton was created one of the first eight Foreign Associates. It is surprising to us that his name appeared as low as seventh in the list. If he had then had the reputation which later he enjoyed, he certainly would have been the first choice, instead of Leibniz; and we can surmise that the Academy would have honoured him further by restricting its first list of foreign members to him, alone. He also became interested in the Royal Society and began to attend its meetings regularly. Montague, who was retiring from public offices, resigned the Presidency and the Lord Chancellor Somers was elected in his stead. In August, Newton exhibited an improved form of his sextant, an instrument for determining longitude at sea. For some reason, perhaps because Hooke, as usual, laid claim to the discovery, it was not followed up. The instrument was rediscovered, years later, and is now known as Hadley's sextant. He also, with Aston and Flamsteed, was elected a member of the Council.[60]

The German Diet had passed a decree, in the year 1699, to reform the Julian Calendar. The two principal provisions were that the day after February 18, 1700, should be changed to March first, and that Easter Sunday should be determined by astronomical observations of the vernal equinox and the full moon following it. Thus began the long confusion of double dating. The second provision affected a church festival and aroused much discussion between theologians and scientists. At the request of Leibniz, the

60 This is on the authority of Edleston. On the other hand Weld, in his *History of the Royal Society,* Vol. I, p. 365, states that he was elected into the Council for the first time, and the Presidency on the same day, in 1703. And he gives the jealousy of Hooke as the reason why he had not been called earlier into the Council.

Royal Society took up the question and referred it to Newton. With Flamsteed's assistance, he drew up a schedule calculating the differences of the time of the equinox at the principal observatories.[61] In the same year, a M. du Verger sent a letter from Rome to the Society in which he offered a solution of those three famous problems,—the trisection of an angle, the duplication of a cube, and squaring the circle. Newton, as the *versatissimus in hisce rebus,* was again consulted and his answer, that they could not be demonstrated mathematically, was forwarded to the deluded author.

In May, 1701, Newton read the only paper on Chemistry which was published except his short articles on acids.[62] Under the title of *Scala graduum caloris,* he described a thermometer which he had invented probably some years previously; at least his note-books show that he was experimenting with thermometers in 1693. It was during those experiments that he discovered his law of cooling bodies; the second discovery was his observation of the constancy of fusion and boiling temperature; and his third, was the graduation of thermometers between these constant temperatures, thus making them comparable.

The lectures which were a part of the duties of his professorship had not been given for several years and, as Newton had decided not to return to Cambridge, he appointed William Whiston as his deputy with the full profits of the place. On December 10th, 1701, he resigned his professorship and shortly after retired from his fellowship.[63] Thus ended his connection of forty-one years with Trinity College. On his recommendation, Whiston was appointed to succeed him as Lucasian Professor and began his lectures on astronomy. The University, in this year of his retirement, showed its appreciation of the great honour Newton had brought to his Alma Mater by electing him one of its representatives in Parliament. Bentley, who was now Master of Trinity, "had the satisfaction of assisting in the return of his illustrious friend."[64] The life of this Parliament was short as it was prorogued in the following May, and dissolved on July 2d, shortly after the death of William III. Newton may have taken part in committee work, but he was a silent spectator of the debates. He

[61] Montucla, *Hist. du Math.* IV, p. 325, and Edleston, p. 304.
[62] Brewster, II, p. 362.
[63] Conduitt seems to have been mistaken when he stated that: "Newton made Mr. Whiston his deputy professor of mathematics at Cambridge [1701], and gave him all his salary from that time, though he did not absolutely resign the professorship till 1703. Turnor, p. 162.—Edleston used the University records to correct this statement.
[64] Monk, *Life of Bentley,* p. 122.

also missed in the House the companionship of his friend, as Montague had moved to the House of Lords. And with the death of King William, both Halifax and Newton lost much of their political power.

In the autumn of 1702, Newton visited Locke at Oates, the country seat of Sir Francis Masham. The two philosophers had been thrown much together during the recoinage and their friendship had ripened. Locke had been for a short time the President of the Board of Trade; but he had been forced to resign because of what he termed the crazyness of his body, due to an asthmatic affection of his lungs. Not being able to endure the air of London,[65] he retired to the country and spent the short remainder of his life with his devoted friends, the Mashams. We learn of Newton's visit from a letter which Locke wrote to his cousin. This letter is probably the best estimate we have of Newton's character from a contemporaneous source; it was written for a private purpose by a keen and appreciative judge who admired his genius and rectitude, but recognised his one inherent weakness of temperament. It is a remarkable evidence of Newton's inordinate sensitiveness and jealous personal pride, that a tried and trusted friend, of Locke's reputation and character, should have felt it necessary to counsel such elaborate precautions in so trivial a matter as to find out the cause for not returning some borrowed papers.

Locke to Lord King

Oates, April 30, 1703.

Dear Cousin,

I am puzzled in a little affair, and must beg your assistance for the clearing of it. Mr. Newton, in autumn last, made me a visit here; I showed him my essay upon the Corinthians, with which he seemed very well pleased, but had not time to look it all over, but promised me if I would send it him, he would carefully peruse it, and send me his observations and opinion. I sent it him before Christmas, but hearing nothing from him, I, about a month or six weeks since, writ to him, as the enclosed tells you, with the remaining part of the story. When you have read it, and sealed it, I desire you to deliver

[65] London, even then, was afflicted with a smoke-laden atmosphere. Evelyn wrote a small tract, with the title of *Fumifugium,* in which he proposed plans for abating the nuisance; one of which was to compel factories and large users of coal to move to the suburbs.

it at your convenience. He lives in German St.: you must not go on a Wednesday, for that is his day for being at the Tower. The reason why I desire you to deliver it to him yourself is, that I would fain discover the reason of his so long silence. I have several reasons to think him truly my friend, but he is a nice man to deal with, and a little too apt to raise in himself suspicions where there is no ground; therefore, when you talk to him of my papers, and of his opinion of them, pray do it with all the tenderness in the world, and discover, if you can, why he kept them so long, and was so silent. But this you must do without asking why he did so, or discovering in the least that you are desirous to know. You will do well to acquaint him, that you intend to see me at Whitsuntide, and shall be glad to bring a letter to me from him, or any thing else he will please to send; this perhaps may quicken him, and make him despatch these papers if he has not done it already. It may a little let you into the freer discourse with him, if you let him know that when you have been here with me, you have seen me busy on them (and the Romans too, if he mentions them, for I told him I was upon them when he was here,) and have had a sight of some part of what I was doing.

Mr. Newton is really a very valuable man, not only for his wonderful skill in mathematics, but in divinity too, and his great knowledge in the Scriptures, wherein I know few his equals. And therefore pray manage the whole matter so as not only to preserve me in his good opinion, but to increase me in it; and be sure to press him to nothing, but what he is forward in himself to do. In your last, you seemed desirous of my coming to town; I have many reasons to desire to be there, but I doubt whether ever I shall see it again. Take not this for a splenetic thought; I thank God I have no melancholy on that account, but I cannot but feel what I feel; my shortness of breath is so far from being relieved by the renewing season of the year as it used to be, that it sensibly increases upon me. 'Twas not therefore in a fit of dispiritedness, or to prevail with you to let me see you, that in my former I mentioned the shortness of the time I thought I had in this world. I spoke it then, and repeat it now upon sober and sedate consideration. I have several things to talk to you of, and some of present concernment to yourself, and I know not whether this may not be my last time of seeing you. I shall not die the sooner for having cast up my reckoning, and judging as impartially of my state as I can. I hope I shall not live one jot the less cheerfully the time that I am here, nor neglect any of the offices of life whilst I have it; for whether it be a month or a year, or seven years longer, the longest any one out of kindness or compliment can propose to me, is so near nothing when considered, and in respect of eternity, that if the sight of death can put an end to the comforts of life, it is always near enough, especially to one of my age, to have no satisfaction in living.

I am your affectionate cousin
And humble servant,
J. L.[66]

We can make a shrewd guess as to the purpose of this visit. Years before, Locke and the Mashams had been the most energetic and persistent of Newton's friends in trying to secure an office for him. Now, he was in grave danger of losing what he had obtained after so many disappointments. Anne was on the throne, Montague was in disgrace, and the Whigs were out of power. The Queen's favourites were the Marlboroughs and their cousin, Abigail Hill, who afterwards married the son of Sir Francis Masham. Thus, the influence of these friends of Newton and Locke had become powerful at Court, and it is reasonable to suppose that he made this visit in order to solicit their aid in retaining his position. Nor, would it be too much to believe that the Queen's continued favour was ascribable more to the influence of the Mashams than to his own record of past achievement.

Some persons, who read the following proposal of marriage to a Lady Norris who has been mentioned before as an intimate acquaintance, may be tempted to think that Newton had resolved to copy Montague's example of mending his fortune by matrimony and so avoid what Brewster would have considered the disgrace of a return to the academic life. At any rate, Brewster found amongst the *Portsmouth Papers* a proposal of marriage to her which he believed to have been made by Newton about this time: "It is in the handwriting of Mr. Conduitt, who, doubtless, intended to publish it, and is entitled, in the same hand, 'Copy of a Letter to Lady Norris by ——,' while on the back is written in another hand, 'A Letter from Sir I. N. to ——.'"[67] Although it is most improbable that Newton, at the age of sixty years and after a life apparently indifferent to love and matrimony, suddenly stooped to this method of securing a livelihood or wrote the letter, yet it must be placed on record.

[66] King's *Life of Locke,* Vol. II, p. 37. [67] Brewster, Vol. II, p. 211.

Newton [?] to Lady Norris

Madam,—Your ladyship's great grief at the loss of Sir William, shews that if he had returned safe home, your ladyship could have been glad to have lived still with a husband, and therefore your aversion at present from marrying again can proceed from nothing else than the memory of him who you have lost. To be always thinking on the dead, is to live a melancholy life among sepulchres, and how much grief is an enemy to your health is very manifest by the sickness it brought when you received the first news of your widowhood: And can your ladyship resolve to spend the rest of your days in grief and sickness? Can you resolve to wear a widow's habit perpetually,—a habit which is less acceptable to company, a habit which will be always putting you in mind of your lost husband, and thereby promote your grief and indisposition till you leave it off? The proper remedy for all these mischiefs is a new husband, and whether your ladyship should admit of a proper remedy for such maladies, is a question which I hope will not need much time to consider of. Whether your ladyship should go constantly in the melancholy dress of a widow, or flourish once more among the ladies; whether you should spend the rest of your days cheerfully or in sadness, in health or in sickness, are questions which need not much consideration to decide them. Besides that your ladyship will be better able to live according to your quality by the assistance of a husband than upon your own estate alone; and therefore since your ladyship likes the person proposed, I doubt not but in a little time to have notice of your ladyship's inclinations to marry, at least that you will give him leave to discourse with you about it.

I am, Madam, your ladyship's most humble,
and most obedient servant.[68]

Brewster discusses at length the authorship of this letter. He, first, decides that Newton did not write it as an intermediary to assist the suit of the unknown "person proposed" on the ground that this was "a quaint and not uncommon form of expression to avoid the use of the first person." To support this argument, he runs over in his mind the names of Newton's acquaintances, and finds no one who would be likely to engage the aid of the philosopher in a matrimonial adventure. We agree with this opinion that no one would

[68] Brewster, Vol. II, p. 211.—I also found this letter in the *Portsmouth Collection.*

look to him as a person having interest or dexterity in this field; but we are surprised that he did not happen upon the name of Montague, who was a widower, keen for money and not scrupulous against obtaining it in this very same manner; and about whom there was a report that he had proposed to a wealthy lady and had been rejected. To have thus assigned the authorship to Montague would have disposed of him as the husband to Mistress Barton.

So Brewter accepts it as an unexpected but regrettable episode in Newton's life. It is odd, it does not seem to have occurred to him that Conduitt may have made a copy of a letter written several years before to Lady Norris by a ridiculous and importunate suitor whose name was deliberately omitted. In support of this interpretation, Newton simply does not fit in the rôle of a go-between in such an affair or as a consoler of a rich widow; and, finally, the style of the letter is totally unlike that of his known correspondence.

Let us hazard a guess of our own. Suppose, Lady Norris, who was an intimate friend as shown by Newton's reference to her in the letter to his niece, had received such an epistle from a professional fortune-hunter and had shown it to him, or to his niece, as a joke. Conduitt may then have copied it later to keep it as an amusing incident, and the unknown endorser have filled in Newton's initials, presuming him to be the author. To make the joke, if joke it was, more striking, Lady Norris had been already married three times. Her last husband was Sir William Norris, a former Fellow of Trinity College and colleague of Newton in his Cambridge days. After leaving the University, he became a prominent member of Parliament and was created a baronet for his services. He then entered the diplomatic service and died, at sea, on his way home from India, October 10th, 1702. Whoever may have been the author of the letter, it should be cancelled as an exhibit of Newton's character.

Two events occurred in 1703 which affected Newton's life and, especially, his relations with the Royal Society. Hooke, who had been such a thorn in his flesh, and had made him vow that he would not submit any work to the Society, died; and Somers, who had been President, resigned at the Anniversary Meeting. At the same meeting, Newton was chosen in his place and was re-elected annually till his death.

CHAPTER XIII

PRESIDENCY OF THE ROYAL SOCIETY. PUBLICATION OF "HISTORIA COELESTIS." KNIGHTED AND STANDS FOR PARLIAMENT. SECOND EDITION OF THE PRINCIPIA

1703–1709

The election of Newton to the presidency of the Royal Society marks a real epoch in his life. It was the full recognition of his work. He was regarded as without a peer in the scientific world, and already the legends of superhumanity were beginning to collect about him; even those who had suffered more or less from his recurrent outbreaks of jealousy were never doubtful of his transcendant genius. Flamsteed protested bitterly against what he believed to be unjust and dictatorial actions but, until the last and final quarrel, he evidently submitted to the domination of that overpowering mind. Locke forgave a cruel and unwarranted accusation of treachery, and was so fearful of giving further offence that he requested his nephew to be diplomatic when asking for the return of one of his own manuscripts. Even Leibniz sought his commendation, and is reported to have said to the Princess of Wales that his rival's achievements in mathematics outweighed the combined accomplishments of all other mathematicians. There could be no stronger evidence of the domination which his character and his genius imposed on his contemporaries, a domination amounting almost to awe. His position as president of the Royal Society was a natural expression of this uncontested leadership, and his reëlection from year to year till his death was uncontested. The last quarter of a century of Newton's life was so centred in the activities of the Society that an account of its foundation and early history is important to a right understanding of his life.

Prior to the sixteenth century, the cultivation of science was carried on by solitary workers whose progress was slow enough to make personal letters and books an adequate means of communicating their ideas and results. But, during that century, the experimental method had so spread, and the interest in medicine and the physical sciences had become so general that, even in the smaller towns of Europe, there could be found groups of men devoted to the New Science. Instead of trusting to an inner sentiment of truth, the inductive method of drawing conclusions from observations was rapidly gaining gound. That universal genius, da Vinci, had foreshadowed this method in his own personal studies in science. His note-books are full of detailed experiments which were a mine from which later scientists unscrupulously pilfered. Almost a century before Kepler, Galileo, and Gilbert had laid the foundations of experimental science, and before Bacon had formulated the principles of the inductive method, the Florentine artist had written: "We should begin with experimentation, and by that means discover the cause."[1] In order, also, to bring together for a mutual exchange of ideas those, who were interested in geometry and other intellectual subjects, he founded an Academy of Arts in Milan.

Towards the end of the sixteenth century, the New Science had become thoroughly rooted and its followers felt the need of association. The first society established for the investigation of physical science was the Academia Secretorum Naturae, or *I Segreti,* in 1560, at Naples, under the presidency of Io. Baptista Porta. This Neapolitan was one of those prodigies who knew everything and wrote a library of books which still are valuable historically, as they give a vivid picture of the learning and superstitions of the day. The members of the society probably threw a veil of mystery about their meetings and work; they, thus, aroused the indignation of the people who denounced the organization to the Pope as a gang of sorcerers, and brought the Academy to an untimely end. But the habit of forming such associations became fixed and, by the close of the century, Tiraboschi[2] lists 171 of them. Many of them adopted fanciful names, such as *Gli Ebbri,*—drunken with the new knowledge. Most of them had a very ephemeral existence, but three deserve special mention; the *Accademia della Crusca,* founded at Florence in 1582, still carries on its useful work in the Palazzo Riccardi; *dei Lyncei,* organised in Rome in 1609, was distinguished by the membership of Galileo, and has since then been the most noteworthy scientific society in Italy; and *del Cimento* of Florence which, though it lasted only ten years, yet was the scene of very important work.

The tendency to form these scholarly associations, outside the

[1] "Dobbiamo comminciare dall' esperienza, e per mezzo di questa scoprine la ragione."
[2] Tiraboschi: *Storia della lett. Ital.,* Vol. VII, p. 495.

universities, spread from Italy to other countries. About 1629, nine men of letters formed a private society in Paris and agreed to meet once a week to converse on all subjects, and especially on literature. Such was the origin of the famous French Academy. A few years later, it attracted the attention of Richelieu who persuaded the members, against their wishes, to enlarge their membership and to incorporate under a royal charter. The Academy began its official life in 1635 and from the beginning of its career its principal object has been to establish a standard French language and to foster a critical taste in literature. The original society was later enlarged by incorporating with it an Academy of Sciences and one of Inscriptions and Belles Lettres. From the start, it flourished under the protection and generosity of Richelieu. In 1699, the Academy was remodelled and eight foreign associates were added to the membership.

England was slower in following the example of Italy in establishing scientific societies,[3] and the Royal Society grew, as did those in the other countries, out of the private meetings of a few men interested in natural philosophy. According to Dr. Wallis, the mathematician, a few friends interested in the new experimental philosophy formed the habit, about 1645, of meeting once a week to discuss scientific affairs at the house of Dr. Goddard in Wood Street, or at the Bull-Head Tavern in Cheapside, or sometimes at Gresham College. Their discourse ranged over a wide field; from the Copernican hypothesis to general medicine, the grinding of lenses, and the latest discoveries in physics. The desire for such meetings seems to have been due to two causes; the first was as a distraction from the desperate social condition of the country, and the other came from the profound influence exerted by the scientific philosophy of Lord Bacon. For example; Sprat says that: "Their first purpose was no more than only the satisfaction of breathing a freer air, and of conversing in quiet one with another, without being engaged in the passion and madness of that dismal age."[4] And he evidently thought that the sobering influence of the Society had a real effect in bring-

[3] The sources for this sketch of the history of the Royal Society are Bishop Sprat's *Hist. R. S.*, written four years after its founding as a defense against its critics; Weld's *Hist. R. S.*, 1848, giving an interesting and valuable narrative to 1830; Birch's *Hist. of the R. S.*, a very valuable collection of its records to 1688; *The Record of the R. S.*, 3rd ed., 1912, edited by its President, Sir Archibald Geikie, which contains an account of the early history of the society and complete lists of officers, members, medallists, etc.; *The Trans. R. S.*, in which are published the important monographs.

[4] Bishop Sprat's *History* undoubtedly exerted a great influence in warding off attacks on the Society. Apparently, also, it was esteemed so excellent in argument and style that others hesitated to continue it. I found in the *Portsmouth Collection* these interesting notes by

ing the nation back to its senses. "What can be more delightful," he writes, "for the Englishman to consider, than that notwithstanding all the late miseries of his country, it has been able in a short time so well to recover itself, as not only to attain to the perfection of its former civility, and learning, but also to set on foot a *new* way of improvement of arts?" Wallis, also, notes the need of such private gatherings when the academical studies in both Universities were much interrupted by the Civil Wars.

We can, however, be certain that some such organisation as the Royal Society would have resulted from the influence of Bacon's inductive philosophy whatever had been the condition of national affairs. In his *New Atalantis* and later in his *Novum Organum,* he had attacked the Aristotelian scholasticism, and had advocated experimentation by associated groups of investigators. Facts of observation on all subjects were to be gathered by an army of seekers after knowledge; they were then to be sorted, and the laws governing each classification would readily come to light. That Bacon was the prime influence in founding the Society is definitely affirmed by its earliest Fellows such as Sprat, Boyle, and others. Thus Sprat says of its founders, "I shall only mention one great man, who had the true imagination of the whole extent of this enterprise, as it is now set on foot; and that is, the Lord Bacon; in whose books there are everywhere scattered the best arguments, that can be produced for the defense of experimental philosophy, and the best directions, that are needful to promote it." And Geikie, in 1912, echoes the same opinion in his preface to the *Record of the Royal Society:* "The foundation of the Royal Society was one of the earliest practical fruits of the philosophical labours of Francis Bacon." There has been a tendency, which still persists, to underrate Bacon's importance as a scientist because he left no experimental discoveries behind him, but such a criticism is very shortsighted, to have directed others in the true scientific method is a work of the highest value and makes him rank amongst the most eminent natural philosophers. There is no doubt that Newton was greatly influenced by Bacon in his adoption of the experimental and mechanistic philosophy, and by his exclusion of hypothesis from science.

Conduitt: "Hans Sloane told me the *History of Royal Society* was written in 1677 and that he had often pressed several to continue it but in vain. Sprat's first sketch which was intended as a sample and to encourage others to continue it was written with such perfection that no one durst continue." Also, "Dr. Swift says the *Hist. of the R. S.* is the best book in the English tongue."

The informal meetings of what Robert Boyle several times in his letters names "our Invisible College" continued till about 1648. At that time several of the members, including Wallis, Dr. Wilkins, and Dr. Petty, moved to Oxford and started a branch society there which met first in Dr. Petty's lodgings, and afterwards in the house of Dr. Wilkins, Warden of Wadham College. The London society, however, continued to prosper and drew to it so many "eminent and noble persons" that its meetings were held regularly, and with more formality, in Gresham College. But in 1658, or 1659, because of what Sprat calls "the miserable distractions of that fatal year," professors and philosophers were driven out of the College in order to turn it into a barracks for the soldiers, who later under Monck's leadership brought about the Restoration.[5] The condition of the lecture halls, after this military occupation, is vividly described in the *Memoirs of the Times* by Bishop Wren: "I went to visit Gresham College, but found the place in such a nasty condition, so defiled, and the smells so infernal, that if you should now come to make use of your tube [telescope], it would be like Dives looking out of hell into heaven. Dr. Goddard, of all your colleagues, keeps possession, which he could never be able to do, had he not before prepared his nose for camp-perfumes by his voyage into Scotland, and had he not such excellent restoratives in his cellar."

In spite of this interruption, the members did not lose hope, and plans were drawn up by Evelyn and Cowley for organising a scientific college or society. When the "fatal year 1659" was followed by the "wonderful pacific year 1660," the meetings were renewed with a membership largely increased by some who had regained their leisure from the cessation of war, and by others who had shared the exile of Charles and who now returned with him in exuberant spirits. On November 28th, the first Journal-book of the Society was opened and plans were begun to establish a permanent organization. Sir Robert Moray, a close friend of Charles, acquainted the King with the design, and brought back the news of royal approval and encouragement. During the years before the Society was incorporated, Moray acted as President and is reported to have been "the life and soul of the body."

The Royal Charter of Incorporation received the Great Seal on July 15th, 1662, and the Royal Society began its honourable career of

[5] There is some doubt about the date. Birch states that Gresham College was not occupied by soldiers till 1659, but Sprat and Wren both state positively that it occurred the year before. *Cf.* Weld, Vol. I, p. 42.

substituting scientific knowledge for the delusions of superstition and witch-craft. Lord Brouncker was elected the first president and continued in that office till 1677. As the first charter did not give the Fellows all the privileges which they desired, a second Charter was granted, and passed the Great Seal on April 22nd, 1663. In this document the King styled himself as Founder and Patron. Although a third Charter was given in 1669, it is the second Charter which ensures the privileges of the Society. By its provisions, the Society was administered by a Council of twenty-one, of whom ten shall retire each year on St. Andrew's day; and the first Register of 119 names constituted the original list of Fellows. Of many of the original Fellows little or nothing is known; they were "gentlemen, free and unconfined" to use Sprat's phraseology. Not more than one-fifth of the members could be called scientists, and they adopted from the beginning the broad and wise policy of associating with themselves a body of men united in a common fellowship for the promotion of natural philosophy.

While the influence of Charles II was essential in giving prestige and protection to the young Society, he rendered very little substantial aid. He granted it a royal coat of arms with the motto of *Nullius in Verba* to signify that its purpose was to depend on facts rather than on words, and that communications should be unadorned with rhetoric; he also presented the Fellows with a mace to lie on the table while the President was in the chair.[6] But, although he made tentative offers of grants of land and money, he was unable, or unwilling, to pass beyond promises. The Society was for a long while poor, and sometimes in desperate need of funds owing to arrears of dues. Nor can we find that much help has ever been given to it by royalty.

The Society met on Wednesday afternoons in their rooms at Gresham College. The annual meeting is held on St. Andrew's Day, November 28, and in honour of him, as their patron saint, the Fellows wore St. Andrew's crosses in their hats.[7] The papers pre-

[6] The legend became current that this mace was the one owned by the House of Commons and which disappeared when Cromwell dissolved the Long Parliament with the curt words, "Take away that fool's bauble." Weld has proved that it was made especially for the Royal Society.

[7] The annual dinner was in the early years less formal than it is today. For example, in 1746, the place of dining was changed from Pontock's Tavern in Abchurch Lane, which was inconveniently situated for the majority of the Fellows, to the Devil Tavern, near Temple Bar. This Tavern was a resort of the wits and writers. Ben Jonson was one of its frequenters and there he drank deeply and often. In its convivial room, he laid the plot and wrote most of the lines of *Volpone,* and planned others of his plays.

sented to the Society have gradually become technical, and often abstruse, but the original plan was to witness experiments performed by members, very frequently by Hooke, who had been given definite problems on which to work. Papers were read on a great variety of subjects and a discussion followed. These early papers are of great historic value; they show, as nothing else can, the state of science and the topics of most interest. The elaborate technical language of modern science had not yet been developed, and most of the papers could be followed by anybody who had a fairly general education. Although the declared purpose of the Society was to depend on experimental evidence, and thus to counteract the prevailing belief in the supernatural, many of the papers gravely discuss prodigies having no foundation except rumour and hearsay. One constantly meets with the same mixture of accurate personal observation and naïve acceptance of wild tales of travellers in distant countries which is so evident in the biological treatises of Aristotle. In many respects, a parallel could be drawn between the early creative periods in the Classical and Renaissance science. In addition to experimental papers and lectures, the Society set up a museum into which flowed a strange mixture of objects of real value with others of only passing interest; and the passion for collecting biological freaks brought many worthless and even fraudulent objects into its cases.

The Society had hardly begun to operate under its Royal Charter, and to settle into its quarters in Gresham College, before it experienced its share of the two great calamities which burst on the nation. On the 28th of June, 1665, the meetings were discontinued because of the plague which was ravaging London and Westminster. Most of the Fellows fled into the country taking with them the exhortation "of the President to bear in mind the several tasks laid upon them, that they might give a good account of them at their return." It has already been told how Oldenburg, the Secretary, stuck to his post and had made arrangements, in case of his expected death, to pass on to others the properties of the Society which he jealously guarded. And it has also been told how this same plague drove the young Cambridge student, Newton, to his rural home where he meditated those astounding discoveries which made him the most illustrious Fellow on the register of the Society.

When the plague subsided, meetings were resumed and experiments on transfusion of blood became the absorbing topic of the Fellows and of the town. Again, the calamity of the great fire, which broke out on Sunday, September 2nd, 1666, threw everything into confusion. Although the fire did not extend to the College, it was requisitioned by the Mayor for the use of fugitives and of supplies, and was afterwards occupied by the Exchange till 1673. During this period the Society removed to Arundel House. After the fire, two of its Fellows, Hooke and Wren, were busily engaged on the plans for rebuilding the city.

The early history of the Society would not be complete without an account of Gresham College. The founder of the College was Sir Thomas Gresham one of the great merchant princes in the time of Queen Elizabeth. Besides having been ambassador to Brussels and financial adviser to the Queen, in which capacity he explained to her his famous principle that "bad money drives out good," he also built the Royal Exchange modelled on the one at Antwerp and a palatial residence at Bishopsgate. In his will he left to the Mayor and Citizens of London a moiety of the building of the Royal Exchange under certain conditions; one was that £50 a year should be given to each of four persons meet to read lectures on divinity, astronomy, music, and geometry in his mansion in Bishopsgate Street. And the other moiety of the Exchange to the "Commonalty of the mystery of the Mercers of London," of which he was a member, with the provision that they should provide for lecturers on law, physic, and rhetoric, under the same terms. At the death of Lady Anne Gresham in 1596, the seven lecturers were chosen and installed in comfortable quarters; and there they delivered their lectures daily in term-time "to the great delight of many, both learned, and lovers of learning."

"Here the Royal Society has one public room to meet in, another for a repository to keep their instruments, books, rarities, papers, and whatever else belongs to them; making use besides, by permission, of several of the other lodgings, as their occasions do require. And, when I consider the place itself, methinks it bears some likeness to their design. It is now a college, but was once the mansion-house of one of the greatest merchants that ever was in England: And such a philosophy they would build; which should first wholly consist of action and intelligence, before it be brought into teaching and contemplation."[8]

The history of Gresham College is a melancholy example of the misuse of a public trust. As the value of the land increased, the two trustee corporations centred their attention on realising money by

[8] Bp. Sprat, *Hist. R. S.*. p. 93.

letting the ground on building leases and allowed the lecturers' quarters to become ruinous. When the Society moved from the building in 1710 the lectures had become futile and the College an object of contempt. In 1767, the trustees agreed to demolish the building and to give up the land, a property really belonging to the public, for the sum of £500 a year in order to build on it an Excise-office. One of the most extraordinary and scandalous provisions of this Act was that the trustees were compelled to commit a flagrant violation of their trust by paying £1800 of Gresham's funds for demolishing Gresham's College.

It is said the University of Cambridge had warned Gresham, one of its alumni, that: "If you design your institution to last, you will place it here." An instructive lesson can be read in the rise of these scientific societies and their relations to the Universities, which is pertinent to the situation today. The cause of the wide-spread founding of learned societies and special colleges in the sixteenth and seventeenth centuries was undoubtedly due to the pressure of the New Science and the rapid expansion of industry. The Universities kept as usual to the conservative learning of the time, the discipline of the Aristotelian scholasticism. The radicals and the young men who had taken up the new ideas, either could not, or were too impatient to, force the Universities into a deliberated modification of the curriculum. In the new institutions subjects and methods were moulded nearer to their hearts' desire. This feeling is expressed in the verses written on the founding of Gresham College and is applicable to the general impatience towards scholastic training:

> "The College Gresham shall hereafter
> Be the whole world's University;
> Oxford and Cambridge are our laughter;
> Their learning is but pedantry;
> These new Collegiates do assure us,
> Aristotle's an ass to Epicurus."

The societies and colleges of that time had a value in causing a modification of the curricula of the universities without, however, inducing them to abandon the fundamental disciplinary studies; but the associations, themselves, mostly vanished or became mere gathering places where the university professors delivered the results of their researches. They were built on too narrow and too shallow a base to endure the changes of time. Today the pressure of industry and humanitarianism has been exerted on the universities, and the claim is made again that they do not fit the youth for the needs of the work-a-day world. The purpose of a university, according to these modernists, is not to make its students acquainted with the thoughts and actions of the past, but to prepare them quickly for a business or profession. The successors to the older scientific societies are the broad elective systems based on the declaration that all subjects are equally effective as an education; the professional schools based on a specialised smattering of science; and pædagogic and sociologic schools based on nothing. Their products may acquire busy minds but they lack the vision and the judgement that come only from the discipline of those classic and philosophic studies which have persisted through the tumults of the past, and must persist in the future if a well-balanced attitude towards life is to endure.

The early history of the Royal Society was not a uniform course of progress. Its final success was due to the devotion and active work of a small group which was keenly interested in promoting experimental knowledge. The bulk of the membership was lukewarm. Attendance seems to have been irregular and the greatest difficulty was experienced in collecting the weekly dues of a shilling. The Journal-book was peppered with melancholy financial reports and at one time the treasurer was directed to solicit dues every day. But an even greater danger was the jealousy and fear which were at once aroused. Bishop Sprat's History was written for the specific purpose of defending the Society. He was careful not to mention individual objections but it is easy to discover what were the chief causes of disapproval. It aroused the jealousy of the universities as tending to detach students from the accepted methods of instruction; the clergy feared lest the reliance on observation and experimentation would lead to atheism and heterodoxy; the physicians looked askance at new-fangled ideas in medicine; the wits and literary men viewed the Society as a collection of solemn pedants curiously investigating matters of little or no importance. Cowley and Dryden extolled it in verse, but Shadwell ridiculed it in his comedy of *The Virtuoso,* and Butler pictures, in the *Hudibras,* the excitement of the learned members who thought they had discovered an elephant in the moon but were chagrined by finding that a fly had lodged in the tube of their telescope. Addison and Steele satirised the Fellows as dull pedants, Pope included them in the *Dunciad,* and Swift bitterly caricatured them in the *Voyage to Laputa.*

When Newton was elected President on November 30th, 1703, he assumed office when the nation was in the throes of political faction and straining its resources to carry on the war of the Spanish Succession. The first and most important problem then confronting the Society was the need of providing new quarters, and Newton, whose duties at the Mint now left him much leisure, assumed active leadership in the movement. Continuance at Gresham College was out of the question, and the time had come when, in the words of Newton, the Society ought "to have a being of their own." The first move had been a petition to Queen Anne to grant them a plot of ground fifty feet by sixty in Westminster on which to erect a suitable building. This plan failed and, considering the affairs of the nation, one can hardly blame the indifference of the Queen's advisers. The Council next applied to the Trustees of the Cotton Library for permission to meet in their apartments. In this connection Burnet mentions; "Lord Halifax moved the House of Lords to petition the Queen, that the Cotton Library and the Queen's Library should be joined, and that the Royal Society, who had a very good Library at Gresham College, would remove, and hold their assemblies there as soon as it was made convenient for them."[9] But all the plans proposed failed and it was not until 1710 that the Council made a successful effort. In that year Newton informed them that the house of the late Dr. Brown in Crane Court was to be sold, "and being in the middle of the town, and out of noise, might be a proper place to be purchased by the Society for their meetings." After a month's negotiations the property was bought for £1450 and a mortgage was given for the entire amount.[10] The repairs and improvements on the building were apparently met by donations and subscriptions. Newton, himself, gave £20 to the Society in January 1709/10, and £100 in December, towards the easing of the debt; and again in 1718 he made a gift of £70. The minute in the Journal-Book of his first gift was followed by the note, "Instead of the like sum he intended after his death. It was ordered to be put by itself and to be subject to such end or benefaction as the President shall direct." According to Edleston, this note is the foundation for Thomas Hearne's scandal that, "he promised to become a benefactor to the Royal Society, but failed."

The purchase of the new meeting place aroused a very considerable opposition in at least some of the Fellows who described the house

[9] Burnet, *Hist. Own Times*, II, p. 441.

[10] Weld, *Hist. R. S.*, I, pp. 387–391.

as small, inconvenient, and so dilapidated as to require £1800 to put it into habitable condition; although the approach to it through a long court was fair and handsome, yet a man could hardly escape being thoroughly wet if there were a heavy rain. It is easy to appreciate the thousand and one objections that would be raised by any proposed move of a Club; but the severest criticism was directed against the dictatorial and high-handed procedure of Newton and the Secretary, Hans Sloane; apparently there were some grounds for this accusation. In a rare pamphlet,[11] one of the malcontents described the events in this caustic manner. After the Council had resolved on buying Mr. Brown's property, Newton gave orders at night to summon as many Fellows as were in town to meet on the night of September 1st. He then told them that a Committee had viewed the house and found it convenient, and that he had called them to hear what objections they had to offer. The general surprise was followed by a profound silence. Those, who opposed the change, argued that the quarters which they occupied were hallowed by the past history of the Society. Till adequate reasons were given for moving it was out of season to enquire into the inconveniences of the house he was recommending. Newton "was not prepared (or perhaps not *instructed*) to enter upon that debate: but freely (though methinks not very civilly) replied, That he had *good reasons for their removing, which he did not think proper to be given there.* The acting Secretary, who has engrossed the whole management of the Society's affairs into his own hands, and despotically directs the President, as well as every other member, took upon him to relate a fact, etc." Finally the opinion was expressed that more time should be given for them to discuss so important an affair. But the President refused to consider any alteration in the plan so unmovably that "some of the gentlemen, with warmth enough, asked him, To what purpose then he had called them thither? Upon which the meeting broke up somewhat abruptly, and not only the members of the Society, but most of those of the Council also, left the President with Dr. Sloane, Mr. Waller, and one or two more, to take such measures at the Council as they best liked."[12] The impression that the acting Secretary, Hans Sloane, had engrossed the whole management of the Society and despotically directed the President may have a basis of truth; in

11 *An account of the late proceedings in the Council of the Royal Society, in order to remove from Gresham College into Crane Court in Fleet Street, 1710.* Weld found a copy of this pamphlet in the British Museum.

12 *Cf.* Weld, Vol. I, p. 391.

most cases where Newton had to act in a public capacity or to contend with others, he seems to have been obstinate but, at the same time, to have followed the guidance of advisers who, unfortunately, were not always actuated by wise or disinterested motives. Whatever may have been the rights of the dispute, the plan was carried through and the Society occupied Crane Court for seventy-two years with apparent satisfaction.

In January, 1704, Newton gave to the Society a powerful burning glass which he had contrived by combining seven lenses, and at several later meetings he demonstrated its power by melting metals, bits of red tile, and other refractory objects. The following month he presented his *Optics*. It is more than probable that the material for this book had been compiled years previously and had been withheld from printing until the death of Hooke had removed the possibility of his bitter criticism. It is remarkable in the fact that it is the only one of his works which was prepared for the press by himself. When it was written or whether it was burned and rewritten, we do not know, but it is likely that the finished manuscript was quickly composed from his lectures, his papers in the *Transactions,* and his voluminous notes and queries. The book became immediately popular. It went into several English editions and was translated into French, German, and Latin.[13] The translation into Latin was done by his friend Dr. Samuel Clarke and was published in 1706; it so pleased Newton by its exactness and elegance that he presented the translator with £500, or £100 for each of his five children, as a token of his approbation and gratitude. Fontenelle, in his *Eloge* of Newton, states that the mathematician, Demoivre, revised and directed the Latin edition, on which he spared neither care nor pains. According to this account they met every evening at a coffee house, probably Slaughter's in St. Martin's Lane, and went from there to Newton's house where they spent the rest of the evening in philosophic conversation. This anecdote seems to be doubtful, or perhaps it refers to some other work of translation; otherwise why was Clarke favoured with so handsome a gift while Demoivre received nothing? Also the reference to St. Martin's Lane is without point if it

[13] A second edition, octavo, bears the advertisement 1717. It was published in 1718, and the date, 1704, of the first edition was added to the preface, apparently to fix the original date in case of dispute. The number of new Queries added begins with the seventeenth. A third edition appeared in 1721, and a fourth edition was published from a copy of the third corrected by the author and left before his death with the bookseller. Recently, a new edition has been issued by Messrs. Bell.

indicates nearness to his house in St. Martin Street, since he did not move there till three years after the book was published.

In the first edition, Newton appended two short treatises on the species and magnitudes of curvilinear figures. The first of these gives a classification of seventy-two curves of the third order, and the second contains the first description of the method of fluxions, and of the binomial theorem. They were omitted from later editions as not being germane to the subject of the book. They were undoubtedly first printed at the solicitation of his friends who saw with anxiety the rapid advance which the calculus of Leibniz was making, and who were preparing to start an active campaign to establish his priority of invention. Newton, again in this preface, reiterates his reluctance to publish. "To avoid being engaged in disputes about these matters [on optics], I have hitherto delayed the printing, and should have delayed it, had not the importunity of friends prevailed upon me." Concerning the publication of the paper on fluxions, he refers to the short description of his method which was published by Wallis in 1679. Then he adds: "And some years ago I lent out a manuscript containing such theorems, and having since met with some things copied out of it, I have on this occasion made it public." This is a covert insinuation that Leibniz had seen this manuscript when in London and had obtained from it hints which led to his discovery of the calculus. In earlier years Newton certainly did not hold this opinion. But in later years he became more and more convinced of this plagiarism. We do not know whether some new fact became known to him, whether he was influenced by his friends, or whether he simply became anxious to believe it. It seems to me unfortunate that his fluxions was published in this manner. His priority of discovery was uncontested and that was all he could hope for. No effort at that late date by him, or by English mathematicians, could substitute his fluxions for the systematic exposition of Leibniz's method; and the insinuation of plagiarism led at once to the great controversy which embittered his last years and left a tarnish on his name.

One of the most honourable bequests to science came to the Royal Society in the early years of Newton's presidency. Sir Godfrey Copley, a Fellow since 1691, left in his will, dated 1704, "one hundred pounds, in trust for the Royal Society of London for improving natural knowledge, to be laid out in experiments, or otherwise, for the benefit thereof, as they shall direct and appoint." On his death, five years later, this bequest came to the society and was administered by Sir Hans Sloane and Mr. Hill, his trustees, jointly till Hill's death, and then by Sloane till 1753. For many years the income from the fund was paid to Dr. Desagulier, Curator of the Society,[14] as a fee for performing experiments. But in 1736, President Martin Folkes proposed to make the gift a signal mark of honour by using it for a medal to be awarded annually to the author of the most important scientific discovery or contribution to science by experiment or otherwise. The Copley medal has long been considered as the highest distinction that the Royal Society can bestow, and the list of Copley Medallists is an almost complete record of the most eminent men of science in the world during the past two centuries. At first, the awards were limited to British scientists and were made on the nomination of the trustees. On Sloane's death, the choice devolved on the President and Council, and all restrictions of nationality were removed. The first Medallist chosen under the new administration was Benjamin Franklin in 1753.

When Newton, as mentioned before, came to the presidency of the Royal Society, he assumed office at one of the most critical periods in English history. At home, the accession of Queen Anne had temporarily postponed the hopes of her brother, the Elder Pretender, but she was in frail health and the prospects of the Jacobites, led by her relatives the Hydes, were high. Abroad, there was the imperative question of carrying on the war begun by William III against France. Whatever sympathies Anne may have had towards her family as rightful heirs to the throne, they were overshadowed by her increasing dislike to the domineering Hydes and by her determination to prosecute the war. Her retired life of an invalid put her in the hands of a small domestic circle over which the Marlboroughs reigned supreme. Up to the time of her final break with her dear friend Sarah Churchill, she backed Marlborough with steadfast loyalty, and made possible that series of brilliant victories which humbled Louis and shattered his dream of world power. Anne began her reign so strong a Tory and so prejudiced against the members of the Junto, that the Whigs had no influence in her first Parliament. As a consequence, the High Tories went so far in alienating her by opposing the war and the influence of Marlborough that it became of the highest importance to manipulate a balance of power. Her fear of the High Tories split that party in two and really gave

[14] Weld, I, p. 384, and *Record R. S.*, p. 174.

rise to three parties. Thus, the Moderate Tories never had a working majority and her reign was marked with a prolonged and fierce political struggle that is unmatched in English history. The excitement, the bitterness, and the character of the political leaders gave vent to an unparalleled license in language and personal slander which must be reckoned with when judging the epithets used in even the altercations of the Royal Society, or in the personal controversies of Newton. The Court was compelled to bid alternately for the votes of the High Tories and of the Whigs, in order to carry on the policies of the Moderate Tories. While the Whigs did not come into power, they still had great influence. They were represented in the Ministry and in the Privy Council; and the five leaders of the Junto, all of whom were then in the House of Lords, were able from that House to guide the policy of the Commons in voting money bills for the vigorous prosecution of the war and for domestic measures. Newton's fear of losing his position at the Mint, because of his Whig affiliations, had, as I believe, led him to solicit the support of the Mashams and Marlboroughs some years previously. And, though Halifax was nominally in disgrace, his support of the war was essential to the Ministry, and his friendship with Newton helped to keep him secure in his office. Unless we take into account the confused political history of Anne's reign, it is difficult to understand why Newton, a confirmed Whig, was so highly esteemed and honoured by the Court, or why he was permitted to retain so envied a political office. This explanation is strengthened by Flamsteed's frequent complaint that Newton was able to crush all opposition to him because he had free and intimate access to the Court, and had the support of a powerful patron, Halifax.

On the Anniversary Day of the Royal Society, when Newton was elected President, the nation was stunned by the effects of the great storm of November 26 and 27, O. S. London streets were piled with heaps of wreckage, and forests of oak and elm trees throughout the south of England were devastated. But the following Anniversary brought great satisfaction to the Society by the election of Prince George of Denmark to membership. The Journal-book stated, that "the Society were extremely pleased with the honour the Prince did them, in suffering them to choose him a member," and the Council desired "the President and Secretary to wait on the Prince with the Statute-book, to have the honour of his subscription."[15] We have

[15] Weld, I, p. 376.

also a note from Newton to Sloane asking him to be ready on December 7th to wait on His Royal Highness. This mark of royal favour, which had been lacking in the previous reign, was important to the Society as a protection against its critics, and it was personally important to the President, since a mark of attention to her husband was a sure means of favour with the Queen. During the audience, Newton succeeded in pledging Prince George to defray the expense of publishing Flamsteed's great catalogue of the stars on which he had been working all the years since his appointment as Astronomer Royal.

Whatever motive may have influenced Newton to undertake an active part in the publication of this monumental work, and it is reasonable to suppose that it was to advance science and perhaps also to repay the assistance he had received for his lunar theory, his procedure in managing the undertaking was as tactless and as arbitrary as it well could be. The printing was delayed interminably; Flamsteed was reduced to a state of passionate and baffled rage; the edition was finally burned and a new one printed at the author's expense. The episode is an interesting and tangled story of two parties trying to do a piece of work when every move of either was opposed by the other. According to the account by Flamsteed, which was set down in letters, and in his diary as the negotiations dragged along, he was treated as if he were but a minor factor in the publication of a work to which he had devoted his life and had accomplished in spite of heart-breaking difficulties.[16]

The relations between Flamsteed and Newton since their last break had remained, as Flamsteed notes, sufficiently cordial for them to converse civilly as often as they accidentally met, and Newton always enquired "how the catalogue went on." But Flamsteed had deepened Newton's hostility by pointing out faults in the *Principia* which he naïvely says, "instead of thanking me for, he resented ill" and "was so presumptuous that he sometimes dared to ask 'why I did not hold my tongue.'" Again, when Newton sent him a complimentary copy of his newly published *Optics,* the Astronomer

[16] The source of our information is to be found in Baily's *Life of Flamsteed* where the letters and diary are published in full. As Baily states, there is absolutely no reason to doubt Flamsteed's direct statements of facts, even though his irritability of temper and intense hatred of Halley led him into exaggerated language and made him difficult and suspicious. Brewster has added a few important facts but his comment is worse than misleading; Flamsteed is all black, and Newton is all white. It never seems to have occurred to him that Flamsteed was the author and had some interest in the publication. I have also examined all the documents and letters contained in the *Portsmouth Collection*.

wrote to his friend Sharp: "My discourse, about the faults of Mr. Newton's *Optics* and correction of my lunar numbers, brought the subtle gentleman down hither [the Observatory] the 12th past [April, 1704]. I thanked him for his book: he said then he hoped I approved it. I told him truly, no." We can be sure that if outwardly civil their private feelings were anything but cordial. At this juncture, after having withstood pressure to publish, and Halley's insinuations of his inefficiency, Flamsteed had not only formed a catalogue of from two to three thousand stars whose positions he had determined with his new mural arc, but had also suggested several corrections to the solar, lunar, and planetary tables. He had spent £2000 for instruments, assistants, and calculators out of his pittance of an income; he had never received any money from the Government except his scant salary; he was now ready to publish his complete work and he hoped it would justify his labour, with some return of money from its subscribers. He gives the following account of the hope he had of royal aid:

"Some friend of mine (that was frequently in company with me, and saw how the work went on with such assistance as I hired and paid myself, and was informed what the charge would be of printing the observations of 30 years, and engraving the maps of the constellations I had prepared) acquainted Prince George of Denmark with my performance. Mr. Newton lived near the Court: I, always at a distance. He was the President of the Royal Society, and had a great courtier [Halifax] as his friend, and one who was frequently at his office [the Mint], required at Court, and attending on the Prince. So that he [Halifax] could not but hear of the Prince's inclination to make me easier in my work; nor could Mr. Newton fail to be informed of it. So, on the 10th of April, 1704, he [Newton] came down to Greenwich, visited me on my request, staid, and dined with me. At his first coming he desired to see what I had ready for the press, . . . which having looked over carefully, he desired me to let him have the recommending of them to the Prince. I was surprised at this proposition. I had formerly tried his temper, and always found him insidious, ambitious, and excessively covetous of praise, and impatient of contradiction. . . . I considered if I granted what he desired, I should put myself wholly into his power, or be at his mercy, who might spoil all that came into his hands, or put me to unnecessary trouble and vexation about my labours."[17]

[17] Baily, p. 73.

The character which Flamsteed invariably gives to Newton is so contrary to the equable, mild, and disinterested behaviour which has been always portrayed to us by his biographers, that his opinion has always been brushed aside as being what Brewster terms Flamsteed's "revolting correspondence"; to which he piously added: "We have hesitated, however, to associate the sacred character of the accuser with systematic calumny; and we hasten to forget that there may be an astronomer without principle; and a divine without charity." Flamsteed was undoubtedly cursed with a suspicious temperament and a pen bitter even for that age which was accustomed to express its feelings with a bluntness of terms that shocks our softer usage. But his estimate of Newton's character cannot be ignored, for he was not lacking in generosity of mind. He had suffered in the past from the contrariness of Newton; he was to suffer still worse in the future, and yet he undoubtedly tried to preserve their friendship. What he predicted would happen about the publication of the Catalogue, did occur. We should not forget that Whiston, who was Newton's successor as Lucasian Professor, a great admirer and an early friend, uses very nearly the same characterisation. "So did I enjoy a large portion of his favour for twenty years together. But he then perceiving that I could not do as his other darling friends did, that is learn of him, without contradicting him, when I differed in opinion from him, he could not, in his old age, bear such contradiction. . . . He was of the most fearful, cautious, and suspicious temper, that I ever knew."[18]

Shortly after Newton's assistance had been refused, Flamsteed drew up a prospectus of his proposed work, estimating the number of pages, the order of contents, and the general scope of his observations. He then gave a copy or two to an acquaintance that it might be shown to those who had unjustly suspected his industry and accomplishment. By chance it was handed to some of the Fellows at a meeting of the Royal Society and was delivered to the Secretary to be read publicly. The interest of the Fellows was aroused and a committee, with the President as Chairman, was appointed to wait on Prince George and to solicit his aid in printing the whole work.

On December 5th, Newton wrote to Secretary Sloane to hold himself in readiness to wait on the Prince on the seventh for the purpose of having the honour of his signature in the Statute-book as a Fellow. During the interview, he gave the Prince a copy of Flamsteed's

[18] Whiston, *Memoirs,* 1st Ed., 1749, p. 294.

prospectus, and persuaded him to undertake the entire cost of the publication which was estimated to amount to £863. Mr. Trevelyan[19] gives us a picture of the loved and loving husband, George of Denmark, Prince Consort, as a man either too dull or too shrewd to take any part in political activities; and to most persons his dullness was his most characteristic trait. He had identified himself with his adopted country but his accent still betrayed the foreigner. He was a kindly man who rarely appeared in public, but he was well liked by his servants. Bishop Burnet bravely asserted that he was "free from all vice"—after his marriage as qualified by Trevelyan. It might be added that he was the father of at least fifteen children. He drank like a fish but that was no vice in those days, and he grew very fat on English food. "After many a succulent meal, he died in 1708—a kindly, negligible mortal." But this can be said in his favour, he was a patron of science, a friend and supporter of Newton, and he profoundly gratified the Royal Society by enrolling his name as a Fellow.

A few days after the Committee had waited on the Prince, Newton received a letter from his Secretary saying that His Royal Highness was desirous of aiding the work and requested that Newton, Mr. Robertes, Sir Christopher Wren, Dr. Gregory, and Dr. Arbuthnot, should act as Referees, (to whom Mr. Francis Aston was later added), to inspect Mr. Flamsteed's papers and consider what was fit to print. A week later, Newton wrote to Flamsteed that the Referees were to dine at his house the next day and he would like him to join the company and to consider the matter. On January 23rd, the Referees reported to the Prince that they had inspected the manuscript "and are humbly of the opinion that *all* the observations which he proposed to be printed in the first and second parts of the work are proper to come abroad, together with his two catalogues of the fixed stars in Latin." The work was estimated to run to about 1200 pages in folio.

It needed no prophet to predict that the printing of the *Historia Cœlestis Britannica* would not run smoothly. The appointment of the membership of the Referees was made without consulting the wishes, or interests, of Flamsteed; and Newton, knowing the suspicious attitude of the author, should have been careful to insist that some of the members be appointed to represent the author. But instead of asking Flamsteed to name persons who would satisfy him, it

19 Trevelyan, *England Under Queen Anne,* p. 177.

is only too evident that the Referees were friends and partisans of Newton. There was only one, Wren, who had sufficient reputation to assert himself against the wishes of the Chairman, and he, as Flamsteed points out, was seventy years of age and far too busy with his multifarious occupations to pay close attention to this duty, so that the whole management was left to Newton. The Referees acted as if the work were their own, or rather the Prince's because of his gift; and as if the author, who was one of the most distinguished of living astronomers, who had spent thirty years of labour and a far larger sum of money than the Prince, were merely a minor actor in the transaction. They did not consult him on what was to be done, how done; and they chose the printer. Flamsteed was suspicious and disgruntled from the start, and he was not one to act complacently under even favourable circumstances. He filled his letters and diary with lamentations and objurgations which usually ended with the pious hope that God would grant him patience. But he was afraid to break entirely with the Referees lest, for lack of money, his great work should never be published. Two criticisms have been made against him. It has been asserted that Newton deserved to have his way because he must have the data printed which he needed for perfecting his lunar theory. But while he may have occasionally contemplated taking "another try at the moon," he gave no evidence after 1700 that he was working on the problem. And it has been proved that he had had access to *all* the observations which Flamsteed had in his possession. It has also been stated that all the observations of the Astronomer Royal belonged to the nation. But that is not true. The manuscripts of Halley, his successor, were *purchased* after his death by the Government. And a test case was made as to the ownership of the books and papers of Bradley, Halley's successor, with the result that they were decided by the court to be the absolute property of his heirs.[20] It would be a waste of space to follow the bickerings and the delays which occurred. After a period of three years, the first volume came from the press in December, 1707, and preparations were made to print the more important second volume of the observations which had been made with the new mural arc.

The sequel of this unpleasant, and even disgraceful affair will be given at the proper time, but one incident should be referred to now. Both Edleston and Brewster place all the blame on Flamsteed and claim that, although they were unable to find the Articles of Agree-

[20] Baily, p. 732.

ment actually signed by Flamsteed and the Referees, we must assume Newton carried out their provisions consistently, while Flamsteed signed but afterwards repudiated them. Brewster flatly declares that Flamsteed had resolved from the beginning not to perform his part of the agreement. Baily found four unsigned draughts amongst Flamsteed's papers, which differ but slightly with each other, and he has published one of them; Brewster found three unsigned draughts of them in Newton's hand-writing which he also published. He then remarks "I regret to say that they are essentially different from those published by Mr. Baily," meaning that Newton's proposed draughts must be identical with the signed articles. Of Flamsteed's draughts, he says "they are only articles *proposed* by Flamsteed, and not *the articles which he signed*. Of these he has left no copies, because he had wilfully violated them,"[21] meaning that he perpetrated a deliberate lie to shield his character. That the two parties to an agreement should have prepared different proposals is natural; and it is to be expected, without definite proof, that the signed covenant would differ from both.

Although no signed copy of the Articles of Agreement has been found, I think a fairly accurate idea of the document can be obtained from a comparison of the tentative draughts of Newton and Flamsteed, and from Flamsteed's diary and letters.[22] It should be remembered, in the first place, that the chief purpose of the agreement should have been to make a contract with the publisher. And it was most unfortunate that the differences of opinion between the Referees and the author were known to the publisher, as he would naturally follow the wishes of the party holding the funds. That the Referees and the author disagreed is evident from Flamsteed's diary and correspondence. He notes on October 12, 1705: "Met Mr. Roberts, Sir C. Wren, and Sir I. Newton, at Sir C. Wren's office: showed my paper of articles: 'twas laid by: Sir I. Newton would like nothing I proposed, though he could not say it was unreasonable: drew up another paper: appointed another meeting on the 18th following.—October 22, when we met: read over all the Articles very [carefully?]: I did not assent to many of them: much talk, little done: in the mean time sent to the Prince, by Mr. L., that I would

21 Brewster, II, p. 223. Italics are Brewster's, not mine.

22 I have before me Flamsteed's draughts (*Cf.* Baily, p. 253), Brewster's copy of Newton's draughts (*Cf.* Brewster, Vol. II, p. 480) and also my own copy of the same made from the original manuscripts of the *Portsmouth Collection* (*Cf. Ports. Coll.*, Cam. Univ. Lib. Add 4006).

throw myself on God's providence and his favour: had a favourable answer from Mr. L. next morning."

Now it is evident that neither Newton's nor Flamsteed's draughts are identical with the signed agreement. The only one of Newton's proposed articles which is dated begins with the words, "Articles of agreement made this — day of October" and we know that changes were made at the meetings during that month. Flamsteed's proposals were dated November 10th, and there was a meeting seven days later when he succeeded in having the catalogue of the fixed stars placed in the second volume, instead of in the first as Newton in one of his draughts had proposed. Thus, the final agreement, as the following letter shows, was not reached till Saturday, November 17, and the articles as then signed contain at least one concession to Flamsteed's wishes.

Newton to Flamsteed

Mr. Flamsteed, Jermyn Street, Nov. 14, 1705.

On Saturday next [Nov. 17] about twelve o'clock, the referees meet at my house, to *finish the agreement and sign the Articles* about printing your book; and I shall be glad to have your company here at the same time, and that you will be pleased to dine with me.

I am, your humble servant,

ISAAC NEWTON.

[The following memorandum was written on the letter by Flamsteed.]

"I was there and signed the Articles, but *covenanted that the catalogue of the fixed stars to make a part of the first volume should not be* printed but with the last. Dr. Arbuthnot was there, with Mr. Roberts, and Mr. Churchill, but neither Sir. Chr. Wren, nor Dr. Gregory."[23]

Brewster made such a point of the differences between the Referees and Flamsteed and condemned the latter so bitterly that a

[23] *Cf. Baily*, p. 253.—The significance of the words which I have italicised clearly is: that the articles were signed only after the place of the catalogue had been changed from the first volume to the second in accordance with Flamsteed's wish and contrary to one of Newton's proposed draughts. This position of the catalogue in the book was one of the principal points of difference and was obstinately adhered to by Flamsteed during all the subsequent contentions. Yet Brewster (Vol. II, p. 224) interprets the italicised phrase in this extraordinary fashion: "This [Flamsteed's covenant] is an express declaration that the articles provided otherwise; and Flamsteed's covenant had this strange character, that after signing the articles, he either said to himself, or wrote upon the document, that he 'cove-

rather detailed comparison of the terms as proposed in the draughts of Newton and of Flamsteed should be made.

The draughts agree that exactly 400 copies were to be printed, and that the author was bound to supply copy promptly and to be solely responsible for correcting proof. He was to have access to the press at all times and to break it when the stipulated number of each sheet had been printed. The publisher was required to print five sheets weekly and was to have no interest in the manuscript or in the finished books. The Referees were responsible for all the financial receipts and expenditures of the Prince's money.

The Referees insisted on employing a publisher or bookseller. They chose Aunsham Churchill without consulting the author and fixed his compensation at thirty-four shillings a sheet. Flamsteed wished to avoid that expense and to employ only a printer; but, when he was forced to concede the point, he made no personal objection to Churchill. He was bitterly disappointed that he, as the author who had spent so many years' labour and so much money on its preparation, should be allowed no share of the Prince's bounty or of the sale of the book, while the publisher was to be well paid. The Referees allowed him £280 for the wages of an amanuensis and of two calculators but nothing for himself.[24] There is only one item in

nanted' something different from them." Brewster either did not, or would not, understand the English language when he had to discuss a question involving Newton's character. He had decided that Newton's draughts (which one of the four he does not say) were the signed articles; therefore, the word "covenant" does not mean an agreement between the two parties.

[24] There is in the *Portsmouth Collection* the following memorandum in Newton's handwriting of his complete account for publishing the *Historia Cœlestis*.

EXPENSE OF FIRST VOLUME; PUBLISHED BY THE REFEREES

Paid to Mr. Churchill for paper and printer	£194—17— 0
To Mr. Flamsteed for his copy	125— 0— 0
To Mr. Machin for correcting the copy by the minute-book, and examining some calculations	30— 0—00
Referees received from Prince George	£349—17— 0

Newton explains: "Some time after this Dr. Halley undertook to finish the book, and the referees of the Prince acted no further. . . ."

EXPENSE OF SECOND VOLUME; PUBLISHED AT EXPENSE OF THE GOVERNMENT

Paid to Mr. Churchill for paper and printing	£ 98—11— 0
Paid for designing and graving the draughts and rolling off the plates	116— 4— 7½
Paid to Dr. Halley	150— 0— 0
	£364—15— 7½

Newton also paid £20 out of his own pocket to the engraver.

the expense account of the first volume which is puzzling. On the face of it, the Referees seem to have violated the contract by paying £30 to Machin, when it was expressly stipulated that the author was to make all corrections and calculations. They undoubtedly drove a hard bargain but, after Flamsteed had agreed to it, he should certainly not have complained constantly of its injustice. The account of the publication of the second volume is another story which will be told in the next chapter. It is sufficient now to point out that the Referees ceased to act after the Prince's death, and less than one-half of his promised grant was used. The death of the Prince and the withdrawal of the Referees certainly terminated the agreement; and, on the evidence available, there could be no justification for the government and the Royal Society to keep the manuscript, and to proceed with the publication of the second volume without his consent and under a new agreement. To add insult to injury, Halley, the bitter enemy of the Astronomer Royal, was made editor and well paid for his services, while the author received not even the balance due him for assistants.

The Referees and Flamsteed also differed as to the disposal of the published volumes. They insisted that Churchill should give the books to them to be sent to the Prince; while he wished them to be forwarded to the Observatory in order that he might have the honour of putting them in the Prince's hands, and perhaps receive some profit from their disposal.

Finally, the most important article of disagreement was the place of the catalogue. And here, Flamsteed apparently won, if my interpretation of the meaning of "covenant" be correct. It is, at least, true that the Referees did not include it in the first volume. Arbuthnot and Halley when they assumed the editorship, treacherously tried to follow the Referees' wishes and print the catalogue from an incomplete copy which they had retained after the agreement was ended.

Although none of the tentative draughts, which have been found, agrees exactly with the signed Articles, it is probable that they were closer in agreement with Newton's draughts than with Flamsteed's, because the latter wrote to his friend Sharp, on November 20th, "Sir Isaac Newton has, at last, forced me to enter into Articles for printing my works with a bookseller, very disadvantageous to myself: but 'tis not time to tell you the story of his behaviour: I shall hereafter, and how much he has thereby injured me." But, even if the signed agreement were identical with one of Newton's draughts, there is absolutely no excuse for insulting Flamsteed's character by asserting, as Brewster did, that he destroyed his signed copy and preserved his preliminary draughts because he knew he had wilfully violated his covenant.

In spite of the vexatious troubles resulting from his contentions with Flamsteed, the first years of Newton's presidency of the Royal Society were marked by pleasant and important events. He enjoyed leisure; apparently his official duties required him to spend only one day a week at the Mint. He had abandoned sustained creative work and now passed his days reading and writing in his favourite subjects of religion, history, and chronology. Under these circumstances, he entertained the idea, in 1705, of representing the University again in Parliament. He had sat in the House of Commons during the Convention Parliament and again in the short session of 1701 which terminated the following summer because of the death of King William. The first Parliament of Anne's reign was certain to be strongly Tory, and Newton could readily see that he would have but a slight chance then of re-election by a University constituency which was normally conservative. He thus wisely wrote to a group of his friends that he preferred not to be a candidate, as the following letter explains.

Newton to ———

[1701?]

Sir,—I wrote lately to Mr. Vice-chancellor, that by reason of my present occasions here, I could very ill come down to your University to visit my friends in order to be chosen your burgess. I would have it understood that I do not refuse to serve you, (I would not be so ungrateful to my Alma Mater, to whom I owe my education, nor so disobliging to my friends,) but by reason of my business here I desist from soliciting, and without that, I see no reason to expect being chosen. *And now I have served you in this Parliament, other gentlemen may expect their turn in the next.* To solicit and miss for want of doing it sufficiently, would be a reflection upon me, and it's better to sit still. And tho' I reckon that all one as to desist absolutely, yet I leave you and the rest of the gentlemen to do with all manner of prudence what you think best for yourselves, and what pleases you shall please—Your most humble and most obedt. servant.[25]

[Is. NEWTON]

[25] Brewster, Vol. II, p. 215.

Brewster found two rough copies of this letter in the *Portsmouth Papers,* neither of which bears a date. He unaccountably assigns the letter to the year 1705, and remarks: "we might suppose that Newton was unwilling to canvass personally for a seat in the new Parliament" which by the Triennial Act would be elected that year. The sentence I have italicised would have no meaning if we accept Brewster's date, as he had not sat in the preceding Parliament; it has a clear meaning if we date the letter, 1701, since he had served in that session. Newton had a fair chance of success in the general election of 1705. The complexion of politics had changed greatly during the first three years of Anne's reign. Her Government had begun with strong Tory tendencies. But, however strongly the Queen desired the Stuart succession, she had subordinated that and other Tory policies to her inflexible purpose to carry on the war against France, and to continue Marlborough's command of the army, which had but the year before achieved the dazzling victory of Blenheim. The Tories had split badly on both of those questions and Government, in order to counteract a strong opposition in their own party, had to secure the support of the Whigs who were committed to the continuation of William's war. Thus, as mentioned before, the Junto, though officially in disgrace, had still much influence. Newton could hope that his great reputation would carry him to victory and, in fact, the election did very well by his party. Though Parliament did not expire till August, that event was anticipated by a prorogation on March 14, and Newton made a visit to Cambridge on election business some time that month. He had the strong support of Halifax as appears from the following letter.

Halifax to Newton

Sir,—I send you the address of the House of Lords, to which the Queen made so favourable an answer, that the enemy are quite enraged. The paragraph in her speech against the Tackers[26] provokes them [the Tories] still more than this [address]. And whatever the ministers may think, they will never forgive them for either. I believe they begin to think so, and will take measures to make other friends.[27] I was in hopes by this post to have sent you an account of several altercations that would have pleased you, but they are not

[26] Tackers was the name given to a section of the High Tories who tried to secure the passage, in 1704, of the Occasional Conformity Bill by *tacking* it on to the Land Tax Bill, but failed.

[27] That is, amongst the Whigs.

yet made, tho' you may expect to hear of them in a very little time. Among other expectations we have, we do depend upon a good Bishop, Dr. Wake is likely to be the man. We are sure Sir William Dawes will not. I think this will have great influence in the place where you are, and therefor I think you may mention it among your friends as a thing very probable, tho' it be not actually settled. He is to hold St. James's *in commendam,*[28] and Dr. Younger will be Dean of Exeter. Mr. Godolphin will go down to Cambridge next week, and if the Queen goes to Newmarket, and from thence to Cambridge, she will give you great assistance. The Tories say she makes that tour on purpose to turn Mr. Ansley out. He is so afraid of being thrown out, that Lord Gower has promised to bring him in at Preston, which they should know at Cambridge. If you have any commands for me, I desire you would send them to me, who shall be very ready to obey them.—I am your most humble, and most obedient servt.,

HALIFAX.[29]

17 March, (1705).

Before the Whig candidates had been decided on, Newton wrote a letter to ask for consideration.

Newton to ———

I understand that Mr. Patrick is putting in to be your representative in the next Parliament, and believe that Mr. Godolphin, my Lord High Treasurer's son, will also stand. I do not intend to oppose either of them, they being my friends, but being moved by some friends of very good note to write for myself, I beg the favour of you and the rest of my friends in the University to reserve a vote for me till I either write to you again, or make you a visit, which will be in a very short time, and you will thereby very much oblige yours, &c.[30]

[Is. NEWTON.]

This visit to Cambridge was brief as Flamsteed wrote to Newton on April 5th about the publication of his Catalogue, and closed by wishing him good success in his affairs, health, and a happy return;

[28] The practice of assigning a benefice, or living, temporarily to a cleric or layman till a pastor was appointed, or even permanently, and permitting the enjoyment of the revenue was not abolished till the reign of William IV.

[29] *Portsmouth Collection.* Also quoted by Brewster, II, p. 216.

[30] This letter is without date or address and was communicated to Brewster by the Rev. Jeffrey Ekins. Brewster, II, p. 217.

but it was not sent as he returned to London too soon. During his visit to Cambridge he renewed his friendship with Bentley who, as Master of Trinity College, was now in the full career of his ambitious projects. In spite of his high-handed misappropriation of funds and his tyrannical treatment of the Fellows, he was rapidly raising its intellectual level and cultivating the Newtonian philosophy. He also restored and adorned its buildings. Amongst his other works, he rebuilt the Chapel at great expense to make it worthy of a new and magnificent organ he had bought for the College. The work, though beautifully executed under the direction of Professor Cotes, caused extreme uneasiness and agitation by creating a large deficiency. Newton, with his customary generosity, contributed £60 towards its completion. Bentley also completely refitted and refurnished the Master's Lodge, and to him is due its great oak stairway.

Not long after the completion of this work, Bentley had the honour of entertaining the Queen. She had passed the month of April, 1705, at Newmarket, and went over on the sixteenth, with her husband and the whole Court, to visit the University. Ostensibly this was a mere visit of ceremony but, from the statement in Halifax's letter, it was really undertaken to strengthen her political position in the University. She spent the day in sightseeing, nominated many persons for honorary degrees, and held a court at Trinity Lodge where she made the day memorable by conferring knighthood on Newton, who went up to Cambridge to receive the honour; and she closed the day with a great banquet.[31] It is not now such a rare thing to confer knighthood for distinguished achievement in science, but so far as I can discover this was the first time anyone had been so honoured for such service. It is true that two of his contemporaries were knighted, but Wren and Sloane owed the honour to their public work rather than to their eminence in science. England was slow to reward scientific achievement by this distinction and I believe that Davy, in the early years of the nineteenth century, was the next to receive royal recognition; and even during that century such physicists as Faraday and Maxwell, and such a biologist as Darwin, were not knighted. Thus, in Newton's case, it was an unprecedented expression of the unique position which he occupied in the world. It marked him as without a peer.

There is no evidence to show that Newton was deeply concerned

[31] Monk, *Life of Bentley*, I, p. 183.

in the outcome of the election, but he was sufficiently interested to canvass again in Cambridge on the twenty-fourth, or twenty-fifth, of April. Flamsteed tells us, "Mr. Newton is knighted; stands for parliament man at Cambridge; and is going down thither, this day or tomorrow, in order to his election. 'Tis something doubtful whether he will succeed or no, by reason he put in too late. I expect him back about a fortnight hence; and, within a month after, we may begin to print, if God spare me life and health. I was with him on Saturday last to wish him joy of his honour; he was more than usually gay and cheerful: but I well perceived the same temper that I had always found under it, and therefore took care to be no more open than formerly. I dealt plainly and sincerely with him as I used to do; and this keeps me always safe: but I take care to inform him no further of my business, than he does me of his, or necessity requires, since he make such uses of it (when I do) as no deserving man would allow. He will see his error in a short time, and be the firmer friend to the Observatory hereafter."[32]

Halifax predicted in a letter to Newton that both he and the other Whig candidate, Godolphin, would be defeated by the influence of the Court.

Halifax to Newton

Sir,—I have sent to my Lord Manchester to engage Mr. Gale for Mr. Godolphin, but I am afraid his letter will not come time enough. There can be no doubt of Lord Manchester's sentiments in this affair. Mr. Gale may be sure he will oblige him and all his friends by appearing for Mr. Godolphin, and he can do you no good any other ways. I am sorry you mention nothing of the election. It does not look well, but I hope you still keep your resolution of not being disturbed at the event, since there has been no fault of yours in the management, and then there is no great matter in it. I could tell you more stories where the conduct of the Court has been the same; but complaining is to no purpose; and now the die is cast, we shall have a good Parliament.—I am your most humble and most obedient servant,

HALIFAX.[33]

5th May, 1705.

[32] Letter of Flamsteed to Sharp. Baily, p. 239.—This passage is significant of the curious attitude of all who came in contact with Newton. They felt the power and the essential integrity of the man; his aloofness baffled them, and they feared the suspiciousness and the influence of a flattering coterie which complicated and distorted his simpler and generous qualities.

[33] Brewster, II, p. 217.

On the polling day, May 17, the two Whig candidates came in last, defeated according to Cobbett on the cry that the "Church was in danger."[34] This ended Newton's political aspirations.

In the autumn, he completed the honour of his knighthood by signing his rather doubtful pedigree and adopted, I suppose, his arms of "two shin bones saltire-wise."[35] He, also, arranged with Sloane to have Francis Hauksbee bring an air-pump to his house some evening when he could "get some philosophical friends to see his experiments, who will otherwise be difficultly got together." The meeting, as first scheduled, was however, postponed as Lord Halifax, the Archbishop of Dublin, and Robertes were out of town.[36]

We have so little direct information about Newton's personal and domestic affairs that his biographer must exercise his ingenuity in piecing them out from inferences. It will be remembered that Halifax was now a widower and, in this year, provided Catherine Barton with an annuity and bequeathed a legacy to her in his will. It will also be remembered that, on the explicit statement of Halifax's historian, she became "the Superintendent of his domestic affairs." If this be a correct statement, and we have no contrary evidence, we must suppose that she left her uncle's house to assume her new duties. Whatever view we may take of the affair, it is exceedingly strange that there should be no allusions, especially by Flamsteed, to such a change in Newton's household. Not even a casual remark by him, or by others, can be found which would clear up the circumstances of his domestic life at this time. We have so few personal letters preserved that the following insignificant incident is worth quoting.

Newton to Sir John Newton

Sir John, [1707?]

I was very much surprised at the notice of Mr. Cook's death brought me this morning by the bearer who being an undertaker came to me to desire that I should speak to you that he might be employed in furnishing things for the funeral. He having married a near kinswoman of mine I could not refuse troubling you with this letter in his behalf believing that he will do it well if you are not

34 Brewster, II, p. 218.

35 Turnor, p. 170.

36 Francis Hauksbee, F.R.S., was a most ingenious experimenter. He was noted for his work with Boyle's air-pump; he accepted Newton's theory of light and colours, and apparently carried out many experimental observations for him on light and electricity. Hauksbee published a collection of his ingenious and interesting experiments in a volume dedicated to Lord Somers, and now very rare, with the title *Physico-Mechanical Experiments on Various Subjects*, etc., London, 1709.

otherwise provided. I had an opinion that my Cousin was not in danger though weak, which makes my concern the greater for the loss. I am

Your affectionate Kinsman
and most humble Servant,
Is. Newton.[37]

Jermyn Street Apr. 1707.
For Sr. John Newton, Baron^{t}
at his house in Soho Square.

Newton, at this time, was asked to assist in drawing up the regulations to govern a new professorship in Cambridge University which was designed to promote the experimental sciences, and which has been filled by a succession of distinguished scientists. In 1704, Dr. Plume, Archdeacon of Rochester, left by his will the rent of an estate, situated at Balsham, of the value of £1800 to found the Plumian Professorship of Astronomy and Experimental Philosophy. It was stated by Professor Smith, who afterwards occupied the chair, that he was induced to make this bequest by the pleasure he had had in reading Huygens's *Cosmotheoros* which the celebrated Mr. Flamsteed had recommended to him. The statutes governing the professorship were drawn up by the trustees of the will with the assistance of Sir John Ellis (Master of Caius), Sir Isaac Newton and Dr. [sic] Flamsteed. As would be supposed, Flamsteed opposed the trustees in the choice of the first incumbent. He had immediately written to Whiston to recommend his assistant, John Witty, to the chair, but was chagrined to find that the matter had practically been settled. He wrote, in his disappointment, to Sharp: "Dr. Bentley has determined [about Dr. Plume's Professor of Astronomy], without even so much as letting me know that he was about such business, and, I fear, directly contrary to the archdeacon's design: wherewith, I am apt to think, none of the trustees in Cambridge were so well acquainted as I am. I had not known of it but by an accident. I have wrote about it to Mr. Whiston, who tells me the thing is done as to the nomination of a Professor, and past remedy. I am sorry for it, because this first election will be a precedent for the future, and I fear a very ill one."

Dr. Bentley was not a person who, when he wished to do anything, permitted his plans to be thwarted. Flamsteed entered in his

[37] Edleston, p. 307. Edleston surmises that Mr. Cook was Edw. Coke, Esq., of Holkham (great-great-grandson of the Chief Justice), who married Cary, daughter of Sir John Newton, and died April 13, 1707.

diary on March 15. "Met Dr. Bentley at Garraway's [Tavern]: Sir I. Newton was there: we discoursed first about Dr. Plume's Astronomical Professorship; the Doctor would have had my hand to a paper for the election of Mr. Cotes to be Professor: I refused till I saw him: he told me Mr. Whiston and Mr. Cotes should wait on me next week." We do not know what impression Cotes made on the irascible and obstinate astronomer, but he was elected October 16, 1707. If his appointment set a precedent for the future it was a most fortunate one; he was an extremely brilliant and promising mathematician, and to him we owe the masterly revision of the second edition of the *Principia.* It was his untimely death at the age of thirty-four which drew from Newton the memorable comment, "If Mr. Cotes had lived we might have known something." When we consider the fact that Newton had had every opportunity of gauging the ability of the young man during their intimate work in editing the *Principia,* such a statement is a remarkable tribute to the genius of the recipient and a fine instance of modesty and generosity by the author.

Roger Cotes was the son of a rector of Burbage parish in Leicestershire. He early showed great proficiency in mathematics and the classics, and was admitted to Trinity College as pensioner from St. Paul's School, London, at the age of seventeen years. He was elected to a minor fellowship in 1705 and two years later, at the early age of twenty-five, he became first Plumian Professor. During his brief tenure of the professorship, he impressed all who came in contact with him by his genius; and his colleagues were deeply grieved when he died at the age of thirty-four from a fever, followed by constant delirium.

Cotes, even during his undergraduate days, had become a great favourite of Bentley who quickly appreciated his ability and amiable character. The Master had gathered about him a small group of the abler scholars, junior Fellows, who were impatient of the domination of the older men and were enthusiastic over the reforms he was introducing. He rashly, and often insolently, restricted his intercourse to this inner circle, in which Cotes stood easily first both in talents and reputation, and treated the other Fellows with harsh contempt. In fact, it was his open hostility towards most of the senior Fellows and his determination to clear the College of dead wood by driving them out, as much as his extravagance and malversation of the funds, that caused him to be accused before two successive Bishops of Ely, Visitors of the College. He was practically ordered by them both to be expelled for maladministration; a sentence that he escaped with great difficulty.

On the Master's side, there was much justification for his attitude towards many of the Fellows. It was common knowledge that the College had sunk to a low level during the preceding masterships. As mentioned before, too many of the Fellows refused to vacate their fellowships after a reasonable time. They preferred to hold on to their college quarters and continued to live in lazy and dissipated idleness. Whiston relates the absolute ruin of two young scholars of exceptional promise who died of drunkenness, apparently believing that heavy drinking was a necessary aid to college preferment. Although it was the custom of the day to use exaggerated expressions which shock our ears and give us a wrong estimate of the characters of the men of the time, yet all the evidence goes to show that laziness, loose living, and drunkenness were undoubtedly too common. As examples of unbridled epithet, we cannot imagine the present Master of Trinity rebuking the habits of his colleagues, whatever they might be, by writing as Bentley did: "I found the College filled (for the most part) with ignorant, drunken, lewd Fellows and Scholars." Or, again, when he wished to describe the Fellows who objected to his arbitrary and illegal acts he wrote: "These very Seniors that were thus asked, are such a parcel of stupid drunken Sots, that the like are not in the whole kingdom: they are the Scab, the Ulcers, the Abhorrence of the whole University." Whiston, who admired the Master for restoring discipline and learning in Trinity College and by consequence in the University also, ascribed the beginning of his later unhappy management to abandoning his commendable rule of giving fellowships for merit only. The first lapse from integrity occurred when he appointed a Mr. Stubbs to a fellowship because his uncle, the Vice-master, was so rich as to be able to give the College £10,000 (though he never gave a groat), and also would be so pleased by the honour as to let Bentley govern as he pleased.

It is a relief to turn to Bentley's distinguished service to the College and University by raising the standard of scholarship and sober living, and by inspiring an enthusiasm for work. Ranking himself as one of the foremost English classical scholars, he was a prodigious worker and could not tolerate indolence in others. He was, from his youth, deeply sympathetic to the New Science and one of the first converts to the Newtonian philosophy. In his Boyle lectures, he used the new discoveries in dynamics and gravitation as an evidence of the design of God to create an orderly world, through a knowledge of which we could best learn His nature. He was thus one of the English divines who influenced the Deistic tendencies of the eighteenth century. He gave every encouragement to promote the sciences. It was his zeal and determination which gave a unanimous election to Cotes as Plumian Professor while still only a Bachelor of Arts. No sooner was that accomplished than he set to work to get subscriptions to build a proper Observatory in order that the study of astronomy, promoted by such a professor, might become naturalised and permanent in Trinity College. And he succeeded in erecting above the King's Gate an Observatory equipped with the best instruments obtainable.[38] He also procured for Professor Whiston chambers adjoining the King's Gate so that he, and his pupils, should be near the Observatory.

Till the death of Cotes and the expulsion of Whiston, those two scientists taught and lectured on Newtonian natural philosophy, and started the school of physical sciences for which Trinity College has been famous ever since. They worked together in complete harmony. Whiston, with rare modesty, stated in his *Memoirs* that he was but a child compared to Cotes. In another place in his *Memoirs,* he noted that "Mr. Cotes and I began our first course of philosophical experiments at Cambridge, May 5, 1707. In the performance of which, certain hydrostatic and pneumatic lectures were composed; they were in number twenty-four; the one half by Mr. Cotes, and the other half by myself. . . . But I esteem mine so far inferior to his, . . . I cannot prevail with myself so much as to revise and improve them, as they ought to be before they are fit for publication."[39] Whiston, also in the same year, published "by the author's permission, Sir Isaac Newton's *Arithmetica Universalis,* or Algebra, from that copy which was laid up in the Archives of the University, as all Mr. Lucas's Professor's Lectures are obliged to be, and where my own Lectures were laid up accordingly: which Algebra had been nine years *Lectiones* of Sir Isaac Newton's; but because that acute mathematician Mr. Machin, Professor of Astronomy at Gresham College (where I formerly read many Lectures for him) and one of

[38] This situation was opposed by Flamsteed who thought the entrance gate of John's, or Caius's College, was more suitable; but he advocated a separate building. This Observatory did not continue long in existence.

[39] Whiston, *Memoirs,* 1st Ed., p. 135.

the Secretaries of the Royal Society, has published this work again, by the author's later desire or permission; I lay no claim to it. It has also been put into English from my edition printed at London."[40]

Bentley also promoted the study of chemistry, and for that purpose he repaired and fitted up an old lumber house as "an elegant chemical laboratory" and there Vigani, the former associate and friend of Newton, barring his lewd story about some nuns, regularly delivered courses of lectures for some years.

But Bentley's greatest service to Newton's philosophy was his energetic prodding of that dilatory author till he was finally induced to undertake a second, and revised, edition of the *Principia*. Apparently also, Bentley intended at first to edit the work, and printing was actually begun. In a letter to Newton, on June 10, 1708, he discussed the need of great care in selecting a printer as English compositors were ignorant and unable to print Latin with the accuracy and elegance attained on the continent. He also sent samples of paper and printing. "By this time," he wrote, "I hope you have made some progress towards finishing your great work, which is now expected here with great impatience, and the prospect of it has already lowered the price of the former edition above half of what it once was. I have here sent you a specimen of the first sheet, of which I have printed about a quire; so that the whole will not be wrought off before it have your approbation. I bought this week a hundred reams of this paper you see; it being impossible to have got so good in a year or two, (for it comes from Geneva,) if I had not taken this opportunity with my friend Sir Theodore Jansen, the great paper merchant of Britain."[41] At this point the enterprise stopped. It is not difficult to surmise the cause. Newton had for years been collecting notes and additional illustrations to support his theory of gravitation, and had been making corrections in the first edition which had been hurriedly printed. His desk copy was inter-

[40] *Ibid.*, p. 135.—According to Biot, page 28, the *Arithmetica* was published by Whiston without Newton's knowledge or consent. He adds: "Science, however, must congratulate itself on the transgression of confidence that has fortunately made this work known; for it were impossible to see a more perfect model of the art by which geometrical or numerical questions may be submitted to algebraical calculation."—It seems to me most improbable that the work was published without the author's permission since the MSS. was in the possession of the University and would not be surrendered without the author's written consent. It is far more probable that another reason caused Newton to republish it in 1712 with Machin's name as editor. Two years earlier, Whiston had been expelled from the University for heterodoxy and irreligion, and Newton would be reluctant to have his name or work associated with one who was a confessed Arian in religion as he was, himself, suspected of that taint.

[41] Brewster, II, p. 248.

leaved with such emendations, but as usual he could not be prevailed on to take the plunge. It must have been realised quickly that the combination of an author, who would not attend to the details himself, and an editor, who could not understand the work, was a hopeless one. It was a most fortunate circumstance that Bentley finally turned the editing over to Cotes who, by his ability and tact, was eminently fitted for the work. As a young man he could show the deference which was a necessity when collaborating with Newton and, like Collins, he had the gift of arousing the finest qualities in him. The result of this combination was a mutual esteem, and an excellent and far-reaching revision.

On May 21, 1709, Bentley and Newton had a conference and the new plan of editing was agreed upon. Cotes was apprised of the agreement by a note, "Sir Isaac Newton will be glad to see you in June, and then put into your hands one part of his book corrected for the press." In July, Cotes went down to London, expecting to have the corrected portion of the manuscript given to him, but was put off with the promise that it would be sent to him in a fortnight. After the delay had been protracted to a month, Cotes became anxious and wrote.

Cotes to Newton

Cambridge, August 18th, 1709.

Sir,—The earnest desire I have to see a new edition of your Principia makes me somewhat impatient 'till we receive your copy of it which you was pleased to promise me, about the middle of the last month, you would send down in about a fortnight's time. I hope you will pardon me for this uneasiness from which I cannot free myself and for giving you this trouble to let you know it. I have been so much obliged to you by yourself and by your book that (I desire you to believe me) I think myself bound in gratitude to take all the care I possibly can that it shall be correct. . . .

I take this opportunity to return you my most hearty thanks for your many favours and civilities to me who am

Your most obliged humble servant

ROGER COTES.[42]

For Sr. Isaac Newton at his House
in Jermin Street near St. James's
Church Westminster.

[42] Edleston, p. 3.—Unless otherwise stated, letters about the second edition of the *Principia* are taken from Edleston. Ninety-one letters dealing with the progress of the work are

Newton paid no apparent attention, for a month or more, to this urgent appeal. The first intimation Cotes had that the work was really to begin was when Whiston, his next door neighbour, unexpectedly put into his hands the greatest part of the copy of the *Principia,* ending with the thirty-second proposition of the second book. A week or so afterwards, a letter from Newton informed him that the copy had been sent to Whiston, and added the modest statement, "Its impossible to print the book without some faults and if you print by the copy sent you, correcting only such faults as occur in reading over the sheets to correct them as they are printed off, you will have labour more than than it's fit to give you." Such was not Cotes's idea of his editorship. He examined carefully each proposition and, by his tactful suggestions and corrections, he finally aroused Newton to put his mind seriously to work. Four years were required for the editing, but when the book was published in 1713 it well repaid the labour. How lucky it was that the earlier plans had failed can be appreciated by considering them briefly.

We have referred to the desire of the pretentious Fatio de Duillier to take the matter into his own hands and improve the work of Newton. It is one thing for Newton to confess that, "The book of the Principles was writ in about seventeen or eighteen months, whereof about two were taken up with journeys, and the MS. was sent to the R. S. in spring 1686; and the shortness of the time, in which I wrote it, makes me not ashamed of having committed some faults." But it is another thing to have it expounded and improved by Fatio. There is a tradition, without specific evidence, that David Gregory was to superintend a second edition.[43] He was a great admirer of Newton, and was one of the group which Flamsteed inveighed against as leading him by flattery into dubious ways. He had gone through the *Principia* with minute care, making notes of what occurred to him, and examining each proposition critically. His notes covered 213 folio pages, and he had published in his *Astronomiae Physicae et Geometricae Elementa* the first exposition of the applications of Newtonian philosophy to astronomy. The text certainly followed the *Principia* very closely; it was for this book that Newton gave to Gregory a summary of his new lunar theory

there given besides others of general interest. This work of Edleston is a most valuable assistance to the biographer, as he has also added an accurate and comprehensive chronological table of Newton's life, amplified with 191 explanatory notes, and much other material.

[43] Rigaud, pp. 89–106.

and thereby broke his express and written promise to Flamsteed,—"I do intend *you* shall be the *first* man to whom I will communicate it." If we can accept Hearne's memorandum[44] of December 10, 1705, "Sir Isaac Newton has complained that Dr. Gregory, who borrowed most of the best materials in his book of astronomy from Sir Isaac, has made little or no mention of him, but just in the preface; so that Sir Isaac, fearing lest that, in the process of time, Dr. Gregory's book might happen to be printed without this preface, and consequently he be thought the author of what Sir Isaac himself had before him discovered, resolved to make another edition of his book called Principia Math." Newton was intolerant of any encroachment on his own preserves, and he may have been piqued because Gregory did not acknowledge more explicitly his indebtedness, but he could not have feared that the originality of the *Principia* would be questioned. Hearne's anecdote, however, has value in proving that Newton as early as 1705 expected to print a new edition. If he had ever seriously looked to Gregory as his assistant, he had changed his mind, and his papers were put into Cotes's hands the year Gregory died.[45]

The manuscript of the *Principia* was no sooner delivered to Cotes than it was turned over to the printer. By the twentieth of October, the energetic Bentley was able to report progress in a letter to Newton in behalf of Cotes who was spending a month in the country.

Bentley to Newton

Trin. Coll., Octob. 20, 1709.

Dear Sir,—Mr. Cotes, who had been in the country for about a month, returned hither the very day Dr. Clarke brought your letter, in which, I perceive, you think we have not yet begun your book; but I must acquaint you that five sheets are finely printed off already, and had not we staid for two cuts that Rowley carried to town to be mended by Lightbody, which we have not yet received, you

44 Hearne was, at the time, one of the keepers of the Bodleian Library, Oxford, and was prejudiced against Gregory, the Savilian Professor of Astronomy. His slur should probably be somewhat discounted.

45 Flamsteed wrote to Sharp, 24 March, 1708/9; "I suppose you have heard that Dr. Gregory is dead. Mr. Caswell, my friend, is chosen to succeed him in the Astronomy Professorship at Oxford. Mr. Keill put in for it. Mr. Halley did all he could to serve him, that he might marry his daughter; but his vile character caused some sober persons concerned to urge Mr. Caswell to accept it; who resigned his Divinity Beadle's place, worth more than

had had sent you six sheets by this time. I am sure you'll be pleased with them when you see them. Besides the general running title at the head of every leaf, PHILOSOPHIAE NATURALIS PRINCIPIA MATHEMATICA, I have added the subdivisions of the book, like Hugenii de Oscillatione,) first, DEFINITIONS, then AXIOMATA SIVE LEGES MOTUS, then DE MOTU CORPORUM LIBER PRIMUS. Next will come SECUNDUS, and lastly, DE MUNDI SYSTEMATE LIBER TERTIUS. All these stand in the top of the margin of the several leaves. Your new corollary, which you would have inserted, came just in time, for we had printed to the fiftieth page of your former edition, and that very place where the insertion was to be was in the compositor's hands. . . . I proposed to our master printer to have Lightbody come down and compose, which at first he agreed to; but the next day he had a character of his being a mere sot, and having played such pranks that nobody will take him into any print-house in London or Oxford; and so he fears he'll debauch all his men. So we must let him alone, and I daresay we shall adjust the cuts very well without him. You need not be so shy of giving Mr. Cotes too much trouble. He has more esteem for you, and obligations to you, than to think the trouble too grievous; but, however, he does it at my orders, to whom he owes more than that, and so pray you be easy as to that. We will take care that no little slip in a calculation shall pass this fine edition. Dr. Clarke tells me you are thinking for Chelsea,[46] where I wish you all satisfaction. I hope my picture at Thornhill's will have your last sitting, before you leave the town.[47] The time you set under your hand is already lapsed. When the two cuts are sent us we shall print

£200 per annum, for this, worth about £120."—Again, on July 5, 1712; "Modest Mr. Caswell is dead: Mr. Keill gives out that he has his place—*at quam dissimilis homo!* It was reported some time since, that if he attained this preferment, he should marry Raymer's [pseudonym for Halley] daughter. Raymer and he are both of the same principles; and 'tis pity two houses should be troubled with them." The succession to the Savilian Professorship is important as Keill became a friend of Newton and was responsible for starting the Leibniz controversy.

46 Newton was then moving to Chelsea.

47 Bentley had engaged Newton to sit for his portrait which he presented to Trinity College. Sir James Thornhill (1676–1734) was a noted painter of many large mural works, the most important of which was the interior of the dome of St. Paul's Cathedral. He also painted several portraits. Besides this one of Newton which now hangs in the reception room of Trinity Lodge where he was knighted, he made two others which are in Hurstbourne Park. Viscount Lymington graciously allowed me to photograph them for the first time. They differ widely from the usual idealised portraits and give, I believe, a faithful likeness of the profile and full face. Their most noticeable features are the width and heaviness of the jaw-bones and the extraordinarily long line without a break from the chin to the crown of the head. It is a great privilege to be permitted to reproduce one of them in this work. Lady Thomson told me that Thornhill's visiting card was found beneath one of the floors of Newton's St. Martin Street house when it was recently demolished.

faster than you are aware of—therefore, pray take care to be ready for us.—I am, Sir, your very obedient humble sevant,

RI. BENTLEY.[48]

To Sir Isaac Newton,
at his house in Jermin Street,
near St. James's Church, London.

This letter augured a rapid completion of the work, but the initial burst of speed was not kept up and the editing required four years. There were other reasons for the delay besides Newton's characteristic dilatoriness. Cotes became increasingly exacting in his revision, and he influenced the author to make additions and changes. Newton, also, was busy with other matters; he had the publication of Flamsteed's Catalogue, and the search for new quarters for the Royal Society, on his hands.

It would be safe to say that Newton's chief interest and pleasure during the later years of his life centred in the Royal Society. He permitted nothing to prevent his attendance at the weekly meetings; he is said to have missed hardly one and, as mentioned before, he changed the day from Wednesday to Thursday as that day interfered with his duties at the Mint. As a President, he would have been ideal in less controversial times, or when the Society had attained to its maturity of power and dignity. But I am not so sure that he was well fitted to guide it at this time. The Society was evidently torn by factions, and Newton, who was strongly biased by the influence of his friends, seems to have allowed it to be governed by an inner and active circle. He lacked the tact to manage by persuasion, and had no ability as a speaker. He was silent and diffident in public meetings. Yet he certainly enjoyed the respect, almost amounting to veneration, of the members, and no criticism of his motives has been found.[49]

The dissensions in the Society clustered around Dr. Hans Sloane,

[48] Brewster, Vol. II, p. 250.

[49] An incident occurred in 1704 which may be noted as it shows that the Royal Society was appealed to for a decision on questions other than scientific. The hypocrite and impostor, George Psalmanazar, published his *Historical and Geographical Description of Formosa* in that year. He had claimed to be a native of that island converted to Christianity. The forgery was so gross a one that it is almost unbelievable that it could have been accepted, but his abuse of the Jesuits was sufficient to create a multitude of willing believers, amongst whom was Compton, Bishop of London. He was brought before the Royal Society and confronted with a Chinese. The fraud must have been disclosed to the members but Psalmanazar continued to profit from his adopted rôle. After forty years of life as a lying hypocrite he was converted to an honest and laborious life by reading Law's *Serious Call*. He, in his last years, became an intimate friend of Johnson who regarded him as a saint.

the Secretary. He was a physician of Scotch-Irish extraction and had studied medicine in London and France. His opportunity came when he accompanied the Duke of Albemarle to Jamaica. He was an indefatigable collector and brought back a prodigious number of botanical specimens from the island. Soon after his return, he published his *Natural History of Jamaica.* He rose to be the leading physician of his time and Physician in Ordinary to George II. His collections formed the nucleus of the British Museum, and his name is still attached to an important district in London. As Secretary, he made enemies by his officiousness, and it was claimed that though Newton may have presided, he managed everything. In the first year of Newton's presidency, Flamsteed wrote that "Our society decays and produces nothing remarkable, nor is like to do it, I fear, whilst 'tis governed by persons that either value nothing but their own interests, or understand little but vegetables [Sloane], and how, by making a bouncing noise, to cover their own ignorance."[50]

The Royal Society early took the stand that it would not be responsible for the ideas of its Fellows, nor would it adjudicate differences of opinion which might arise between them. A precedent was established when Secretary Sloane was ordered by Council to acquaint Dr. Bidloo, who had attacked certain statements of Mr. Cowper "that the Society are not erected for determining controversies, but promoting natural and experimental knowledge, which they will do in him or anybody else." But they were equally determined to seek out and, if possible, to discipline those who attacked the Society. An occasion arose in 1700 which caused much disturbance and led to rather serious results. An anonymous author published a satire on the Society in which a bitter attack was directed especially against Sloane, who as Secretary was editor of the *Transactions.* It was entitled *The Transactioneer, with some of his Philosophical Fancies, in two dialogues.* The preface, which was mainly an attack on Sloane as editor of the *Transactions,* begins: "By the following dialogues it is apparent that by industry alone a man may get so much reputation, almost in any profession, as shall be sufficient to amuse the world, though he has neither parts nor learning to supply it." Weld, who examined a copy in the British Museum,[51] considered it of so low and ridiculous a nature that he was surprised the Council paid any attention to it. But he overlooked the fact that,

[50] Baily, p. 218.
[51] Weld, Vol. I, p. 353.—The library of the R. S. does not possess a copy.

at the time, the Society was subjected to constant criticism and ridicule; he also forgot that it was a day of scurrilous pamphlets which made or broke many a reputation. At any rate, the Council took up the matter vigorously and made every effort to discover the author.

According to Dr. Johnson the author of the pamphlet was "Dr. William King, a man of shallowness." But some of the Fellows, amongst whom was Secretary Sloane, suspected Dr. Woodward. He was a man of fine parts, who from a humble origin became one of the great pioneers in the science of geology. His temper was quick and his tongue was sharp, but he was not one to hide behind anonymity. He indignantly denied that he had had any hand in the pamphlet in a letter to the Society, which clearly indicated the dissatisfaction amongst the members, and placed the blame on Sloane. The gist of his grievance can be given by quoting two passages: "I am sorry to find two or three Members of the Society, and my particular friends, ill-treated in it: the writer of it is but meanly qualified for what he undertakes; though whether there was not occasion given, may be worth your consideration. This I'm sure, the world has been now for some time past very loud upon that subject: and there were those who laid the charges so much wrong, that I have but too often occasion to vindicate even the Society itself, and that in public company too. . . . The matter is this: Dr. Sloane and his friend Mr. Pettiver cause it to be spread abroad that I am the author, or at least concerned in writing the aforesaid pamphlet. They do not directly charge me with it: that is not their way, but they do the thing as effectually by insinuating in their clubs and meetings, from whence all the rumour comes, that the world ascribes the pamphlet to me. At other times they assert that it was wrote by a Member or Members of the Society. I cannot but believe they know the true author all the while: at least they know I utterly disown it."[52]

It is probable that the incident of the *Transactioneer* was smoothed over but it, and other differences of opinion as to the conduct of the Society, aroused a bitter feeling which was directed mainly against the Secretary and, to a less degree, against the President. The quarrel came to a head in 1709 when Sloane was up for re-election as Secretary and the removal to new quarters was under discussion. It is clear that Newton publicly supported the Secretary, but his personal feelings towards him are not so certain. Flamsteed evidently thought this supposedly undue influence of the Secretary was to the disad-

[52] Weld, Vol. I, p. 354.

vantage of the Society, for he wrote to Sharp in that year: "Newton is now removing to Chelsea, and has been lately much talked of; but not much to his advantage. Our society is ruined by his close, politic, and cunning forecast; I fear past retrieving, for our Doctor's Transactions have been twice burlesqued publicly; and now we have had none published I think this four months."[53] Again he wrote the following July: "Sir I. Newton has put our Royal Society into great disorder by his partiality of E. Halley and Dr. Sloane, upon a small and inconsiderable occasion: so that they have broke up some few weeks before their time."[54] On the other hand, one of the friends of Woodward, stated in an anonymous letter to Newton: "You had complained of Dr. Sloane's artifices in surprising you with things at the Council, frequently very unfit, without having given you any previous account. As upon others, you had declared to more than one friend, how little qualified he was for the post of Secretary, so upon these occasions you as freely declared him a *tricking fellow;* nay, *a villain* and *rascal,* for his deceitful and ill usage of you in the affair of Dr. Wall."[55]

In spite of opposition, Sloane was re-elected Secretary. At one of the regular meetings shortly afterwards, he read a translation from the *Memoirs* of the French Academy of Sciences[56] in which it was maintained that the Bezoar is a gall-stone.[57] To this statement Sloane added the information that gall-stones caused colic. Woodward was quick to contradict these opinions and, while he was speaking, the Secretary made faces at him or, in the language of the writer, "when he was not able to maintain what he had asserted in words, he had recourse to grimaces very strange and surprising, and such as were enough to provoke any ingenuous sensible man to a warmth, at least equal to that which Dr. Woodward used." Apparently, Sloane

53 Baily, p. 272.—Dr. Sloane was editor of *The Transactions.* Flamsteed's gloomy opinion should, perhaps, be discounted somewhat as Edleston has noted that he was suspended from the Society during that year for non-payment of dues.

54 *Ibid.,* p. 276.

55 This letter is preserved in the *Portsmouth Collection.* The author did not hide behind his anonymity as he offered to have a personal interview with Newton if it was desired. I think Newton must have considered the letter important and reliable as he kept it amongst his papers. Brewster thought that Newton had no such terms in his vocabulary, because he never used towards Flamsteed in public "a harsher term than Puppy."

56 The following account of this extraordinary scene is taken from the anonymous letter referred to above. It is instructive in showing the license of speech and action indulged in during the Augustan age. The general reliability of the account is confirmed by the action of the Council.

57 A Bezoar or Bezoar Stone is a concretion occasionally found in the stomach or intestines of ruminant animals. It was believed to be an antidote to poison. The oriental bezoar is burned as incense.

made his grimaces in such a way that only a few members saw them. But Woodward was one of the number, and he attacked him warmly, using the words, "no man that understands anatomy, can assert that the stones in the gall-bladder are the cause of the colic." During the altercation, the opinions were asked of some of those present, especially of Dr. Mead,[58] who was forced to decide against Sloane. The altercation became so bitter that it was formally taken up by the Council. Sloane denied that he had made grimaces in such a way that Woodward retorted, "Speak sense, or English, and we shall understand you." As a result of this renewed quarrel, Woodward refused to apologise, and he was expelled "from the Council for creating a disturbance by the said reflecting words," and Sloane was thanked for the pains and fidelity with which he had served the Society as Secretary. Woodward brought an action at law to be re-instated but was unsuccessful. What side Newton took is not known, but he evidently retained the respect of both the disputants. He continued to support the Secretary; and although he is reported to have said, "Dr. Woodward might be a good natural philosopher, but he was not a good moral one," that irascible geologist dedicated his great work on the *Classification of Fossils* to him as the *Vir illustris* by whose influence the book had its being. This is, I think, another example of that profound impression which Newton's genius made on his contemporaries and which made them judge him in all respects by it rather than by his personal actions. But Sloane did not escape censure. He lost his secretaryship in 1713 and, apparently, he almost brought about the defeat of Newton, if we can give credit to a statement by Flamsteed in a letter written a week or so after the election: "On St. Andrew's day, Dr. Sloane laid down his secretaryship of the Royal Society: but either he, or another, had so managed the business, that Sir Isaac Newton had like to have been left out of the presidency. There were high and furious debates. Dr. Halley is Secretary in Dr. Sloane's room; and Dr. Keill is brought into the Council. Sir I. Newton sees now that he is understood." If Newton's authority was thus shaken, he came out of the contest stronger than ever as is shown by the results of the election. Sloane, also, recovered from the mischance, as he later was created a baronet and succeeded Newton in the presidency.

[58] Dr. Mead was one of the most distinguished physicians of the day. He was medical adviser of George II; a warm friend and the physician of Newton; and head of St. Thomas's Hospital. His ludicrous duel with Woodward has been already referred to. He also introduced Pemberton, who edited the third edition of the *Principia*, to Newton.

CHAPTER XIV

CONTROVERSY WITH FLAMSTEED. SECOND EDITION OF PRINCIPIA

1709–1713

WHILE Newton was occupied with the disturbances in the Royal Society, with the exasperating business connected with the publication of Flamsteed's *Historia Cœlestis,* and with the editing of the *Principia*, he moved in 1709 from Jermyn Street to Chelsea. A year later, he returned to the city and occupied a house on the east side of St. Martin's Street just off Leicester Square, where he lived till 1725, when because of illness he was taken to Kensington in the vain hope that the purer air of the village would restore his health. The appearance of the house, during Newton's occupancy, is well known from an old print, and indeed it was still standing with but little change till about 1915 when the building was demolished to the first story. It was left in that melancholy state for a decade and, when the bicentenary of his death was celebrated, workmen were picking away the foundations. After another long delay, a new public library of the City of Westminster now occupies its site.

The house was one of considerable size and of some pretensions. It was three stories in height, built of stone with a slated attic on which rose a low wooden structure used, according to tradition, as an observatory. Shortly after Newton's death, the Conduitts removed to George Street, Hanover Square, a more fashionable part of the town, and I believe it is unknown who were its next tenants. But Dr. Charles Burney lived there in 1779 and gathered in the pleasant Jacobean house, with its panelled rooms and charming little staircase, a musical, literary, and artistic coterie so various, and so brilliant, that it could not be matched in the stateliest mansions of Grosvenor Square. Such men as Garrick, Reynolds, Burke, and Dr. Johnson,[1] frequently passed in and out the low doorway level with

[1] Boswell frequently mentions the visits and intimacy of Dr. Johnson and erroneously adds "in the house where the great Newton lived and *died*."

the street. Here Fanny Burney wrote *Evelina* and, like Catherine Barton before her, charmed her distinguished friends.

The question whether Catherine Barton presided over her uncle's household at this time, or was acting as housekeeper for Lord Halifax, will have to be decided by the reader from the evidence previously presented. It is irritating that Swift, who was in London in 1710–1711 and sent to Stella a detailed account of what he did, and of whom he met, should not have left a clue as to where she lived. He mentions frequently his great affection for Mrs. Barton, and that he often visited and dined with her. He also tells us that, although he had turned Tory, he kept up his friendship for Lord Halifax, and visited him occasionally. But he never couples their names together, although they were intimate friends, nor indicates where either of them lived. De Morgan believed that Swift deliberately suppressed this information because they were privately married, and he wished to respect the delicacy of her equivocal position. In the *Diary to Stella,* Newton's name is not mentioned, and this fact strengthens De Morgan's opinion since the names of so many other less distinguished men, whom he met, are carefully recorded. We know also that he was commissioned by Bolingbroke to offer a large pension to Newton and that he proposed the plan to Catherine Barton. It seems reasonable to assume that he would not have chosen such an indirect method if he had known Newton personally, or if he met Mrs. Barton at her uncle's house. Swift's long and affectionate friendship with his niece is shown by the following letter, written many years later, the only one of hers which has been preserved.

Catherine Barton to Dean Swift

George Street, November 29, 1733.

Sir,

Mrs. Barber did not deliver your letter till after the intended wedding brought me hither. She has as much a better title to the favour of her sex than poetry can give her, as truth is better than fiction, and shall have my best assistance. But the town has been so long invited into the subscription, that most people have already refused or accepted, and Mr. Conduitt has long since done the latter. I should have guessed your holiness would rather have laid than called up the ghost of my departed friendship, which since you are brave enough to face, you will find divested of every terror, but the remorse that you were abandoned to be an alien to your friends, your country, and yourself. Not to renew an acquaintance with one who can twenty years after remember a bare intention to serve him, would be to throw away a prize I am not now able to repurchase; therefore, when you return to England, I shall try to excel in, what I am very sorry you want, a nurse. In the mean time I am exercising that gift to preserve one who is your devoted admirer.

Lord Harvey has written a bitter copy of verses upon Dr. Sherwin, for publishing, as 'tis said, his Lordship's epistle, which must set your brother Pope's spirits all a working. Thomson is far advanced in a poem of 2000 lines, deducing liberty from the patriarchs to the present time, which, if we may judge from the press, is now in full vigour. But I forget I am writing to one who has the power of the keys of Parnassus, and that the only merit my letter can have is brevity. Please therefore to place the profit I had in your long one to your fund of charity, which carries no interest, and to add to your prayers and good wishes now and then a line to

Sir, your obedient humble servant,

C. CONDUIT.

Mrs. Barber, whom I had sent to dine with us, is in bed with the gout, and has not yet sent me her proposals.[2]

We have no record of the furnishing of the house when it was first occupied, but at the time of Newton's death a true and perfect inventory[3] of all his possessions was made by his nephew, Conduitt. From it we can obtain an idea of the appearance of a comfortable home in the early part of the eighteenth century. Newton was partial to crimson since that colour largely predominated throughout the house. His own bedroom, with its dressing-room, contained rather simple furniture and more draperies than one would expect. His niece's rooms were furnished in crimson and more in sympathy with feminine ideas of taste. Oddly enough, in neither room were any washing accommodations catalogued and, as there were certainly no separate bathrooms, the ablutions of all were performed with four pails and washing tubs listed amongst the kitchen utensils. In the dining room, the most notable object was a bust of Newton

[2] Brewster, Vol. II, p. 494.

[3] The recent discovery of this important document is due to the diligent search of Colonel R. de Villamil. The inventory, which was drawn up by order of the Prerogative Court of Canterbury, is a document sixteen feet long and five inches wide, written on strips of vellum and each officially stamped. For a complete list of Newton's household goods and library, *Cf.* his *Newton: The Man.*

carved in ivory under a glass frame. This work of art, of which he was proud, is not the excellent ivory bust by Le Marchand now in the British Museum. His study, where he lived the latter years of life, and where he meditated and worked with a book or pen constantly in his hand, is the room that most excites our interest. Situated just above his bedroom, its significant articles were a walnut cabinet writing desk and a large table, both with drawers. Around the walls stood six book-cases containing his library. Other items included 210 prints, a small piece of tapestry, some Irish stitch lace hangings, two platen busts and library chairs. Colonel de Villamil pictures Newton as being quite indifferent to his personal surroundings, and states that there were no beautiful or valuable pieces of furniture anywhere in his house. He kept two servants, and a man who slept in the hall on a "settle bedstead." He kept no coach but owned a sedan chair. Colonel de Villamil quotes Seward that "backagmmon was a favourite recreation with him, at which he used to play with Flamsteed." The total appraised value of his household goods was £520-6-6, and it seems to me that this is a sum which would argue a well furnished house and rather contrary to Colonel de Villamil's opinion. In addition to the furnishings there were listed 1896 books appraised at £270 and personal manuscripts at £250.

The disappearance of the library and its discovery have been previously referred to; now, thanks to the diligent enquiry of Colonel de Villamil the wanderings of this collection can be followed.[4] Living also in St. Martin's Street was the notorious warden of the Fleet Prison and, at Newton's death, he pounced on the library which he bought for £300 and gave to his son, Charles Huggins, Rector of Chinnor, near Oxford. The owner pasted his book-plate in all the volumes. Later, the benefice was presented to Dr. James Musgrave who purchased the collection for £400, and his book-plate was pasted over that of Huggins. By marriage, the descendants of Dr. Musgrave have now the name of Wykeham-Musgrave of Thame Park, Oxfordshire and Barnsby Park, Gloucestershire. About 1920, Thame Park was sold and a large part of Newton's books were sold in bundle lots, and were scattered or destroyed. But Colonel de Villamil found 896 volumes and Dr. Musgrave's original catalogue still remaining at Barnsby Park. Thus much of this library so useful to students of Newton's character has come again to light after its disappearance of two centuries.

[4] *Cf. Newton: The Man*, pp. 2–7.

It has been shown in the previous chapter how the strained relations between Newton and Flamsteed had gone from bad to worse during the publication of the *Historia Cœlestis*. After long and vexatious delays, accompanied by constant bickering on both sides, the first volume was finally printed in December, 1707, and the sheets were left with Churchill till the question was decided whether the catalogue of stars should be included in it. Flamsteed was paid the £125 which had been agreed upon,[5] and then months passed without any progress being made towards the printing of the second volume.

Although the Referees and the author had had no difference of opinion as to the question of the contents of the now finished volume, they were hopelessly at issue as to the arrangement of the second volume. The Referees had wished to prefix the catalogue of the fixed stars to the first volume, but Flamsteed insisted that it be printed at the end of the second, and that it be set up under his immediate superintendence and control. On the order of arrangement he was steadfast, but he appears to have been kept in ignorance that the Referees were meanwhile editing and mutilating his observations. Apparently, also, to conceal this real cause of the delay, they met in July and adopted a resolution that "the press should go on without delay: and that if Mr. Flamsteed do not take care that the press be well corrected, and go on with dispatch, another corrector be employed."[6] Flamsteed answered, a week later, by a letter addressed to Wren as he feared a communication sent to Newton might be suppressed. He protested vigorously that he had not delayed the first volume, and pointed out that he could not be the cause of the present stoppage of the press as he had deposited with the Referees, on March 20th last all the observations made between September, 1689 and 1705, complete on 175 sheets of paper, in order that the printing might begin. Then he states, what was evidently the real trouble, that Newton insisted on placing the catalogue in the first volume and that he would not consent to the arrangement. Also Flamsteed persisted in maintaining his contractual right to correct all proofs: "The catalogue is of that importance that I shall never consent that any page of it should be printed off till I have fully corrected and received from the press a proof without faults."

[5] Flamsteed either forgot that he had been paid on 12 April, 1708, or else complained that his payment had been maliciously deferred in order to add weight to his grievance for what he felt to be a niggardly treatment.

[6] *Cf. Baily,* p. 87.

Flamsteed had made a good case for himself, but its effect was to stiffen Newton's obstinate pride and to make him more determined than ever to have his own way. What would have been the final outcome, no one can say, but the press was stopped the rest of the year. In October, Prince George died and that event ended the agreement. Newton returned the unexpended balance of the Prince's grant and, as he noted in his accounts, previously given, the Referees ceased to act. No progress on the second volume could now be made till someone provided the funds and a new contract should be drawn. But Newton had not relaxed his determination to manage the business as he wished, and he had still in his possession 175 sheets of the observations.

However mild and equable Newton's temperament might be in his ordinary contact with men, he was aroused to intense, and even vindictive, resentment by any personal criticism which reflected on his integrity and honour. And Flamsteed, especially in his letter to so eminent a man as Wren, had not hesitated to denounce both his conduct and motives. He had by now reached the point of such exasperation that he would be satisfied only when he had not merely thwarted Flamsteed's wishes about his book, but had also broken his authority at the Observatory. Although it has often been said that Newton was a Whig and a Churchman by habit, he had managed to hold his lucrative office during Tory governments, and he also enjoyed the friendship and admiration of Bolingbroke. However, at the time of Prince George's death, the ministry had changed, and the time was not propitious for getting a new grant to continue the publication. Nothing was done about the book for two years till, in 1710, Bolingbroke returned to office as Secretary of State; with his help and that of Dr. Arbuthnot, who was high in Queen Anne's favour, Newton obtained a royal grant to continue the printing of the work, and also secured the appointment of a Board of Visitors of the Observatory; both of these plans were placed under the direction of committees of the Royal Society with himself as chairman.

It is very probable that the appointment of Visitors has been to the advantage of the Observatory, but it was an ungracious and unwise act at the time. Flamsteed was a distinguished astronomer; he was old and had been neglected; the least the Government could have done for him as a reward for his services was to publish his great book as he wished and to let him manage his work without hindrance till his approaching retirement. Coming at the time it did, the appointment of the Visitors was undoubtedly the result of Newton's revenge and plan of subjecting Flamsteed to his will. The minutes of the Royal Society have constant references, for the next few years, to orders for the Royal Astronomer to send reports of his observations to the Visitors, and directions by them as to what he should undertake. On the other side, Flamsteed petitioned the Queen to dispense with the Visitors, and he paid but scant attention to their wishes.

The feeling between the Visitors and Flamsteed became so bitter that Newton, as President, desired him to attend a meeting of the Council on October 26, 1711, "to know of him if his instruments be in order, and fit to carry on the necessary celestial observations." This request was an extraordinary one as Newton, by reason of his frequent visits to the Observatory, knew the condition of the instruments, and he had used Flamsteed's lunar observations as the most accurate ever made. It would be difficult to view such an order as anything but an effort to humiliate the Astronomer Royal. Flamsteed attended and a disgraceful scene ensued. It was fortunate for the Society that there was not a quorum present and that there is consequently no entry of the humiliating occurrence in their records.

Flamsteed narrated the interview in a letter written two months later: "I have had another contest with the President of the Royal Society, who had formed a plot to make my instruments theirs; and sent for me to a Committee, where only himself and two physicians (Dr. Sloane, and another [Dr. Mead] as little skilful as himself) were present. The President ran himself into a great heat, and very indecent passion. I had resolved aforehand his kn—sh talk should not move me; showed him that all the instruments in the Observatory were my own. . . . This nettled him; for he has got a letter from the Secretary of State for the Royal Society to be visitors of the Observatory; and he said '*as good have no observatory as no instruments.*' I complained then of my catalogue being printed by Raymer [Halley], without my knowledge, and that I was *robbed of the fruits of my labors.* At this he fired, and called me all the ill names, puppy, etc., that he could think of. All I returned was, I put him in mind of his passion, desired him to govern it, and keep his temper."[7]

[7] *Cf.* Baily, p. 294. There seems to be no doubt as to the correctness of his statement of this scene. Flamsteed has left three accounts which differ only in minor details. Even Brewster [Vol. II, p. 239] grudgingly admits its probability. "How simple minded" he remarks, "Newton must have been in whose vocabulary of vituperation the epithet [puppy] given to Flamsteed was the most prominent." Somehow, he seems human but not simple minded on account of this outburst.

During the squabble Mead also ran into the same passion as Newton, but Sloane said nothing all the while, and Flamsteed thanked him for this civility. Shortly afterwards he met Halley, drank a dish of coffee with him, and told him calmly of the villainy of his conduct, and called it blockish. This is a striking example of the license of talk indulged in even by sedate men of high position and today, two persons, who had accused each other of such base conduct as had Flamsteed and Halley, would hardly enjoy a dish of coffee together.

We can now return to Newton's plan for publishing the second volume of the *Historia Cœlestis.* A royal grant to defray the cost had been obtained through the influence of Arbuthnot,[8] and the former Referees were replaced by the Royal Society. All this was done without Flamsteed's knowledge and, although the old Agreement was thus abrogated, he was left at their mercy as no new contract was drawn. His first intimation of what was in store for him was a letter from Arbuthnot.

Arbuthnot to Flamsteed

London, March 14, 1710/11.

Sir,

Her Majesty having commanded me to take care that the *Historia Cœlestis,* which was begun by his Royal Highness's order, and carried on at his charge, should be finished as soon as possible, and that it should appear in a dress suitable to the honour of such a patron, I should fail in my duty if I did not acquaint you that there remain several things to be performed on your part towards the perfection of so useful a work; and particularly what retards us at present is, the want of your most accurate catalogue of the fixed stars, which the world has so long wished to see. The copy you have hitherto delivered is imperfect. . . . Therefore, I desire you will deliver into my hands, as soon as possible, a perfect copy of your catalogue of the

[8] Dr. Arbuthnot, born in 1667, was a native of Scotland and received his medical education at the University of Aberdeen. He moved to London and, not being able to support himself by his profession, he taught mathematics in which he was proficient. His first success in medicine resulted from a lucky accident. Prince George was suddenly taken ill at Epsom, and Arbuthnot who happened to be near at hand was called to attend upon him. His treatment was so successful that he became the physician and great personal friend of the Prince; and the year following, physician in ordinary to Queen Anne. A man of great wit and learning he was a prominent Fellow of the Royal Society and a friend of Newton, Pope and Swift. Dr. Johnson spoke of him as an illustrious physician and believed that he was the author, aided by Pope and Swift, of the *Memoirs of Martinus Scriblerus.* With Pope, he annotated the *Dunciad,* in fact, Johnson thought he excelled Swift in coarse humour, and ranked him as the most eminent writer in Queen Anne's reign.

fixed stars, and you shall have a receipt, in due form, upon the delivery of it. . . .[9]

Flamsteed was greatly encouraged by the news that the work of printing was to be resumed, and informed Arbuthnot that he had enlarged and corrected his observations and catalogue to the advantage of the book. But his hopes were dashed by the answer that his, Arbuthnot's, commission permitted him to publish only the observations which had been given to the Referees before his Royal Highness's death. After, however, they were printed he would be ready to solicit the Queen to add the new material to the work as an Appendix.

The history of the negotiations can now be followed from Flamsteed's letters and autobiography; the facts are doubtless true even if their presentation is coloured by his chagrin. "March the 19th, 1710/11, I received a letter from Dr. Arbuthnot, one of the Queen's physicians, signifying that the copy of a part of my catalogue, which had been delivered into Sir I. Newton's hands at his desire, sealed up, was now in the Doctor's, who desired that I would give him four constellations that were wanting in it, with the variations, etc. for the rest. For, when the part of my catalogue was put into Sir I. Newton's hands (March the 15th, 1705/6) these constellations were not begun, and the rest unperfect: which, though Sir Isaac knew very well, he still persisted to have the keeping of it in his hands, sealed up; that, as he said, he might have all things in his power." Two years later, March 20, 1707/8, the packet was opened with Flamsteed's consent, in order that the magnitudes of the stars might be inserted in their proper places; the packet was then resealed and left with Newton. On March 25, 1711, he was informed by a friend that the packet had been opened again and without his knowledge; the catalogue was in press and some sheets of it had been printed. On March 29, four days later, Arbuthnot and Flamsteed met at Garraway's Tavern when Arbuthnot stated categorically before two witnesses that not a sheet had been printed. Flamsteed was certain that this statement was false since, at the same time, he was offered £10 for every press fault that could be found in it, and only four days later he received the first printed sheet.[10]

9 For the correspondence of Arbuthnot and Flamsteed, *cf.* Baily, pp. 280–289; pp. 93–95; and also p. 291.

10 Baily comments on this episode: "Flamsteed was right: and it seems scarcely possible that Dr. Arbuthnot could have been ignorant of the fact. Some gross deception was evidently

The incident of the sealed packet must be discussed however it may affect Newton's integrity. There is no doubt that the incomplete catalogue had been deposited in his hands sealed, and by his own request. In fact, the precautions then taken are a commentary on the lack of confidence between the Referees and Flamsteed. It is also certain that it was opened by mutual consent that necessary data might be inserted. The only doubt, as to the conduct of Newton, is whether it was again sealed; and Brewster's only argument to the contrary rests on his opinion that such an act was not in accordance with Newton's character as he understood it. But if it were not re-sealed in accordance with the explicit promise that its data could not be used without Flamsteed's approval then his whole complaint falls to the ground. Now Flamsteed definitely charges Newton with this breach of faith several times in letters to his friend, Sharp, and in one of them claims Newton justified himself that he had done it by the Queen's order. But the Queen must have issued the order on either Newton's or Arbuthnot's request.

It may be claimed that statements in personal and private letters are not proofs of fact. But Flamsteed made the same accusation in public and before witnesses. He also requested an unknown correspondent to lay the matter before the Duke of Bolton, who later was instrumental in getting the published volumes returned to him; finally, he included his charge in a remonstrance to Queen Anne. Such evidence must be conclusive, and the subsequent history of the packet confirms it, and shows Newton's determined obstinacy and unrelenting hostility when once he had decided on a line of conduct. In 1716, Flamsteed wrote him a formal note demanding the return of the catalogue and the 175 sheets of observations. As that demand produced no effect he sent an attorney to Newton, but he refused to be seen and the attorney left a note for him. No considerations of right ever prevailed, and he never returned Flamsteed's property. Nor did Newton's vengeance limit itself to mutilating Flamsteed's life-work. When the second edition of the *Principia* appeared, in 1713, his name was erased in nearly all the places where recognition for his great services had previously been made.

The subsequent history of the book can be told briefly. As Flamsteed was unable to stop the press, Halley continued to act as editor, and Baily states that he made many misrepresentations and misstate-

carrying on: and Flamsteed was justified in breaking off all negotiation with parties that could act in this manner. Nevertheless it appears that he was still willing to abide by his original agreement with the Referees." *Cf.* p. 94.

ments and, in his preface, gave a colouring to facts which leave a false impression in the mind of the reader. Halley's edition appeared in 1712 and contained, besides the spurious catalogue and the garbled observations, nearly the whole of what now forms the first volume of the *Historia Cœlestis.*[11] In the meanwhile, Flamsteed recopied his enlarged catalogue and observations, at great personal labour and expense. Political changes brought the Duke of Bolton and Sir Robert Walpole into office and he had the great satisfaction, through their interest, of having 300 copies delivered up to him. These were probably all of the 400 printed which remained after the presentation copies distributed by Newton and a few sales were deducted. He immediately committed them to the flames "that none might remain to show the ingratitude of two of his countrymen, who had used him worse than ever the noble Tycho was used in Denmark." Although he made every effort to complete his work, he died before the second volume was finished. The remainder of the second and the third volumes were edited by Joseph Crosthwaite, his assistant, with the aid of Abraham Sharp; and the whole work was published in 1726, six years after Flamsteed's death.

It is pleasant to turn from the sordid and devious quarrels in which Newton was involved; if for no other reason than that the emphasis which I am forced to put upon his peculiarities of temperament may seem to include me in the class of biographers who delight in detracting from the characters and achievements of the men they portray. At the same time in which he was directing the publication of the *Historia Cœlestis,* he was engaged in editing with Cotes the second edition of the *Principia.* In this work he shone at his best. As I pointed out previously, his relations with young men, Collins, Gregory, Halley, Fatio, and now Cotes, were charming in their mixture of dignity and modest friendliness; and in Cotes he had found the most amiable and the most brilliant of this very exceptional group. In a former chapter, the early stages of the work were described to the year 1709. In the beginning, Newton's interest in the undertaking had been listless. He felt that, if the marginal notes and corrections which he had made in his desk copy of the first edition were put into shape by Cotes, it was as much as could be expected. This was not at all the idea of the young and enthusiastic

[11] It is but fair to Halley to quote a remark of the mathematician, Jones, made in a letter to Cotes: "Dr. Halley has almost finished the printing of the Greenwich Observations, which will be a work of good use; especially as it is now freed from the trifles it was loaded with." Edleston, p. 208.

editor who was determined to make a thorough revision of the work. Newton quickly recognised the industry and ability of Cotes, and soon formed the habit of accepting his corrections. No better illustration of his own curious and haughty indifference to his intellectual children could be given than the following: "You need not give yourself the trouble of examining all the calculations of the scholium. Such errors as do not depend upon wrong reasoning can be of no great consequence and may be corrected by the reader." But that was not Cotes's method and he answered: "I received your letter of June 15th in which you consent to the alterations that I proposed in that scholium. I have examined the whole calculation and done it anew where I thought it necessary."

It will be remembered that Cotes received the greater part of the manuscript in October, 1709 and by April 15, 1710, nearly one-half of the whole work had been printed; that is, as far as the scholium to proposition x of the second book. Greater speed was possible at the beginning because little new matter was added to the earlier portion, and Cotes could usually manage the correction of errors and misprints by himself. At least, he had but little assistance from Newton, as there is a break in their correspondence for six months. He then wrote: "I have ventured to make some little alterations myself whilst I was correcting the press such as I thought either elegancy or perspicuity or truth sometimes required. I hope I shall have your pardon if I be found to have trusted perhaps too much to my own judgement, it not being possible for me without great inconvenience to the work and uneasiness to yourself to have your approbation in every particular." Newton is probably to be excused for his dilatoriness as he was excessively occupied in other business. He moved his household twice within the year, and he was unusually busy at the Mint coining the silver necessary to meet war expenses of the army in Flanders. During this time also he was negotiating for the house in Crane Court and preparing it for the Royal Society; his troubles with Flamsteed were at their height both in the matter of publishing and in that of the Visitors to the Observatory; and the controversy with Leibniz had reared its ugly head.

The first real snag was struck when editing the problem on the velocity of efflux of a fluid through an orifice in the base of a cylindrical vessel.[12] Newton had made a mistake in the first edition and,

[12] Newton had made a mistake in Prop. XXXVII, Book II, in his first edition (Prop. XXXVI in Motte's English Trans.) where he stated that a jet of water from an orifice rose to half the height of the fluid in the vessel. This error was exposed by experiments made by the

when his attention was called to his error, he made some strikingly ingenious experiments, discovered the unknown effect of the *vena contracta,* and solved the problem correctly. The incident is well worth noting as it shows that his ability in experimentation and his powers of scientific deduction were unimpaired; only his inclination was wanting. Another case of an error made by Newton can be instanced in order to show that even he was fallible. The mistake occurred in finding the value of the resistance to the motion of a projectile in air, and was pointed out to him by Nicholas Bernoulli.[13]

The most important revisions were made in the theories of the moon and of comets,[14] derived from the observations which Newton had received years before from Flamsteed. While this part of the work was in progress, he became keenly interested, and there was a quick interchange of letters. We can, therefore, ascribe the last two years required to finish the work to the important changes and additions in the text rather than to dilatoriness.

During the progress of the revision, the controversy between Newton and Leibniz on the invention of the calculus had reached an acute stage. It had been reawakened by an article of Keill's published in the *Philosophical Transactions* in 1708 which led to a review of the case by the Royal Society. The continental men of science were almost unanimously on the side of Leibniz and, as rumours had arisen that a new edition of the *Principia* was in preparation, they opened an attack on the Newtonian philosophy. Since it was difficult to find fault with his mathematical exposition of the law of universal gravitation, they concentrated on his claim that his philosophy involved no hypotheses and thus was superior to the Cartesian postulate of vortices.[15] The gravamen of their criticism was

Royal Society in 1691. The discrepancy in calculating the velocity of efflux from the observed height of the jet and from the quantity of fluid discharged was not reconciled till Cotes, after performing some new experiments, forced Newton's attention to the subject, and he then investigated anew and by experimentation discovered the principle of the *vena contracta.*

13 Bernoulli was on a visit to England during the months of September and October, 1712. Newton mentioned in a letter (Macclesfield's *Collection,* Vol. II, p. 437) "Having been shown an error in Prop. X, Book III by Nicholas Bernoulli, I corrected the construction of the proposition, and showed the correction to him, and I took care to have it printed not deceitfully but with his knowledge." He also repaid the Bernoullis by proposing John Bernoulli as a member of the Royal Society, into which he was elected December 1st, 1712.

14 As early as 1694, Newton began to revise his lunar theory, and there are in Sect. I, § IX B of the *Portsmouth Collection* many memoranda on the subject and "a list of propositions in the lunar theory, prepared for a 2d. edition of the *Principia,* but not used." This list has been published in an Appendix to the Preface of the *Cat. of the Ports. Coll.* and also in Ball's *Essay on the Principia,* p. 126.

15 Professor Jones wrote to Cotes, October 25, 1711: "I have nothing of news to send you; only the Germans and French have in a violent manner attacked the philosophy of Sir Is.

that Newton held attraction at a distance to be an essential property of matter; if so, then they argued, he had introduced an occult quantity, and his philosophy was as hypothetical as the Cartesian hypothesis of vortices in an occult medium.[16]

It is evident that Bentley and Cotes were worried lest the new criticism of the *Principia* should affect Newton's reputation and also the sale of the new edition, now rapidly approaching completion. They agreed that a preface should be prepared which would defend Newton against the charge of introducing occult quantities, and attack Leibniz's priority in invention of the calculus. Newton, also, was to defend his philosophy by a general statement to be added to the body of the text. On March 2, 1712/3, he wrote to Cotes that he enclosed the last batch of copy which finished the book. This he says is "the scholium which I promised to send you, to be added to the end of the book." Before taking up the subject of the preface, it is important to consider the scholium, itself, because he there sums up the essence of both his scientific and religious philosophies.

The celebrated General Scholium begins with the sentence: "The hypothesis of vortices is pressed with many difficulties." Its chief difficulties are then discussed: first, the necessary periodic times of the vortices do not conform to the periodic times of the planets, secondly, the rotations of the sun and the planets do not correspond with the motions of their vortices; thirdly, the motions of comets are exceedingly regular and their eccentric orbits are incompatible with a vortex and, in addition, their paths cut through the planetary orbits and vortices in all directions. He next argues that the regularity and beauty, or rather the rhythmic harmony, of the solar system presuppose the existence of a designing and intelligent Creator, whose attributes are to be discovered from a study of his works.

To answer the insinuations of Leibniz, that he believed God to be merely a part of the mechanical universe and to be defined as the sensorium of infinite space, in agreement with the Cambridge Platonists, Newton emphatically declares that God is a true spiritual being who "governs all things, and knows all that are or can be done.

Newton, and seem resolved to stand by Descartes; Mr. Keill, as a person concerned, has undertaken to answer and defend some things, as Dr. Friend, and Dr. Mead." Edleston, p. 210. That the attack on the *Principia* was the result of the Leibniz controversy, and that it was directed against the hypothetical character of the Newtonian philosophy is evident from the letters in Edleston, pp. 149–160.

[16] The particular meaning of *occult* should be carefully noted. An occult substance is one which cannot be directly perceived by the senses, *e. g.* the luminiferous æther; an occult force is one unknown to experience, *e. g.* action at a distance.

He is not eternity or infinity, but eternal and infinite; He is not duration or space, but he endures and is present. He endures forever, and is everywhere present; and by existing always and everywhere, he constitutes duration and space." This declaration of faith is important. In spite of his personal beliefs, it is certainly true that naturistic Deism found one of its strongest supports in the mechanistic philosophy of the *Principia*. In Leibniz's debate with Clarke, it was claimed that Newton's God was but the creator of an universal machine which was self-acting and needed but a mechanician to keep it in repair. In this discussion, an important matter was overlooked, Newton confined his mechanisms to the physical world; it was not till the nineteenth century that man, unfortunately, was made a part of the machine. It seems from his former statements on the æther, and his present ones on God, that he regarded absolute space, not as God, but as the divine sensorium of God. Here he apparently did not go quite so far as Henry More who came, at times, almost to the point of identifying space with God, as Aristotle did celestial motion. The following passage is, perhaps, the most definite statement by More on the subject: "For if after the removal of corporeal matter out of the world, there will be still space and distance in which this very matter, while it was there, was also conceived to lie, and this distant space cannot but be conceived to be something, and yet not corporeal, because neither impenetrable nor tangible, it must of necessity be a substance incorporeal necessarily and eternally existent of itself; which the clearer *Idea of a Being absolutely perfect* will more fully and punctually inform us to be the *self-subsisting* God."[17]

Newton, then, combats the charge of having introduced occult quantities by saying that he had explained the phenomena of the heavens and of the sea by the power of gravity, but that he had not as yet assigned the cause of this power. And then he fortifies the statement by adding: "But hitherto I have not been able to discover the cause of those properties of gravity from phenomena, and I frame no hypotheses; for whatever is not deduced from the phenomena is to be called an hypothesis; and hypotheses, whether metaphysical or physical, whether of occult qualities or mechanical, have no place in experimental philosophy. In this philosophy particular propositions are inferred from the phenomena, and after-

[17] More. *Antidote Against Atheism.* Appendix, 2d edition, p. 338.—The influence of More and the Cambridge Platonists on Newton's ideas of space, time, and God, was direct and important; it would be interesting to work it out more fully.

wards rendered general by induction. Thus it was that the impenetrability, the mobility, and the impulsive force of bodies, and the laws of motion and of gravitation, were discovered. And to us it is enough that gravity does really exist, and act according to the laws which we have explained, and abundantly serves to account for all the motions of the celestial bodies, and of our sea."[18] Such were the limits which he would impose on himself and on the scientific method.

After he has thus shown the will to refrain from conflating speculation with true knowledge, he turns on his accusers and proves that his humility does not result from a lack of imagination equal to those who, then and now, confidently discuss the causes and nature of the universe. For, he concludes, if we prefer an occult substance to an occult cause, he might add something about a subtle Spirit which pervades all bodies and whose actions are the cause of gravitation, electrical energy, light, heat, sensation, and nervous stimuli: "But these are things that cannot be explained in a few words, nor are we furnished with that sufficiency of experiments which is required to an accurate determination and demonstration of the laws by which this electric and elastic Spirit operates." And we wonder whether the army of scientists and pseudo-scientists, who are today telling us all about this "subtle Spirit" which governs the universe, have a knowledge so accurate as to make their statements anything but futile guesses. Those, who are now speaking so confidently of the age and nature of the universe, of its contracting or expanding, are in Newton's opinion neither philosophers nor scientists. They are merely juggling with a word which signifies the negative of finite time and space. As Galileo long ago said, the scientist should restrict himself to a world of experience and not one of paper.

I had long puzzled over the reason for the addition of the General Scholium. The text of the first edition ends in a most inconspicuous manner with the solution of the proposition of how to determine the trajectory of a comet, and there is no summing up of the purpose of the book. The reader is left with the impression that the author stopped merely because he did not choose to discuss any more prob-

[18] The most important phrases in this memorable statement of Newton's conception of the limitations of the scientific method are: "Sed causam gravitatis nondum assignavi. . . . Rationem vero harum Gravitatis proprietatum ex Phaenomenis nondum potui deducere, et hypotheses non fingo. Quicquid enim ex phaenomenis non deducitur, *Hypothesis* vocanda est; et hypotheses, seu Metaphysicae, seu Physicae, seu Qualitatum Occultarum, seu Mechanicae, in *Philosophia Experimentali* locum non habent."

lems. In the later editions, the masterly Scholium was added with its broad sweep covering in a few words the author's confession of faith, and his philosophy of science; golden words which should be engraved on the minds of all students of natural phenomena. I had supposed, as I believe many others had also, Newton penned those words in order to teach the general lesson that the chief purpose of science is to inspire character and religion. It interested me greatly to discover that so broad a philosophical discussion had its cause in the desire to repel a personal attack on his character.[19]

But this apologia did not fully satisfy Bentley and Cotes. It did not sufficiently crush the Cartesians or manifest the glory of the *Principia;* it softened the denial that occult qualities had been introduced; it was silent as to Leibniz and the invention of the calculus. Most important of all it did not hurl back with scorn the charge of the materialism of his philosophy, and the irreligion of its author, which Leibniz had insinuated in the ear of that royal blue stocking, the Princess of Wales, who had just come to England from Hanover and the teaching of Leibniz. After a conference, they decided that these matters were very necessary and should be incorporated in a preface. Three days later, Bentley went to London and obtained Newton's consent. In order that there might be no misunderstanding they wrote a joint letter to Cotes in which Bentley's share was, "I have Sir Isaac's leave to remind you of what you and I were talking of, an alphabetical index, and a preface *in your own name;* if you please to draw them up ready for the press, to be printed after my return to Cambridge, you will oblige. Yours. R. Bentley."

Cotes answered the letters separately. To Newton, he wrote he would undertake the index, and would write to Bentley about the preface. To Bentley, he points out that he should know what Newton thinks to be proper for the preface. In his opinion, the defense

19 How great an effect this attack on Newton had made in England can be judged from an anecdote given in the *Biographia Britannica, Art. Newton.* "Leibniz renewed the charge of irreligion against Newton and attempted to disparage his philosophy because of pique over fluxions. This blackening method had its effect. It is supposed that Pope added two lines to the *Denial* as a censure of Newton's philosophy:

> 'Philosophy that lean'd on Heav'n before,
> Shrinks to her hidden cause, and is no more.'

Dr. Warburton remarks that if Pope's excellent friend Dr. Arbuthnot had been consulted, 'so unjust a reflection had never disgraced so noble a satire.' On the hint of Warburton, Pope changed the lines with great pleasure into a compliment, as they now stand, on that divine genius.

> 'Shrinks to her second cause, and is no more.' "

of Newton which the Royal Society had recently published in the *Commercium Epistolicum* gave such an indubitable proof of Leibniz's want of candour that he would like to speak out the full truth of the matter if it were thought convenient. Then he adds, knowing Newton's invincible reluctance to attack over his own name: "I think it will be much more advisable that you or he, or both of you, should write it whilst you are in town. You may depend upon it that I will own it and defend it as well as I can if hereafter there should be occasion."

So wary a fox was not to be drawn by such a plea. Bentley held a conference with Newton, and his instructions were sent to Cotes in the following letter, which throws some light on his character.

Bentley to Cotes

At Sir Isaac Newton's March 12.

Dear Sir,

I communicated your letter to Sir Isaac, who happened to make me a visit this morning, and we appointed to meet this evening at his house, and there to write you an answer. For the close of your letter, which proposes a preface to be drawn up here, and to be fatherd by you, we will impute it to your modesty; but you must not press it further, but go about it yourself. For the subject of the preface, you know it must be to give an account, first of the work itself, 2dly of the improvements of the new edition; and then you have Sir Isaac's consent to add what you think proper about the controversy of the first invention. You yourself are full master of it, and want no hints to be given you: However when it is drawn up, you shall have his and my judgement, to suggest any thing that may improve it. Tis both our opinions, to spare the name of M. Leibniz, and abstain from all words or epithets of reproach: for else, that will be the reply, (not that its untrue) but that its rude and uncivil. Sir Isaac presents his service to you.

I am Yours

R. BENTLEY.[20]

For Mr. Roger Cotes Professor of
Astronomy at Trinity College in
Cambridge.

On receipt of this letter, Cotes sent to Newton an outline of his proposed preface. He received two letters in reply, devoted mostly

[20] Edleston, p. 150.

to an explanation of what is meant by the mutual attraction of two bodies, and a definition of what he meant by an hypothesis. It is interesting to note that the remarkable passage in the General Scholium, beginning "Whatever is not deduced from phenomena must be called an hypothesis . . ." was not included in his original draught, but was first given in this letter to be inserted. In the second letter, Newton drew up a short note describing what had been done in the new edition which he desired to be printed below his original *Praefatio ad Lectorem*. And, as a postscript, there is this warning, "If you write any further preface, I must not see it, for I find that I shall be examined about it."

Hampered by these restrictions, Cote's preface is a rather tame affair, confined to a general exposition of the Newtonian philosophy. There are no references to the controversy over the calculus, or to the charges of materialism and irreligion; only a veiled reference is made to Leibniz in a general condemnation of the system of Cartesian vortices.

The last package of manuscript was sent to Cotes on March 2d, 1712/3, but the publication was delayed till the latter part of June and, a month later, Newton waited on the Queen to present her with a copy. The edition, judging from a statement of Cotes, was limited to 750 copies of which 200 were sent to France and Holland at a great abatement of price. In England the book, in quires and unbound, sold for 15s. When bound the price varied; Flamsteed paid 18s. for his copy, Charles Morgan gave a guinea, and Keill obtained his for a pound. The expense of publishing this second edition was met by Bentley, and he received all the profits from its sale; it is said that the author, even, was charged for some of the printer's corrections. Conduitt mentioned that he once asked Newton, "how he came to let Bentley print his *Principia,* which he did not understand—'Why,' said he, 'he was covetous, and I let him do it to get money.' "[21]

It is evident that the Master of Trinity did not confine his financial exactions entirely to the Fellows of his college. He also had the audacity, unknown to Newton and Halley, to alter the Latin verses, which the latter had composed for the first edition. Cotes's reward for his arduous part in the undertaking was a gift of twelve copies. Although it was quite in accord with Bentley's character to take advantage of the obligations which the young professor was under

[21] Conduitt's MSS. *Portsmouth Collection.*

and to pay him nothing for his work, it is not in accord with Newton's custom. He had always been more than generous to those who assisted him. He gave lavish presents of money to Clarke, Pemberton, Pound, and repeatedly offered compensation to Flamsteed. It seems very possible that Cotes declined to accept a reward other than the honour of assisting in the editing of a *Principia.*

Six months after the publication of the book, Newton sent to Cotes a formidable list of corrections and additions through Cornelius Crownfield, the University Printer. Cotes's feelings were apparently hurt, and his justification shows the prevalent lack of care in proofreading which would not be tolerated today. Thus, he answered: "I observe you have put down about twenty errata besides those in my table. I am glad to find they are not of any moment, such I mean as can give the reader any trouble. I had myself observed several of them, but I confess to you I was ashamed to put them in the table, lest I should appear to be too diligent in trifles. Such errata the reader expects to meet with, and they cannot well be avoided. . . . I am sure it is much more correct than the former, which was carefully printed; for besides your own corrections and those I acquainted you with whilst the book was printing, I may venture to say I made some hundreds, with which I never acquainted you."[22]

What a fortunate thing the *Principia* was edited by Cotes instead of by Duillier can be judged by the spirit of the two men. Duillier wrote to Huygens that he hoped to enlarge and improve the treatise by his emendations, and he modestly [!] inscribed these verses in his personal copy of the third edition:

> "Insculptoque basi Newtoni nomine; in ipso
> Culmine scribatur, Facius multum addidit aedi:
> Aedi, quae immensi typus est templi Omnipotentis."[23]

Cotes wrote: "I never think the time lost, when we stay for Sir Isaac's further corrections and improvements of so very valuable a book, especially when this seems to be the last time he will concern himself with it. I am sensible his other business allows him little time for those things, and therefore I cannot hasten him so much as I might otherwise do. I am very well satisfied to wait till he has leisure."[24] Cotes was certainly the most amiable and brilliant of the

[22] Edleston, p. 167. [23] Ball, p. 125.
[24] Macclesfield, *Corr.*, I, p. 260; Edleston, p. 209.

young men who fell under the spell of Newton's genius. In early manhood he had given fame to the new Plumian professorship and had become one of the most respected and influential Fellows of Trinity College. His death in 1716, on the threshold of his career, was a great loss to science and a personal sorrow to Newton.

One of Cotes's most intimate friends was William Whiston, and to him we are indebted for many of the incidents of Newton's life and an estimate of his character. Whiston's life[25] had become increasingly eccentric; endowed with great ability, he early became obsessed with the idea of restoring the Christian Church to its primitive state and gave up his career and prosperity for conscience's sake. Like many of the mathematicians and scientists of the day he was more interested in theology than in science except as it might serve as a handmaiden to religion; like Newton, he studied the Scriptures persistently in order to explain the prophetic writings, and to draw up a chronology of sacred history. By some twist in the mind, he saw in the law of gravitation a prognostication of a happy return to the primitive state of the Christian Church, but when he considered Newton's religious and chronological writings he found only folly and imbecility. The vanity of the *irritabile genus* is to be allowed for in his estimate: "As to this wonderful man, Sir Isaac Newton, I mean wonderful in mathematics, and natural philosophy, and their consequences: he is one of the greatest instances that ever was, how weak, how very weak, the greatest of mortal men may be in some things, though they be beyond all men in others. . . . Sir Isaac, in mathematics, could sometimes see almost by intuition, even without demonstration. . . . And when he did but propose conjectures in natural philosophy, he almost always knew them to be true at the same time; yet did this Sir Isaac Newton compose a Chronology, and wrote out eighteen copies of its first and principal chapter with his own hand, but little different one from another, which proved no better than a *sagacious romance,* as I have fully proved in my confutation of it."[26] One of Whiston's earliest works bore the stupendous title—*A new theory of the earth, from its original to the*

[25] When he was eighty-two years old he published his *Memoirs of Mr. Whiston* (London, 1749) which was popular enough to require a second and corrected edition four years later, and is a valuable book for the student of the times. Brewster invariably throws discredit on its accuracy, but it is manifestly because Whiston indulges in severe criticism, as well as high praise, of Newton. So far as can be discovered, Whiston was truthful, and his testimony should not be discredited because he found fault with Newton, or because he was willing to be a martyr for his religious beliefs.

[26] *Memoirs,* p. 38,—2d edition, p. 34.

consummation of all things, wherein the creation of the world in six days, the universal deluge, and the general conflagration, as laid down in the Holy Scriptures, are shewn to be perfectly agreeable to reason and philosophy. This book was shown in manuscript to Dr. Bentley, Sir Christopher Wren, but chiefly laid before Sir Isaac Newton himself, on whose principles it depended, and who well approved of it. And the great John Locke wrote in commendation of it.

Whiston gives a striking illustration of Newton's almost morbid sensitiveness to any personal criticism. It seems that Bentley was deeply offended by Bishop Lloyd because he interpreted a day in the prophecies of *Daniel* and the *Revelation* to denote the duration of a year, "And long afterwards The Master bluntly asked Newton, who had expounded the prophecies in the same manner, whether he could *demonstrate* the same. Sir Isaac Newton was so greatly angered at this, as invidiously alluding to his being a mathematician; which science was not concerned in this matter; that he would not see him, as Dr. Bentley told me himself, for a twelvemonth afterwards." On such questions did the greatest minds of the time exercise themselves and grow heated in discussion.

After Whiston returned to Cambridge, he continued his study of the Bible, in addition to his scientific work, and became an ardent propounder of primitive Christianity and Unitarianism. His first public utterance of those heretical doctrines was made, I think, in the Boyle lectures which he delivered in St. Paul's Cathedral, in 1707. One of the heads of the lecture was, "The new prophets entertain vulgar untrue notions in divinity; such as the Athanasian Trinity." His friends became alarmed, foreseeing that he was headed towards serious trouble, and begged him to renounce the Arian heresy. But his answer was that they might as well try to persuade the sun to come down from the firmament as to turn him from his resolution. Conscious of the fate before him, he began to prepare himself for martyrdom, being satisfied that no other death was so eligible to a Christian. While he did not suffer the extreme penalty for his faith, he was expelled from Cambridge, on October 30, 1710, as an obstinate heretic by the Heads of the Colleges after he had twice convented before them.[27] A month later Cotes urged him to

[27] Bishop Monk, *Life of Bentley,* Vol. I, p. 290, says: "He was *twice* convened before the academical court; and, remaining obstinate in his resolution to propagate opinions hostile to those of the Church, was banished from the University by the sentence of the Vice Chancellor and eleven Heads. In these proceedings the Master of Trinity took no share: he entertained

recant and submit to the judgement of the Convocation; but Whiston never changed his opinions and was never permitted to return to the University.

The effect on Whiston of banishment from the University was to add the fervor of martyrdom to his writing. He not only attacked the trinitarian doctrine of Athanasius and accused him of forgery, but he also advocated a return to primitive Christianity and the necessity of infant baptism. In all these ideas, he was confident that he had the support of Newton, and must have greatly embarrassed him by publishing that opinion. For example, he sent his paper on infant baptism to Newton by a mutual friend for his criticism and stated: "He was so hearty for the Baptists, as well as for the doctrines of Eusebius and Arius, that he sometimes suspected they were the *two Witnesses* in the *Revelation*." Thus to tear the veil behind which Newton carefully concealed his private opinions and to expose them to public criticism, aroused his bitter resentment and, perhaps also, his fear of being involved in a similar punishment. Whiston claimed that Newton, having first greatly favoured him for twenty years, finally grew to hate him because of his independence of mind. He shocked the public by the blunt statement that Newton's cautious and suspicious temperament had been so fed by the flattery of his friends as to make him unable, in his old age, to bear the least contradiction. As proof of this opinion, Whiston cites the fact that he was refused admission to membership in the Royal Society: "The case was this: Sir Hans Sloane, and Dr. Edmund Halley, and myself were once together at Child's Coffee-House, in St. Paul's Churchyard, and Dr. Halley asked me, Why I was not a member of that Society? I answered, Because they durst not choose an heretic. Upon which Dr. Halley said to Sir Hans Sloane, that if he would propose me, he would second it: which was done accordingly. When Sir Isaac Newton, the President, heard this, he was greatly concerned; and, by what I then learned, closeted some of the members, in order to get clear of me; and told them, that if I was chosen, he would not be President. Whereupon, by a pretence of deficiency in the form of proceeding, the proposal was dropped, I not insisting upon it."[28]

for Whiston a personal regard." Anti-trinitarianism was regarded as more dangerous than out-right atheism. Halley did indeed fail to obtain a professorship at Oxford because of his openly professed infidelity, yet he afterwards secured a like professorship there without making any pretence to a belief in Christianity.

[28] Whiston's *Memoirs*, p. 202.

One other incident recorded by Whiston will be narrated not so much for its intrinsic value as for the inferences Biot drew from it. In 1714, several captains in the navy and of merchantmen, with merchants of London, petitioned Parliament to offer a large reward to the person who should discover an accurate method of determining longitude at sea.[29] Whiston and a Mr. Ditton, the same year, discovered a method of finding longitude by signals. They first communicated it to Newton and then, at his desire, to Halley, Dr. Samuel Clarke, and Cotes; and with their approval they applied to the House of Commons for the reward. A large Committee was appointed, whose report was taken into consideration on June 11th, and the four persons mentioned above were summoned to attend. According to the report of the Committee, which Brewster examined, Whiston and Ditton stated that they had found a method of taking longitude at sea, and that they had explained their method to the four persons mentioned, who all approved the theory but found difficulties in its practical application. Newton then reported on four possible methods for finding longitudes which may be given in condensed form: 1. By a watch to keep time exactly, but such a watch had not yet been made. 2. By observing eclipses of Jupiter's satellites; but, because of the length of the telescopes needed and the motion of a ship, the eclipses cannot yet be observed. 3. By observing the place of the moon, but the lunar theory was not yet exact enough for the purpose. 4. By Mr. Ditton's project. He then discussed briefly and clearly the possibilities of the four methods, but the Committee were unable to follow his reasoning or to understand whether or not he thought the proposed method was practical. Whiston gave the following inside account of the meeting. "As soon as the Committee was set, which was a very large one, Newton, Halley, Clarke, and Cotes appeared. A chair was placed for Sir. I. Newton near the Chairman, and I stood at the back of it. What the rest had to say they delivered by word of mouth, but Sir I. Newton delivered what he had to say in a paper. Upon the reading of this paper, the Committee were at a loss, as not well understanding its contents: Sir I. Newton sitting still and saying nothing by way of explication. This gave the chairman an opportunity, which it was perceived he wanted, of trying to drop the bill; which he did by declaring his

[29] For the details of this incident see the Historical Preface inserted in some copies of Whiston's *Longitude Discovered*, London, 1738. Quotations from it and comments on what took place are to be found in the *Biographia Britannica, Art. Newton;* Edleston, p. lxxvi; Brewster, Vol. II, p. 257; and Biot, p. 37.

own opinion to be that 'Unless Sir I. Newton would say that the method now proposed was likely to be useful for the discovery of the longitude, he was against making a bill in general for a reward of such a discovery'; as Dr. Clarke had particularly proposed to the Committee. Upon this opinion of his, not contradicted by any other of the Committee; and upon Sir I. Newton's silence all the while, I saw the whole design was in the utmost danger of miscarrying. I thought it therefore absolutely necessary to speak myself: which I did nearly in these words, 'Mr. Chairman the occasion of the puzzle you are now in is nothing but Sir I. Newton's caution. He knows the usefulness of the present method near the shores (which are the places of greatest danger).' Whereupon Sir Isaac stood up and said that 'He thought this bill ought to pass, because of the present method's usefulness near the shores.' Which declaration of his was much the same with what he had said in his own paper, but which was not understood by the Committee, and determined them unanimously to agree to such a bill."[30] This report by Whiston is held to be unreliable; Edleston says, "the requisite allowance must be made for the forwardness and vanity of the reporter" and Rigaud, with Brewster's later approval, believed the story to be tinctured by his spleen and disappointment. But I can find no grounds for their opinion except their predetermined dislike to the unfortunate Whiston who, although he always expressed the highest admiration for Newton's genius, found certain faults in his character, and had suffered from their effects. His story, so far as it can be checked, agrees with the report of the Committee; and so far as Newton's personal part is described, Whiston makes no slur on his character. To me, it seems to be quite in line with what one might expect. Newton was undoubtedly not a ready speaker; he had written an excellent report and he was not accustomed to express himself in terms which the layman could understand. When he found that he was not understood he would very likely be puzzled to give a simple explanation, and when the decision was forced on him by the Chairman his caution and characteristic dislike of argument and contentions might very well keep him sitting and silent, and finally merely repeat Whiston's explanation. When the above commentators condemned Whiston, they were really exasperated by what Biot read into his statement. Biot was obsessed with the idea that Newton's

[30] The *Biographia Britannica* states that as a result of Newton's report the House of Commons threw aside the petition of Ditton and Whiston.

break-down in health in 1693 had left him with a permanent and fatal aberration of the intellect, and had been the cause of his forsaking science for religion and chronology. He cited this incident as a proof of Newton's imbecility in this extraordinary fashion: "Newton then repeated word for word what Whiston had said, and the project of the bill was accepted. This almost puerile conduct,[31] in a circumstance so solemn, could lend itself to stranger consequences, above all if the fatal accident which Newton experienced in 1695 [1693] be recalled, though it might have been merely the effect of excessive shyness, produced by the retired and meditative habits of his life. For, to judge from a letter of Newton, written some time before the disastrous epoch, in which he points out the conduct to be pursued by a young traveller, it would appear that he was very ignorant of the habits of society."[32]

[31] Whiston made no such insinuation.

[32] The "disastrous epoch" was in 1693 and the letter to Aston was written in 1669 so the "sometime before" was a stretch of twenty-four years. As Newton was a youth of twenty-seven years when he wrote the letter he might well have been "ignorant of the habits of society" but it is ludicrous to use it as an example of Newton's social experience at the age of seventy-two and after his life in London. *Cf.* Biot, *Life of Newton,* p. 37.

CHAPTER XV

CONTROVERSY WITH LEIBNIZ ON INVENTION OF THE CALCULUS

1699–1718

A FEELING of embarrassment is the lot of the biographer who must unravel the long and complicated controversy which arose over the invention of the calculus. It is undoubtedly the bitterest and most notorious dispute in the history of science; it engaged its principals and their sympathisers in recriminations for a quarter of a century; it will never lose its interest and never be satisfactorily settled. The charge and countercharge of actual plagiarism have been dismissed by documentary evidence; we know that Newton discovered and developed the method of fluxions first, and that Leibniz invented the method of the calculus at a later date and independently. But whether fluxions and calculus are identical is a matter of opinion; whether either inventor, unconsciously or deliberately, was influenced by the other in the later development of his ideas, is a second undecided question; and lastly the conduct of both men seems unaccountable on the grounds of common sense and honour. In the end, Newton lost the fruit of his great invention; his last years were embittered and his character smirched; Leibniz reaped a great reward, but the suspicion of being a plagiarist still clings to him; he betrayed a friend, and stooped to anonymous attacks.

When we judge the motives and actions of those immediately involved in this controversy, we must remember that they were playing for a great stake, one so great that cool judgement was clouded, and they were swayed by the passions of gamblers. The invention of the calculus was, in mathematics like the discovery of universal gravitation in physics, one of those unique pieces of good fortune that can come but once, and but to one man. Almost the whole modern science of mathematics is derived from the postulate of infinitesimally variable quantities; all problems in theoretical physics are stated as differential equations, and are solved by the integral calculus. Such a prize was sufficient to excite the passions of nations and to involve in it those lower and more brutal standards of conduct which influence men when they act in concert, and are absolved from personal responsibility. This evident double standard now passes under the rather foolish name of mob psychology, although it is merely the natural consequence of the fact that the individual can in such cases soothe his conscience by dividing the shame with others.

The temperaments of the principals involved in this altercation have a direct bearing on its history. Leibniz was essentially a teacher as well as a thinker, and he was not content till he had developed his idea of the calculus into an organised mathematical system. He communicated his work freely to others, and his reputation was increased by the contributions of his followers. He, himself, was impulsive, and his occasionally rash and boastful statements irritated the English intensely; Cotes once described him as "swaggering upon the occasion, according to his usual vanity"; and Conduitt, who must have discussed the matter with Newton, wrote to Fontenelle, that Leibniz's manner of defending himself would convince everybody that he had taken his calculus from Newton. Thus, Leibniz's contradictory statements of the sources of his idea, his subterfuges, his betrayal of his friend and his anonymous articles were easily exposed by his adversaries. The conviction became fixed that a man who would stoop to such methods of defense must have done so from the guilty knowledge of having plagiarised. Even though the publication of his early papers has made it clear that he developed his calculus honourably, yet the suspicion of having received help from fluxions in some unknown manner still clings to him, and sullies his reputation.

On the other hand, Newton never once evinced any desire to make public his invention or the least interest in public approval. After he had written to Leibniz, that he had discovered a method of fluxions and had safely secured priority of invention by two sentences dissected into a jumble of letters which could not possibly be deciphered, he persistently refused to discuss the subject with him, or any one else. His refusal to publish and his apparently sphinx-like indifference to popular fame impressed his contemporaries as the indication of modesty. On the contrary, it resulted from his dominant passion for meditation and for being free from the distractions which arise from the publication of new ideas. In his youth, he had made a bid for popular approval and the mild criticism, which his work on light received, made him declare science to be a taskmaster which he would in the future be rid of; in his old age, when his character had hardened and he had become dictatorial from adulation and flattery, he could not endure any opposition. While he cared little for what is ordinarily classed as fame, the least reflection on his personal character, or an intimation that he had been dependent on others for help, aroused in him an unrelenting hostility. So far as we can see, Leibniz might have published any number of papers on the calculus; he and his followers might have developed it to any extent without interesting Newton in the least. But we know he secretly nursed a grudge against Leibniz for not having acknowledged in his first published paper that he was merely the second inventor of the calculus and that his later invention in time had no merit. And he was aroused to an implacable and cold rage when the continental mathematicians intimated that he had received aid from his rival in the development of the fluxions.

In contradistinction to Leibniz's subterfuges which were easily exposed, Newton never made clear his part in the controversy till after Leibniz's death. The public charges against his rival were made under the cover of his friends, Fatio, Keill, Raphson, and of the Royal Society. The countercharges were directed against them, and they were supposed to have had no aid from him; while the truth is that he directed most, if not all, of the attacks without acknowledging his participation in them. He packed the investigating committee of the Royal Society, supplied it with data and directed its enquiry; and he anonymously wrote the preface for their published report, and made changes in the text. The leading part he personally took in the quarrel was not guessed till his manuscripts were examined by Brewster a century and more after his death, and till De Morgan disclosed many unknown facts in a series of critical essays. Even with this knowledge, I was amazed, during my own examination of the *Portsmouth Papers,* to find the mass of notes and manuscripts on the subject which Newton preserved. It is shocking to find that two such eminent men as the principals, and practically all of those associated with them, wantonly made statements which were false; and not one of them came through with a clean record. In such a tangled story, all the biographer can hope to do is to set the facts down as clearly and as accurately as possible, and let the reader apportion the degrees of blame as he best may.

In order to make the subsequent history of the controversy clear a brief résumé of the earlier events will aid the reader.[1] Leibniz had discovered, and had developed, the method and notation of both the differential and integral calculus about 1675 or 1676. This is now certain from his early papers in the Hanover collection recently published by Gerhardt, and by his letters to Newton; and it seems thoroughly established that, in agreement with his statement, the first idea of the calculus came to him from his study of Pascal's work on series. In 1684, he published his first paper on the calculus in the Leipzig *Acts,* in which he made no mention of the fact that Newton had invented a similar method some years prior to his own discovery. His explanation of this omission was the reasonable one that, as Newton had not explained to him his method of fluxions, and had refused to publish it, he was not at liberty to refer to a discovery which the author declined to reveal. By 1695, Leibniz and the two Bernoullis had developed the calculus into a powerful mathematical tool, and a year later de l'Hôpital published his systematic text-book on the subject. Amongst the continental mathematicians it was generally referred to as Leibniz's calculus, and few of them had any knowledge of Newton's prior invention.

There is no doubt that Newton invented the fluxions in 1665, or 1666, and had, at times, used dots over the symbols to signify a velocity. How far he developed his method during those early years, we do not know. In 1669, Barrow sent the tract *De Analysi* to Collins. He and Oldenburg discussed the work and showed the tract to a number of mathematicians in England and on the continent, among whom was Leibniz. We now know that Leibniz saw the tract when in London and made extracts from it; but it is still a debatable question with mathematicians whether the *De Analysi* discussed the method of the fluxions and calculus, or whether it was limited solely to the method of solution of problems by infinite series.

When Newton published the *Principia* in 1687, he introduced a Scholium to Lemma II in which he paid a compliment to Leibniz for having invented a calculus similar to his own except for its system of notation and language; but he gave no explanation of either method. He stated that Leibniz had described his method to him but that he had concealed his own invention in two sentences with transposed letters. There can be no doubt he thereby acknowledged

[1] *Cf. supra,* Chapter VI.

that Leibniz had made a later and independent invention of the calculus, for such a statement would have been ridiculous if he had suspected him of plagiarism. Furthermore, the world would also be forced to judge that Newton could have received aid more readily from Leibniz, than Leibniz from him, if the question were to be decided on this statement in the *Principia.* In 1693, Wallis published in volume II of his *Collected Works* a brief account of Newton's fluxions with the solution of a few problems and, in the preface, he mentioned the calculus as being another name for fluxions. This was the first opportunity mathematicians had had for comparing the two methods.

Thus, towards the end of the century, mathematicians found themselves equipped with a magnificent new tool; and, being far more interested in the perfection and accessibility of the instrument than in the abstract question of its inventor, they currently referred to it as Leibniz's calculus. So far as we can learn the scientific world was at peace till 1699, when Fatio de Duillier published a tract which opened the whole question and started a bitter controversy which raged for twenty-five years, aroused international jealousies, and still smoulders.

The publication by Wallis of the method of fluxions, even in an abbreviated form, and his statement that the calculus was the same thing under a different name, were clear indications that the English were preparing themselves to claim the honour of the invention. Leibniz and Bernoulli, who had adopted a rather boastful tone in their publications, were much perturbed and devised a test to show that certain classes of problems could be solved only by those who had studied and had become proficient in their method. According to the custom of the day, Bernoulli published in the Leipzig *Acts* for June, 1696, a challenge problem "to the acutest mathematicians of the world." The problem was,—To determine the curve line connecting two given points, at different distances above the horizon and not in the same vertical line, along which a body passing by its own gravity shall descend to the lower point in the shortest time possible.[2] Originally, six months was allowed for the contest. As no solutions were received during that period, on the advice of Leibniz, the time was publicly extended for a year longer so that French and

[2] This curve for shortest time of fall, or *brachistochrone,* is the well-known cycloid,—a curve which had been much studied as it is the apparent path of a planet in the Ptolemaic system. But this was a new property and it required the calculus for solution.

Italian mathematicians might have an equal opportunity with those in Germany. According to Conduitt's *Memoirs,*[3] Newton received two copies of the problem from France on January 26, 1696/7, at four o'clock in the afternoon, when he was very tired with the business at the Mint, where he had been employed all day, and yet he solved it before he went to bed that same night.

This story, which has been related in an earlier chapter, is always given as a detached event in Newton's life, and it had greatly puzzled me as it seemed so contrary to his habit of avoiding just such distractions. It occurred when he was newly appointed to the Mint, and even two years later, when he was not so deeply immersed in its affairs, he wrote in that curious letter to Flamsteed: "I do not love to be printed upon every occasion, much less to be dunned and teased by foreigners about mathematical things, or to be thought by our own people to be *trifling* away my time about them, when I should be about the King's business."[4] This reference, to being teased by foreigners, is meaningless unless it refers to this problem sent by Leibniz and Bernoulli. Why should he take the time from the King's business for it, and yet rebuke Flamsteed about the lunar problem in which he was deeply interested? The answer is perfectly simple; Newton suspected the problem had been devised and sent to him to prove, by his inability to solve it, that his fluxions was not the general and powerful method he claimed it to be. And, by exerting his matchless powers, he routed his adversaries and vindicated himself.

It can be shown easily that Newton's suspicion was justified. Bernoulli had proposed the problem to illustrate the unique power of the new calculus; the only solutions were sent in by Leibniz and de l'Hôpital, and they had naturally used that analysis. From 1696 to 1699, the correspondence of Leibniz and Bernoulli[5] is full of references to this problem and of their speculations about its success as a test case. Leibniz proposes to name the curve the *Tachystoptota,* but is told that it is to be called the *Brachystochrone.* He surmises that solutions could be expected only from l'Hôpital, James Bernoulli, and Newton, to whom Hudde might have been added if he had not too long laid aside his mathematical meditations. They show their anxiety lest the solutions will not prove the necessity of the use of the calculus, and when one comes anonymously from Eng-

[3] Turnor, p. 161. Also, the *Portsmouth Collection.*

[4] Baily, p. 166.

[5] *Commerc. Phil., Leib. et Bern., passim.*

land they both guess it to be from Newton, "tanquam ex ungue leonem." They are chagrined by this upset of their plan, and they discuss how closely the methods of fluxions and the calculus agree; finally, Leibniz writes to explain their differences so far as he can determine them from Wallis's short exposition of his rival's work.

Since Bernoulli's answer to this letter contains the first accusation, that he believed Newton was indebted to their work, it is important to quote from it at some length: "Wallis explains Newton's method in very few words; yet as I understand them, it by no means differs in substance [in re neutiquam] from the differential calculus, as Newton himself acknowledges in his *Principia,* page 254. What in the one is called a *differential,* in the other is a *fluxion,* and what is called an *integral* [summa], is there a *fluent.* And the strength of his method, as also of the differential calculus, rests on the two problems: Given fluent quantities, to find their fluxions; and on the other hand, Given fluxions, to find their fluents. Instead of your letter, *d,* to designate a first differential, or fluxion, he uses a dot over the symbol. Thus dx is $\dot{x}$, ddx is $\ddot{x}$, etc. Otherwise the method of procedure is the same for both, so that I do not know whether Newton had developed his method till after he had seen your calculus; especially since, from the passage cited, I see that you had communicated your calculus to him, before he had published his method."[6] Thus, they satisfied themselves that the problem had been a test of the power of the calculus, and Newton, by solving it, had shown that his method was similar to theirs. The reason why they were the same, Bernoulli suggests, was because Newton had benefited by knowing Leibniz's work. Bernoulli and Leibniz were to regret that they had aroused Newton to action, and still more that they had fostered the poisonous idea of his plagiarism. He was justified in his suspicion that the problem had been sent to test his claims, and nothing was more certain to arouse him from his indifference than thus to touch his personal pride. He laid aside the King's business and struck back at them; by solving the problem at a sitting, he performed an incredible feat, and proved that his unmatchable mathematical powers were as vigorous as ever. He had forsaken mathematics not because his power had failed, but because the subject had ceased to interest him.

Leibniz seems, at this time, to have lost his head completely, for he took the unfortunate step, in 1699, of publishing in the Leipzig

[6] *Commerc. Phil. Leib. et Bern.,* Vol. I, p. 190.

Acts a review of the solutions of Bernoulli's problem which he heralded as a triumph for his own calculus. In the article, he told of his prophecy to Bernoulli that it could not be solved except by the aid of his earlier inventions. And, in fact, only those, he boasted, had solved it who had penetrated sufficiently into the mysteries of his calculus; they were the two Bernoullis, de l'Hôpital, and Newton; of other possible contestants, Huygens had recently died and Hudde had abandoned mathematical studies. "These I repeat, that it may not seem as if I despised those excellent men who either had no desire or no time to occupy themselves with our inventions." Thus, to publish to the world that Newton was his pupil was more than the English mathematicians could stomach. The chance to take their revenge on Leibniz fell to Fatio.

If one depends only on the biographies of Newton, the reason why Fatio undertook his defense and attacked Leibniz is not at all clear, for the fact is baldly stated as if it were an act of pure loyalty. But the causes, leading to his explosion of resentment, go back several years; and it is evident, from the correspondence of Leibniz and Huygens, that he was giving two blows for himself to one for Newton. He had gone to England in 1687 to live and had been made a Fellow of the Royal Society the same year. In 1690–1691, he paid a visit to Huygens, at The Hague, whom he had met the year before he went to England.[7] While he was in Holland, he showed Huygens a new mathematical work on tangents and quadratures of his own which greatly interested Leibniz also as he was working in the same field. As a result, the correspondence of Leibniz and Huygens mentions Fatio frequently, and they both express a high appreciation of his ability.[8] Leibniz offers to help him; and it is proposed to exchange their notes on the subject by the mediation of Huygens. While they are extremely complimentary to each other, it is easily seen that Leibniz adopts the tone of the mentor; Fatio resents the idea that his method is inferior; and each fears to expose his incomplete manuscript lest an advantage be given to the other. Finally, Huygens suspected how the matter stood and

[7] Brewster, Vol. II, p. 37, states that, except for a visit to Switzerland in 1699–1701, he did not leave England and so overlooked the important stay in Holland. Huygens wrote to Leibniz on 21 April, 1691; (*Cf. Briefwechsel von Leib.* Ed. by Gerhardt, Vol. II, p. 647) "Mr. Fatio is still here"; and on 16 November, he wrote that Fatio had left two months previously for England. Newton also refers to Fatio's visit to Holland in a letter to Locke (Oct. 28, 1690): "I suppose Mr. Falio [sic] is in Holland, for I have nothing from him for the half year." *Locke's Life,* I, p. 404.

[8] *Briefwechsel von Leib.,* Vol. II, pp. 603–727, *passim.*

wrote to Leibniz, "You do not believe you will profit much by his method, he does not greatly desire yours."

Fatio, towards the end of the year, 1691, returned to England, exasperated by what he believed to be Leibniz's contemptuous attitude towards his work. The year following, he paid a visit to Newton in Cambridge, and deeply aroused his interest and sympathy. It is easy to guess that they discussed his work on tangents, and what Leibniz was accomplishing with the calculus. Also we may suppose Newton explained his method of fluxions and referred to their former correspondence.

After Newton moved to London, their intimacy increased. Besides their common interest in the Royal Society, Fatio had become an eager disciple of the Newtonian philosophy, and he boasted that he had mastered the *Principia* more thoroughly than anyone else; so thoroughly, indeed, that he hoped to edit a second and improved edition. Besides their intellectual interests which drew them together, a deeper personal sympathy had strengthened the tie; the young man had sought Newton's help in his religious doubts and had been comforted when he was ill and thought he was in danger of death. He gives the impression of having been of a neurotic temperament and afflicted with doubts which he stilled by joining the mystical sect of the Camisards. He became their secretary and had sufficient influence on Newton to excite in him "a strong inclination to go and hear these prophets, and was restained from it, with difficulty, by some of his friends, who feared he might be infected by them as Fatio had been."[9] The relations between Newton and Fatio became so intimate as to have been a matter of comment even on the continent. Leibniz and his friends frequently couple their names together as if they held their ideas in common, and as if Fatio's influence were harmful. Thus, Leibniz wrote to Huygens, in 1694, that Newton and Fatio persisted in believing in the corpuscular theory of light and ascribed the cause of gravitation to the pressure of an æthereal fluid.

Fatio and Huygens maintained a correspondence, in which Fatio evidently expressed his resentment towards Leibniz and his belief that he was not the inventor of the calculus. Thus, Huygens warned Leibniz that trouble was brewing: "Fatio believes Mr. Newton knows on this subject [the calculus] both all that he, and all that you, Monsieur, have ever found and even more, and also that he will

[9] Spence's *Anecdotes*.

publish a tract on the subject." This is the first intimation that Newton had been persuaded to publish an account of his fluxions, and the persuasion very possibly came from Fatio.[10] This news brought the following sarcastic reply from Leibniz: "I am obliged to M. Fatio who offers me his methods of tangents, but believing that I have gone almost to the bottom of it, I would not wish to give him the trouble. I am seeking a more general method, which will apply to the reduction of transcendental curves, and I have made a beginning in that direction. I am not surprised to learn that Mr. Newton has gone far in the subject. But still each follows his own path; I perhaps have found one, with which he is not yet acquainted."

It is evident that Fatio[11] had a personal resentment against Leibniz and had become a hot partisan of Newton. He had been working for some time on Bernoulli's test problem of the Brachistochrone and on the solid of least resistance to motion in a fluid. His work was now ready for the press[12] and it gave him a convenient opportunity to revenge himself and Newton on Leibniz. For this purpose he inserted the following passage:

"The distinguished Leibniz may perchance enquire from whom this calculus, which I use, may have been learned. At all events, its general principles, and very many of its rules, I INVENTED BY MY OWN EXERTIONS, about the month of April and the following

[10] This tract, under the title of *De Quadratura* was published as an appendix to the *Optics* in 1704.

[11] Fatio is a person who aroused very different opinions. I have collected the following notes about him. Brewster (Vol. II, p. 37) calls him an eminent mathematician and favours him for his advocacy of Newton. Guhrauer always refers to him in most contemptuous terms, and attributes the motive of his attack on Leibniz to wounded vanity. Lefort (*Commerc. Epist.* Ed. Biot, p. 224) says: "Fatio deserves as a juster title the qualification of *rogue,* which Keill gave so liberally to the editors of the Leipzig *Acts* [Leibniz, Bernoulli, *et al.*] in the effusions of a private correspondence with Newton. . . . He was successively a conspirator, a common informer, geometer, prophet, condemned and exposed in the pillory. It is regrettable that Newton should have accepted, and perhaps solicited such an auxiliary." While in London he taught mathematics at the Spitalfields School. The Camisards, or French prophets, which he joined, were fanatical believers in prophecy and miracles accomplished by women and girls afflicted with epilepsy. After they were expelled from France many of them emigrated to England. Unscrupulous men preyed on the weakness of the women and Hearne relates an indecent incursion made into Oxford by one of their bands. According to Spence, he received in a heavenly inspiration the knowledge that an æthereal fluid was the cause of gravitation which Newton also believed. His connection with the Camisards came to an ignominious end, in 1707, when he was stood in the pillory at Charing Cross for terrifying the people by his prophecies. He spent the rest of his life in Worcester, where he died in 1753.

[12] Nicolaii Fatii Duillierii R. S. S. *lineae brevissimi descensus investigatio geometrica duplex. Cui addita est investigatio solidi rotundi, in quod minima fiat resistentia.* Londini: 1699. . . . The passage quoted is translated by me from the extract in the *Commerc. Epist.* Ed. Biot, p. 223. Brewster (Vol. II, p. 39) also translates the same passage, but he certainly softened its terms.

months of the year 1687, and during the succeeding years. At the time I thought no one, except myself, used that kind of a calculus. Nor would it have been less known by me, if Leibniz had not then been born. And so he may brag of other disciples but certainly not of me. This fact will be fully established if, in the future, the letters which passed between the distinguished Huygens and me are made public. But I am now fully convinced by the evidence itself on the subject that Newton is the first inventor of this calculus, and the earliest by many years; whether Leibniz, its second inventor, may have borrowed anything from him, I should rather leave to the judgement of those who had seen the letters of Newton, and his original manuscripts. Neither the more modest silence of Newton, nor the unremitting vanity of Leibniz to claim on every occasion the invention of this calculus for himself, will deceive anyone who will investigate, as I have investigated, those records."

By this insulting attack, Fatio stood out as the eager defender of Newton's reputation; but it is rather a vicious attack on Leibniz because of his treatment towards himself. The personal animus, behind his feeling of hatred, was his chagrin because Leibniz had formerly treated his claim to the discovery of a general method with indifference, and had later omitted his name from the list of distinguished mathematicians who could be expected to solve Bernoulli's test problem by the calculus. The conclusion of the passage can be interpreted as a thinly veiled charge of plagiarism, under the politer term of borrowing.[13] This is the first time that the accusation had been made openly on either side. It is true, Leibniz had inferred in his article that Newton had been aided in the later development of fluxions by his more systematic calculus, but he never denied that his rival was the first inventor of a calculus; there is a real distinction between the two statements, since the first involves legitimate aid and the second, plagiary.

The question whether Fatio's attack was made entirely on his own initiative, or whether Newton and his circle knew about it and collaborated with him, is a difficult point to decide.[14] It seems hardly pos-

13 Brewster comments thus: "Strong as these expressions are, they cannot be regarded as charging Leibniz with plagiarism. He is styled *second inventor,* the title with which he, on many occasions, expressed himself satisfied, and he is blamed only for everywhere ascribing the invention to himself" (Vol. II, p. 40). If the passage had been directed against Brewster, would he not have used *insulting,* rather than *strong,* to describe these expressions, and would he not have known that he had been charged with plagiarism?

14 Guhrauer held that Newton prompted the attack of Fatio. But Brewster notes that he inspected all the manuscripts of Newton and did not find "the slightest evidence in support

sible that Fatio would have acted as a spokesman for the honour of English science without the knowledge, and even connivance, of his friends; his vanity, if not his caution, would lead him to read his declaration to those who were equally hot against Leibniz. On the other hand, it was contrary to Newton's fixed habit to take an active part in an altercation. His early dealings with his critics through the medium of Collins and Oldenburg and his refusal to read the preface to the second edition of the *Principia* by Cotes, point to the probability that he now refused to read what Fatio had written in his defense. But I do not believe that anyone, who knew him well, would dare to defend him in such a manner without previously obtaining his consent. There are also grounds for believing that Newton was not pleased with the form Fatio's vindication took, as Bernoulli refers to a rumour of a grave quarrel between them. I think, myself, that he would also be offended by the author's undue emphasis on his own achievements.

Leibniz was indignant over what he declared to be an unwarranted attack. He wrote to his friends that Newton was ignorant of the affair and would vindicate him, since he had acknowledged in the *Principia* the independent discovery of the calculus. But, when Newton maintained a haughty silence, Leibniz published a defense of his conduct in the Leipzig *Acts,* in which he dismissed the charges as emanating from a boorish and jealous young man. Fatio attempted to publish an answer, but the editors declined to accept it on the principle that the journal was not a proper medium for personal disputes.

After this the controversy subsided for five years. The indirect cause of its revival, and the beginning of its virulent phase, was the publication, in 1704, of Newton's *Optics*. He took that opportunity to add two mathematical tracts[15] to the main body of the work. In the preface to this first edition of the book, he inserted the following passage to explain his reason for including these tracts: "In a letter written to M. Leibniz in the year 1676, and published by Dr. Wallis, I mentioned a method by which I had found some general theorems about squaring curvilinear figures [i. e. finding their areas] on

of a charge which deserves the severest reprobation." The attention of the reader hardly needs to be called to the fact that Newton may have prompted the attack, wholly or partly, and not have preserved a written record. Both opinions are really guesses.

[15] *Tractatus duo de speciebus et magnitudine figurarum curvilinearum,* 1st. *Tractatus de quadratura curvarum; 2d. Enumeratio linearum tertii ordinis.* The tract *De quadratura* is the first published exposition of fluxions given by Newton, himself. Both tracts were omitted in later editions of the *Optics* as being of an extraneous character.

comparing them with the conic sections, or other the simplest figures with which they might be compared. And some years ago I lent out a manuscript containing such theorems; and having since met with some things copied out of it, I have on this occasion made it public."

The reference to matter purloined from a manuscript refers to Leibniz. Even in the earlier days Newton felt that Leibniz had found out more of his work than he admitted; and as time went on he became more and more convinced that Leibniz had in some way got the key to his calculus while he was in England. The following passage, from a paper in the *Portsmouth Collection* which, I believe, has never been published, is important as a confirmation of this suspicion:

"Mr. Collins, having received from me and Mr. James Gregory several series for squaring the circle and conic sections, was very free in communicating them to the mathematicians both at home and abroad in the years 1670–1– and 2, and Mr. L. was in London in the beginning of the year 1673 and went from thence to Paris in the end of February, carrying with him Mercator's *Logarithmotechnia* along with him and kept a correspondence with Mr. Oldenburg till June following about arithmetical questions.

"Upon the news of Mr. James Gregory's death he wrote for a collection of Gregory's paper and the derivation of my series—meaning my method of finding them and promised Mr. Oldenburg a reward for my method and told him that Mr. Collins could help him to it. I suppose he meant my *Analysis per series numero terminorum infinitas*. For that was the only paper in which I had sent my method of series to Mr. Collins."

It is an extraordinary fact that, from the time of Newton to the present day, nearly everyone, who has treated the subject, has either accused Leibniz of plagiarism or has, even when defending him, left his reputation to some extent tarnished. He, himself, stated that his first idea of the calculus came to him suddenly when reading a little book by Pascal written, under the pseudonym of Dettonville, as letters to Carcavi. As more and more of Leibniz's early papers are published, we find that his statements about the sources of his invention are true, however much he may have twisted the truth when defending himself. Thus, Dietrich Mahnke has recently examined his unpublished papers, and states that the notes which Leibniz made when he was reading Pascal's *Traité des Sinus* are still among his papers, and they show his gropings towards his more general method.[16]

An anonymous review of Newton's two mathematical tracts was published in the Leipzig *Acts* for January, 1704/5. After criticising the mathematical contents, the following passage was given in an appendix:

"The very ingenious author precedes the discussion of the quadrature of curves with a brief Preface. In order that this Introduction may be better understood, the following facts should be known. When any quantity increases continuously, as for example a line increases by the flow of the point which describes it, those momentaneous increments are called differences, that is between the quantity which was before and that which has been produced by means of the momentaneous mutation. And hence has arisen the differential calculus and its converse the integral calculus. The elements of this calculus have been given to the public by its inventor Dr. Gottfried Wilhelm Leibniz in these Acts, and its various uses have been shown by him and by Drs. the brothers Bernoulli, and by Dr. the Marquis de l'Hôpital. Instead of the Leibnizian differences, then, Dr. Newton employs, and has always employed, fluxions [adhibet, semperque adhibuit, Fluxiones], which are very much the same as the augments of fluents produced in the least equal intervals of time; and these fluxions he has used elegantly in his *Mathematical Principles of Nature* and in other later publications, just as Honoratus Fabri, in his *Synopsis of Geometry* substituted [substituit] progressive motions for the method of Cavalieri."[17]

There is no doubt that Newton, who immediately suspected Leibniz to be the author of the review, took the passage to be a direct and cowardly accusation of plagiarism. Besides the account in the *Portsmouth Collection* which Brewster published, I found more than a dozen other articles all bearing on the same subject as if it had be-

[16] *Isaac Newton 1642–1727.* Ed. by Greenstreet, p. 135.—The latest defender of Leibniz is Professor Child. He is certain that Leibniz invented his calculus independently of Newton, and he considers that Gerhardt made but a feeble defender. And yet Child spends much effort in trying to show that Leibniz did not receive his inspiration from Pascal, but that he was deeply indebted to Barrow, and carefully suppressed the facts relating to this indebtedness. (*Early Math. MSS. of Leibniz,* 1920.) His thesis seems quite unnecessary as Leibniz mentioned freely those from whom he obtained assistance, and there was no earthly reason why he should try to conceal help from Barrow, whose work was read and known by everyone. And now five years later new material comes out which shows that his early work *was* based primarily on Pascal and not on Barrow.

[17] This translation was made from the article in the Leipzig *Acts* as published verbatim in the *R. S. Commerc. Epist.* As this is the crucial statement of Leibniz which aroused Newton's wrath and on which he based his counter-attack, I submitted the text to classical scholars

come an *idée fixe* with him. In every one of these papers, his bitterness against Leibniz is directed against this article in the Leipzig *Acts:* For example: "There is some ambiguity in the words, but the most proper sense is that I always used fluxions instead of the differences of Mr. Leibniz. And is not this to make the readers believe that I always knew the differential method of Mr. Leibniz and invented the method of fluxions by using fluxions instead of differences? This gave occasion to Mr. Keill to represent, on the contrary, that Mr. Leibniz used his differences instead of my fluxions. And if this derogates from the candor of Mr. Leibniz, the contrary derogates from my candor, and that unjustly."

Till now he had let others defend his reputation, but from this time he directed the attack, usually under cover of others' names. He had no scruples about using any weapons as if a man, who would reflect on his personal honour, had put himself without the pale of the law; he met Leibniz's false statements with chicane; he never forgot, nor ever spared, his enemy even after his death; but he did forget that Fatio had accused Leibniz first of plagiarism, and he had said nothing.

If Newton, himself, admitted there was some ambiguity in Leibniz's words,[18] we may be sure that writers on this controversy will take opposite sides. The Committee in the *Commercium Epistolicum* give, in a foot-note, their interpretation to be that Newton substituted fluxions for the differences of Leibniz in the same manner as Fabri had substituted progressive motion for the method of Cavalieri; that is, Leibniz was the first author of this method and Newton took the same from Leibniz by substituting fluxions for differences. English writers down to, and including, Brewster take the same view. De Morgan, who criticised Brewster's *Life of Newton* so severely and who, in a series of brilliant essays, was the first Eng-

and checked their translation with my own. I especially asked for the implied significance of the words in brackets. Brewster (Vol. II, p. 41) gives a free and sufficiently accurate statement of that portion of the passage. He follows this with the Latin text of the whole passage which he found copied in Newton's MSS., with some inserted explanatory words. Oddly enough there are several errors in this text which may have been due to carelessness by Newton, but they are such grammatical mistakes as to make parts of it untranslatable. I may mention here, as an aside, that Thos. Hearne, in his *Diaries,* stated that Newton "understands not one bit of classical learning, nor can he, as I hear, write Latin, but is beholden to others to do that for him." He repeats this on two other occasions, but there is certainly no truth in the sneer.

[18] The passage in the Leipzig *Acts* which raised the storm is "Pro differentiis igitur Leibnitianis D. Newtonus adhibet, semperque adhibuit, Fluxiones, . . . iisque tum in suis *Princ. Nat. Math.* tum in aliis postea editis eleganter est usus, quemadmodum et Honoratus Fabrius in sua Synopsi Geometrica, motuum progressus Cavallerianae methodo substituit."

lishman to break down the legends of perfection which had been created about Newton, says flatly that it "was by no means a charge of plagiarism."[19] But we should remember that De Morgan was the first to combat the national idea that Leibniz was all black and Newton, pure white. While his acute and unwearied research brought many unknown facts to light, he was at times, carried away by scorn of the injustice towards Leibniz.

On the other side, Leibniz denied in 1716, in a letter to the Countess de Kilmansegg, that the passage meant that Newton had plagiarised from him.[20] And again, in the same year, he wrote to the Abbé Conti more fully; "the Editors of the *Commercium Epistolicum* had," he declared, "interpreted the meaning to be that *Newtonus Fluxiones differentiis Leibnitianis substituit.* That is the malicious interpretation of a man who seeks a quarrel. It seems that the author [i. e., Leibniz himself] of the words, inserted in the Leipzig *Acts,* expressly wished to avoid that meaning by selecting the words, *adhibet* SEMPERQUE *adhibuit,* in order to insinuate it was not after seeing my differences, but before then that he made use of fluxions. And I defy anyone to give any other meaning to the words *semperque adhibuit;* instead of which *substituit* was used when speaking of what Père Fabri had done after Cavalieri."[21]

Most of the continental historians, more or less, actively side with Leibniz. For instance, Rosenberger, one of the most thorough and reliable critics of Newton's work and character, gives as his opinion that Leibniz, by publishing a pointed comparison between Newton and himself, committed an impolitic and foolish act, but any unbiased person must deny that he planned a deliberate attack against Newton's services to science.[22] On the other hand Guhrauer, the biographer of Leibniz, holds that the author has point-blank, and without any subterfuge, accused Newton of plagiarism. The authorship of the review aroused much discussion and Leibniz persistently denied that he was responsible for it. Guhrauer, however, settled the question; by the aid of Ludovici, the Director of the Pauline Library in Leipzig, the original manuscript of the review was discovered, and it bore the signature of Leibniz.[23]

While there may be ambiguity in the passage, it seems to me to be, in fact, an accusation of plagiarism. The possible ambiguity lies in the meaning of the phrase, "*adhibet semperque adhibuit,*" which

[19] *Essays on Newton,* p. 27, f.-n. [20] *Commerc. Epist.* Ed. Biot et Lefort, p. 243.
[21] *Ibid.,* p. 244. [22] Rosenberger, p. 473. [23] Guhrauer, p. 311.

can safely be translated, *employs and has always employed;* and *"adhibuit"* has practically the same meaning as *"substituit,"* used further on, in spite of Leibniz's specious explanation that the two words were used to express a difference of implication. What is to be understood by *"semperque adhibuit"* will depend rather on the time when Newton first employed fluxions for differences. Since none of the details of his work on fluxions was known till after the publication of the calculus, the reader would assume that he had always trailed after Leibniz from the beginning. Priority of discovery has always been based on priority of publication, or at least on documentary evidence dated in the presence of a witness, and Leibniz's inference is apparent. And this is a proper custom for, without it, there would be no guaranty against false claims. Few great discoveries have been made which have not been guessed, or have not been worked on, by others. Even granting as a fact, which is rarely denied, that Newton discovered first the method of an infinitesimal calculus, he had only himself to blame for losing the undisputed fruits of his invention by his dilatoriness. Several of his friends, and especially Wallis, urged him in vain to publish, as they foresaw this danger. And Newton, himself, on another occasion took the position which he now opposed. When he published his discovery of the universal law of gravitation, others, and especially Hooke who had in fact written a paper on the subject, claimed a share in the discovery. Newton's letter to Halley will surely be remembered in which he bitterly complained that Hooke, who having merely guessed there was such a law, was now trying to rob him of the fruits of his labour although he had first successfully demonstrated and published the law.

If there be left any doubt whether Leibniz meant to imply that Newton had been helped, (not perhaps in grasping the original idea, but in devising a nomenclature, and in developing the idea into a systematic method), it must be abandoned when we consider his comparison of Newton and himself with the well-known case of Fabri and Cavalieri. Fabri knew Cavalieri's work and changed it in no essential particulars when he published it as his own. He had greatly damaged his reputation by the publication, in 1669, of his *Synopsis of Geometry* which would have been forgotten, as a work of little value, except for its mention in this connection.[24] And Leibniz had instanced this flagrant case of plagiarism by an insignificant

[24] Cantor, *Gesch. der Math.,* Vol. III, p. 293.

Fabri as a parallel to the case of the incomparable Newton. One might forgive the bad taste shown by a reviewer anonymously praising his own achievements; one might excuse the temptation to make a counter-charge of plagiarism; but to place Newton on a level with Fabri was an outrageous insult. There is only one possible explanation of Leibniz's conduct in publishing this review; the same reckless insinuation, which had been made about him by Newton's intimate friend, Fatio, had spread its evil contagion over all the participants.

In spite of the anger which Leibniz's review aroused, no public notice was taken of it for three years; Fatio dropped permanently out of sight, and the controversy was reopened even more bitterly by John Keill, who became from that time the chief defender of the English cause. Keill, who was a Scotchman, had gone with James Gregory to Oxford as a student, and had thus early been inducted into the Newtonian philosophy. In 1708, he was a Master of Arts and had completed a paper on *The Laws of Centripetal Forces.* This paper, he addressed as a letter from Christ Church to Halley, who was Savilian Professor of Geometry in Oxford; and under his auspices it was published in the *Philosophical Transactions* for September-October of that year. We need not discuss this work except to cite the following passage which was evidently inserted as a counterblast to Leibniz: "All these [laws] follow from that very celebrated arithmetic of fluxions which without any doubt Dr. Newton invented first, as can readily be proved by any one who reads the letters about it published by Wallis; yet the same arithmetic afterwards, under a changed name and method of notation, was published by Dr. Leibniz in the *Acta Eruditorum.*"[25]

There can be little doubt that the offensive passage was known to Halley and others; but Newton was not involved in its preparation, and was annoyed when it was published.[26] The volume of the

[25] *Commerc. Epist.* Ed. Biot., pp. 171 and 228.—Of the three accusing passages Brewster claims that Fatio's was not a charge of plagiarism, as Leibniz is allowed to be the second inventor, but he does not mention the scarcely veiled charge that the invention was borrowed; he holds that Leibniz's review was a virtual, but ambiguous, charge of plagiarism; he states that if the reader finds Keill retorts the charge of plagiarism he must admit it was not coarsely or insidiously made. He indignantly wrote that "who dares accuse a man like Newton, or indeed any man holding a fair character in society, of the odious crime of plagiarism, places himself without the pale of the ordinary courtesies of life, and deserves to have the same charge thrown back upon himself." But, of the wickedness of the charges made against Leibniz by Fatio and Keill, he writes not a word.—As for myself, I can see little difference in the three accusations, except that Fatio's came first and Leibniz exonerated Newton of any share in it; and the other two charges were retorts discourteous.

[26] *Cf.* Edleston, p. lxxii; where a detailed summary is given of the minutes of the Royal Society pertaining to the controversy.

Transactions containing Keill's article was not published till 1710; and, as Leibniz was then in Berlin, the copy sent to him by Secretary Sloane was further delayed. Thus, it was not till March 4th, 1710/11 that Leibniz wrote to Sloane to complain of this second attack on his integrity. He mentioned in the letter, that Fatio had attacked him first, and that he had taught him a lesson; and both Sloane, himself, as he knew from his letters, and Newton, so far as he knew, had disapproved of that attack. And now, he complained, Keill seems to have renewed the same inept accusation of plagiarism. "That it is false no one knows better than Newton. Assuredly I had not heard the name of the calculus of fluxions by report, or had seen with these eyes the characters which Dr. Newton used, before they were published in Wallis's *Works*. . . . Yet I do not believe Dr. Keill to be a calumniator, but rather I think he offended more from rash judgement than from malice." He concluded by demanding Keill to testify publicly that he did not mean what his words seemed to imply.

The letter would have rung truer if it had not been preceded by Leibniz's anonymous review. When it was read to the Royal Society, Newton, as I mentioned, was irritated by Keill's attack. However, Keill sent him a letter with the Leipzig *Acts* containing the review, and later described at a meeting of the Society the unjust treatment accorded him; then Newton, from the Chair, gave a short history of the fluxions, the date of its discovery, and the letters published by Wallis. After a discussion, Keill was desired to draw up an account of the matter in dispute and to set it right. Further discussions followed at later meetings, and finally his reply, addressed to Secretary Sloane, was read and ordered to be printed in the *Transactions* as soon as Leibniz's reply should have been received. The author's importance had greatly increased since the publication of his scientific article, as he had been elected a Fellow of the Royal Society and Savilian professor of Astronomy in Oxford. While he gave no distinction to either position, he proved himself to be an eager partisan and a keen polemical writer. To him was given a leading part in the defense of Newton, but after the publication of this letter he became rather the mouth-piece than the originator of ideas, for Newton really furnished the materials and really directed the campaign. Brought up in an atmosphere of violent political strife, Keill adopted the fashionable tone of the day, and his correspondence, with its constant reference to rogues and the shameless actions of his opponents, is not attractive. His flattery of Newton makes one realise the temptation to become dictatorial which would have been difficult for even the most modest man to withstand.

While Keill's second letter[27] of May 24th, 1711, to Leibniz, reviews the question of priority in a way to give the credit to Newton, the former passage against Leibniz is softened, and one suspects that the Fellows had counselled more moderation. Thus he explained: "I acknowledge I had said that the arithmetic of fluxions had been invented by Dr. Newton and, with a changed name and method of notation, had been published later by Leibniz. But I do not wish these words to be so understood as if I contended that either the name which Newton had given to his method, or the form of the notation which he had used was known to Leibniz; but I meant only that Dr. Newton had been the first inventor of the arithmetic of the fluxions, or of the differential calculus. Also I meant that, in the two letters written to Oldenburg and sent by him to Leibniz, there was given information sufficiently obvious to so perspicuous a genius; whence Leibniz derived [*hausit*] the principles of his calculus or at least could have derived them." The remainder of the letter, which reiterates the charge that Leibniz had published nothing before the receipt of the Oldenburg letters, is undoubtedly intended to impress on the mind of the reader the suspicion that he did get the clue to the calculus from them. This matter has already been discussed and it is generally agreed that Leibniz did not get, and could not have got, his discovery from the correspondence. The letter closes with the compliment that anyone should be satisfied with the glory which the development of so noble an invention had given to him.

While it was a lame and incomplete apology, Leibniz could, and should, have accepted it; and have left to posterity the decision. The development of the calculus by the work of his school had so far outstripped the fluxions that his great reputation was secure. But he smarted under the feeling of injustice; he was badly counselled by Bernoulli, who had given his opinion that Newton was indebted to him; and he decided to put the decision to the test of a public investigation.

In a letter[28] to Secretary Sloane of date December 29th, 1711, Leibniz claimed that Keill had again attacked his candour and worse than before; and, in a sense, it is true that the explanation as given did strengthen the accusation. He claims that it was done without

[27] *Commerc. Epist.*, p. 172.

[28] *Commerc. Epist.*, p. 181.

Newton's authority or consent; there, of course, he was quite in error, and his complaint against the author was indirectly one against Newton. It was in vain, he wrote, that the anonymous review in the Leipzig *Acts* had been cited as "I do not find that any injustice had been done to anyone, but rather each one had been given due credit." As this matter involved a knowledge of events long ago and documents which must be examined, it could not be left, he declared, to a man learned, but young, and thus an advocate too little acquainted with what had happened before his time.[29] And he concluded by requesting the Society to repress "such vain and vociferous clamours."

It was a tactical blunder for Leibniz to appeal to the Royal Society. In the first place, he was really attacking its President since, contrary to his idea, Newton was responsible for Keill's second attack; and, in the next place, the government under Bolingbroke was hostile to the Hanoverian succession and everything connected with that interest. He should have known that the English Society would defend its President and would find in his favour; and if the conditions had been reversed does one doubt that a German commission would have sided with Leibniz? On receipt of Leibniz's first letter, demanding a public investigation, the Society discussed what their procedure should be at almost every meeting from March to the following January. Newton, as has been remarked, was opposed to continuing the dispute, but after he became acquainted with Leibniz's Review and his two letters, he became passionately determined to manage his defense. At the meeting of 6 March, 1711/12, a Committee was appointed to examine all the documents, letters, etc., in the possession of the Society which pertained to the matter, to publish them, and to draw up a report of their findings. The finished Report was read on April 24, 1712 and during the following January, it was published with the title *Commercium Epistolicum*.[30] The names of the Committee appear nowhere in the report; all that was

29 The phrase is: Cum homine docto, sed novo, et parum perito rerum ante-acturum cognitore. Brewster (Vol. II, p. 46) renders it in this inexcusable fashion: "He brands Keill with the odious appellation of an *upstart*, and one little acquainted with the circumstances of the case."

30 *Commercium Epistolicum D. Johannis Collins et aliorum de Analysi Promota:* Jussu Societatis Regiae. In lucem editum. Londini. Typis Pearsonianis, Anno MDCCXII. As the Report was printed in a very limited edition and was not for sale, it soon became scarce and this quarto edition is almost impossible to find; in 1722, a second edition in octavo, purporting to be an exact reprint, was published, and copies are not so rare. In 1856, Biot and Lefort edited an edition, giving comparative readings of the two editions, critical notes, extracts of other pertinent documents, and a critique of the controversy. This is a remarkably fine piece of work and is invaluable to anyone attempting to follow this tangled history.

known of its composition was that Newton stated, ten years later, in the Recensio for the second edition: "*Numerosus quippe consessus erat, e viris eruditis diversarum nationum lectus,*" and in a letter to the Abbé Conti, in 1716, he wrote, "The materials for the *Commercium Epistolicum* were collected and published by a numerous committee of gentlemen of different nations."

The names of this Committee were not known to the public till Turnor printed, in 1806, the following minutes of the Royal Society which pertain to the present subject:[31]

"March 11, 1711/12. Upon account of Mons. Leibniz's letter to Dr. Sloane, concerning the disputes formerly mentioned, a committee was appointed by the Society to inspect the letters and papers relating thereto, viz. Dr. Arbuthnot, Mr. Hill, Dr. Halley, Mr. Jones, Mr. Machin, and Mr. Burnet, who were to make their report to the Society."

"1712, April 24. The Committee, appointed to inspect the papers, letters, and books of the Society, on account of the dispute between Mr. Leibniz and Mr. Keill, delivered in their report, which was read as follows: etc. . . .

"To which report the Society agreed *nemine contradicente,* and ordered that the whole matter from the beginning, with the extracts of all the letters relating thereto, and Mr. Keill and Mr. Leibniz's letters, be published with all convenient speed that may be, together with the report of the said Committee. [The report is in the handwriting of Dr. Halley.]

"Ordered, that Dr. Halley, Mr. Jones, and Mr. Machin, be desired to take charge of the said impression (which they promised,) and Mr. Jones to make an estimate of the charges, against the next meeting."

"1712/13. Jan. 8. Some copies of the book entitled *Commercium Epistolicum,* etc. printed by the Society's order being brought, the President ordered one to be delivered to each person of the Committee, appointed for that purpose, to examine it before its publication."

The personnel of the Committee, as given by Turnor, hardly agreed with Newton's statement that it was numerous and of different nations. The discrepancy was not explained till De Morgan discovered in 1846[32] that Mr. Robartes was added to it on March

[31] *Town and Soke of Grantham,* p. 181, Extracts [1671–1713] from Journal Books of the Royal Society relating to Sir Isaac Newton. And, in a foot-note, Turnor states that these extracts have not previously been printed and were made by Dr. Rutty, for Mr. Conduitt, in 1728.

[32] *Phil. Trans.,* Vol. XLVI, pp. 107–109.

20; M. Bonet, the Prussian Minister to England, on March 27; and Mr. Demoivre, a French refugee, Mr. Aston, and Dr. Brook Taylor, on April 17. Of this Committee, only two were foreigners and only one of the two, Demoivre, was a mathematician; six were mathematicians; and seven, at least, were intimate personal friends of Newton and Keill. It had been generally assumed that this was a judicial committee to enquire impartially into the whole matter, and that its report was adopted by the Society. On the contrary, its function was to examine the archives and to defend Newton and Keill; and this it did without giving any notice to Leibniz, still less giving him any invitation to produce documents or to defend himself. Besides the inference which can be drawn from its composition and method of action, direct evidence of its partisanship is available. Demoivre (who, with Aston and Brook Taylor, had only seven days to examine the mass of documents) considered himself, according to an intimate friend, as then drawn out of the neutrality which he had observed before he had joined the Committee.[33] Burnet, another of the Committee, wrote to John Bernoulli in August, 1712: "We are, at present, occupied in the Society in *proving,* by the original letters, that the method of fluxions had been known more than seven years before M. Leibniz published anything on it, and that M. Leibniz could have seen the principles of it at the house of a Mr. Collins. . . ."[34] Lastly, the Royal Society, apparently, made itself responsible for the report of this anonymous and partisan Committee. The opposite to this opinion has been stated by Brewster and De Morgan.[35] The origin of this grave error may be readily shown. Leibniz wrote a letter to John Chamberlayne,[36] who later

33 De Morgan, *Essays,* p. 28.

34 *Commerc. Phil. et Math. Leibniz et Bernoulli,* Vol. II, p. 283.

35 Brewster, Vol. II, p. 58, supports his opinion against Weld on the grounds that the Society "agreed to *receive* it, and ordered it to be printed" and on a statement of Newton to Conti in 1716 (*Cf.* Raphson, *Fluxions,* p. 112); "If the Royal Society *have not yet given judgement against him,* it is because the Committee did not act as a jury, nor the Royal Society as a formal court of justice. The Committee examined old letters and papers, and gave their opinion on them alone, and left room for Mr. Leibniz to produce further evidence for himself. And it is sufficient that the Society ordered their report, with the papers upon which it was grounded, to be published." Since the title page states that it was published by the Society without any reference to an irresponsible Committee, it certainly makes itself responsible for the work. From their action of May 20, 1714, it would seem that, worried by the effect of the book on the Continent, the members wished to hedge. It is difficult to follow Newton's argument that Leibniz was given an opportunity to produce his evidence. One may suspect that the members were sick of the mess into which they had been led. Also I suspect that the troubles which arose in the Society about this time may have come partly from this cause.

36 John Chamberlayne was educated at Oxford and was later Chamberlain to George, Prince of Denmark. He was elected F. R. S. in 1702 and contributed three papers to the *Transactions.* He died in 1723.

tried to act as mediator, inveighing against the *Commercium Epistolicum* and requesting him to lay a complaint before the Society. Chamberlayne complied with this request, but either he reported the action of the Society erroneously or gave Leibniz a mistaken impression, for Leibniz answered: "I am obliged to you for the attempt you made with the Royal Society. The extract of its *Journal* of May 20th makes known that it does not consider the report of its Committee should pass for a decision of the Society."[37] He also wrote to Bernoulli that Chamberlayne had written to him and had told him, the Society "denied it had decided the controversy."[38] What really happened was, the Society, on May 20th, 1714, adopted the following resolution which certainly implies its own full responsibility:

"It was not judged proper (since this letter [from Leibniz] was not addressed to them), for the Society to concern themselves therewith, nor were they desired so to do. But that if any person had any material objection against the *Commercium*, or the Report of the Committee, it might be reconsidered at any time."[39]

When the report of the Committee was read, it was approved unanimously at an ordinary meeting of the Society and ordered to be printed without apprising Leibniz of its findings. By this action the Society, if it so wished, could disclaim responsibility. While the controversy was about a purely scientific question, there is little doubt that it served as a political document, since the health of Queen Anne was precarious, and a desperate intrigue was in progress to prevent the Hanoverian succession; nothing was thus easier than to colour a personal controversy between Newton and Leibniz with a political issue between England and Hanover.[40]

The report of the Committee was published under the title of the *Commercium Epistolicum*, in 1712. This original edition, in quarto, was edited by Halley, Jones, and Machin. The book was not for sale, but was given to important individuals and institutions. Twenty-five copies were sent to Johnson, a bookseller at The Hague and editor

[37] Des Maizeaux's *Recueil.* 2d Ed., Vol. II, p. 128.

[38] *Com. Phil. Bern. et Leib.*, Vol. II, p. 340.

[39] *Journal-book*, Vol. XII, p. 481. Quoted by Weld, *Hist R. S.*, Vol. I, p. 415, Historians have thus followed Leibniz's letters rather than the unpublished minutes of the Society.

[40] Leibniz wrote to Bernoulli, 19 August, 1713, that an English friend had written to inform him the action of the Society was not one on mathematics but one of the Tories against the Whigs.—*Commerc. Leib. et Bern.*, II, p. 321.—Brewster scouts this idea because Newton was a Whig and consequently Hanoverian. But I have pointed out that he always had sufficient influence with the Tories to keep his lucrative office, and that Bolingbroke admired him sufficiently to offer him a great pension and to be his staunch supporter during the Flamsteed controversy. Nor should we forget that Swift was a friend of his niece, and that Anne knighted him.

of the newly founded *Journal Littéraire,* to be distributed on the continent. It is now thoroughly established that Newton was the directing power behind the Committee; he chose the documents which, though accurately copied, were extracted so as to put his case in the most favourable light; he made a running comment in foot-notes which interpreted obscurities in the documents, and turned them to his own advantage; he thus directed anonymously his own defense and laid the burden of responsibility on his friends, and on the Society of which he was President. The evidence of his personal direction of the Committee is to be found in his papers preserved in the *Portsmouth Collection,* and also in a rough draught of a critique on three papers of Leibniz's which formerly belonged to Keill and is now preserved among the Lucasian papers. Edleston,[41] who found this paper, states that its language is in close agreement with that used in the *Commercium Epistolicum* and the editors must have seen the document or perhaps a corrected form of it.

In 1722, a second edition, which purported to be an exact reprint, was published in octavo. A *Recensio* and an *Ad Lectorem* were prefixed. As this edition was larger and was put into the hands of book-sellers, the reading public has had to depend on it, and did so in the belief that the text was a *verbatim* reprint of the original report. The title page is an exact copy of the original, and there is no mention of its being a second, or revised, edition. Some copies bear the date, 1725, but it has been established that all the copies were published in 1722, and that the false titles with the later date were pasted over the originals. The first intimation, that the reprint contained variations from the original text, came from De Morgan, who, in 1846, was loaned a copy of the first edition by the Royal Society and compared the two texts.[42] In spite of De Morgan's disclosure neither Brewster or Edleston referred to it, and it was left to Biot and Lefort to publish in their superb edition of the *Commercium Epistolicum* issued in 1856 at the expense of the French Government, the variations in the two editions, extracts from many documents which related to the subject, and a critical review of the report of the Committee.

[41] Edleston, p. 307.

[42] "One testimony to the significance of the *variantes* is that of Sir D. Brewster, who holds it wise to omit all mention of them. After my paper, which I took care he should have, and with a full knowledge of the new work being *reprinted* under *the old date,* he calls it 'a new edition with notes, a general review of it and a preface of some length.' [Vol. II, p. 75.] He did not even give the true date (1722), but sticks by that of the second title-page (1725). This is of some consequence; for three years, at Newton's age, then made a difference in the palliation which years and infirmities may be made to give." De Morgan, *Essays,* pp. 190–192.

As for the supposed reprint of 1722, Keill was its editor, but Newton was really responsible for it. He inserted, omitted, and changed passages in the text; and, as it was not published till six years after Leibniz's death, and when the original was almost inaccessible, the alterations were not suspected for a century and a quarter. The *Ad Lectorem* which serves as a preface, and the *Recensio* which follows it, were ascribed to Keill; but they were written by Newton. This charge was first advanced by Biot; it was contradicted by Brewster in his first *Life of Newton* in 1831; and finally established by De Morgan, in 1852, by an examination of the style and on the authority of Dr. Wilson, a friend of Pemberton. Finally, when Brewster was given the privilege of examining the *Portsmouth Collection* he found an almost complete manuscript of the *Recensio* and five or six copies of the *Ad Lectorem* in Newton's own hand-writing, and retracted his former opinion.

The *Recensio* contains a polemic against Leibniz, and a justification of his own conduct, which Newton prepared in his letters addressed to the Abbé Conti in 1716. The history of this *Recensio* is a curious one. It was first written in English by Newton and published anonymously in the *Philosophical Transactions* for 1715 with the title, "An account of the Book entitled *Commercium Epistolicum.*" It was then translated into French by Demoivre according to Lefort, and sent by Keill to the *Journal Littéraire* where it appeared, again anonymously, in 1715–16. Finally, it was translated by Newton into Latin, and prefixed anonymously to the second edition of the *Commercium Epistolicum.* And to make his authorship even less suspected he, indirectly in an *Annotatio,* attributes it to Keill.[43] Knowing the facts of the case, as we now do, it does not seem possible that he could have dared to write the following in the *Recen-*

[43] The above account of the proof of Newton's editorship of the *Commerc. Epist.* and authorship of the *Recensio* follows the generally accepted story. But De Morgan, Brewster, and Lefort seem to have overlooked a contemporaneous statement which should have made their research unnecessary. In 1719, Des Maizeaux, a friend of Newton, published a collection of documents on the Newton-Leibniz controversy and, in a preface, he gave a summary of its history. In a foot-note (Des Maizeaux's *Recueil,* 2d edition, Amsterdam, 1740, p. lxx.) I find the following: "To make it [*Commerc. Epist.*] more public, Mr. Newton prepared a second edition in 1722 in 8vo, preceded by an Advertisement [the *Ad Lectorem*] where he gives an idea of his dispute with Mr. Leibniz. This Advertisement is followed by a Latin Translation [the *Recensio*] of the Extract of the *Commercium Epistolicum,* which after having appeared in English in the *Philosophical Transactions,* was then translated into French and printed in London. . . . This Extract was inserted in Tome VII of the *Journal Littéraire.* At the end of this second edition, Mr. Newton printed the *Judgement* of a Mathematician (Mr. Bernoulli) on the first Inventor of the fluxions or the differential calculus, with a short refutation of what this illustrious mathematician had advanced."

sio to this second edition, (p. 26): "Nemo in causa propria sibi testis est. Iniquus admodum fuerit Judex, omniumque gentium jura conculcaverit, qui quemquam in sua causa pro legitimo teste admiserit."[44] Of all the regrettable events in this lamentable altercation, this is to me far the worst. That one should thus secretly condemn himself for self-witnessing and use it to buttress the impression that he was being vindicated by others is a depth of hypocrisy impossible to excuse.

We can now turn to the report of the Committee of the Royal Society, and to present their findings more clearly, each article will be given and then followed by a critical comment. After examining the documents in their archives, abstracts of those portions which were considered pertinent to the controversy were printed and the case was summed up: "By these letters and papers we find,—

"I. That Mr. Leibniz was in London in the beginning of the year 1673, and went thence in or about March to Paris, where he kept a correspondence with Mr. Collins by means of Mr. Oldenburg, till about September, 1676, and then returned by London and Amsterdam to Hanover: And that Mr. Collins was very free in communicating to able mathematicians what he had received from Mr. Newton and Mr. Gregory."

Comment: These are undisputed facts.

"II. That when Mr. Leibniz was the first time in London, he contended for the invention of another differential method properly so called; and notwithstanding that he was shown by Dr. Pell that it was Mouton's method, persisted in maintaining it to be his own invention, by reason that he had found it by himself, without knowing what Mouton had done before, and had much improved it. And we find no mention of his having any other differential method than Mouton's, before his letter of the 21st of June 1677, which was a year after a copy of Mr. Newton's letter, of the 10th of December 1672, had been sent to Paris to be communicated to him; and above four years after Mr. Collins began to communicate that letter to his correspondents; in which letter the method of fluxions was sufficiently described to any intelligent person."

Comment: This is a clever bit of camouflage, made in order to predispose the reader against Leibniz, by charging him with an earlier indiscretion. If he took his first method from Mouton, and

[44] "No one is a proper witness for himself. He would be an iniquitous Judge, and would crush under foot the laws of all the people, who would admit anyone as a lawful witness in his own cause."

his series for finding the arc of a circle from Gregory which was intimated in the body of the text by the anonymous commentator, it was only natural to believe that he would take from Newton the method of fluxions, and disguise it by a different name and notation. Thus a feeling of suspicion was injected into the mind of the reader.

In the first place, the facts are misleading because Leibniz frankly admitted that Dr. Pell's criticism was correct but, as he had not seen Mouton's work at the time, his work had been done independently.[45] Although the question of discoveries by the method of infinite series, such as Mouton's, bulks so largely in the text of the *Commercium Epistolicum* and in the *Recensio,* we should remember that it is not germane to the controversy about the invention of the calculus. Newton's great work on infinite series, and his discovery of the binomial theorem were expansions of the work of Barrow, Wallis, and others. Leibniz never claimed to be in the same class with Newton and Gregory in that field, and frequently urged Newton to continue and publish his work. He claimed to have found only one series (that for finding the arc of a circle from a tangent) by his own invention, and the claim was substantiated by Huygens.[46]

Next, as to the famous letter of December 10th, 1672, which the Committee declare was sent to Leibniz and that in it "the method of fluxions was sufficiently described to any intelligent person."[47] The history of this letter, its content and its dispatch to Leibniz, has already been discussed. Even if the extract containing the example

[45] In regard to the Mouton incident Leibniz had a curious lapse of memory. In his *Hist. et Origo Calc. Differ.* (first published by Gerhardt, now translated and made more accessible by Child in his *Early MSS. of Leib.,* Chicago, 1920), Leibniz states "Pell told him that they were not new, but that it had been recently made known by Nicolaus Mercator . . . this made Leibniz obtain the work of Mercator." Child notes on page 37: "What Pell told him was that his theorems on numbers occurred in a book by Mouton entitled *De diametris apparentibus Solis et Lunæ.* Leibniz, *to defend himself from a charge of plagiarism,* made haste to borrow a copy from Oldenburg and found to his relief that not only had Mouton got his results by a different method, but that his own were more general." The words italicised are interesting in connection with the present accusation by the Committee.

[46] In his *Hist. et Origo,* Leibniz points out this device of his opponents who "neither from the *Commercium Epistolicum* that they have published, nor from any other source, brought forward the slightest bit of evidence whereby it might be established that [Newton] used the differential calculus before it was published by [Leibniz]; therefore all the accusations that were brought against him by these persons may be treated with contempt as beside the question. They have used the dodge of the petti-fogging advocate to divert the attention of the judges from the matter on trial to other things, namely to infinite series. But even in these they could bring forward nothing that could impugn his honesty, for he plainly acknowledged the manner in which he had made progress in them." Child, p. 57.

[47] The Committee used the words "intelligent person" for their English readers, and translated them with the word "cognitori" for foreigners. As the meaning of "cognitori" is an advocate, or one skilled in a subject, the delicate change in significance for home and foreign consumption is evident.

published in the text by the Committee had been sent to Leibniz, there would have been no possibility of his having received a clue to the calculus from it. De Morgan answers this charge in the following vigorous manner:[48] "We are obliged frequently to recur to the assertion of the Committee that Newton's example, which we have translated, was description enough of the method of fluxions for any intelligent person. That this, which we shall believe to be the most reckless assertion ever made on a mathematical subject, until some one produces its match, was solemnly put forward by the Committee, is not in our day excuse enough for dwelling upon it. But the sufficient excuse is that writers of note, upon the Newtonian side of the question (Brewster, *et al.*), still quote the assertion with approbation." But the question, whether an intelligent person could have received a hint from the example, is academic because it is certain beyond dispute that Leibniz never saw the example.

There are two manuscripts in the Archives of the Royal Society which clear up the whole matter.[49] One of these, the manuscript referred to by the Committee as the *Collectio* or *Historiola* of Collins, is entitled *Extracts from Mr. Gregories Letter;* it contains the full text of Newton's letter of December 10th, 1672, including the problem: the other has the superscription, *To Leibniz the 14th of June 1676 About Mr. Gregories remains;* it is an abridgement of the *Collectio,* and does not contain the problem on the tangent. Fortunately, we now know what Leibniz actually received from Oldenburg. From papers of Leibniz found in the Royal Library of Hanover and published by Gerhardt, it is certain that Oldenburg wrote to him from London, *July 26th, 1676,* not forwarding Collins's *Collectio,* but merely describing it. He quoted the descriptive part of Newton's letter of December 10th, 1672, but he did not even mention the example of the tangent which the Committee states "sufficiently described the method of fluxions to any intelligent person." Thus, it is difficult to explain the conduct of the Committee in making the statement in this Article II, when they had at their disposal the abridgement marked to be sent to Leibniz. If we must condemn the Committee for making such a grave and inexcusable charge against Leibniz in the edition of the Commercium of 1712, what must we think of the editor of the reprint of 1722 (that is,

[48] *Essays,* p. 85.

[49] They were found by Edleston and commented on by him, p. xlvii. Unfortunately his conclusions are made to shield Newton and the Committee rather than to make clear the significance of his discovery. *Cf.* De Morgan, *Essays,* p. 73.

Newton) who secretly added the following sentence to the original text "This *Collectio* was sent to Dr. Leibniz on June 26, 1676"?[50]

"III. That by Mr. Newton's letter of the 13th of June 1676 it appears, that he had the method of fluxions above five years before the writing of that letter. And by his *Analysis per Aequationes numero Terminorum Infinitas,* communicated by Dr. Barrow to Mr. Collins in July 1669, we find that he had invented the method before that time."

Comment: This section is quite disingenuous. No one, certainly not Leibniz, had ever claimed that Newton had not invented the method of fluxions when he claimed to have done so. The letter of 13th of June 1676 is the *Epistola prior* already discussed in a former chapter. It, and the *Epistola posterior* of October 24th, 1676, announce the invention of the method of fluxions. But it is generally admitted that Leibniz could not have found a clue to the calculus from the problems in infinite series, or from the jumble of letters, contained in them.

As for the *de Analysi,* it is the opinion of mathematicians that it does not show Newton had then developed a method which could be called the calculus.

From the research of Gerhardt,[51] we can learn what acquaintance Leibniz had with the *De Analysi* and the *Collectio* of Collins. Gerhardt found that Leibniz acquired nothing of importance with reference to mathematics during his first visit to London in 1673. During the following three years he made great progress in the subject. The letter of Oldenburg dated July 26, 1676, that is the *abridgement* of Collins's *Collectio,* excited his curiosity to learn what the English were doing, and induced him to return to Germany by way of London in October of the same year. "He stayed there about a week and made the acquaintance of Collins who willingly let him have access to his collection of treatises and letters. What Leibniz found in them, that he thought worth noting, he set down on two

[50] The last two sentences of Section XLVI in the edition of 1722 are: "Habetur et Epistola D. Newtoni ad D. Collins, 10 Decemb. 1672 data, et superius impressa, in qua Newtonus se Methodum generalem habere dicit ducendi Tangentes, quadrandi Curvilineas, et similia peragendi; et Methodum Exemplo ducendi Tangentes exponit: quam Methodum D. Leibnitius differentialem postea vocavit. Haec *Collectio* ad D. Leibnitium missa fuit 26 Junii 1676."—After comparing this passage with the original text, Biot and Lefort, p. 100, found that the last sentence had been added. It should be noted that there were also two interpolations made in the text of this section which, although not important in themselves, are illustrations of the unwarranted changes made in this edition.

[51] Published in the *Sitzungsber. Akad. zu Berlin,* 1891. For translation of this article, *cf.* Child, Chap. VI.

folios; the one has the heading, *Excerpta ex tractatu Newtoni de Analysi* . . ., the other sheet has the heading, *Excerpta ex Commerc. Epist. inter Collinium et Gregorium.*" It is apparent, since he made these notes from the *De Analysi* and the *Collectio* of Collins, that he had not seen, nor had had in his possession either of these documents before October, 1676.[52] From the extracts made during this week, Gerhardt states that "what Leibniz found in Collins's collection relating to algebraic analysis was new to him and excited his interest; also the verbal interchange of ideas between himself and Collins was upon the same subject. On the other hand, as regards the infinitesimal calculus, Leibniz obtained nothing during his second visit to London."[53]

"IV. That the differential method is one and the same with the method of fluxions, excepting the name and mode of notation; Mr. Leibniz calling those quantities differences, which Mr. Newton calls moments or fluxions; and marking them with the letter *d,* a mark not used by Mr. Newton. And therefore we take the proper question to be, not who invented this or that method, but who was the first inventor of the method. And we believe that those who have reputed Mr. Leibniz the first inventor, knew little or nothing of his correspondence with Mr. Collins and Mr. Oldenburg long before; nor of Mr. Newton's having that method above fifteen years before Mr. Leibniz began to publish it in the *Acta Eruditorum* of Leipzig.

"For which reasons, we reckon Mr. Newton the first inventor; and are of opinion, that Mr. Keill, in asserting the same, has been no ways injurious to Mr. Leibniz. And we submit to the judgement of the Society; whether the extract of letters and papers now presented to you, together with what is extant to the same purpose in Dr. Wallis's third volume, may not deserve to be made public."

Comment: Almost at the time the Committee wrote article IV, Newton issued the 2d edition of the *Principia* in which it is stated that "the two methods were scarcely different, except in the forms of

[52] In connection with this visit and the examination of Collins's collection the following dates are important. The *Epistola prior* of Newton to Leibniz is dated 13 June 1676. In it he discusses the binomial theorem but not fluxions. On August 27, 1676, Leibniz wrote asking for more information. Newton's answer, the *Epistola posterior,* was written on October 24, 1676. In this letter he elaborates the binomial theorem and mentions nothing about fluxions except to announce an invention in his famous jumble of letters. Leibniz was in London for a week in October and so missed the letter if it was sent to Paris. It was received in Germany some time after March, 1676/7. On June 21, 1677, he wrote to Oldenburg a letter giving a full and clear statement of the calculus. All these letters, in full or in extract, were published in the *Commerc. Epist.*

[53] Child, pp. 162–170.

terms and notation, and *in the idea of the generation of quantities,"* which is an essential difference. But if the identity of the two methods be granted, then the honour of priority of invention by accepted practice would be given to him who first publishes or, at least, can exhibit a certified paper describing satisfactorily the same method,—in other words, to Leibniz. And I have already cited Newton's previous stand against Hooke on the discovery of gravitation.

The Committee is not honest in its statement of the question given it to decide. Leibniz had never denied that Newton had invented an unknown method of fluxions, but he had claimed the independent discovery of the calculus; and he had demanded of the Society to vindicate him from what he asserted to be an accusation of plagiarism made by Fatio and Keill. Since the Committee certainly did not prove such plagiarism their statement that "Mr. Keill, in asserting the same, has been no ways injurious to Mr. Leibniz" was preposterous. In spite of the fact that the charge of plagiarism has been proved to be false, the baneful effect of the Committee's conclusion still persists. The controversy, which led to the preparation of the *Commercium Epistolicum,* will always excite a deep interest because it involved a great question, and the honour and passions of great men. I have endeavoured to discuss it critically and dispassionately, and to support my opinions on documentary evidence. The more thoroughly the question is studied the stronger the conviction becomes that the President, the Committee, and the Fellows of the Royal Society are to be condemned for a reckless and disgraceful exhibition of injustice against one of their oldest and most illustrious members. In coming to the decision that the chief blame must fall on the Society, I in no degree palliate the conduct of Leibniz and his friends: the difference lies in this; when it accepted the adjudication of the dispute, the world believed that the taint of partisanship had been eliminated, and that its report was based on justice. We can be charitable towards the faults of passion of those immediately concerned; but no such excuse pertains to such a body as the Royal Society.

We can now go back and pick up the thread of events which followed the first printing of the *Commercium Epistolicum.*[54] The

[54] The principal sources for this account are: *Commerc. Phil, Bern. et Leib.;* Des Maizeaux *Recueil; Commerc. Epist.* Biot et Lefort; Corr. of Newton and Keill; the *Portsmouth Collection.*

correspondence on this subject between Bernoulli and Leibniz begins on 28 February, 1712/13, with a letter to Leibniz who was making a long stay in Vienna: "I have shown to Newton some of his errors, but gently, lest I should offend him; besides he has been friendly to me, seeing that he recently proposed me for membership in the Royal Society and secured my election, which dignity he promised also should be conferred on my son. . . . The history of the differential calcalus of Collins [*Commerc. Epist.*], as Demoivre wrote me recently, has not yet appeared; he said it would certainly be issued the week following his letter was written. Without doubt it will be sent to you more quickly than to me. . . . I agree with you that the fluxions flowed from the differential calculus, and that this is self-evident although the English dissimulate it."

In his answer, Leibniz congratulates Bernoulli, or rather the Society, on his election. He has not received the *Commercium*. Then Bernoulli writes to him the important letter of June 7th, 1713, which Leibniz afterwards published, and which caused its author such trouble. This letter has passed into history under the title of *Judicium Mathematici.*

"My son has received a copy of the *Commercium Epistolicum,* given to him in Paris by the Abbé Bignon who had several copies sent to him from London for distribution. I have read it, but not carefully. In the first place, the method of proceeding is displeasing. You are, at the start, accused before a tribunal which, it appears, is composed of the plaintiffs themselves and their witnesses, so to speak the one accused of plagiarism, after the documents are produced against you is put to vote; you fall under the law, you are condemned. . . . It is certain, therefore, that Newton was ignorant of the correct method of taking second differentials a long time after it was familiar to us. But I must break off; I ask you [*rogo*] to use properly what I write, and not to commit me with Newton and with his countrymen; I do not wish to be mixed up with these quarrels."

The next interchange of letters contains a warning from Leibniz, that Newton is trying to curry favour with Bernoulli; and the reply that there is no danger. In the meanwhile, both sides began a campaign to win supporters in France and, especially, the good opinion of Abbé Bignon, of Varignon, whom Newton thought the most acute geometer in Europe, and of Rémond de Montmort.

Keill, under the guidance of Newton, published a letter in the *Journal Littéraire* in which he gave an account of the dispute much as it was later given in the *Recensio,* the Report of the Commitee, and the letter of December 10th, 1672. He also stated: "The Report must be regarded as the judgement of the Society."

On his side, Leibniz without waiting to see the *Commercium Epistolicum* retaliated by spreading over Europe one of those anonymous *Flying Sheets,* or a *Charta Volans,* without date or place of publication, which were commonly in use by politicians. Leibniz, who wrote the paper, speaks of himself in the third person and says that, being in Vienna, Leibniz had not seen the attack on himself, and had left its answer to the judgement of a very eminent mathematician, impartial and quite capable of judging; then, without giving Bernouilli's name, the *Judicium Mathematici* letter of June 7th, 1713, was included. Leibniz also published anonymously this same letter, in the November-December number of the *Journal Littéraire*[55] for 1713, with amplifications. He points out that the eminent mathematician believed Newton should be content with the honour of having perfected the synthesis by infinitesimal lines, since he could not pretend to have found the differential calculus. As a confirmation of Newton's habit of injustice towards himself and others, he cites the mortification of Flamsteed and Hooke because due credit had not been given to them in connection with the formulation of the law of planetary attraction; he also asserted that the series which expresses the arc of a circle in terms of its tangent had been taken from Gregory. Finally, the author concludes: "I shall not particularise on what Newton and his disciples do not know about the exponential calculus, which is the highest branch of the transcendental calculus. M. de Leibniz has used it first, and M. Bernoulli has found it later independently. Nor shall I stop to show what errors some disciples of Newton have made, when they have wished to use the differential calculus."

The wrath of the English was raised to a white heat by the *Charta Volans;* Newton, when he received a copy from Chamberlayne, pronounced it to be an infamous libel; and Keill exclaimed that "they had thrown all the dirt and scandal they could without proving anything," and dubbed them those "Leipzig rogues." Newton did not at once guess that the author was Leibniz, himself, but the charge stung him so sharply that he asked Keill to prepare an answer.[56]

[55] *Cf.* Biot et Lefort, p. 230. Newton also published the *Judicium Mathematici* as an Appendix to the 2d edition of the *Commerc. Epist.*

[56] For the letters of Newton to Keill, see Edleston, pp. 169–178; the answers of Keill are in the *Ports. Coll.*

Newton to Keill

Sir,

Your letter of Feb. 8th I delayed to answer till the *Journal Littéraire* for November and December should come out. It has just come from Holland and I desired Mr. Darby to send you a copy which I doubt he has not done because he sent one to me this morning which I reckon to be for you, and I design to send it to you the first opportunity by the carrier. Mr. Leibniz in August last, by one of his correspondents, published a paper [the *Charta Volans*] in Germany containing the judgement of a nameless mathematician in opposition to the judgement of the Committee of the Royal Society, with many reflections annexed. This paper has been sent to Mr. Johnson with remarks prefixed to it. And the whole is printed in the *Journal Littéraire,* page 445. And now it is made so public I think it requires an answer. It is very reflecting upon the Committee of the Royal Society, and endeavours to derogate from the credit of some of the letters published in the *Commercium Epistolicum* as if they were spurious. If you please when you have it, to consider of what answer you think proper, I will within a post or two send you my thoughts upon the subject, that you may compare them with your own sentiments and then draw up such an answer as you think proper. You need not set your name to it. You may write either in English, or Latin, and leave it to Mr. Johnson to get it translated into French. Mr. Darby will convey your answer to the Hague.

I am

Your most humble servant,

Is. Newton.

For Dr. John Keill, Professor of
Astronomy, at his house in Oxford.

In agreement with this request, Keill prepared an elaborate reply of forty-two pages with the constant advice and suggestions of Newton. They both soon penetrated the thinly disguised fact that Bernoulli was the eminent mathematician, but Newton counselled that his name should be omitted: "The *Acta Eruditorum* for the last year are but just come to London, and I find thereby that John Bernoulli is the great mathematician who accuses me on this account. But I believe its better not to reflect upon him for it, nor so much as to name him any otherwise than by the general name of the great mathematician. They are seeking to pick a quarrel with me, and its better to let them begin it still more openly without a provocation." Halley also was consulted; and when the paper was finished, Keill sent to Newton "the whole of his answer to Bernoulli and the Leipzig rogues, for you and Dr. Halley to change or take away what you please."

Keill's paper is an able and bitter attack on Leibniz and his anonymous great mathematician. The arguments, to prove Newton's priority of invention, are practically the same as those he used later in the *Recensio;* and the charge of Newton's injustice towards Hooke and Flamsteed is dismissed as the slur of a cowardly calumniator. The conclusion is a retort in the best style of the current political pamphlets: "M. Leibniz censures M. Descartes sharply for having published the discoveries of other men, and for having concealed the names of those from whom he took them; meanwhile there are not nearly such proofs that M. Descartes had appropriated the ideas of others, as there are that M. Leibniz has published the discoveries of Messrs. Newton and Gregory, without making the least mention of them."[57]

As early as January 10th, 1713/14, Leibniz had written to Bernoulli[58] that he intended to attack Newton, and that he would use Bernoulli's now famous letter, but would protect his anonymity by giving it as the opinion of an eminent mathematician. Bernoulli answered that Leibniz would do well to use anonymously what he had written him in his Apology [the *Charta Volans*] against the *Commercium Epistolicum;* and, in his next letter, he gives further advice on how to make an effective attack. Leibniz did not return to Hanover till the end of the year, and his *Charta Volans* was a shot in the dark as he published it before he had seen the *Commercium Epistolicum.* Bernoulli also informed him about the first paper by Keill in the *Journal Littéraire,* which he described as a *famosus Libellus* and most injurious to themselves. He had become worried lest his share in the pamphlet should become known and continued to criticise Keill after Leibniz apparently had dropped the subject. Leibniz, in fact, had impulsively taken up a new line of attack. He had been an intimate friend and counsellor of Caroline who, on the accession of George I, became Princess of Wales. He seized the opportunity to write her a letter in which he warned her to beware lest her simple German faith should become sophisticated by the irreligion of the English in general, who had been carried away by the

[57] *Journal Littéraire,* July–August, 1714. Extract in Biot et Lefort, p. 236.
[58] *Commerc. Phil.* Leib. et Bern. II, p. 329.

atheism of Hobbes, and of Newton in particular, whose *Principia* fostered the idea of a mechanical universe and of a God who was merely a super-mechanician. Her Most Serene Highness, however, imparted this warning to Dr. Samuel Clarke who made it the topic of a sermon. As a result Leibniz became involved in a lengthy philosophico-religious debate. Leibniz described it to Bernoulli in this terse manner: "Clarke sent the sermon to me, I responded, he replied; I duplicated, he triplicated; I have just quadruplicated; that is, I have answered now his third letter." One may add, that the successive replies of this famous discussion embraced an ever greater and vaguer field.[59]

Two other excerpts from their correspondence should be given as they throw light on what has been called "the betrayal of Bernoulli by Leibniz."

Leibniz to Bernoulli

Hanover, 13 April, 1716.

The English quarrel has been renewed, Newton himself, when he saw that I considered Keill unworthy of a reply, descends into the arena. . . . You will be amazed at the trifling arguments he advances. . . . He knows the letter [in the *Charta Volans*] was yours, he says it was written by a mathematician or by one aspiring to mathematics [par un mathématicien ou prétendu mathématicien] as if he were ignorant of your merit. He claimed the entire article, in which your letter was inserted, to be defamatory, as if his reputation could be more injured than by the *Commercium Epistolicum*. . . .

Bernoulli to Leibniz

Bâle, 20 May, 1716.

I am pleased that Newton himself has descended into the arena; the contest will be fought under his own name and the mask be laid aside. . . . Whatever happens, I hope now the true history will be better revealed. If Newton, because of his freedom from prejudice which I assume and trust, narrates faithfully what happened and what you have done, the public may know the truth. . . .

I wonder how Newton could know that I was the author of the

[59] Leibniz referred to the discussion in this fashion in a letter to Bernoulli (*Commerc. Phil.*, Vol. II, p. 381): "Serram etiam Philosophicam nunc cum Newtono, vel quod eodem redit, cum ejus Hyperaspita Clarkio Regis Eleemosynario me reciprocare fortasse jam intellexeris. Scis Keillium et Praefatorem novae Editionis *Principiorum* Newtoni etiam Philosophiam meam pungere voluisse. Itaque scripseram ego forte Serenissimae Principi Regiae Walliae, pro excellenti ingenio suo harum rerum non incuriosae, degenerare nonnihil apud Anglos Philosophiam, vel potius Theologiam Naturalem.

letter, which you inserted in the *Charta* against Newton[60] since no mortal man knew I wrote it, except you to whom it was written, and I by whom it was written. Perhaps the expression, "by a mathematician or so-called mathematician," has a meaning other than you suppose. It could be assumed to mean that Newton believed the letter to be supposititious and yet composed by a certain mathematician; written in fact, yet invented and inserted by the author of the *Charta,* himself; if you read the matter so, you will understand "by a so-called mathematician" one who was created for the purpose and never existed.

As Leibniz had temporarily engrossed himself in the philosophical discussion with Clarke, a reply to Keill's last article was prepared and published by Bernoulli in the Leipzig *Acts* for July, 1716, under the title of *Epistola pro eminente Mathematico, Do. Johanne Bernoullio, contra quendam ex Anglia antagonistam scripta.* In some ways, Bernoulli's conduct in this controversy was worse than that of either Newton or Leibniz, as he added the trait of cowardice to the sins of the others. His interest in the business was almost as keen as Leibniz's; he was the first to put the charge of plagiarism by Newton into his friend's mind, and he supplied him with materials for attack; but he also tried by anonymity to avoid being entangled; he tried to keep friendly with Newton for favours shown him, and he was afraid of Keill. So he now sent his paper to Christian Wolf, one of the editors of the *Acts,* and asked him and Leibniz to alter it, and to publish it in an anonymous form. For he wrote "it would be exceedingly unpleasant to me to be anointed with Keill's bile and contumeliously traduced as his antagonists are accustomed to be, after he has so far treated me quite courteously." The article was accordingly put into the third person, abridged and considerably changed. But these precautions were all to no purpose, as the editors overlooked in one place the words *meam formulam* which, by the context, gave the

[60] The editor of this correspondence remarks: "Newton knew it from Leibniz's letter to Bothmar." This is easily proved to be wrong. Leibniz wrote letters to his friends the Count de Bothmar and the Countess de Kilmansegg in the month of April, 1716, and in both of them he defends himself, and states that Bernoulli was the author of the letter accusing Newton of plagiarism. But Newton and Keill, in their correspondence *two years previously,* had been in no doubt that Bernoulli was the author; in fact, he was the only one who could have written it. If Leibniz's editor could do him such a turn, it is easy to imagine that Brewster totally misrepresents the incident and makes it seem as if Leibniz had publicly betrayed his friend. Furthermore, Bernoulli had so deeply involved himself in this controversy that he was not justified in keeping his opinion of Newton's plagiarism secret, if he really believed it.

clue to the authorship. It was not till a year later that the unlucky *meam* was called to his attention. Much chagrined, he desired Wolf to insert as an *erratum,* "for *meam* read *eam.*" As that was no refuge he finally, on the advice of de Montmort, employed his son Nicholas to get him out of the scrape. The son wrote to de Montmort that his father was annoyed by the rumour of his authorship. He admits that, at the request of a friend, he put down in writing the main facts contained in the letter, but the form of the letter was not his, but his friend's. Truly Leibniz was not blessed with friends as courageous as Newton's, who rushed eagerly into the fray and shielded him from all attacks.

Bernoulli's letter added fresh fuel to the wrath of the English. Keill, the avowed champion of Newton in this quarrel as Halley calls him, again dipped his pen in vitriol and prepared to hit back; but his answer was not published, and perhaps because of the following letter.

Newton to Keill

Dr. Keill,

I received about a month ago the inclosed letter from Mr. Montmort. It contains some extracts of letters to him from Mr. Bernoulli and his son. The chief point is that Mr. Bernoulli denies that he is the author of the Memoir entitled Epistola pro eminente, etc., that is inserted in the Acts of Leipzig 1716. The Memoir itself lays it upon Mr. Bernoulli by the words *meam solutionum* [sic, for *formulam*], and if Mr. Bernoulli is injured thereby it is not you but the author of the Memoir who has injured him. The injury is public and in justice requires a public satisfaction, not from you but from him that has done the injury. The question is therefore whether you will take notice of Mr. Bernoulli's excusing himself in private or leave him to do it in public. I have not yet returned any answer to Mr. Montmort, because I thought it best to stay till I had your sense upon this matter. I think to discourse also your friends Dr. English and Dr. Bower about it. I am

Your faithful friend and
humble Servant
ISAAC NEWTON.

London, 2 May, 1718.

[P.S.] I pray return Mr. Montmort's letter by Dr. Halley because I am to answer it.[61]

For Dr. John Keill, Professor of
Astronomy at Oxford.

[61] Edleston, p. 185.

As the dispute increased in bitterness and in its unscrupulous methods, the continental mathematicians showed an increasing distaste of the whole affair. Varignon and Montmort sympathised with Leibniz and disapproved strongly of the method and action of the Royal Society; but they both refused to commit themselves on the questions of priority of invention and of plagiarism; they thus kept both sides on the anxious seat.

Leibniz had not changed his original opinion that Newton had had the idea first of a method of solution by infinitesimals, or fluxions; but he had come to believe, largely I am convinced by the suggestions of Bernoulli, that Newton, when he developed the fluxions into a workable system of analysis, had used the information given in his own frank disclosures. A statement, in a letter from him to M. la Croze supports this opinion:[62] "M. Bernoulli, who knows the matter better than any one, and who is absolutely impartial, believes that M. Newton has invented his calculus later than mine, and in fact did not give any sign of it before. But I should not have contradicted his pretensions of having known it previously to my work, if he had not attacked me."

Newton, also, had been shaken from his early generous acknowledgement in the *Principia* of Leibniz's independent work by the insinuations of his friends till he, too, had become convinced of his rival's plagiarism. The best evidence of this exists in the six copies of a letter varying but slightly which I found in the *Portsmouth Collection*. This letter expresses his conviction that Leibniz got his information from a correspondence with Collins and Oldenburg.

Such a dispute was certain to beget mediators, but the uncompromising attitude of both the principals foredoomed their efforts to failure. Chamberlayne was the first to make the attempt, but he merely made matters worse. His plan was to interchange letters between Leibniz and Newton; whereupon, each of them merely declared his own innocence, and a perfect willingness to forgive the other, if he would withdraw his charge of plagiarism. One incident, which occurred during the negotiations of Chamberlayne, should be discussed.

After Chamberlayne had sent to Leibniz the decision of the Royal Society that it was not responsible for the Report of the Committee, Leibniz answered: "Since it seems that there are letters which con-

[62] This letter is to be found in a rare book entitled *Epistolae Leibnitii*, edited by Kortholtus, Lpzg. 1734, p. 449.

cern me, amongst them some of Mr. Oldenburg's and Mr. Collins's which have not been published, I desire the Royal Society to communicate them to me. For, when I return to Hanover, I also may publish a *Commercium Epistolicum,* which may add to literary history. I shall be disposed to publish the letters opposed to me as well as those which favour me. And I shall leave the judgement to the public."

This letter was read to the Society, but Newton represented that the statement was injurious to the honour of the Committee; that he, personally, had had no part in the *Commercium Epistolicum,* and had left complete liberty to the Committee in its choice and use of documents; that he had abstained from presenting two letters favourable to himself; and that he believed it would be improper for Mr. Leibniz to publish a *Commercium Epistolicum.* He added that it would be dangerous to send the originals of the letters demanded, but attested copies might be forwarded. Also, if Leibniz had any letters favourable to himself, he could send the originals to some of his English friends; they could then be examined by members of the Society, who knew the hand-writing, and be returned. He, lastly, proposed that these letters might be published in the *Philosophical Transactions,* or in Germany, as Mr. Leibniz might prefer.[63] There was not much chance, after such an uncompromising attitude by Newton, that Leibniz could expect any consideration, or justice, from the Society, or from the English.

The other mediator was the Abbé Conti, a Venetian nobleman, who visited England in 1715. He had had a correspondence with Leibniz on a philosophical question and, to a letter written at the end of the year, Leibniz added a long postscript reviewing his dispute with Newton. This postscript, or *Apostille,* begins sarcastically: "I am overjoyed that you are in England; you will profit by it as it is true that there are able men there; but they wish to pass as almost the only inventors and that is apparently what they will not succeed in doing."[64] He then reviews his claim of being, on the authority of

[63] Des Maizeaux *Recueil,* Vol. I, pp. lxxvii–lxxx and Vol. II, p. 188.—Leibniz never published a *Commercium Epistolicum.* But he prepared an answer to the charges against him that was apparently ready for the press but was not published because of his death. Gerhardt discovered the manuscript in the mass of papers preserved in the Royal Library of Hanover and published it in 1846. This *Historia et Origo Calculi Differentialis* has now been translated by Child into English, and included in his *Early Math. MSS. of Leibniz,* Open Court Pub. Co., 1920.

[64] The account of Conti's mediations and the correspondence relative to them is to be found in Des Maizeaux's *Recueil.*

Bernoulli, the first inventor of the calculus. He follows this up with an attack on Newton's conception of gravitation, of a vacuum, and of his idea of God. The note closes with a problem which he sent "to feel the pulse of our English analysts."

Leibniz's challenge excited a lively interest at the English Court. Conti, and other distinguished people, tried to induce Newton to reply, but they could not prevail against his aversion for personal contests. Finally, Newton requested Conti to assemble the foreign Ambassadors and Ministers in the rooms of the Royal Society. After they had examined the letters and documents in its archives, the Hanoverian Minister, the Count de Kilmansegg, said to Newton that this was not sufficient, as the way to end the quarrel was for him to write a letter personally to Leibniz. All the other Ministers approved the idea. Ten days later, Newton gave his answer, dated 26 February, 1715/16, and addressed to Conti, who forwarded it with a covering letter of his own. The King read and approved it, with the remark that the explanations were very simple and clear, and the facts difficult to answer.

Newton's defense is a long and temperate review of the entire dispute from the beginning, and ends with the statement that as Leibniz had been the aggressor, so he should prove his accusations. Leibniz answered what he termed the *Cartel de Défi* in a letter addressed to Conti on April 14, 1716. He was greatly provoked with Conti and wrote that "it was undoubtedly only a love of truth which induced you to concern yourself with a sort of challenge from Newton." The letter to Newton was a heated vindication of his own conduct, and he adopted a method of sending it calculated to wound Newton's susceptibilities most deeply. He sent his letters, and copies of Newton's and Conti's letters, to de Montmort to be read, and then to be forwarded to London, for the purpose as he cynically remarked that he might have "neutral and intelligent witnesses of our dispute."

The way of the peacemaker is proverbially difficult, and Conti's was no exception. He afterwards lamented that Leibniz had been deeply irritated against him; the Germans had reproached him; the French had turned against him. And to cap the climax Newton, in spite of the honour and respect shown to him, had changed his attitude, and now accused him of having instigated the quarrel with Leibniz.

The controversy died down as Newton, sick and weary of it, refused to be drawn into a further discussion. Leibniz, who had been suffering from gout which had gone from his feet into his hands and shoulders, was seized with a sharp attack and attempted to relieve it by taking a triple portion of a decoction recommended by a Jesuit at Ingolstadt. His constitution was too feeble to react, and he died suddenly on November 14th, 1716. The last act of Newton in this affair has been severely condemned by some, notably De Morgan, and excused by others. He wrote a reply to Leibniz's last letter, after his death, which he communicated only to some of his friends. "As soon as he learned of Leibniz's death, he had printed at London the Apostille and letter of Leibniz to Conti, his own letter to the Abbé, and his Remarks; he preceded the Remarks with a Preface where he explained the subject and the occasion."[65] These documents, which could not be answered, were given to Raphson who appended them to his *History of Fluxions.*

To conclude a long, and perhaps wearisome, discussion of this most famous of scientific disputes, two passages may be quoted from a letter of Rémond de Montmort to Brook Taylor, written December 18th, 1718, and which admirably sum up my own opinion: "I agree with you as to the merit of M. Newton. I always speak of him as a man above others, and that one cannot too much admire. But I cannot agree with your opinion that the public has received from M. Newton, and not from MM. Leibniz and Bernoulli, the new calculus and the art of making it serve in all the researches that have been made with it in geometry. That is an error of fact. It is unsustainable to say that MM. Leibniz and Bernoulli are not the true, and almost sole, promoters of this calculus. . . . There is nothing more beautiful, nor better of its kind, than the treatise *De Quadratura Curvarum* of M. Newton, but it appeared too late. The date of issue of this work is unfortunate, not for M. Newton, who has attained so much glory that the most ambitious man could not desire more, but for some Englishmen who seem to envy those who had discovered and published first these new methods which have so greatly advanced geometry."[66]

[65] Des Maizeaux *Recueil,* Vol. I, p. lxxxvi.
[66] Brewster, Vol. II, p. 511, and Biot et Lefort, p. 248. A copy of it is in the *Portsmouth Collection.*

CHAPTER XVI

ANCIENT CHRONOLOGY. THEOLOGY. RELIGIOUS BELIEFS

THE historical and theological work of Newton has been slighted and considered to have been of little importance,—even often condemned as a waste of effort. Yet, if we can judge from the amount of time he spent upon it, and the care with which he preserved it, Newton himself must have regarded it as of major importance; even to the point of stating that the chief value of his scientific work lay in its support of revealed religion. The commanding position which he holds as a scientific thinker necessarily affects our judgement of his achievement in other fields; we unconsciously adopt too severe a standard of criticism, and condemn work by him which by another would receive our commendation. We have progressed so much further in our knowledge of archæology and ancient history, and have so shifted our sympathy from the religious questions which occupied the seventeenth and eighteenth century thinkers, that the positive value of his work in those fields is almost negligible. Yet we must estimate Newton as one of the foremost chronologists of his day, and as one who laid the foundations for later scholars. Nor can we dismiss his theological work as trifling as is done so lightly by scientists. He discussed the questions which were then of true importance, and he was regarded as an erudite theologian. In proof of his reputation, Conduitt states[1] in his intended life of his uncle that "Archbishop Tenison offered him, if he would take orders, the Mastership of Trinity College when it was given to Montague, and importuned him to accept any preferment in the Church; saying to him: 'Why will you not? You know more divinity than all of us put together.' Why then, said Newton, 'I shall be able to do you more service than if I was in orders.'" In the minds of his contemporaries, I think, his work was looked upon as important in trying to replace the authority of the Roman Church by

[1] *Portsmouth Collection.*

the authority of the Bible, and to counteract the sceptics who were beginning to question its miracles and prophecies.

When we turn to the consideration of this work as a phase of Newton's personal life, and as a criterion of his interest and character, then history and divinity play most important rôles. It is altogether probable that ancient history and theology were constantly in his thoughts from youth to extreme old age. He was brought up in a religious atmosphere; it is likely that he went to Cambridge with the expectation of being ordained and of being appointed to a rural parish. And from such a career he was diverted, apparently, by the discovery of his mathematical and scientific genius, and by a certain intellectual leaning towards Arianism and unorthodox Protestantism.

While the world will always regard his scientific work as an end in itself, he seems always to have felt it was a hard and dreary taskmaster, and not of intrinsic value except as it should give evidence of the laws and attributes of God. It is altogether a mistake to suppose that his interest in religion served as a relaxation for his mind when exhausted by his scientific studies. He read constantly in history and theology, and he must steadily have made notes, or have turned the corners of the pages of his books in his peculiar manner, in no other way could he have left such a mass of papers on those subjects. It is true, he told Conduitt that his studies in chronology were the work of his vacant hours and a relief from his scientific studies, and this is true in the sense that he loved to disentangle complicated numerical puzzles, but he read persistently in theology and especially after he had forsaken science. He wrote draught after draught of many of his papers for the sheer love of noting down his meditations, nor was this labour undertaken to prepare them for publication.

As his great achievements in science were ascribed to the sane balance of an extraordinarily fertile imagination and a passion for practical handicraft or experimentation,—a balance which checked either from dominating the other;—so, also, the same characteristics are to be found in his historical and theological work. Attention has already been drawn to his early dominant traits, his solitary meditation and his passion for constructing toys, and they were mentioned then as the source of his future power. Later, his introduction to his great enquiry into the nature of light grew out of his practical work in grinding lenses. If he had followed the custom of scientists he would at once have proposed an hypothesis to explain the cause of light; but, even as a youth, while he may have pictured in his mind metaphysical æthers and corpuscles as causes of phenomena, he refrained from incorporating them in his finished essays. The same is true of his work on gravitation; his imagination again led him to picture a sort of universal and æthereal cause; but such ideas he considered to be only Queries outside his search for scientific law based on experimental observation. Thus, this restraining balance prevented his imagination from sweeping him into the scientific mysticism which has so dominated the minds of Professor Einstein and his school. To Newton the universe was an objective reality, whose phenomena and laws we could to a limited extent verify and establish; to them it is a mental phantasmagoria as foreign to experience as were the mediævalists' conceptions of heaven.

On the other hand Newton's imagination lifted his manipulation out of the rut of mere statistical observations. For pleasure and relaxation, he made an astonishing number of chemical manipulations. His curiosity led him into the most unexpected fields; one of his most surprising ventures is entered in the Journal Books of the Royal Society: "Newton mentioned a remarkable experiment he made, formerly in Trinity College kitchen at Cambridge, upon the heart of an eel which he cut into three pieces, and observed every one of them beat at the same instant and interval: putting spittle upon any of the sections had no effect, but a drop of vinegar utterly extinguished its motion."[2] But such observations were made for the pleasure of satisfying his boundless curiosity; when he was engaged in systematic experimentation, like Galileo, "he said that he first proved his inventions by geometry and only made use of experiments to make them intelligible, and to convince the vulgar."[3] And his youthful skill with tools proved to be a major factor in making him one of the great experimentalists. When Conduitt once enquired of him where he got his tools with which to make his telescope, he answered that he made them himself, and laughingly answered: "If I had stayed for other people to make my tools and things for me I had never made anything of it. The only help I had in those operations was from my next chamber fellow who was stronger than I and used to help me on with my kettle sometimes, for he had several furnaces in his own chambers for chemical experiments."[4]

So also Newton's imagination tempted him to explore the mys-

[2] Edleston, p. lix.

[3] Conduitt's intended life of Newton, *Ports. Coll.*

[4] *Ibid.*

teries of alchemy; made him sympathetic with the mysticism of Boehme and of the Camisards; and led him to enquire into the doctrine of the Trinity, the prophecies of Daniel, and of the Apocalypse. If we were to look for other examples of this combination of religious fervour and scientific caution, we should find it best exemplified in Kepler and Pascal. Of the three only Pascal and Newton could balance those two mastering forces and Newton's colder and more cautious nature alone could stand the strain. Religious mysticism might tempt him, but in the end he strove to prove by facts the authority of the Bible. If we keep in mind that he was essentially a Protestant and constantly sought to prove the usurpation of authority by the Roman Church, we shall find the cause of his chronological and theological work, and realise that he was one of the chief actors in the acute conflict in England between Protestantism and Romanism.

Newton may have lightly spoken of his work in chronology and divinity as a pastime for his vacant hours, and as a relaxation when mentally fatigued; but no one who follows his thought can fail to recognise that he was deeply read in the Bible, in the Christian literature, and in the classical authors; and the catalogue of his library[5] shows that it was rich in theological and classical works. We can be certain that he acquired these books for use as he was not one to spend money for show. And we may be pretty certain that he read such authors for historical information rather than for literary pleasure.

We can easily dispose of Biot's opinion that Newton's religious and historical work is to be dated after what he calls "the disastrous epoch of 1695" when his nervous break-down had produced an aberration of the intellect and "his mind, fatigued by long and painful efforts, had need of complete and entire repose. At least we know, that thenceforward he only occupied his leisure with religious studies, or sought relief in literature or in business."[6] Against such a guess there is need only to place his own statement that he employed his leisure in such studies during his whole life. However little value they may have in comparison with his scientific work they are not the fruit of a morbid state of mind. He did not turn to religion as a solace from discouragement or from fear, but cultivated it steadily

[5] R. de Villamil. *Newton: the Man.*

[6] Biot, p. 37. Newton's correspondence with Locke proves that his most important religious work was completed in 1690. And it will be shown later that he was discussing the prophetic books with Henry More in 1680.

because he believed it to be the noblest occupation of the mind. His estimate of the comparative values of science and religion is best shown by the fact that he considered his *Principia* and *Optics* to be useful since they had helped to make manifest the laws of God, and had revealed His nature. The failure to publish his theological and historical work is no evidence of its time of composition or of his opinion of its importance, as his dislike of criticism and of contention would operate even more strongly in such controversial subjects than in the more impersonal field of science.

The history of the events leading up to the publication of Newton's chronological summary of ancient times is a curious one, and it exemplifies the trouble which his dilatoriness caused him. After the accession of George I, the Princess of Wales, Caroline of Anspach, carried her interest in philosophy from Hanover, and created a salon in the English Court. She set aside one evening a week to the discussion of philosophical questions and Newton became a frequent and welcome guest at the Court. In fact, Caroline seems to have transferred her favour from Leibniz to him, and to have declared herself fortunate in having lived in an age which had produced so illustrious a man. These discussions centred on the mechanistic philosophy of the *Principia* which was warmly espoused by Dr. Samuel Clarke and Bishop Hoadly, and as strongly attacked by the idealists, Bishops Berkeley and Sherlock.

One day the Princess and Newton discussed the education of her children, and he was led to explain to her a new system of ancient chronology which he had devised during his Cambridge days. The Royal Lady was so pleased with the ingenuity of the plan that she asked for a copy of the work. As it existed only in loose papers which were incomplete, and in a state of confusion, he promised in a few days to draw up an abstract for her private use. This manuscript was entitled *A Short Chronicle from the First Memory of Things in Europe to the Conquest of Persia by Alexander the Great*[7] and some time after, at the request of the Princess, Newton permitted the Abbé Conti to make a copy, but with the distinct promise that it should be kept strictly private as it probably contained some errors.

In spite of his promise, Conti loaned the manuscript to several persons in Paris as soon as he left England. Amongst others, it was given to Freret, a learned chronologist and antiquary, who translated it into

[7] It was not intended for publication; but it was later prefixed to Conduitt's edition of Newton's *Chronology* published in 1728, and also to Horsley's *Op. Omnia Newtoni*, Vol. V, pp. 265–291.

French, and added a commentary for the purpose of refuting some of its principal results. Newton seems to have been quite ignorant of this breach of faith for some years, and to have been taken quite by surprise by a letter in 1724 from Cavelier, a book-seller in Paris.

Cavelier to Newton

à Paris le 11me May 1724.

il m'est tombé en main un petit manuscrit que l'on assure venire de vous, Monsieur, comme votre nom est tres estimé par toute l'Europe jay voulu le faire imprimer, mais l'on me assuré quil y avait des fautes et que cela pouvait vous faire de la peine de le voir paraitre sans votre illustre nom ce qui fait que je prens la liberté de m'adresse a vous et de vous prier, Monsieur comme le manuscript que jay est peu de choses, de vouloir bien me marquer, si vous pouviez m'en faire tenire une copie corecte *de votre Chronologie* plusieurs personnes qui en ont des copies defectueuses seront bien aises de'n avoir de correctes et moy Libraire qui ne cherches que de bonnes choses suis persuadé quil ny a rien de meilleur que ce qui part de votre plume j'afens L'honneur de votre reponse et suis avec un profond respec

Monsieur Votre tres humble et tres
obeissant serviteur
G. Cavelier fils Libraire
rue S. Jacques.[8]

Newton, unfortunately for his later peace of mind, took no notice of this request. About a year later, Cavelier wrote a second time to warn him that a failure to answer would be taken as a tacit consent to publish the manuscript in the French translation, and with the comments of Freret. When he found that Newton paid no attention to a direct appeal, he finally, by the aid of a friend in London, obtained the following answer.

Newton to Cavelier

I remember that I wrote a chronological index for a particular friend, on condition that it should not be communicated. As I have not seen the MS. which you have under my name, I know not whether it be the same. That which I wrote was not at all done with

[8] This letter and a later one of Cavelier's were preserved by Newton. I have given the above verbatim from the original in the *Ports. Coll.*

the design to publish it. I intend not to meddle with that which hath been given you under my name, nor to give any consent to the publishing of it.—I am, your very humble servant,

Is. Newton.[9]

London, May 27th, 1725 St. Vet.

But the refusal of consent, whether it would have had any effect or not is a question, was received too late as the tract was already published[10] and a copy was sent to the exasperated author. When Newton received this work he published a reply in the Philosophical Transactions.[11] In this paper, he quite rightly charged Conti with a breach of faith which had greatly embarrassed him; and with less justice blamed the printer. He then defended his chronological system against the criticisms of Freret. We must believe that Brewster thought it unnecessary for a biographer to make himself acquainted with the subject of ancient chronology. To him it was sufficient that Newton had been criticised and he merely remarked, "To all the observations of M. Freret, Sir Isaac returned a triumphant answer." We may greatly admire Newton's labour and ingenuity in assigning dates, and in explaining so imposing a number of legendary and historical incidents; but, as will be shown later, the results he obtained are practically worthless. Since both chronologists, as did all others of the day, accepted the Mosaic account of the creation and placed it some 4000 years B. C., they necessarily had to compress the whole unrecorded and recorded history of man, and also of the earth, within that period. A single example will suffice to prove that, as both chronologists were hopelessly wrong, it would be an act of supererogation to compare their excellence: Newton calculates the important event of the Argonautic expedition in Greek history as occurring in 937 B. C.; Freret assigns the same event to the year 1469 B. C.; while modern research places it about 1200 B. C. Newton's defense closed with a bitter complaint against Conti who, he charged, treacherously to befriend Leibniz had first engaged him in philosophical and mathematical quarrels and since then "what he hath been doing in Italy may be understood by the disputes raised there by one of his friends [Rizzetti] who denies many of my optical experiments, though they have been all tried in France with suc-

[9] Brewster, Vol. II, p. 303.

[10] It was entitled: *Abrégé de Chronologie de M. Le Chevalier Newton, fait par lui-même, et traduit sur le manuscript Anglois*. Paris, 1725. I have not seen a copy of this tract.

[11] *Remarks on the Observations made on a Chronological Index of Sir Isaac Newton, translated into French by the Observator, and published at Paris. Phil. Trans.*, 1725.

cess; but I hope that these things and the perpetual motion[?] will be the last efforts of this kind."

The Nemesis of contention dogged Newton to the very end of his life, for Father Souciet attacked his new chronology in five most virulent dissertations. Although Newton was now eighty-one years old and was suffering from attacks of stone, gout, and inflammation of the lungs, he set himself resolutely to the work of preparing his chronology in proper form for the press. Although he finished this work of 376 quarto pages in less than three years, it was, after his death, left to his nephew, Conduitt, to publish with a dedication to Queen Caroline.[12] Conduitt was not a practical writer and he was perturbed with the responsibility of "ushering into the world, under Your Sacred Name, the last work of as great a Genius as any age ever produced." In his trouble, he turned for advice to Pope, whom he had met at the house of a Mrs. Howard, because "anything connected with that great man concerns the whole world and the honour of the nation." The poet criticised the dedication in a most urbane and tactful manner. His principal caution was not to overdo the praise of Royalty for "it takes very much from the praise of Sir I. N., and I fear unjustly, to imagine that any Prince's reign can *make* Newtons, however it might *encourage* or *admire* them." The letter closes with this fine and just tribute: "I could wish it were enlarged with some memoirs and character of him, as a private man. I doubt not his life and manners would make a great discovery of virtue and goodness and rectitude of heart, as his works have done of penetration and the utmost stretch of human knowledge."

Except to the person inquisitive about the intellectual movements of the eighteenth century, or to one especially interested in the life of Newton, the *Chronology Amended* is hardly worth reading since its positive value is very slight. In six chapters the author tabulates with a descriptive comment the important events in the early history of Greece, Egypt, Assyria, Babylonia, and Persia, and describes the Temple of Solomon.

Our modern archæological discoveries, defective as they still may be, have carried our knowledge of the recorded history of ancient civilisations so far back in years; and our conviction, that a slow course of many millennia was necessary to advance primitive peoples to a state recorded civilisation, has so changed our point of view

12 *The Chronology of Antient Kingdoms Amended.* Printed for J. Tonson. London, 1728. Horsley also included it in his edition of the *Opera Omnia,* Vol. V.

as to make the chronologies of Newton and his contemporaries practically useless.

To the scholars of his time, there were two fixed events which served as definite starting dates. From the genealogical tables in the Old Testament it was possible, with the ingenious exercise of the imagination, to establish the date of the creation of the world. The year 4004 B. C., as calculated by Bishop Ussher, was universally accepted in England as the beginning of things and was early adopted in the King James Version of the Bible.[13] The other date was that of the Deluge, 1656 years later or 2348 B. C., when the human race, after that drastic eugenic experiment, began again from the family of Noah.[14] Now Newton[15] accepts the account of the early history of mankind given in the Old Testament as accurate. From casual mention of foreigners inserted in Jewish history; from a careful examination of classical authors, and from vague astronomical data, he was able by cross references to build up a consistent chronology of the other great ancient kingdoms which in his opinion was accurate. So certain of his ground was he, that he closed his introduction with the *modest* statement: "I have drawn up the following chronological table, so as to make chronology suit with the course of nature, with astronomy, with sacred history, with Herodotus the Father of History, and with itself; without the many repugnancies complained of by Plutarch. I do not pretend to be exact to a year: there may be errors of five or ten years, and sometimes twenty, and not much above."[16] Alas, for the complacency of the human mind, his errors are more often to be measured in centuries or millennia.

Newton, quite rightly I think, gave a historical background to many of the legends of heroes and gods, but the following example will be sufficient to show that he could not distinguish between myths and history: "1035, B. C. Erectheus reigns in Attica. Aethlius, the

[13] The chronology of Bishop Ussher was published in his *Annales Veteris et Novi Testamenti* (1650–1654), and the dates there determined have been inserted in the later editions of the Authorised, or King James, Version.

[14] There are three genealogical tables in the Old Testament. I have followed in my calculations the numbers of the Hebrew text, rather than those of the Samaritan or the LXX texts, as I believe it was the one used by Newton. The period between the Creation and the Flood differs widely in the three texts; 1656, 1307, and 2242 years, respectively.

[15] I wish to acknowledge my thanks to my colleague, Dr. Allen West, Professor of Ancient History in the University of Cincinnati, who was kind enough to examine the *Chronology Amended,* to unravel the complexities of Newton's system, and to compare his deductions with those of modern scholarship. Without this generous aid I should have hesitated to present this critique.

[16] P. 8, or p. 7. The first page references are to Conduitt's edition and the second to Horsley's.

grandson of Deucalion and father of Endymion, builds Elis. The Idaei Dactyli find out iron in Mount Ida in Crete, and work it into armour and iron tools, and thereby make a beginning to the trades of smiths and armourers in Europe; and by singing and dancing in their armour, and keeping time by striking upon one another's armour with their swords, they bring in music and poetry; and at the same time they nurse up the Cretan Jupiter in a cave of the same mountain, dancing about him in their armour."[17]

With the assumption of the historical accuracy of the Book of Genesis, Newton was able to fix from its genealogical tables a date from which he could reckon the whole history of every nation. The time of the scattering of the human race, after the Deluge, is determined from the account in Genesis, Chapter XI, of the abortive attempt of the descendants of Noah to dwell permanently together in the land of Shinar: "All mankind lived together in Chaldaea under the government of Noah and his sons, until the days of Peleg: so long they were of one language, one society, and one religion: and then they divided the earth, being perhaps disturbed by the rebellion of Nimrod, and forced to leave off building the tower of Babel: and from thence they spread themselves into the several countries which fell to their shares, carrying along with them the laws, customs, and religion, under which they had till those days been educated, and governed, by Noah, and his sons and grandsons."[18]

It was also easy to calculate the date of Abraham's birth. Taking the Deluge as 2348 B. C. and Shem to be 100 years of age at that time, then Peleg, the fourth generation in descent, was born 99 years later or 2249 B. C.; and the five succeeding generations of 191 years to Abraham fix the date of his birth in 2058 B. C.

Having established to his satisfaction that the first spread of mankind over the earth had happened not long before the time of Abraham, Newton could assume that the population of the various countries was small. And he found confirmation of his opinion in Exodus I, 9 and 22, which he paraphrased as follows: "Pharaoh[19] said of the Israelites; behold the people of the children of Israel are more and mightier than we: and to prevent their multiplying and growing too strong, he caused their male children to be drowned."[20]

17 P. 14, or p. 11.

18 P. 186, or p. 139.

19 The Pharaoh of the Jewish captivity has been positively identified with Rameses II, the Sesostris of the Greeks. His date is about 1350 B.C. As we shall see later, Newton identifies Sesostris with Sesac who reigned in the time of Rehoboam, he thus makes the son of Solomon contemporary with Moses.

20 P. 186, or p. 139.

If Egypt was thus sparsely inhabited, he could take it for granted that Greece also was occupied only by nomad tribes, especially as he accepted Herodotus's statement that Cadmus, with a small band of Phœnicians, had a large share in the settling and civilisation of Greece. He then, from references to Egyptians and other foreign persons mentioned in the Bible, fixed certain dates in the histories of those countries. And, from similar instances in Greek history, he drew up a comparative table in which he attempted to make a synthesis of ancient legends, to explain chronological discrepancies, and to bring secular history into conformity with Biblical tradition.

Although Newton agreed with other chronologers in assigning three generations to a century, he thought he had discovered their chief source of error in the fact that many of the dates are stated in terms of the length of the reigns of successive kings and "by the ordinary course of nature kings reign, one with another, about eighteen or twenty years apiece."[21] To prove this point, he listed all the reigns of ancient kings, and also those of France and England, and so determined eighteen to twenty years to be what he can call the average length of a reign. Thus, he believed that chronologers, by taking the length of a reign to equal the longer period of an average generation, had lengthened the lapse of time by about one-third.

Also Newton believed that chronologies had been greatly lengthened by duplication of persons. For example; tradition records two rulers with the name of Minos; by assuming them to be the same person, one generation is struck out. In order to compress by this means the long histories of the Greeks and Egyptians within the fixed Biblical dates, he is led into deep water. One of the most remarkable instances of the historical confusion so introduced is the protean form he gives to Sesac. He starts with the statement in 2d Chronicles, XII, 2, "that in the fifth year of King Rehoboam, Shishak king of Egypt came up against Jerusalem." This king's name is elsewhere spelled Sesac, and Newton places him as the second king of Egypt. And, apparently, for no other reason than that the first syllables of their names are spelled the same, he is identified with Sesostris, mentioned by Herodotus and known to us as Senusret, who ruled in Egypt more than a thousand years before the time of Sesac and Rehoboam.[22] By this simple and effective method he makes the

21 P. 52, or p. 39.

22 This identification of Sesac and Sesostris was not original with Newton as he cites Josephus and the great English chronologer, Sir John Marsham, as authorities for his merger of these two into one.

beginning of the dynastic history of Egypt contemporaneous with the reign of Solomon.

Not content with this slight discrepancy of a thousand years, he proceeds to make Sesac-Sesostris a name to conjure with, and by him to correlate Greek and Egyptian history by the following ingenious identification: "Osiris, Bacchus, and Sesostris lived about the same time, and by the relation of historians were all of them kings of all Egypt, and reigned at Thebes, and adorned that city, and were very potent by land and sea: all three were great conquerors, and carried on their conquests by land through Asia, as far as India: all three came over the Hellespont, and were there in danger of losing their army: all three conquered Thrace, and there put a stop to their victories, and returned back from thence into Egypt: all three left pillars with inscriptions in their conquests: and therefore all three must be one and the same King of Egypt; and this King can be no other than Sesac."[23] But the ubiquitous Sesac had still other uses, as he also becomes a son of Jupiter-Ammon. By these means, Newton telescoped more than two millennia of Egyptian history into a single generation.

Sesac-Osiris also is the link connecting up Greek history since all legends regarding Dionysus or Sesac-Bacchus can now be dated in the reign of the Biblical Sesac, or between 1002 and 956 B. C. The sons of Dionysus and Ariadne were the Argonauts, and their famous expedition is thus placed one generation later than Sesac. As Dionysus loved a woman named Venus, who became the mistress of Anchises and the mother of Æneas, the fall of Troy occurred not long after the Argonautic expedition. And since Ariadne was the daughter of Minos of Crete, his date is also settled. To make confusion worse confounded, Sesac is finally merged with Ægyptus, and so becomes the brother of Danaus and the grandson of Io, who turns out to be no other than the Egyptian goddess Isis. But Isis was certainly the wife of Osiris and so must be also his grandmother. And Epaphus, the son of Io, turns out to be no other than the father of Sesac-Ægyptus, yet Newton also identifies Epaphus with Sesac.

By such devious devices, Newton dates the capture of Troy in 904 B. C., despite the fact that ancient writers placed it about 1200 B. C., an approximate date now generally accepted. One more example will suffice. The first dynastic king of Egypt, supposed to have founded Memphis, was called Menes by the Greeks; Newton con-

[23] P. 193, or p. 144.

fuses him with Amenophis or Memnon, who is probably Amenhotep III, a ruler some 2000 years or more later.

Besides these methods of constructing his calendar, Newton thought he had confirmed the date of his Menes-Amenophis by an astronomical method.[24] The Egyptian year of 365 days was divided into twelve lunar months, to which were added five extra days dedicated to five gods. In the temple of Menes-Amenophis, there was a golden circle divided into 365 equal parts, and on it were noted day by day the heliacal risings and settings of the stars. Newton, from this legend, conjectured that the solar calendar was established "in the reign of Ouranus, or Ammon, the father of Sesac," who ruled shortly before Amenophis. Since this calendar year is about six hours shorter than the true solar year, the New Year's day moves backward one day in every four years. This year of 365 days was later adopted in Babylonia in 747 B. C., the first year of the so-called era of Nabonassar, and the New Year began on February 26th of the old Roman Calendar. If, as Newton was convinced, the era of Amenophis began on the vernal equinox, or thirty-three days later, then the date of Amenophis becomes 884 B. C. But it has since been discovered that the Egyptian astronomers chose July 20th, the constant date of the heliacal rising of Sirius, to initiate the new calendar, instead of the March 22d, the vernal equinox, so his calculations are quite erroneous. According to Breasted the calendar of 365 days was introduced into Egypt in 4241 B. C., some 3400 years earlier than Newton's calculation.

Newton made use of another astronomical calculation, the precession of the equinox, in order to establish his chronology.[25] Chiron, he says,[26] was a practical astronomer and mapped the stellar sphere to aid the Argonauts during their long and perilous voyage. According to this map, he claimed that the "points of the equinoxes and solstices were [then] in the middles of the constellations of Aries, Cancer, Chelae, and Capricorn." He then from the positions of these

[24] For Newton's discourse on ancient astronomy, *cf.* pp. 71–94, or pp. 55–75.

[25] The Greek astronomer, Hipparchus, was the first to note that the sun arrived at the equinox a little earlier each year. According to the observations of Flamsteed this annual precession amounts to 50″ of arc which agrees very closely with the present accepted value. Newton had discovered its principal cause to be the moon's attraction on the earth's equatorial belt which makes the pole of the earth to describe a slow circle. At the rate of 50″ a year it takes the pole 25920 years to make the complete circuit, and evidently in that period the calendar gains a year. Thus, if we observe the equinoctial point in the constellations at two different times we can measure the precession and if we know one of the dates the other can be calculated on the basis of 50″ per year.

[26] P. 83, or p. 64.

points in the year 1689 A. D. found that the equinox was gone back 36°, 44′ which, at the annual rate of 50″, is equivalent to a lapse of 2646 years. Thus, the date of the Argonauts would be 956 B. C. Because of the coarse observations of the ancients, he introduced various corrections till he made the date agree with his former statement of 937 B. C., or twenty-five years after Solomon. But, as the correct date is approximately 1260 B. C., we must accept the opinion of modern astronomers that the astronomical observations recorded before Hipparchus are too vague to be used as a basis for chronology.[27]

	NEWTON	MYRES
Deucalion and the Flood	ca. 1045	ca. 1430
Cadmus comes to Greece	1045	1400
Erechtheus reigns in Athens	1033	1360
Minos reigns in Crete	1015– 964	1230
Io	1047	1530
Œdipus	958	1260
Argonauts	937	1260
Trojan War	904	1200

It must be evident that Newton's long labour on his chronology was thrown away if we consider its practical value, but it is important as evidence of his love of calculating and fitting together the pieces of a puzzle. If he had lived today, he might have solaced his vacant hours by omnivorous reading of detective stories, or by working cross-word puzzles, instead of ancient chronologies and Biblical prophecies. It is a similar example of his youthful confession of having calculated the area of a hyperbola to fifty-two decimal places. His love of detailed work, and of drawing, is also shown by his devoting Chapter V of his *Chronology* to an elaborate description, with three detailed plates, of Solomon's Temple. I shall omit any comment on this work except to note an anecdote of Dr. Stukeley which I discovered in the *Portsmouth Papers.* Dr. Stukeley relates that he discoursed with Newton on Christmas (1720) about Solomon's Temple: "He says it was older than any other great temple. From this model Sesostris built his temples in Egypt and from thence the Greeks borrowed their architecture and religion." With this last example of confusion introduced by Sesac-Sesostris-Osiris, *et al.,* I shall leave the subject.

Newton's interpretation of the prophecies of Daniel and of the

27 I have as an illustration of the errors of Newton's system made a comparative table of his dates with those given in Mr. Myres's, *Who were the Greeks?*

Apocalypse brings out even more clearly his mystical tendencies, and his love of practical details, than does his chronology. In his interpretations of mystical and prophetic writers, he sought to verify their vague statements by intricate chronological tables and to support their philosophy by mathematical analysis. There is sufficient contemporaneous evidence for this opinion. William Law, the author of *The Serious Call,* stated that Newton "did but reduce to mathematical form the central principles of nature revealed in Behmen."[28] Henry More thought he was misled in his interpretation of Daniel by his mathematical genius.[29] And there is also the anecdote of his anger when Bentley accused him of expounding the prophecies, as he would demonstrate a mathematical proposition.[30] It seems to us an utter waste of time to try to interpret the symbolism of the Biblical writers as a prediction of future events. Modern scholarship has proved conclusively that such books were written during times of political disruption and conquest. They narrated the past history and sufferings of the Jews under their conquerors in order to keep up their national spirit, and to encourage them by foretelling the advent of a Messianic ruler who would institute a reign of spiritual righteousness and restore their ancient power. These chronicles were disguised in symbolic language because it would not have been safe to mention such matters openly.

We also have grown to be lax in seeking for any religious authority, but in Newton's time the effort to replace the authority of the Roman Church by that of the Bible was an all important question. The growth of science and, especially, Newton's own work were fostering a critical examination of Biblical miracles and natural history; and the English had entered upon a period of scepticism and irreligion as a reaction against the rigors of the Commonwealth. To meet the unanswerable attacks on the literal revelation of the Bible as a whole, the belief was gaining ground that only those parts necessary to salvation were infallible, and that they had been expressed so clearly as to enable any enquiring mind to understand them. The attempt was also being made to use the mechanistic philosophy of Newton's *Principia* as a proof of God's revelation by the establishment of natural law. The leaders of the Church of England, and such men as Locke and Newton, accepted the Scriptures as a divine revelation and remained professing churchmen; while they might

28 Conway Letters. Ed. by Nicolson. Oxford, 1930, p. 381 n.
29 *Ibid.*, p. 479.
30 Whiston, *Memoirs*, p. 107.

question the authenticity of some passages, they withstood the attacks of the then obscure Deists who denied the truth of miracles as being contrary to the invariability of natural law. But, the fact is, Newton and Locke gave a much greater impulse to modern mechanistic naturism than did the professed Deists, for their philosophy was adopted by Voltaire and the French philosophers of the eighteenth century and, through them, the mechanistic evolutionists of the nineteenth century transmitted to us our rejection of all knowledge not based on the scientific method of sense perception.[31]

Thus Newton, who was essentially a Protestant and who was also heterodox enough to be classed as an Arian and therefore sceptical concerning the doctrine of the Trinity, would still find deep satisfaction in reconciling the prophecies with future history. By that means he would strengthen his belief in the authority of the Bible at least so far as spiritual miracles were concerned. There is no doubt that his profound belief in the rigor of natural law must have made him doubt many of the natural miracles of the Old Testament. A note, which is preserved in the *Portsmouth Papers* and which apparently has not been published, is almost conclusive evidence of his scepticism:

"For miracles are so called not because they are the works of God but because they happen seldom and for that reason create wonder. If they should happen constantly according to certain laws impressed upon the nature of things, they would be no longer wonders or miracles but might be considered in philosophy as a part of the phenomena of nature [notwithstanding their being the effects of the laws impressed upon nature by the powers of God] notwithstanding that the cause of their causes might be unknown to us."[32]

Newton's boyhood had been passed in a religious atmosphere; and, from the evidence of the verses on King Charles, which he at least preserved even if he may not have been their author, we should suppose that he, and his family, were High Church and Royalist in sympathy. But there were two influences which would exercise a

[31] This indirect influence of Newton's mechanistic philosophy, which he would have scorned, is too intricate to be treated here; but I hope in a future work to show that it is the dominant factor in our present philosophy of life.

[32] This note was most carefully written and interlined with corrections. It was apparently to be used in combating Leibniz's charge of the irreligious tendencies of the *Principia*. The passage in brackets was written and then crossed. Newton's explanation of natural miracles can hardly be considered orthodox.

great effect on his growing mind. He lived in the heart of Cromwell's country, and he must have listened to many advocates of the Protestant movement; also the feeling of Cambridge was much less Royalist in sympathy than at Oxford. At all events, he became a confirmed Whig and anti-Romanist. We may suppose that his friendship with the young Charles Montague affected his sympathies; but we can ascribe the principal causes of his change of opinions to the moral laxity of Charles II, which would deeply shock him, and to the steady drift of the Stuarts to the Roman Church. At all events, the attempt of James II to bring the Universities to tolerate, at least, that faith aroused in him such unqualified opposition as to make him take the leading part in refusing to obey the King's mandate to give a degree to Fr. Alban, and to represent the University in the Convention Parliament. From that time, his steady adherence to the Whig party and to the Anglican Church was summarised in the gibe that he accepted his politics and his religion without doubt or question. No opinion could have less accurately described him. No subject occupied his thoughts more than religion and, while he was critical of some of the tenets of the Church of England and a rather lax attendant on public worship, he evidently felt that it and the Whigs were the strongest bulwarks against the encroachments of Rome. If the fear of Rome so affected his religion, it was entirely consistent for him to be a Whig as that party was committed to the Protestant Church and opposed to the restoration of the Stuarts. His opposition to Rome was so strong that, fearing the effect of Jacobite plots at the accession of George I, he drew up the following declaration against the Roman Catholics which was evidently intended to be circulated and presented to Parliament:

"Whereas of late years some opinions have been propagated by superstitious men among the Christians of the Church of England which tend to incline those of the Church of England to break all communion and friendship with the Protestant Churches abroad and to return into the communion of the Church of Rome; such as are the opinions that the Church of Rome is a true Church without allowing her to be a false Church in any respect, and that the Protestant Churches abroad are false Churches and that they have no baptism and by consequence are no Christians, and that the Church of England is in danger, meaning by the succession of the House of Hanover. . . ."[33]

[33] *Portsmouth Collection.*

This introduction should make clear Newton's purpose in his study of the prophetic books of the Bible. Before considering his work I shall sketch the modern interpretation of the Book of Daniel.

It is generally agreed amongst Biblical scholars that Daniel is the most important, and most easily understood, of the apocalyptic books. It describes the historical events of the four captivities of the Jews by the Babylonians, the Medes, the Persians, and the Greeks, disguised as visions in symbolic language. It was written by a single author during the reign of Antiochus Epiphanes and, probably, in 165 B. C. Of the successors of Alexander the Great, Antiochus Epiphanes of the Seleucid Dynasty was the bitterest oppressor of the Jews; he had despoiled the Temple, thereby committing "the abomination of desolation," and was attempting vigorously to stamp out their religion. In this desperate state of the nation, the purpose of the prophet was to enhearten the people by showing that, as the troubles of the three former conquests had passed away, so also would this bitterest of all, the Greek domination. And if they would have courage and faith, they could expect a Messianic, or spiritual Kingdom of great power and glory.

The scene of the Book is set during the third year of the reign of Jehoiakim in the sixth century, B. C. Nebuchadnezzar, king of Babylonia, had conquered Jerusalem and had carried off some of the golden vessels of the Temple and many captives, among whom were Daniel and three other noble youths. Daniel rises to great favour with the king by interpreting his dream of a great image whose head was of gold, his breast and arms of silver, his belly and thighs of brass, his legs of iron and his feet part of iron and part of clay. And a stone cut without hands smote the feet of the image and broke them. Later Daniel, himself, has a vision of four ravening beasts, each more terrible than the former. Without going into details, Daniel interprets both dreams as foretelling successive conquests by the Babylonians under Nebuchadnezzar and his son Belshazzar; by the Medes under Darius; by the Persians under Cyrus; and by the Greeks under Alexander, and his successors of the Seleucid Dynasty. The author finally predicts the success of the insurrection of the Maccabees in 167 B. C. but he does not mention the re-dedication of the Temple in 165, nor the death of Antiochus in 163, and thus establishes the date of the composition with approximate accuracy. The portion of the book which describes the Greek conquest and, especially, the events of the reign of Antiochus Epiphanes is exact and detailed, but there are several serious errors in the narrative of the earlier events. For example, there is no record of a Babylonian conquest in the third year of Jehoiakim; Belshazzar was neither the son of Nebuchadnezzar nor a ruler, but was the commander of the army in the reign of his father, Nabunahid; and there is no historical record of a king Darius the Mede preceding Cyrus.[34]

Newton's work on Daniel and the Apocalypse of St. John was not published till six years after his death, and was then edited by Benjamin Smith, the son of his half-brother Benjamin.[35] It was afterwards included by Bishop Horsley in his *Opera Omnia* of Newton in 1785. There is no known record of when Newton began this work, but it was evidently well under way in 1690 for he referred to it several times in his correspondence with Locke.[36] In one letter he wrote: "The Son of man, Dan. VII, I take to be the same with the word of God upon the white horse in heaven, Apoc. XIX. and him to be the same with the man child, Apoc. XII., for both are to rule the earth with a rod of iron; but whence are you certain that the Ancient of Days is Christ? Does Christ any where sit upon the throne?" Evidently, at this time, Newton was sceptical of Daniel's prophecy as predicting the coming of Christ, for he wrote again: "Concerning the Ancient of Days, Dan. VII. there seems to be a mistake either in my last letter, or in yours, because you wrote in your former letter, that the Ancient of Days is Christ; and in my last, I either did, or should have asked, how you knew that."

In the first two chapters of his book, Newton gives a rapid summary of the history of the Old Testament, and the key for interpreting prophetic language. He declares his protestant faith in these vigorous terms: "The authority of emperors, kings, and princes, is human. The authority of councils, synods, bishops, and presbyters, is human. The authority of the prophets is divine, and comprehends the sum of religion, reckoning Moses and the Apostles among the prophets; and *if an angel from heaven preach any other gospel,* than what they have delivered, *let him be accursed.*" Of Daniel, he says "to reject his prophecies, is to reject the Christian religion. For

[34] Dictionary of the Bible. Scribners, New York, 1901.

[35] *Observations upon the Prophecies of Daniel and the Apocalypse of St. John.* In two parts. By Sir Isaac Newton: Dublin, 1733. Printed by S. Powell.—The book is dedicated to Peter, Lord King, who was a relative of John Locke and wrote his life. In 1733 he was Lord Chancellor.

[36] For this correspondence, *cf.* pp. 360, 361.

this religion is founded upon his prophecy concerning the Messiah." He parted company with many of the other interpreters in that he believed future events were not predicted with sufficient clarity to be understood beforehand but, after they had happened, one could recognise they had been foretold and thus be fortified in the faith of revelation.

Newton believed the first six chapters to be a collection of historical papers written by later, and unknown, authors who narrate the incidents of Daniel's life at the Babylonian Court; and the last six chapters to contain the prophecies of future events as foreseen and written by Daniel, himself. He identified the composite image, and the four beasts, with Babylonia, Persia, Greece, and Rome. It would be quite a waste of time to follow Newton as he tried to reconcile the many events of ancient times with the imagery of Daniel; he is ingenious, and he went to prodigious labour in reviewing history, but his guesses were no better than were those of other interpreters. It will pay us, however, to consider his interpretation of the fourth beast of Chapter VII, which to him foretold Rome, instead of King Antiochus. It will be remembered this beast had ten horns, and Daniel saw that there came up among them another little horn which plucked up three of the first horns by the roots; and this horn had eyes like the eyes of a man and "a mouth that spake very great things, whose look was more stout than his fellows. I beheld, and the same horn made war with the saints, and prevailed against them; until the Ancient of days came, and judgement was given to the saints of the most High; and the time came that the saints possessed the kingdom."

Now Newton had identified this beast with the Roman Empire, and the ten horns with ten kingdoms into which that Empire broke about the time it was conquered by the Goths. It is quite evident his long and meticulous discussion of the fourth beast was for the purpose of showing that the prophecies are accurate, and can be proved to have been true from our knowledge of later events of Roman history. His real interest in writing the book was, on the strength of this background, to show that the little horn of the fourth beast was prophetic of the Roman Church.

The little horn, Newton states, is a little kingdom; since it belonged to the fourth beast, Rome, and rooted up three kingdoms, he looked for it among the nations of the *Latin* Empire, established after the break up of the *Roman* Empire into the ten kingdoms. His ingenious argument for his identification of the Roman Church with the little horn should be told in his own words:[37]

"It was a kingdom of a different kind from the other ten kingdoms, having a life or soul peculiar to itself, with eyes and a mouth. By its eyes it was a see; and by its mouth speaking great things and changing times and laws, it was a prophet as well as a king. And such a see, a prophet and a king, is the Church of Rome.

"A see, episcopus, is a bishop in a literal sense of the word; and this Church claims the universal bishopric.

"With his mouth he gives laws to kings and nations as an oracle; and pretends to infallibility, and that his dictates are binding to the whole world; which is to be a prophet in the highest degree.

"In the eighth century, by rooting up and subduing the Exarchate of Ravenna, the kingdom of the Lombards, and the Senate and Dukedom of Rome [the three horns], he acquired Peter's patrimony out of their dominions; and thereby rose up as a temporal prince or king, or horn of the fourth beast."

To confirm this identification of the Church of Rome with the little horn, Newton reviews the early history of the Church and its relations with the secular powers in great detail and with astonishing erudition. But his great endeavour is to announce the downfall of Papal authority and the succeeding dominion of the saints; and this conclusion he gives in the following words which reveal the passionate depths of a man who ordinarily appeared so restrained and aloof:

"By the conversion of the ten kingdoms to the Roman religion, the Pope only enlarged his spiritual dominion, but did not yet rise up as a horn of the beast. It was his temporal dominion which made him one of the horns: and this dominion he acquired in the latter half of the eighth century, by subduing three of the former horns as above. And being arrived at a temporal dominion, and a power above all human judicature, he reigned 'with a look more stout than his fellows, and times and laws were hence forward given into his hands for a time, times, and half a time', or three times and a half; that is, for 1260 solar years, reckoning a time for a calendar year of 360 days, and a day for a solar year. After which 'the judgement is to sit, and they shall take away his dominion', not at once but by degrees, 'to consume, and to destroy it unto the end. And the kingdom

[37] *Cf.* p. 75.

and dominion, and greatness of the kingdom under the whole heaven shall', by degrees, 'be given unto the people of the saints of the most High, whose kingdom is an everlasting kingdom, and all dominions shall serve and obey him.' "[38]

It is not necessary to comment on Newton's interpretation of the Apocalypse of St. John as it is not nearly so detailed or important. Nor would so much space have been devoted to Daniel if by doing so a most important trait of his character had not been disclosed for the first time. It is clear to me, and I hope now to others, that Newton had been deeply affected by the Protestantism of the Commonwealth from 1642 to 1660 and, while he never left the Church of England, he regarded Roman Catholicism with hatred and fear. And I believe the chief purpose of his religious study was to satisfy his hope of the downfall of the papal power, which he confidently predicted would happen about the year 2000 A. D. If he were living today he would be torn by two fears, the revival of Roman temporal and spiritual power, and the decadence of Protestantism.

Like all the other scholars of his day, Newton regarded Mede as the great source for chronological and prophetic study. It is not likely that he took counsel with Whiston as they disagreed on almost every question. Whiston caustically wrote, "how weak, how very weak, the greatest of mortal men may be in some things" and gave as an example Newton's *Chronology* which after all his painstaking effort was "no better than a *sagacious romance*." Again, he criticised the interpretation of Daniel and of the Apocalypse as so imperfect, "even after the successful labour of the great Mr. Mede (whom I have heard him own as the best of expositors), . . . I could hardly assent to more than one of his expositions.[39]

Newton found a most sympathetic friend and adviser in Henry More. In fact, the earliest information of his interest in the prophetic writings is to be found in a letter, written in 1680, by More to Dr. Sharp, who had asked about Newton's apocalyptic notions. To this question, More answered: "I remember I told you how well we were agreed. For after his reading of the *Exposition of the Apocalypse* which I gave him, he came to my chamber, where he seemed to me not only to approve my *Exposition* as coherent and perspicuous throughout from the beginning

38 This passage is to be found on pp. 113, 114; and the quotations he inserted are from Daniel, VII, verses 20, 25, 26, and 27.

39 Whiston, *Memoirs*, p. 40.

to the end, but (by the manner of his countenance which is ordinarily melancholy and thoughtful, but then mightily lightsome and cheerful, and by the free profession of what satisfaction he took therein) to be in a manner transported. So that I took it for granted, that what peculiar conceits he had of his own had vanished." Then there follows a disapproval of some of Newton's "extravagant conceits," but in a postscript More adds: "When my *Exposition* of Daniel comes out with this appendage, I hope you will easily discover that Mr. N. was over sudden in his conceits. I have told him myself of this appendage, and that if he be not convinced thereby, he has free leave from me to enjoy his own opinions. We have a free converse and friendship, which these differences will not disturb."[40]

We cannot learn much about Newton's religious beliefs from his Chronology, or from his interpretation of Daniel. But from his tract on *Two Notable Corruptions of Scripture* which was published posthumously, and from his manuscript papers, some of which were published by Brewster and others examined by myself, it is possible to arrive at a fairly clear knowledge of his personal beliefs.

During Newton's life there were pretty definite rumours of his heterodoxy, in so far as his acceptance of the doctrine of the Trinity was concerned. And in those days to deny the doctrine of the Trinity was a serious matter as it prevented one from holding any position of trust, and if persisted in the penalty was imprisonment.[41] Whiston, in his *Memoirs,* twice stated that Newton, like himself, was an Arian, and a Baptist, and that he thought these two sects were the two witnesses to the truth in the book of Revelations. Hopton Haynes, who was a clerk in the Mint, declared that Newton was a Unitarian and lamented that his friend, Dr. Samuel Clarke, had stopped at Arianism.[42] On the other hand, the *Biographia Britannica* stated in the article on Newton: "Mr. Whiston, who represented Sir Isaac as an Arian, which he so much resented that he would not suffer him to be a member of the Royal Society while he was President."

40 *Conway Letters,* p. 478.

41 The anti-Trinitarians can be classed under three main divisions: the Arians who denied that the Son was coeternal with the father, though he was begot before time began and by him the Father created all things. Arius was the chief opponent of Athanasius who held that the Son is of the same substance (homoousion) as the Father; the Socinians who believe that he did not exist before his appearance on earth, but that he was an object of prayer; the Humanitarians, or Unitarians, who believe him to be a man, and not an object of prayer.

42 This latter evidence is not direct, as it was reported by the Unitarian minister, Richard Baron, a friend of Haynes. *Cf.* De Morgan, *Essays,* p. 55.

This statement is however not to be found in either edition of Whiston's *Memoirs*.[43]

The stigma of being an Arian, if such it be, would probably have died out after Newton's death if it had not been re-awakened by the publication of his tract on the *Two Corrupt Passages*, which he had first intended to print anonymously and had then suppressed. And even this manuscript purports to be merely a critical examination of a Biblical text and not a criticism of the doctrine of the Trinity. The fact of the matter is that the belief in Newton's heterodoxy does not rest on such statements as Dr. Johnson's that in his youth he was a furious atheist, but rather on the insinuations of his apologists. When Bishop Horsley was preparing his edition of Newton's works, he had the opportunity given to him of examining the Portsmouth manuscripts; and there is a widespread tradition that he found many papers on religion which he deemed unfit for publication as they would have great weight and would encourage atheism or, at least, heterodoxy.

It was most unfortunate that such a man as Bishop Horsley had the first chance to examine Newton's private papers, and to foster the rumour that there was something sinister in his religious beliefs. It was still more unfortunate that Brewster, when he wrote his first *Life of Newton* in 1830 and without any real examination of the question, had no hesitation in declaring that he was a believer in the Trinity. After De Morgan had made public his critical researches, Brewster, who had in the meantime examined the *Portsmouth Papers* while preparing his later *Memoirs of Newton*, qualified his opinion by the admission that Newton's orthodoxy was not proved, "but in the charity which thinketh no evil, we are bound to believe that our neighbour is not a heretic till the charge against him has been distinctly proved."[44] While Brewster did publish some of the *Portsmouth Papers*, he failed to publish others which in my opinion are decisive, and he added to the suspicions of heterodoxy by stating that "Dr. Horsley exercised a wise discretion in not giving them formally to the world."[45] The day is long past, if it ever existed, when such

[43] De Morgan first pointed out the falseness of this statement. I have verified De Morgan in both editions of Whiston. On page 206 (edition 1749), and on page 178 (edition 1753), Whiston merely says that Newton was an Eusebian or Arian; on pages 293, 294 (edition 1749) and on pages 249, 250 (edition 1753) he states that Newton refused to let him be elected to the Royal Society because he could not bear to be contradicted and so was afraid of Whiston the last thirteen years of his life. Thus the biographer deliberately joined these two detached statements together to bolster up Newton's orthodoxy. Brewster rests part of his plea for orthodoxy on this false evidence.

[44] Brewster, Vol. II, p. 340.

[45] *Ibid.*, Vol. II, p. 355.

mild heterodoxy as Newton's can encourage atheism; and a dispassionate review of his theological opinions will settle the question.

We shall examine his most important theological tract first published posthumously in a slightly mutilated form in 1754, and afterwards included in Horsley's edition of Newton's works under the title of *An historical account of two notable corruptions of Scripture* ("in a letter to a friend, now first published entire from a MS. in the author's hand-writing in the possession of the Rev. Dr. Ekens, Dean of Carlisle"). The history of the composition of this work has been made accessible by Lord King.[46]

On November 14, 1690, Newton wrote to John Locke: "I send you now by the carrier, Martin, the papers I promised. I fear I have not only made you stay too long for them, but also made them too long by an addition. For upon the receipt of your letter reviewing what I had by me concerning the text of 1st John v. 7, and examining authors a little farther about it, I met with something new concerning that other of 1st Timothy III. 16, which I thought would be as acceptable to inquisitive men, and might be set down in a little room. . . . If at present you get only what concerns the first done into French, that of the other may stay till we see what success the first will have. I have no entire copy besides that I send you, and therefore would not have it lost, because I may, perhaps, after it has gone abroad long enough in French, put it forth in English."

Locke was expecting to make a trip to Holland and Newton's purpose was that he should take the manuscript with him and, through the medium of some literary acquaintance, have it translated into French and published anonymously. As the texts criticised are the two on which the doctrine of the Trinity is principally based, Newton, with his characteristic timidity and dislike of contention, desired to see how the work would be received before publishing it in England. But Locke either postponed, or abandoned, his trip, and forwarded the manuscript to his friend Le Clerc with instructions to have it translated and published. Newton, who had learned that his friend was still in England, wrote on February 16, 1691/2, "Your former letters came not to my hand, but this I have. I was of opinion my papers had lain still, and am sorry there is news about them. Let me entreat you to stop their translation and impression as soon as you can, for I design to suppress them." In a third letter written three months later he merely said that he was "glad the edition was

[46] *Cf.* King's *Life of Locke,* Vol. I, pp. 401, 409, 415, 423–434.

stopped." We learn from the letters of Le Clerc to Locke that he faithfully carried out his instructions, although he appreciated the value of the dissertations and was most anxious to publish them. After Locke's death in 1704, he apparently deposited the manuscript in the library of the Remonstrants in Holland as the name of the author had not been divulged to him, and he did not know where to return them. There they lay for fifty years when they were published by an anonymous editor who, as some of the first and last pages were missing, supplied them as best he could. Porson, the Greek scholar, in his Preface to his *Letters to Travis* comments on this work: "Between the years 1690 and 1700, Sir Isaac Newton wrote a Dissertation upon 1 John v. 7, in which he collected, arranged, and strengthened Simon's arguments, and gave a clear, exact, and comprehensive view of the whole question."[47]

The two texts which Newton criticised are:

1st Epistle of John v. 7,—For there are three that bear record in heaven, the Father, the Word, and the Holy Ghost: and these three are one.

v. 8,—And there are three that bear witness in earth, the Spirit, and the water, and the blood: and these three agree in one.

1st Epistle to Timothy III. 16,—And, without controversy, great is the mystery of godliness: God was manifest in the flesh, justified in the Spirit, etc.

It will not be useful or interesting to follow Newton's detailed argument. In brief, he agrees with Simon[48] that verse seven of John's Epistle is not to be found in any of the early Greek texts, or mentioned by the early Greek fathers. The one exception of Cyprian is explained by both as not being authoritative, as he merely states that we should understand the water, blood, and spirit, as being

47 Richard Simon (1638–1712) was a French biblical critic whose work was the standard for the time. His *Histoire critique du Vieux Testament* (1678) aroused a storm of criticism and forced him to secede from the Congregation of the Oratory. Later, he published his even more famous *Histoire Critique du Texte du Nouveau Testament.* My quotations are from the Rotterdam edition of 1689. Newton possessed both of these works and also three others by Simon. In support of his thesis, Newton referred to an astonishing number of the Church Fathers, and I found it interesting to check them up from Villamil's catalogue of his library published in his *Newton: the Man.* In almost every case the author's works were in his collection. It is evident also that he did not read Greek fluently as all the editions of the Greek fathers were in both Greek and Latin.

48 *Critique du Nouveau Testament,* Chap. xviii.

significant of the Father, Son, and Holy Ghost, which is quite different from saying they are the same, or that the Holy Ghost is a person.

After Newton had disposed of the verse as a late interpolation in the canon of the Scriptures, he accuses Jerome of having deliberately inserted it in the Vulgate when he translated the then existing Greek versions into Latin, about 385 A. D. One of his strongest arguments is the fact that during the long and bitter controversy at the Council of Nicæa in 325 A. D., which was waged on the doctrine of the Trinity, none of the Athanasian party makes any reference to this witness of "the Three in Heaven." From this and other evidence, he concludes that later scholars, finding the passage in the Vulgate, made a note of it in the margins of their Greek copies; and from such Scholia it ultimately crept into the subsequent Greek versions.

In thus flatly accusing Jerome of a forgery and of falsifying the Scriptures, Newton differs from Simon. The French scholar admits that verse seven is a spurious insertion in the Vulgate, but he claims that it was interpolated in the Latin text by Victor, Evêque de Vite, who lived a century after Jerome. He also claims that the *Prologue* of the Canonic Epistles attributed to Jerome was not written by him, and cites its unknown author who "complains that the interpreters have not translated the Epistles faithfully, and especially this verse in St. John. He accuses them of having fallen into great error when they retained in their Version only the three words, the water, the blood, and the spirit, and of having omitted the Father, the Son, and the Holy Ghost who are authentic witnesses of the belief of Catholics in the mystery of the Trinity."

In his criticism of the verse in Timothy, Newton was breaking new ground as Simon does not mention it. His argument is that the verse should read: "Great is the mystery of godliness, which was manifested in the flesh." He cites that all the churches of the first four or five centuries, and all the authors of the ancient versions, even Jerome's, give it in that form. Also it reads the same in the Ethiopic, Syriac, and Latin versions down to Newton's time. But the Greeks, he claims, changed ὅ into CΘ, the abbreviation of Θεός, so that the passage now reads, "Great is the mystery of godliness: God manifested in the flesh." As he does not hesitate to charge Jerome with falsifying the Epistle of St. John so he summarises on the falsification of the Epistle to Timothy: "The man that first began thus to alter the sacred text, was Macedonius, the patriarch of Constantinople, in the beginning of the sixth century. For the emperor Anastasius banished him for corrupting it."

In order to complete the investigation of these two passages, I am permitted to include the following statement of my colleague Professor Robert P. Casey who, because of his study of Athanasius, is eminently fitted to sum up the case.

"The verse is a gloss which originated either in Spain or Africa before the end of the fourth century. It is first quoted as part of 1st John by a Spanish author Priscillian in 381 A. D. [?]. There are only three late Greek witnesses, all dependent on the Latin. It was natural for Newton to suppose Jerome inserted the verse since the Vulgate was the earliest source in which he could find it. Brook summarises his exposition of the evidence:

" 'The gloss was certainly known as part of the text of the Epistle in Africa in the fifth century. Its acceptance as part of the text cannot be found in any country except Spain in the fourth century. There it was undoubtedly used by Priscillian (380 ?). The influence of his works and writings on the Latin texts of the Bible, which passed over into orthodox circles through Peregrinus is an undoubted fact. It is through the Theodulfian recension of the Vulgate that the gloss first gained anything like wide acceptance.'[49] It appears quite certain, however, that Jerome took over what was already in existence.

"With regard to 1st Timothy III. 16, there is no doubt that the right reading is ὅς, although there is inferior manuscript authority for ὅ and Θεός. The difficulty lies in the absence of an antecedent for ὅς, and it is generally held that the verse is a clumsily introduced quotation, perhaps from some early Christian hymn. The theory, that ὅς was altered to Θεός by Macedonius, is first advanced by Hincmar of Rheims. Liberatus of Carthage, in the sixth century, in an anti-heretical tract, accuses Macedonius of changing ὅς to ὥς. The editor of this treatise in Gallandi's *Bibliotheca Patrum* suggested that the original editor should have emended the text of Liberatus to agree with that of Hincmar on the supposition that Hincmar was acquainted with Liberatus. This conjecture was unhappily adopted by Tischendorf, and the text of Liberatus is thus quoted in its emended form in his apparatus. It is, however, not the reading of the manuscript and I am inclined to think that the editor of Gallandi was wrong."

49 *Cf.* A. E. Brook, *Commentary on the Johannine Epistles.* International Critical Commentary. New York, 1912.

Our chief interest in this work of Newton is not whether he proved the spuriousness of these important texts, but to learn why he spent such time and labour on the problem, and whether we can find evidence in it of his own belief. There can be no doubt that he considered the doctrine of the Trinity as of fundamental importance in theology, and by proving the spuriousness of these verses he had shattered the chief and most definite source of the mystery. Simon could come to the same opinion without disturbing his acceptance of the doctrine as an article of faith, since he could hold that the doctrine of the Trinity had been established by the infallible authority of the Œcumenical Councils of the Church; but Newton was a Protestant, who denied the authority of the Church Councils and rested his whole belief on the authentic words of the Bible. If he thus proved that this verse had not been incorporated in the New Testament before the fourth century he was absolved in his own mind from accepting it. Also by fastening the act of falsifying the Scriptures on Jerome he confirmed one more grievance against the Roman Church.

It has been claimed that Newton, by countermanding the request to have this tract published, had thereby indicated that he had not convinced himself as to the truth of his research. But this argument is without weight when we consider his characteristic reluctance to publish anything, and especially a work on such a topic which involved actual danger to his position and liberty. While he is discreet, there are several passages which show his sympathy with Arianism.

The tract opens with the significant statement of his purpose, "I have done it the more freely, because to you, who understand the many abuses which they of the Roman Church have put upon the world, it will scarce be ungrateful to be convinced of one more than is commonly believed. . . . But whilst we exclaim against the pious frauds of the Roman Church, and make it a part of our religion to detest and renounce all things of that kind, we must acknowledge it a greater crime in us to favour such practices, than in the Papists we so much blame on that account: for they act according to their religion, but we contrary to ours." He then explains that he is not discussing an article of faith, but only the authenticity of a text of Scripture; but he omits to say that for Protestants the two questions are hardly separable.

Again, Newton does directly attack the doctrine of the Trinity and, what is extremely rare in his writings and occurs only when he is deeply moved, he indulges in sarcasm. When discussing the opinions of Cyprian he remarks, Cyprian "does not say, the Father, the Word, and the Holy Ghost, as it is now in the seventh verse; but the Father, the Son, and the Holy Ghost, as it is in baptism; the place from which they tried at first to derive the Trinity."[50]

We find here also Newton's very emphatic statement of his Protestantism. He says of this seventh verse as it now appears in the Bible: "Let them make good sense of it, who are able. For my part, I can make none. If it be said that we are not to determine what is scripture, and what not, by our private judgements, I confess it in places not controverted: but in disputable places, I love to take up with what I can best understand. It is the temper of the hot and superstitious part of mankind, in matters of religion, ever to be fond of mysteries; and for that reason, to like best what they understand least."[51] This dependence on the reason was the attitude not only of the extreme Protestants, but it might also serve as the fundamental doctrine of the English Deists who held that all the portions of the Bible essential for salvation were revealed in language so clear they would not be subject to dispute: thus, since he found this text subject to dispute, the doctrine of the Trinity was not essential.

One more passage will be quoted, as it shows Newton's tenderness towards the Arians and is an example of his power of sarcasm. "Yes, truly, those Arians were crafty knaves, that could conspire so cunningly and slily all the world over at once (as at the word of a Mithridates) in the latter end of the reign of the emperor Constantius, to get all men's books into their hands, and correct them without being perceived: ay, and conjurors too, to do it without leaving any blot or chasm in their books, whereby the knavery might be suspected and discovered; and to wipe away the memory of it out of all men's brains; so that neither Athanasius, or anybody else, could afterwards remember that they had ever seen it in their books before; and out of their own books too."[52]

50 Horsley, Vol. V, p. 498.—The Bishop, although he published this tract, was none too well pleased with its tone, and probably included it only because it had already appeared in a mutilated form. He notes on this passage: "The insinuation contained in this expression, that the Trinity is not to be derived from the words prescribed for the baptismal form, is very extraordinary to come from a writer who was no Socinian." As the Socinians were a shade worse in the eyes of the orthodox than the Arians, the Bishop certainly was convinced of Newton's heterodoxy and refused to publish other of his documents which would reveal his Unitarianism.

51 Horsley, Vol. V, p. 529.

52 *Ibid.*, p. 508.—Perhaps I should add a note of explanation as there seems to be prevalent not only ignorance of the great questions of theology but also a curious apathy towards

Newton's purpose in writing this dissertation, and then deciding to suppress it, is obvious enough. He was deeply interested in the mystery of the Trinity. Its chief support, in the New Testament, is verse seven of John's epistle. He finds, following the lead of the French critic, Simon, that it was fraudulently inserted into the text of Jerome as late as the fourth century and after the Council of Nicæa. As a Protestant he could reject the doctrine of the Trinity if it is not legitimately in the Scriptures; and also he finds support for Deism in that it is not intelligible. Lastly I think he rejoiced to uncover a pious imposture of the Roman Church which he holds would be worse still for the Protestants to conceal. And one can understand that, when so dangerous a manuscript was out of his hands, he began to fear lest its authorship would be discovered, and so he not only suppressed it but, after Locke's death, he did not dare to write to Le Clerc to ask for its return.

One of Newton's important papers, judging from the care with which it was written, is the *Irenicum: or ecclesiastical polity tending to peace*. As Brewster has published this document,[53] a running commentary on its main points will be sufficient. The author sketches the history of church government from the earliest Jewish times down to his own, with the purpose of showing that the Protestant, rather than the Roman, form is the true successor of the primitive Jewish church. Before the Babylonian captivity, he states, the cities of Israel were governed by elders who sat at the gates of the cities. The place of worship was nearby, and sometimes there was an altar for sacrifices on a neighbouring hill. After the captivity, the King of Persia, Artaxerxes Longimanus, commissioned Ezra to restore the government, and to appoint magistrates and judges. Newton supposes that he revived, as nearly as possible, the ancient customs. Of the new courts of judicature, the highest was the Sanhedrin, and the lower courts sat in the synagogues whose development was due to Ezra. The government, thus established, continued to the time of Christ, and was then extended over all the Roman Empire by the scattered Jews. This same government passed from the Jews to the early Christianised Gentiles who merely changed the name of synagogues to that of churches, and of the Chief Rulers and Princes

enquiring about them. Newton is referring to the vital controversy between Athanasius and Arius at the Council of Nicæa in 325 when the Arian view of the nature of the Son was decided to be heresy. Newton is of course sarcastically stating that the Arians had erased the seventh verse of John from the early Greek texts and writings of the Fathers so that the Athanasians would not find any support for their pronouncement on the Trinity.

[53] Vol. II, p. 526.

of the synagogues, to Bishops and Presbyters. According to continuous precedent the duty of Bishops and Presbyters is to govern, but not to make laws.

The laws of the King extend only to things undetermined by the laws of God; he is supreme head of the church in all things indifferent to the faith and can nominate or depose Bishops and Presbyters. The being of the church does not depend upon an uninterrupted succession of Bishops and Presbyters for it was broken in the time of Ezra, and, having been broken once, it may be broken again.

All persons baptised are members of Christ's body, called the Church, even those who are not yet admitted into the communion of the synagogue of any city. "The commission to teach and baptise was given to the Apostles as the disciples of Christ, and to their disciples, and the disciples of their disciples, to the end of the world, there being no bishops or presbyters or church government yet instituted among the Christians. But after the institution of governments, the governors appointed men to catechise and baptise, except in cases of necessity, where the original right returned."

The main line of Newton's argument is, therefore, that the government of the true church goes back continuously to the establishment by Ezra, after the Babylonian captivity, of synagogues without priests or sacrifices, and that the institution of the Temple and its High Priest was an usurpation of authority. Thus, he argues the continuity of the Protestant Churches, and the usurpation of the Bishops of Rome from the example of the Temple; that is, the primitive Christian Church and its successor the Protestant Church were a continuation of the synagogue and modelled on it. Since, also, a break in the succession occurred in the time of Ezra so an uninterrupted succession of Bishops is not necessary for the being of a church as the Roman Church claims. But his reasoning is defective, because he forgets that the Temple, and the authority of the High Priest, grew out of the synagogue, as the Pope and the Bishop grew out of the Temple.

In general, Newton subscribes to the state government of the Church of England. His ideas on baptism are correct in that it is a requirement for the Christian, but he is wrong in affirming that it can be performed by any one except in cases of extreme urgency. If his statement that baptism may be performed on those "who are not yet admitted into the communion of the synagogue of any city" is one defining his own belief, he cannot have accepted the doctrine of the Baptist Church of his day. But the *Irenicum,* or peace, may be a compromise to consolidate the Protestant Churches against the papacy, and may not be a declaration of his own principles.

If we can rely on the evidence of the manuscripts which Newton preserved to determine what religious questions in addition to his faith in Protestantism and antagonism to Rome, most occupied his thought, we shall find that they group themselves about the doctrine of the Trinity. He enquired into the Biblical authority for the doctrine; the controversy between Arius and Athanasius at the Council of Nicæa; the doctrine of consubstantiation or whether the Father and the Son are of the same essence; and lastly he examined whether Jesus is an object of worship, and whether the Holy Ghost is a person. I found eight documents on these subjects; they were written most carefully, corrected and interlined, and often repeated. Of these eight documents, Brewster published only two, and he apparently selected those of an historical nature which could be regarded as an enquiry into facts rather than as an expression of personal belief.

The first of these documents published by Brewster[54] proposed sixteen *Paradoxical questions concerning the morals and actions of Athanasius and his followers.* Newton questions the report spread by Athanasius that Arius died in a house of prostitution and several other scandals of the same sort; whether Athanasius was a properly constituted Bishop; and whether the Council of Nicæa was truly an œcumenical council. To every question, he finds the answer favourable to the Arians.

The other document published by Brewster[55] is a list of twenty-two *Quaeries regarding the word homoousios.* While these questions are not answered, the drift of Newton's sympathy is evident. *Homoousios* is the battle cry of the Trinitarians as it signifies the belief in the identical, and uncreated, essence of the Father and Son. Newton asks whether such metaphysical questions have any meaning, or are essential to religion. Then he asks whether the Emperor Constantine did not interpose his authority to defeat the wish of the majority, and whether even then the Council did not decide that Christ was merely the express image of the Father. He also proposes the questions whether the doctrine of the equality of the three substances was not first set on foot by Athanasius and others in the reign of Julian the Apostate, and so later than the Council of Nicæa; whether

54 Vol. II, p. 342.—Brewster thought that the manuscript had been written for publication; I think he was mistaken as no one with any public position or reputation would have dared to publish such scandals about the Council of Nicæa.

55 *Ibid.*, Vol. II, p. 532.

the worship of the Holy Ghost was not first decreed after the Council of Sardica; and whether the doctrine of the three Persons in one was not also the decision of that Council.[56] Newton's last questions turn again to the subject of the usurpation of authority by the Bishops of Rome.

What we can learn from the published theological works of Newton is obscured by his caution, a caution which must have been increased by the misfortunes of Whiston. When I was generously given permission to examine, and to make extracts from, the *Portsmouth Collection* I was particularly anxious to see whether the vexed question of his religious opinions could not be answered from the documents which Horsley and Brewster did not feel it wise to publish. And I think the answer can now be given.

There are, in the *Portsmouth Collection,* a set of seventeen Quæries and one of ten Observations on the history of the Council of Nicæa which do not greatly differ from those published by Brewster. But there are other papers which give his personal beliefs on these religious questions, and have never been printed. It was a curious attitude for Brewster to take in suppressing such documents. He devoted a long biography to show that Newton was not only the greatest of all scientists, but also a man with almost no human faults. And yet he undoubtedly thought that Newton's religious convictions, the subject which he had meditated deeply and held to be the most important of all, should not be divulged lest they should weaken the faith of others, and lead them towards atheism. One can better appreciate the pressure which was put upon a writer, in the middle of the last century, to suppress any enquiry into matters held to be orthodox from the rebuke administered to Brewster because of his very mild questioning of Newton's orthodoxy. His short *Life of Newton* had no sooner been published than he received a letter from Dr. Burgess, Bishop of Salisbury, protesting against his conduct, and enclosing the advance sheets of an article which included the following passage:

"The name of Sir Isaac Newton has been lately employed by So-

56 Newton's purpose, in trying to prove that the doctrine of the Trinity was first decreed by the Council of Sardica, seems to be that he believed he would thus weaken it even in the minds of Catholics. Many mediæval theologians held the decisions of a council to be binding only when they were received as such by the whole Church. That resolved itself into the question of which councils were œcumenical. The Council of Nicæa was the first of such councils, and that of Sardica is never included in the list. But, if such were his purpose, it has no value since the doctrine, however it may have originated, has been affirmed in later œcumenical councils.

cinians and Unitarians. in opposition to the doctrine of the Trinity, on the authority of a Tract, which he anxiously and deliberately suppressed. Dr. Brewster, in his recent publication of the Life of Sir Isaac Newton, *has, it is much to be regretted, done the same injustice to the memory of Sir Isaac* by his restatement and revival of the general contents of the suppressed Dissertation on the controverted verse of St. John, and by omitting to notice Sir Isaac's suppression of the Tract."[57] It is fortunate for me that the Bishop cannot thunder against me for I shall be far more bold, as I think the time has come to give to the world even his most private thoughts.

In a hitherto unpublished and unmentioned paper, Newton lays down fourteen *Argumenta* in Latin, with supporting passages from the Scriptures, to show that the Son is neither coeternal with, or equal to, the Father. The most important arguments are the following.[58]

2. Because the Son is called the Word: John I. 1.
4. Because God begot the Son at some time, he had not existence from eternity. Prov. VIII. 23, 25.
5. Because the Father is greater than the Son. John XIV. 28.
6. Because the Son did not know his last hour. Mark XIII. 32,—Matt. XXIV. 36,—Rev. I. 1, and V. 3.
7. Because the Son received all things from the Father.
9. Because the Son could be incarnated.

In addition to adducing the support of the Bible against the doctrine of the Trinity, Newton wrote another paper giving seven *Rationes* or reasons against it. For example:

1. *Homoousion* is unintelligible. 'Twas not understood in the Council of Nice (Euseb. apud Soc. . . .) nor ever since. What cannot be understood is no object of belief.

6. The Father is God, creating and a person; the Son is God, created and a person; and the Holy Ghost is God, proceeding and a person; *et tamen non est nisi unus Deus.* He follows this statement by an illustration; there is a Western Church, an Oriental Church and an Egyptian Church, *et tamen non est nisi una Ecclesia.* The ambiguity in both cases is that each is a particular individual and in that sense cannot be said to be one.

57 Brewster, Vol. II, p. 523.

58 These, and the following *Rationes,* are given *verbatim.* The reader may, by consulting the citations, discover Newton's evidence for his opinions.

7. The Person is intellectual substance [*substantia intellectualis*], therefore the three Persons are three substances.

Besides these hitherto unnoted papers, there are two short memoranda which really amount to a declaration of his faith in Christ, and they can mean only that he did not believe in the divinity of Jesus. I quote the most significant portions of them:

"God has the prophecy originally in his own breast and Christ received it from God, and delivers it to his messenger, and by his messenger to John, and by John to the Churches in a continual subordination. He delivers it not as having it originally in his own breast, but as a faithful and true witness of what He received from the Father as a witness or prophet whose testimony is the spirit of prophecy. And to deny this subordination would be to deny Jesus Christ as he is a Prophet, the only Prophet to whom God reveals himself immediately, and who is therefore called the Word of God."

His Unitarianism is, I think, even more pronounced in the following: "Jesus therefore by calling himself the Son of God and saying I and the Father are one meant nothing more than that the Father had sanctified him and sent him into the world." Then Newton justifies "the calling them Gods to whom the word of God came lest the Scriptures should be broken; and that by consequence that he, being a man, might have called himself a God in the sense of the Scriptures without blasphemy, and much more may he call himself the son of God."

Newton had thought out his religious beliefs with sufficient clearness, and there would not have been a long controversy about them if those, who had access to his papers, had not tried to make him appear orthodox. He was wholly committed, as was Milton, to the Protestant doctrine against the authority of the Church Councils. He was especially interested in proving that the Council of Nicæa was dominated by the Emperor and by the evil machinations of Athanasius, and should not even be credited as authoritative by the Catholics. His purpose was not to do away entirely with the interpretation of the Athanasian doctrine of the one substance, but to show that the argument over *homoousios* was not an important, or rather not a fundamental doctrine. He would have us believe that the Church was all the while Arian. His scholarship was weak in the modern sense, and he had not grasped the broader aspects of the problem as did the great English divines, such as Hooker, or he would have realised that the doctrine of the substance is a fundamental one, since without it the Christian God becomes a vague sort of a creative action.

Personally, Newton was an Arian since he states definitely that the Father and the Son are not one substance; that the Son was created and therefore of a different substance for, if they were of one substance then, the Father having created the substance of the Son, He must have created his own substance. Having placed the source of authority in the Bible and not in the Councils, he shows that the Holy Ghost is not a person or substance by calling the two passages in the New Testament spurious which specifically mention the Holy Ghost as a person.

But Newton goes much farther than merely to deny the doctrine of consubstantiation. He had rationally adopted the Unitarian position that Jesus was sent by the Father into the world as a Prophet who differed from the other Prophets only in the immediacy of the message delivered to him. Thus he explains the claim that "I and my Father are one" as a unity of purpose and not one of identity. Like so many other Unitarians of the day, such as Locke, he here makes a break between reason and practice, since he maintained his affiliation with the Church of England. But, as I have remarked before, I find in this the cause of his refusal to take orders; as a private worshipper he felt he was justified in making reservations which his conscience was too tender to permit him to make as a priest.

The natural philosophers of Newton's time were wiser than the scientists of today because they saw more clearly the inevitable conflict which must always exist between materialistic science and idealistic religion. They saw that the doctrine of the Trinity was a vital and fundamental question, and not a matter of words as it is so frequently and contemptuously assumed to be by those who find truth only in what appeals to the senses. It is, at bottom, the answer of the Christian Church to the question of the reality of immaterial substance; it is the question which most occupied Plato and Aristotle; and it is the question which made them, and Newton also, condemn the philosophy of materialism.

While Newton's specific statement that "what cannot be understood is no object of belief" might have been quoted as the fundamental tenet of the Deists, he cannot be classed with them. Even if no other consideration had weighed with him, he would have repudiated a connection with that movement because all the dignitaries of church and state of his time looked upon the professed

Deists as out of the pale. But, on the other hand, his world of rigorous mechanical law as portrayed in the *Principia* became by the skillful pen of Voltaire the chief source of the later deistic philosophy. Nor would it be difficult to show the influence of Newton's mechanistic philosophy on the agnosticism of Huxley and the humanitarianism of the present day.

Although Newton wrote so voluminously on religious subjects, he never seems to have anticipated that his mechanistic natural philosophy could have any effect on religion other than to strengthen our belief in the Christian faith. He was therefore taken entirely by surprise when Leibniz, in a letter to the Princess Caroline, expressed his disapproval of the *Principia* on the ground that its philosophy was materialistic and subversive of the Christian religion. Newton's God, he claimed, was merely a super-mechanic who could not even create a satisfactory universe, but to keep it going must constantly repair its worn parts.

This criticism aroused a storm of indignation in England and the animus of Leibniz was attributed, with some apparent justification, to the personal jealousy of its author who was irritated by the charge of plagiarism which had been made against him. By most people, the purity and piety of Newton's life was instanced as a sufficient evidence of the wickedness of the accusation, although it should have been clear that his religious faith and practice had nothing to do with the question. Since Newton was considered not to be skillful in philosophic debate, the task of defending his philosophy was left to Samuel Clarke.[59] The fact is that Newton's philosophy and religion were two separate things, and he does not seem to have concerned himself with the problem of reconciling them. Intellectually, he could develop a system in which God and man had but a minor rôle in comparison with Nature; but practically he remained a confessing member of the Church of England whose doctrines are not in conformity with rigorous laws of mechanics.

From brief statements scattered through his scientific writings, a fairly accurate idea of Newton's conception of the physical universe, and of man's place in it can be formed. This universe, at least so far as it can be examined scientifically, he regarded as a vast and complicated machine created by a personal and spiritual God, who also

[59] A spirited correspondence passed between Clarke and Leibniz which has been published in Des Maizeaux's Collection—*Recueil de diverses pièces, par Mss. Leibniz, Clarke, Newton, et autres.* 2d edition corrected and enlarged. 2 vols., Amsterdam, 1740.—Also an edition by Dr. Sam'l Clarke giving the collection of Papers in French and English. London, 1717.

ordained rigorous laws according to which it must operate. While the world was young, God may have set aside the orderly operation of natural law in order to teach ignorant men His power; the age of such miracles is now past. The record of those intimate relations of God and men is found in the Old Testament; but now He reveals to us His purpose and His power through natural laws which He no longer miraculously contravenes. Thus, if we, by diligent seeking, discover the laws of the universe we are at the same time making manifest the Divine purpose; and science becomes one of the chief aids to religion. The miraculous power which men, with Divine aid, could exercise formerly to alter the motions of the stars and to suspend the laws of nature was taken from us when the full revelation had been granted in the death and resurrection of the Messiah; since then it is sufficient for us, as detached observers, to learn and obey natural and spiritual law. So strong was his conviction of the universe as a rigorous machine that he thought the planets must, because of friction, gradually lose their motion. One might sum up this philosophy by saying that God had created the world machine and, having in its early history experimented with it, now limited Himself to repairing and adjusting its worn parts. Possibly even it might wear out and have to be recreated at intervals.

If we are thus limited to a mere observation of an objective world, how shall we conduct ourselves in it during our life, and how shall we learn from our sensations what is the Divine purpose towards us? Newton, apparently without regard to the difficulties involved, accepted the ideas of the Cambridge Platonists. According to that philosophy, the flux of external events comes to us as mechanical agitation of the sense organs which is then transferred to the brain by motion in our nerves. Although the brain, as a whole, contributed to the translation of these motions into the sensations of sight, touch, etc., their interpretation as emotion and thought was the function of a small and imaginary organ situated somewhere in the brain. This organ, the *sensorium* as it was named, was the seat of the self-conscious soul, and in it were concentrated all those processes which together constitute the intellectual and spiritual personality. As the flux of events which comes to our sense organs is very limited in quantity and confused in character, so also its interpretation by the human *sensorium* is equally limited and distorted by our imperfect and finite nature. To the approximation with which we can conceive of an infinite and omniscient *sensorium* that receives the universal flux and translates it absolutely without limitation of time and space, we have to the same degree defined the nature of God. Since the *sensoria* of God and man differ thus only in degree and not in kind, we can by the exercise of accurate observation and thought understand more clearly the divine nature, and obey more readily the divine will.

It is quite evident that such a philosophy left man entirely outside of the physical world in which he lived. And for the most part men of science were content, during the eighteenth century, to study the material and the living worlds as quite separate from each. With the growth of the biological sciences in the nineteenth century, there was an attempt by the evolutionists to close this gap, and to regard life and its functions as special configurations and motions of material atoms. Thus biology became but a branch of mechanics. The height of this movement was attained by the cosmic evolution of Spencer who pictured a continuous evolution, from a primordial chaos to the present state of the universe, controlled by the laws of mechanics. Man had indeed been made a part of the universe, but he had also entirely lost his self-conscious identity. It is safe to say that the trend of thought is at present to regard life as an entity distinct from matter and subject to its own laws.

By the irony of fate, Newton's religious heterodoxy, which was so much feared, has now not a particle of influence; but his scientific work, which was heralded by Bentley and others as a bulwark for orthodox faith, has been built upon as a basis for the attacks on the Christian religion by such scientists as can recognise no phenomena and no laws except those of matter, space, and time.

CHAPTER XVII

THE LAST YEARS

1718–1727

THE last years of Newton's life were passed in the enjoyment of the honour and respect which his achievements merited. At the advanced age of seventy-five years, he still enjoyed excellent health, and his mental powers were unimpaired except for some decay of memory; with his snow white hair and with the bloom and colour of youth, he presented a notable and venerable appearance. While he had suffered from the inevitable death of acquaintances, yet his habitual isolation from society would enable him to bear such losses with composure of mind. The death of Halifax, however, must have made a great difference in his life, if, as seems probable, his niece, Catherine Barton, returned to his house. She was now a rich woman and, whatever her status may have been as Halifax's housekeeper, within two years she married John Conduitt, a man of influence several years younger than herself. Without any positive evidence, except the statement of Conduitt that Newton's niece lived with her uncle twenty years before and after her marriage, it is believed the Conduitts lived with him in St. Martin's Street. A year after their marriage, their only child, Catherine Conduitt, was born.

In spite of the additional life which these new relationships brought to Newton, we still picture him as living mostly in his private study, eating his meals alone and passing his days reading and writing. Occasionally, he had visitors, and occasionally he met Halley and others at taverns and coffee houses. His duties at the Mint were light and required attendance only one day a week, and he went regularly to the weekly, and to the Council, meetings of the Royal Society. How rarely he travelled is strikingly illustrated by the fact that he had never been in Oxford till, at the age of seventy-eight, he visited Keill.

Although the active phases of the controversies with Flamsteed and Leibniz had died out, they still affected his life and occupied his time. The visits of Flamsteed and their morning games of backgammon had long since ceased. The *Historia Cœlestis* had been published in spite of the exasperated protests of its author, but Newton had suffered the bitter mortification of learning that Flamsteed had triumphantly burned all the copies undistributed, and was pushing his own edition with desperate haste. All that Newton could do to delay this work was to refuse obstinately to return the sealed packet of data, and now he knew that although his former friend had sunk under his infirmities and labours, yet the catalogue was to be published posthumously.

Also the Pyrrhic victory over Leibniz had left Newton embittered and determined to vindicate himself. Nor did the death of Leibniz in 1716 end the matter; for Bernoulli's *Epistola pro Eminente Mathematico* had had a great influence in securing the support of the continental mathematicians; and now Bernoulli was alternately denying the authorship of the letter, and trying to excuse himself to Newton. The bitterness of this controversy had eaten into his very soul and he spent hour after hour drawing up a vindication of his own conduct, and a proof to show that Leibniz had plagiarised his ideas. Raphson had published a *History of Fluxions* in 1715, and now Newton turned over these papers to him in order that they might appear as an appendix, which was not added to the copies till after Leibniz's death.[1]

It seems probable that Newton was even more exasperated by Leibniz's attack on the anti-Christian influence of the *Principia* than by the controversy over the invention of the calculus. To justify himself, he aided Des Maizeaux in preparing for publication the long debate between Leibniz and Samuel Clarke on the religious significance of the Newtonian philosophy. For this purpose he gave to the author the documents relating to the controversy, and assisted him in preparing an historical preface which reviewed the whole affair. Nor did he stop with these efforts; it has already been told that he personally revised and edited the *Commercium Epistolicum*,

[1] De Morgan (*Essays*, p. 31) states: "Leibniz died in November, 1716, and Newton forthwith handed the whole correspondence, with his final notes, to Raphson, whose *History of Fluxions* was then in process of printing. The book appeared with this correspondence as an appendix: it is dated 1715, but the publication was retarded."—This is, I am convinced, an error. The book was published in English and in a Latin translation in 1715. As it happens I own a Latin copy without the appendix and another copy with the appendix which includes documents dated 1716. I conclude that the appendix was added to the copies which were sold after Leibniz's death in 1716. The books, themselves, support this opinion as the appendix begins with a new sheet, marked Bb, and the paper has turned a deep brown while the body of the book is white, which indicates a different stock had been used.

which had had a very limited distribution, and that he did not hesitate to alter the text or to write an anonymous *apologia* which was attributed to Keill.

If one were to seek for the cause for this almost feverish desire on Newton's part to vindicate himself and to crush his opponents, one would be apt to lay it to personal vindictiveness; but such a trait was not consonant with his character since it was natural for him, when opposed, to retire into silence. It seems more plausible to accept Flamsteed's judgement that he was prone to be swayed by the flattery and influence of those he trusted. And at this time he was led by those who counselled active retaliation; such a spur acting on his sensitive personal honour and his obstinate patience to exhaust a subject would account for what must appear to be a cold blooded ruthlessness.

As a result of his renown, many requests for Newton's portrait were made. He had given one by Jervase to the Royal Society in 1717 and three years later he sat for Sir Godfrey Kneller. At this time, Dr. Stukeley seems to have been a frequent visitor and, in particular, he was present during the sittings. He afterwards wrote to Dr. Mead: "I was with him in the year 1720 when he sat for his picture to Sir Godfrey Kneller to be sent into France. 'Twas pleasant to hear Sir Godfrey, in his wild way of discourse, sifting Sir Isaac about his notions of religion, and with what caution and modesty he was answered." Stukeley also wrote to Conduitt that he had hoped Newton would sit for his profile. "What says Sir Isaac, would you make a medal of me and refused it, though I was then in highest favour with him"? While Stukeley mentions that he frequently visited Newton during these last years, he relates two incidents,[2] occurring in 1721, which may well have happened at the same time and which indicate strikingly Newton's fixity of opinion when once it had been formed and also his sensitiveness or "niceness" to opposition. "23 February, 1721, I breakfasted with him in company with Dr. Halley. Sir Isaac mentioned the poverty of the materials he had for making his theory of the moon's motion. Mr. Flamsteed would not communicate any of his observations to him, that he could as then finish it, if he would go about it, but that he left it to others." It should be remembered that this conversation occurred in the same year in which he refused to give Flamsteed's attorney the sealed packet of observations, and when he must have been mortified because of the

[2] *Portsmouth Collection.*

destruction of Halley's edition of the *Historia Cœlestis.* If he so forgot his former correspondence with Flamsteed as to make such a statement, it is no wonder that the rumour of the astronomer's lack of help became fixed. The other incident related to Stukeley's assistance in supplying Conduitt with memoranda. He excused himself for not sending more anecdotes on the ground that: "I had the misfortune to fall under Sir Isaac's displeasure for many years on account of putting up for Secretary against Dr. Jurin: or these papers would have been much fuller, for I should have taken pains in it in his lifetime."[3]

Mention has been made that Newton lived simply, although in his later years he was a wealthy man; and it was shown he had enjoyed a much larger income from the Mint than was supposed, because of perquisites in addition to his salary. At his death, he left an estate of almost 32,000 pounds. The principal items in his inventory were:

Stock in the Bank of England at 126½, with accrued div.	£18,130
Stock in the South Sea Company at 104	5200
Annuities, South Sea Company at 97½, with accrued div.	5000
Cash	1711

Now Newton, although he was singularly generous, was a man not at all likely to be carried away by impulsive excitement and, at the time of the debauch of speculation in South Sea Stock, Lord Radnor is quoted in Spence's *Anecdotes* as saying: "When Sir Isaac Newton was asked about the rising of the South Sea Stock, he answered that he could not calculate the madness of the people." The investment of so large a sum in the Bank of England stock bears out this opinion of his character; but what can we say of a third of his estate having been put in the notorious gamble of the South Sea Company? Did he join the excited throngs in Change Alley, or had he made a conservative investment? It was evidently believed by many at the time that he had been bitten by the greed of gain. Seward, in his *Anecdotes of Some Distinguished Men,* expressed what was evidently an accepted opinion:

"Sir Isaac Newton, indeed, was in one respect but too like the common race of mortals; his desire of gain induced him to have some concern in the fatal Bubble of the South Sea; by which (as his niece

[3] The date of this incident is settled by the election of Dr. James Jurin as Secretary of the Royal Society in 1721. He "was a very respectable philosopher of the Newtonian school, who cultivated medicine and mathematics with equal success." Weld, Vol. I, p. 435.

used to say) he lost twenty thousand pounds. Of this, however, he never much liked to hear." And Macaulay fastened on him, from this report, the absurd characterisation that "with all his genius, he was as simple as a child,"—a statement about as far from the truth as could well be.

The most confirmatory evidence of this "desire for gain" was given by Weld.[4] He found, amongst the Newtoniana in the possession of the Royal Society, the following note in Newton's handwriting accompanied by a letter of the donor, Dr. Wollaston.

Mint Office, 27th July, 1720.

Sir,

I desire you to subscribe for me and in my name the several Annuities you have in your hands belonging to me amounting in the whole to six hundred and fifty pounds per ann. for which this shall be your warrant.

ISAAC NEWTON.

To Dr. John Francis Ffouquier.

The letter of Wollaston reads:

Dorset Street, December 4, 1828.

"Dr. Wollaston has desired that an autograph of Sir Isaac Newton be presented to the Royal Society.

"It is an order, addressed by Newton to Dr. Francis Ffouquier,[5] directing him to supply certain sums in his possession belonging to Newton in purchasing on Newton's account South Sea Stock; and is dated July 27th, 1720, a time when the price of that stock had nearly reached its maximum.

"Dr. Wollaston, not knowing that any such occurrence in the life of Newton had ever been made public, was for many years unwilling to divulge this transaction; but, having found that the losses which Newton sustained by the South Sea scheme have been noticed in the biographical memoir drawn up on the authority of Mr. Conduitt, who married the niece of Newton, he no longer hesitates to present the document; being satisfied that it will be considered by every reflecting mind an instructive instance of the soundest understanding being liable to have its judgement perverted by the appear-

[4] *Hist. of R. S.*, Vol. I, p. 440.—*Cf.* also Villamil, *Newton: the Man,* who found the inventory and who investigated the transaction with great care.

[5] Fouquier was a French Huguenot who went to England after the revocation of the edict of Nantes and became a Governor of the Bank of England. Dr. Wollaston was an eminent chemist and physicist. His father married Fouquier's daughter.

ance of enormous profit; and to forget that such profit can only be aimed at with proportionate risk of failure."

Weld, in commenting on this letter, merely softens the judgement that Newton had been perverted by the appearance of enormous profit by bidding us to remember he was not the only great man implicated in this foolish adventure. Fortunately, Col. de Villamil has now investigated the affair thoroughly and has quite cleared Newton of either folly or greed of gain. He first points out that Dr. Wollaston has added another instance to what might be termed a concerted conspiracy to suppress any facts which seemed to reflect adversely on Newton's character: as if it were, like a delicate porcelain vase, too fragile to bear any rough handling, and thus this mistaken policy has served to increase those rumours which flourish on suspicion. Col. de Villamil also points out Dr. Wollaston's false interpretation of the note to mean that Newton bought with cash South Sea Stock when it had nearly reached its maximum price. He is thus accused of gambling wildly, and thereby lost 20,000 pounds. On the contrary, the warrant is clearly an order to subscribe for Annuities, and was in no sense a gamble as can be easily shown by a brief history of the South Sea Company.

Looking backwards, our ideas are confused by the term Bubble which is always attached to the South Sea Company, and by the fact that it is synonymous with the most disastrous crash in the history of British finance. But, in the beginning, it was a legitimate trading company on the lines of the East India and Hudson Bay Companies. It was incorporated, in 1710, by an Act which gave it a monopoly of trading in the Pacific Ocean and along the east coast of South America. Also, by an Assiento Treaty, it obtained from the Spanish Government a lucrative and practical monopoly of the slave trade with her colonies. In return, the Company took over about 10,000,000 of the National Debt on which the Government paid 6 per cent in the form of an issue of unredeemable "Annuities." In 1717, the Company advanced another 5,000,000 to the Government on the security of 5 per cent "Annuities." They were thus "gilt-edged" securities; and Newton had evidently invested in them considerably more than the 650 pounds worth per annum which he ordered to be exchanged for capital stock in 1720, since he still possessed some at his death. Up to this time the Company had been highly successful in the slave trade. But in 1720, the Company offered to pay off the whole National Debt of some 57,000,000 and to buy up the irredeemable "Annuities" amounting to £800,000 a year. After a debate in Parliament, the proposal was accepted; the moot question was whether the holders of the unredeemable "Annuities" would convert them into capital stock. On April 13th, the Company opened a subscription of 2,000,000 of capital stock at 300 per cent, declared a stock dividend of 10 per cent and, besides offering liberal terms to holders of the "Annuities" for conversion, inflamed the cupidity of the public with glowing tales of gold and silver awaiting exploitation in South America. There ensued one of the wildest gambles in history, and the stock rose to £1000 per share. The few, who subscribed and immediately sold their stock, made fortunes, but the great majority, who bought during the inflation and held on, were ruined as the stock dropped to £135 a share.

By a simple calculation Col. de Villamil shows Newton's part in this affair. He decided, on July 27, 1720, to subscribe for stock equivalent to £650 per year of 5 per cent "Annuities" for which he must have paid £13,000. He received £5000 in capital stock and £4000 in cash; and, as he still held this same amount of stock at his death when it was quoted at 104, he lost about £9000. It is quite clear that he could have made a great profit by selling his stock immediately after conversion. He had acquired his stock at 180 per cent, while the market price had stood at about 300 per cent during the past three years and had risen to over 600 per cent during the latter part of July, 1720. Any conservative banker, such as Dr. Fouquier, would have advised him to sell; and, if he had taken such advice, he would have profited by something like £20,000. Is it not probable his niece's statement of his loss in South Sea Stock meant he could have gained that sum but lost the opportunity because he neglected to sell?

Is not the conclusion then to be drawn that Newton invested his money honourably and conservatively? He invested a large sum in South Sea 5 per cent unredeemable "Annuities" which were "gilt-edged" securities backed by the Government. He transferred a part of them to capital stock and could have reaped a great profit. But, if the statement by Lord Radnor be authentic, he regarded the subsequent speculation as a "madness" of which it would be improper to take advantage, and thus sustained a loss for the sake of his principles. Besides his personal loss, his heirs must have suffered heavily since the proprietors and subscribers finally got back about one-third of their money by a composition with the Government.

It is extraordinary how the persistent efforts to suppress the truth about Newton's character succeeded in obliterating all the strong points of his personality. To make him orthodox, his earnest enquiries in the dogmas of religion were slurred over; he is made so meek that he could not appreciate the transcendent power of his work, or when aroused to wrath or indignation would not express himself in blunt and even coarse terms; when opposed he is pictured as being always forbearing instead of obstinate and, occasionally, vindictive. Thus, he, a man of mixed passions, has been made into a lifeless monument of lath and plaster which must be protected from every harsh wind lest it fall to pieces. But, of all the efforts to suppress the facts, the fear lest he be accused of gambling in stocks was the most foolish. It is simply grotesque to suppose that he, who had all his life been uniformly frugal in his own habits, and lavishly generous to all who were related to him or who in any way aided him, should suddenly in his old age and when rich, be seized with a greed for gain. Many instances, when he gave large sums to those who had little call upon him or secured positions for mere acquaintances, have been previously mentioned; before leaving this subject, I shall present a number of others without troubling to sort them by their dates or subjects. Some of these examples of his generosity are almost quixotic; and from some of them a caustic humour peeps out which makes one wonder whether he was quite so sedate as he has been made to appear.

We can pass over Newton's constant support of his niece, Catherine Barton, and frequent gifts to all the other members of his family. To those who aided him in his work, he gave all the proceeds of the first edition of the *Principia* to Halley; the proceeds of the second edition he gave to Bentley, and enraged Flamsteed by repeatedly offering to compensate him and his assistants; Pemberton was presented with 200 guineas for editing the third edition and the astronomer Pound with 100 guineas for furnishing observations. Dr. Clarke pleased him so much with a Latin translation of the *Optics* that he received a gift of 500 pounds, delicately offered as a present of a hundred pounds to each of his five children.

Conduitt is the authority for the following anecdotes which are worth repeating just as he noted them down roughly for his intended life of his uncle.

"His arithmetic was first printed by Whiston, against Newton's inclination but, being full of errors, he afterwards printed it himself, corrected the faults and Machin overlooked the press, for which he intended to have given him 100 gs.; but he made him wait 3 years for a preface and then did not write one but left it to the bookseller to put one in."

"Dr. Arbuthnot told me—he told I. N. that Cheyne had writ an ingenious b[ook] upon mathematics—but that his [?] had not money to print.—Bring i[t] to me says I. N. and when he brought it—I. N. offered Cheyne a bag of money,—which he refused and I. N. would see him no more."

"He offered Cheselden[6] for a fee a handful of guineas out of his coat pockets, and when he refused them and said, I should have only one or two—I. N. answered suppose I do give you more than your fee."

"When he missed banknotes of £3000 or more and there was [some] reason to suspect one of his [——], Will Whiston, a nephew of Whiston's, had picked his pocket, because [—al] time he left him and bought an estate in land of that value without any visible means, he never could be prevailed to prosecute him. And when I asked him how much he had lost,—he said too much."

"When he was imposed on and gave double the value for an estate, he said he would not for the sake of £2000 go to Westminster Hall to prove he had made a fool of himself."

There is, as I have said, an element of whimsicality, or of blunt humour, in these stories which consorts oddly with the staid, and may I say dull, demeanour in society which his associates seem determined to invest him with. The two following anecdotes, show such a fine appreciation of worth that they will be given at some length. The first is related in Rigaud's *Life of Bradley:*

A young and brilliant Scotch mathematician, James Stirling, educated at Oxford, became involved in the Jacobite rebellion of 1715 and fled to Venice. While there he wrote several important papers; in particular, a commentary on Newton's work on curves of the third degree. Newton was so impressed with the young man's promise that he sent to him a present of money, arranged to have his work published in England, and finally succeeded in having him pardoned. Stirling was deeply touched by such an interest in his wel-

[6] William Cheselden was a famous surgeon. He was surgeon at the St. Thomas's, St. George's and Westminster hospitals, and his skill as an operator has seldom been surpassed. The lateral operation for stone in the bladder was his invention. He was a friend of Newton and attended him when he suffered from that affliction. The equally famous Richard Mead was Newton's physician and friend.

fare and wrote that: "As your generosity is infinitely above my merit, so I reckon myself ever bound to serve you to the utmost; and, indeed, a present from a person of such worth is more valued by me than ten times the value from another." After his return to Scotland, Stirling had a varied career and ended as a manager of a coal mine.

The second example of Newton's generous and sympathetic aid to young men of genius refers to his relations with Colin Maclaurin, probably the most brilliant of Scotch mathematicians, and certainly the ablest contemporary expositor of the Newtonian philosophy. Maclaurin[7] was appointed professor of mathematics in Marischal College, Aberdeen, at the unusually early age of nineteen years and after a competitive examination lasting ten days. During the two summer vacations following his election, he went to London and met, amongst others, Bishop Hoadly, Dr. Samuel Clarke, Martin Folkes, and Sir Isaac Newton; "whose friendship he ever after reckoned the greatest honour and happiness of his life." He was also made a Fellow of the Royal Society. He became an ardent Newtonian and was one of the first to teach the fluxions and mechanics. At the age of twenty-seven years, he offered himself to the Curators of the University of Edinburgh as a candidate to be assistant and successor to James Gregory "whose age and infirmities had rendered him incapable of teaching." He had several difficulties to overcome,—"particularly, the competition of a gentleman eminent for mathematical abilities, who had good interest with the patrons of the university; and the want of an additional fund for the new professor."

In order to assist his young friend, Newton wrote to him the following letter with permission to show it to the university authorities: "I am very glad to hear that you have a prospect of being joined to Mr. James Gregory in the professorship of the mathematics at Edinburgh, not only because you are my friend, but principally because of your abilities, you being acquainted as well with the new improvements of mathematics, as with the former state of those sciences: I heartily wish you good success, and shall be very glad of hearing of your being elected; I am, with all sincerity, your faithful friend and most humble servant."

Maclaurin, however, answered that he had some scruples about

[7] *Cf.* the life of Maclaurin prefixed to his *Account of Sir Isaac Newton's Philosophical Discoveries*. Published posthumously by his children. London, 1748. This work is probably still the best survey of the *Principia*.

making public a letter addressed to him, personally; so Newton wrote a recommendation to the Lord Provost of Edinburgh.

Newton to the Provost of Edinburgh

My Lord,

I received the honour of your letter, and am glad to understand that Mr. Maclaurin is in good repute amongst you for his skill in mathematics, for I think he deserves it very well. And, to satisfy you that I do not flatter him, and also to encourage him to accept of the place of assisting Mr. Gregory, in order to succeed him, I am ready (if you please to give me leave) to contribute twenty pounds per annum towards a provision for him, till Mr. Gregory's place become void, if I live so long, and I will pay it to his order in London. When your letter arrived at London I was absent from hence, which made it the later before I received it, otherwise I might have returned an answer a little sooner.—I am, my Lord, your Lordship's most humble and most obedient servant.

ISAAC NEWTON.[8]

To his Lordship the
Provost of Edinburgh,
in —— Scotland

Maclaurin was elected on the strength of this influence and occupied the chair of mathematics with great distinction for some twenty years. When the Jacobite uprising of 1745 occurred, he took the side of the English and was among the first to point out the importance, and at the same time the defenceless condition, of Edinburgh. "He made plans of the walls, proposed the several trenches, barricades, batteries, and such other defences as he thought could be got ready before the arrival of the rebels, and by which, he hoped, the town might be kept till the King's forces should come to its relief. The whole burden, not only of contriving, but also of overseeing the execution, of these hasty fortifications fell to Mr. Maclaurin's share; he was employed night and day, in making plans, and running from place to place; and the anxiety, fatigue and cold to which he was then exposed, affecting a constitution naturally of weak nerves, laid the foundation of the disease of which he died."

Maclaurin lived little more than a year after his arduous exposure,

[8] *Portsmouth Collection.* There are preserved two draughts of this letter, written on the same page and differing slightly. The copy as given in Maclaurin's *Life* ends with the words, "order in London."

nd died while dictating the last chapter of his commentary on the *Principia.* Brewster tells how, when he was a youth at college in Edinburgh, he often gazed upon the tablet in memory of Maclaurin attached to the south wall of the Greyfriar's Church, and envied the unique tribute to his genius,—*Newtono Suadente.*

The first warning of the final decay of Newton's constitution came to him in 1722 in the form of a bladder trouble. At first, he seems to have been seriously ill; but under the direction of Dr. Mead he improved in health and was able to write to Varignon in July that he was slowly recovering his strength and hopes soon to be well. But from this time to his death, he was forced to live very quietly and to leave off dining abroad or having much company at home. Since any motion increased his disorder he substituted a sedan chair for the jolting motion of a coach. And he was advised to eat but little meat, but to live chiefly on broth, vegetables, and fruit, "of which he always eat very heartily." It was during these last five years when he was confined to his room that the persistent reading of the Bible became so noticeable to his friends. He seems to have realised that the end of his life was imminent and he bravely and patiently set himself the task of putting his house in order. Since his attendance at the Royal Society was precarious he had Martin Folkes appointed as his deputy or vice-president; and he offered to resign from the Mint, but his nephew, Conduitt, undertook to carry on that work for him.

Newton's first concern was to arrange for a new edition of the *Principia.* The second edition had been a small one, copies of it are about as rare as those of the first, and it was again out of print. The demand on the continent was being met by a reprint at Amsterdam which did not appear till 1714, and as that supply was exhausted a second reprint had been issued nine years later. Newton, himself, had continued to insert marginal notes in his own desk copy and to make corrections and memoranda which are to be found in the *Portsmouth Collection.* He also seems to have hankered to have another try at the problems of the moon and of comets, for he wrote to Halley on December 3, 1724,[9] asking him to examine two of the calculated places in the elliptic orbit of the comet of 1680, and to calculate another place, supposing the orbit to be a parabola. He stated that he wished this information for use in the third book of the *Principia,* second edition, page 459. However, either he did not carry out his intention or Halley did not accommodate him as the material was

[9] Macclesfield, Vol. II, p. 435.

not used in the third edition. But at the age of eighty, he found it to be too heavy a task to revise the work by himself and he sought to find an assistant to help him. He was again fortunate, as he established another congenial relationship with a young man, Henry Pemberton, who has left a charming account of his courtesy and kindliness.

Pemberton,[10] while studying medicine at Leyden under Boerhaave, was loaned a copy of the *Principia* and to his surprise he did not find it too difficult to understand. Greatly pleased with this success, he studied Newton's fluxions and his *De Quadratura*. On his return to England he made the acquaintance of Keill; and when Leibniz sent his problem by Conti to test the English mathematicians, Keill wrote to Newton that not only he, himself, had solved the problem, but so had Mr. Stirling, an undergraduate at Oxford, and Mr. Pemberton who sent him also solutions of several other problems.[11] But, when Keill introduced Pemberton to Newton, "some ill offices done by a malevolent person who then had Sir Isaac's ear," according to Dr. Wilson, made him receive the eager young man but coldly. Still determined to succeed, Pemberton projected his popular exposition of the *Principia;* but a fortunate chance brought him to his goal by a quicker path. A certain Professor Poleni of Padua had brought out a paper which was supposed to overthrow Newton's law of gravity and to support the contrary views of Leibniz, and this thesis, Pemberton cleverly disproved. This was so well approved by Newton that he sought his friendship and asked him to edit the proposed new edition of the *Principia.*

For the third time Newton seems to have cast the spell of his personality over a young assistant and to make him feel as if the work were his own intellectual child. It is well for us, when thinking on Newton's true character to bear in mind Pemberton's tribute to him:[12]

"Though his memory was much decayed, I found he perfectly understood his own writings, contrary to what I had frequently heard in discourse from many persons.[13] This opinion of theirs might arise perhaps from his not being always ready at speaking on these subjects,

[10] For a short statement of the relations between Newton and Pemberton, *cf.* his *View of Sir Isaac Newton's Philosophy*, 1728, which gives a popularised exposition of the *Principia*. Pemberton became professor of physic at Gresham College. He also lectured on chemistry. These lectures were published after his death by his friend, Dr. Wilson, who prefixed a short biographical sketch.

[11] Macclesfield, Vol. II, p. 424.

[12] Preface, Pemberton's *View*.

[13] The old rumours of his mental breakdown seem still to have persisted.

when it might be expected he should. . . . As to the moral endowments of his mind, they were as much to be admired as his other talents. But this is a field I leave others to expatiate in, I only touch upon what I experienced myself during the few years I was happy in his friendship. But this I immediately discovered in him, which at once both surprised and charmed me: Neither his extreme great age nor his universal reputation had rendered him stiff in opinion, or in any degree elated. Of this I had occasion to have almost daily experience. The remarks I continually sent him by letters on his *Principia* were received with the utmost goodness. These were so far from being any ways displeasing to him, that on the contrary it occasioned him to speak many kind things of me to my friends, and to honour me with a public testimony of his good opinion."

The printing of the new edition of the *Principia* was begun late in 1723, or early in the following year, and was not finished till February, or March, 1726. During the progress of the work, a great many letters passed between them, as they lived at some distance apart. Most of Pemberton's letters have been preserved and they will be valuable if a critical edition of the treatise should be undertaken: Newton's answers, however, have been lost; it is possible they may merely have been notes, jotted down on the proof-sheets. No such important corrections and additions, as were made in the second edition, were attempted.[14]

One charge of a personal nature was made which has subjected Newton to criticism. He omitted the paragraph in the Scholium, which was believed to acknowledge Leibniz's independent discovery of the calculus. He explained elsewhere, in a manner which seems inadequate and artificial, that the original passage had not been intended to convey the meaning commonly given it, but "his silence put me upon a necessity of writing the Scholium upon the second Lemma of the second Book of Principles, lest it should be thought that I borrowed that Lemma from Mr. Leibniz." Whether Newton took this step on his own initiative or on the advice of others, it was undoubtedly a mistake; the words had been written and allowed to stand without comment too long to make any explanation satisfactory, or free from the suspicion that an advantage was taken of an opponent whose death had prevented any reply.

[14] Brewster (Vol. II, p. 549) has drawn up a very complete list of the alterations and additions made in the third edition.

Newton's last important work, which he carried on with an indomitable will in spite of rapidly failing health and of suffering, was to try to counteract the faulty and pirated French edition of his *Chronology* by rewriting and preparing it for the press. This task he finished just before his death, and the manuscript was left for Conduitt to publish.

The remaining three years of Newton's life are a melancholy chronicle of successive attacks on his vigorous constitution before it finally succumbed. In August, 1724, the presence of a dread disease declared itself by his voiding, without any pain, a stone about the size of a pea which passed in two pieces. While this afforded him a temporary relief, he suffered from a slight attack of the gout and, in the following January, was seized with a dangerous cough and inflammation of the lungs. As the bad air and smoke of the city aggravated his condition, he was persuaded with great difficulty to take a house in the village of Kensington.[15] Conduitt tells us that, "though he found the greatest benefit from rest, and the air at Kensington, and was always the worse for leaving it, no methods that were used could keep him from coming sometimes to town." It is probable that the Conduitts did not accompany him to his new home but moved then to their house in George Street, Hanover Square; for in Newton's inventory there is the item "Manuscripts in a box sealed up at the house of John Conduitt, Esqre.", and it is reasonable to suppose that they were deposited there for safe-keeping when Newton left his own house.[16] We get the impression that Conduitt and Stukeley were often with him; the latter visited him for the last time in April, 1726, and Conduitt reports a long conversation with him which will be given in abstract.

"I was on Sunday, the 7th of March 1724/5," Conduitt wrote,[17] "at Kensington with Sir Isaac Newton, in his lodgings, just after he was come out of a fit of the gout, which he had in both of his feet, for the first time, in the eighty-third year of his age; he was better after it, and his head clearer, and memory stronger than I had known

15 The house he took, and in which he died, was known as Orbell's Buildings, afterwards called Pitt Buildings. It is situated in Pitt Street, west of Church Street and north of the High Street.

16 These manuscripts were the *Chronology*, published posthumously by Conduitt (valued at £250) and the history of the prophecies. This latter manuscript is referred to as unfinished which argues that Newton had contemplated another work on the subject. Conduitt's use of the phrase of "*coming* sometimes to town" is significant for, if they had been with him, the natural expression would have been "going."

17 Turnor, p. 172.

them for some time." During the course of the conversation, Newton conjectured that the heavenly bodies were periodically subject to decay and replenishment; that the vapours and light emitted by the sun "gathered themselves by degrees into body, and attracted more matter from the planets; and at last made a secondary planet [a moon], and then by gathering to them and attracting more matter, became a primary planet; and then by increasing still, became a comet, which after certain revolutions, by coming nearer and nearer to the sun, had all its volatile parts condensed, and became a matter fit to recruit, and replenish the sun, which must waste by the constant heat and light it emitted." To illustrate this idea he cited the probability that the comet of 1680 would, after perhaps five or six revolutions, drop into the sun; and when such a catastrophe occurred "it would so much increase the heat of the sun, that this earth would be burnt, and no animals in it could live."

How far Newton was from being a mechanist in the modern sense of the term is shown by Conduitt's statement that: "He seemed to doubt whether there were not intelligent beings superior to us, who superintended these revolutions of the heavenly bodies, by the direction of the Supreme Being. He appeared also to be very clearly of opinion, that the inhabitants of this world were of a short date, and alleged as one reason for that opinion, that all arts, as letters, ships, printing, needle, etc. were discovered within the memory of history." When Conduitt "asked him how this earth could have been repeopled if ever it had undergone the same fate it was threatened with hereafter by the comet of 1680; he answered, that required the power of a creator." Again, when Conduitt asked "why he would not publish his conjectures, as conjectures, and instanced that Kepler had communicated his. . . . His answer was, I do not deal in conjectures." The conversation closed by Conduitt wishing to know why he would not, in the *Principia,* acknowledge that the sun was replenished and recruited by comets dropping into it, when he had made a similar statement about the fixed stars ["stellae fixae refici possunt"]. "He said, that concerned us more; and laughing, added that he had said enough for people to know his meaning."

Such were the last recorded thoughts of Newton on the world system, whose laws he had done so much to discover; and it is well to remember that he said of himself: "I kept an eye upon such principles as might work with considering men for the belief of a Deity, and nothing can rejoice me more than to find it useful for that purpose." However he may have regarded himself in comparison with other men, he was piously humble in the presence of the mystery of God and the universe. Just a little while before his death he said: "I do not know what I may appear to the world; but to myself I seem to have been only like a boy, playing on the sea-shore, and diverting myself, in now and then finding a smoother pebble or a prettier shell than ordinary, whilst the great ocean of truth lay all undiscovered before me."[18]

As so frequently happens, Newton's thoughts, while his life hurried towards its end, turned back to the scenes of his childhood. He wrote to the Rev. Mr. Mason, Rector of Colsterworth, that he wished to subscribe £12 towards erecting a gallery in the church, also £3 to repair the floor; and, when he learned the work was finished, he authorised the surplus to be applied "to the use of the young people of the parish that are learning to sing Psalms." And, only a month before his death, he took the trouble to have assays made of some ore sent to him by a Woolsthorpe friend of Mason and sent word that it contained no iron. So, too, he retained his interest in the affairs of the little village and wrote the following homely note to his tenant.

Newton to Percival of Woolsthorpe

Sir,

I desire you acquaint John Groves, and the rest of the neighbours in the parish of Colsterworth and Woolsthorpe, that I agree to the design proposed to me of bringing their commons to a rule, suppose, by allowing eighty sheep commons to a farm, and ten to an ancient cottage, and settling the beast commons according to ancient right, to be set down in a list of them; and where any dispute arises, the commons may be proportioned to the annual value of the farm or cottage. And I should be glad to see the settlement finished. There are one hundred and twenty sheep commons due to me by ancient right, on account of the royalty.

I am, &c.

ISAAC NEWTON.[19]

London, May 12, 1725.

There is little more to relate; on Tuesday, 28 February, 1726/7, Newton, having sufficiently recovered from a second attack of the

[18] Conduitt's MSS. *Portsmouth Collection.*

[19] Turnor, p. 158.

gout, went to London to preside at a meeting of the Royal Society. He stayed in town till Saturday; and, when Conduitt assured him that he was looking better than for many years past, he answered with a smile that he was sensible of the fact, as he had slept the Sunday before, from eleven at night to eight in the morning, without waking. The fatigue and motion of the journey, however, were fatal to him, as he became ill on arriving home. Dr. Mead and Dr. Cheselden, who were summoned, pronounced the cause to be stone in the bladder and gave him no hope of recovery. From this time he suffered from violent attacks of pain and, though the sweat rolled down his face from the agony, he neither complained or cried out. And during the short intermissions of the torture, he would smile and talk with his usual cheerfulness. It is probable, also, that he sorted and burned a great number of his personal papers.

The following account of Newton's death and funeral is taken from Conduitt's letter to Fontenelle of the French Academy.

"On Wednesday the 15th of March, he seemed a little better, and we conceived some hopes of his recovery, but without grounds. On Saturday morning, the 18th, he read the newspapers, and held a pretty long discourse with Dr. Mead, and had all his senses perfect; but that evening at six, and all Sunday, he was insensible, and died on Monday the 20th of March, between one and two o'clock in the morning. He seemed to have *stamina vitae* (except the accidental disorder of the stone) to have carried him to a much longer age. To the last he had all his senses and faculties strong, vigorous, and lively, and he continued writing and studying many hours every day to the time of his last illness."

"On the 28th past, the corpse of Sir Isaac Newton lay in state in the Jerusalem Chamber, and was buried [April 4th] from thence in Westminster Abbey, near the entry into the choir. The pall was supported by the Lord High Chancellor, the Dukes of Montrose and Roxborough, and the Earls of Pembroke, Sussex, and Macclesfield, being Fellows of the Royal Society. The Hon. Sir Michael Newton, Knight of the Bath, was chief mourner, and was followed by some other relations, and several eminent persons, intimately acquainted with the deceased. The office was performed by the Bishop of Rochester, attended by the prebends and choir."

Newton had kept himself too aloof from society, and his work had been too far removed from the ordinary occupations of life, for his death to call forth a wide-spread feeling of personal loss; it rather aroused in the people a national consciousness that so great a philosopher had been their countryman. Thus the notices of his death took the form of a review of his work, and of moral reflections that such intellectual power had been exemplified in so virtuous a life. The Royal Society forbore to make any public expression of the genius and discoveries of the most eminent Fellow and President on their rolls from the beginning even to the present time. Appended to the minutes of Council is the simple, but eloquent, note "Sir Isaac Newton departed his life on Monday the 20 March, 1726/7: and in the minutes of the Journal-book for the ordinary meeting on the next Wednesday, "The chair being vacant by the death of Sir Isaac Newton, there was no meeting this day."

When the weight of his great authority was lost to the Society, trouble broke out while seeking to find a successor who would unite the factions which had existed in the membership. Thus, Stukeley wrote, "I don't wonder that there are divisions in the Society now the great soul and genius of it has left them."

Since Newton died intestate, his personal property was divided equally amongst his nephews and nieces, and his manor descended to his heir-at-law John Newton, great grandson of his father's next oldest brother, Robert. There seems to have been some doubt as to his being the heir, or perhaps a hope that one nearer of kin might be found, since Conduitt wrote to Mason for information and received the following reply.

Mason to Conduitt

Good Sir: 23 March, 1726/7.

This morning I received from you the melancholy news of that truly great and good gentleman's death, Sir Isaac Newton, and I have according to your desire made Sir Isaac's heir and representative, who is the bearer of this acquainted with it, but God knows, a poor representative of so great a man, but this is a case that often happens. There are two families of the Newtons in this Parish, both descended from the 2^d^ and 3^d^ brothers of Sir Isaac Newton's father. The 2^d^ brother was Robert Newton from whom the bearer of this, John Newton, is descended. The 3^d^ was Richard from whom descends Robert Newton now living in this Parish, so that without dispute John Newton, the bearer, is heir to the estate now devised by will [there was no will]. . . . Neither do I exactly know how long the Manor of Woolsthorpe has been in Sir Is. Newton's family, but the first Newton that I can find at Woolsthorpe was Robert Newton, Sir Isaac's grandfather, and him I take to be the first lord thereof, but I may be mistaken. . . . THO. MASON.

P. S. Sir Isaac, in the days of his health and prosperity, used to talk pretty much about founding and endowing a school in Woolsthorpe for the use of the Parish, as the neighbours and his relations inform me. I, myself, never knew him but in his declining years, having been but six years Rector; but he used to talk pretty much upon that subject, though his dying without a will leaves no room for any such hopes.

To John Conduitt
in Great George Street
Hanover Sq.

The disparaging comment on the heir was justified by his subsequent history. He sold the Manor in 1732 to Edmund Turnor of Stoke Rochford, whose family have preserved it with solicitous care as a memorial. The heir, himself, "being dissolute and illiterate, soon dissipated his estate in extravagance, dying about his thirtieth year, in 1737, at Colsterworth, by a tobacco pipe breaking in his throat, in the act of smoking, from a fall in the street, occasioned by ebriety."[20] Thus Newton's family name is preserved only in the memory of his undying fame.

There is no need to elaborate a eulogy on the character and achievement of Newton, they speak for themselves. No one can be better aware than the biographer of the imperfections of his work; but he can find some excuse for his faults in the lapse of time and in the scarcity of materials, and still indulge the hope that something of the real Newton has been made more accessible. On the twentieth of March, 1927, the bicentenary of Newton's death, I first entertained the idea of writing his biography. As I now finish this long and arduous task, which has kept my mind absorbed in the life and philosophy of such a consummate genius, satisfaction is mingled with regret,—a regret made the more poignant by the recollection that so

20 Maude, *Wensleydale*.

many of those who found pleasure in its beginning are not witnesses of its conclusion. To the abiding memory of one, who, far more than I, would have rejoiced in its success and have excused its failure, I dedicate this *Life of Newton*.

CINCINNATI,
20 March, 1934.

INDEX

Abbreviations: N for Newton; Roy. Soc. for Royal Society

CATALOG OF DOVER BOOKS

BOOKS EXPLAINING SCIENCE AND MATHEMATICS

THE COMMON SENSE OF THE EXACT SCIENCES, W. K. Clifford. Introduction by James Newman, edited by Karl Pearson. For 70 years this has been a guide to classical scientific and mathematical thought. Explains with unusual clarity basic concepts, such as extension of meaning of symbols, characteristics of surface boundaries, properties of plane figures, vectors, Cartesian method of determining position, etc. Long preface by Bertrand Russell. Bibliography of Clifford. Corrected, 130 diagrams redrawn. 249pp. 5⅜ x 8.
T61 Paperbound **$1.60**

SCIENCE THEORY AND MAN, Erwin Schrödinger. This is a complete and unabridged reissue of SCIENCE AND THE HUMAN TEMPERAMENT plus an additional essay: "What is an Elementary Particle?" Nobel Laureate Schrödinger discusses such topics as nature of scientific method, the nature of science, chance and determinism, science and society, conceptual models for physical entities, elementary particles and wave mechanics. Presentation is popular and may be followed by most people with little or no scientific training. "Fine practical preparation for a time when laws of nature, human institutions . . . are undergoing a critical examination without parallel," Waldemar Kaempffert, N. Y. TIMES. 192pp. 5⅜ x 8.
T428 Paperbound **$1.35**

PIONEERS OF SCIENCE, O. Lodge. Eminent scientist-expositor's authoritative, yet elementary survey of great scientific theories. Concentrating on individuals—Copernicus, Brahe, Kepler, Galileo, Descartes, Newton, Laplace, Herschel, Lord Kelvin, and other scientists—the author presents their discoveries in historical order adding biographical material on each man and full, specific explanations of their achievements. The clear and complete treatment of the post-Newtonian astronomers is a feature seldom found in other books on the subject. Index. 120 illustrations. xv + 404pp. 5⅜ x 8.
T716 Paperbound **$1.50**

THE EVOLUTION OF SCIENTIFIC THOUGHT FROM NEWTON TO EINSTEIN, A. d'Abro. Einstein's special and general theories of relativity, with their historical implications, are analyzed in non-technical terms. Excellent accounts of the contributions of Newton, Riemann, Weyl, Planck, Eddington, Maxwell, Lorentz and others are treated in terms of space and time, equations of electromagnetics, finiteness of the universe, methodology of science. 21 diagrams. 482pp. 5⅜ x 8.
T2 Paperound **$2.00**

THE RISE OF THE NEW PHYSICS, A. d'Abro. A half-million word exposition, formerly titled THE DECLINE OF MECHANISM, for readers not versed in higher mathematics. The only thorough explanation, in everyday language, of the central core of modern mathematical physical theory, treating both classical and modern theoretical physics, and presenting in terms almost anyone can understand the equivalent of 5 years of study of mathematical physics. Scientifically impeccable coverage of mathematical-physical thought from the Newtonian system up through the electronic theories of Dirac and Heisenberg and Fermi's statistics. Combines both history and exposition; provides a broad yet unified and detailed view, with constant comparison of classical and modern views on phenomena and theories. "A must for anyone doing serious study in the physical sciences," JOURNAL OF THE FRANKLIN INSTITUTE. "Extraordinary faculty . . . to explain ideas and theories of theoretical physics in the language of daily life," ISIS. First part of set covers philosophy of science, drawing upon the practice of Newton, Maxwell, Poincaré, Einstein, others, discussing modes of thought, experiment, interpretations of causality, etc. In the second part, 100 pages explain grammar and vocabulary of mathematics, with discussions of functions, groups, series, Fourier series, etc. The remainder is devoted to concrete, detailed coverage of both classical and quantum physics, explaining such topics as analytic mechanics, Hamilton's principle, wave theory of light, electromagnetic waves, groups of transformations, thermodynamics, phase rule, Brownian movement, kinetics, special relativity, Planck's original quantum theory, Bohr's atom, Zeeman effect, Broglie's wave mechanics, Heisenberg's uncertainty, Eigen-values, matrices, scores of other important topics. Discoveries and theories are covered for such men as Alembert, Born, Cantor, Debye, Euler, Foucault, Galois, Gauss, Hadamard, Kelvin, Kepler, Laplace, Maxwell, Pauli, Rayleigh, Volterra, Weyl, Young, more than 180 others. Indexed. 97 illustrations. ix + 982pp. 5⅜ x 8.
T3 Volume 1, Paperbound **$2.00**
T4 Volume 2, Paperbound **$2.00**

CONCERNING THE NATURE OF THINGS, Sir William Bragg. Christmas lectures delivered at the Royal Society by Nobel laureate. Why a spinning ball travels in a curved track; how uranium is transmuted to lead, etc. Partial contents: atoms, gases, liquids, crystals, metals, etc. No scientific background needed; wonderful for intelligent child. 32pp. of photos, 57 figures. xii + 232pp. 5⅜ x 8.
T31 Paperbound **$1.35**

THE UNIVERSE OF LIGHT, Sir William Bragg. No scientific training needed to read Nobel Prize winner's expansion of his Royal Institute Christmas Lectures. Insight into nature of light, methods and philosophy of science. Explains lenses, reflection, color, resonance, polarization, x-rays, the spectrum, Newton's work with prisms, Huygens' with polarization, Crookes' with cathode ray, etc. Leads into clear statement of 2 major historical theories of light, corpuscle and wave. Dozens of experiments you can do. 199 illus., including 2 full-page color plates. 293pp. 5⅜ x 8.
S538 Paperbound **$1.85**

BRIDGES AND THEIR BUILDERS, David Steinman and Sara Ruth Watson. Engineers, historians, everyone who has ever been fascinated by great spans will find this book an endless source of information and interest. Dr. Steinman, recipient of the Louis Levy medal, was one of the great bridge architects and engineers of all time, and his analysis of the great bridges of history is both authoritative and easily followed. Greek and Roman bridges, medieval bridges, Oriental bridges, modern works such as the Brooklyn Bridge and the Golden Gate Bridge, and many others are described in terms of history, constructional principles, artistry, and function. All in all this book is the most comprehensive and accurate semipopular history of bridges in print in English. New, greatly revised, enlarged edition. 23 photographs, 26 line drawings. Index. xvii + 401pp. 5⅜ x 8. T431 Paperbound **$2.00**

FADS AND FALLACIES IN THE NAME OF SCIENCE, Martin Gardner. Examines various cults, quack systems, frauds, delusions which at various times have masqueraded as science. Accounts of hollow-earth fanatics like Symmes; Velikovsky and wandering planets; Hoerbiger; Bellamy and the theory of multiple moons; Charles Fort; dowsing, pseudoscientific methods for finding water, ores, oil. Sections on naturopathy, iridiagnosis, zone therapy, food fads, etc. Analytical accounts of Wilhelm Reich and orgone sex energy; L. Ron Hubbard and Dianetics; A. Korzybski and General Semantics; many others. Brought up to date to include Bridey Murphy, others. Not just a collection of anecdotes, but a fair, reasoned appraisal of eccentric theory. Formerly titled IN THE NAME OF SCIENCE. Preface. Index. x + 384pp. 5⅜ x 8. T394 Paperbound **$1.50**

See also: **A PHILOSOPHICAL ESSAY ON PROBABILITIES, P. de Laplace; ON MATHEMATICS AND MATHEMATICIANS, R. E. Moritz; AN ELEMENTARY SURVEY OF CELESTIAL MECHANICS, Y. Ryabov; THE SKY AND ITS MYSTERIES, E. A. Beet; THE REALM OF THE NEBULAE, E. Hubble; OUT OF THE SKY, H. H. Nininger; SATELLITES AND SCIENTIFIC RESEARCH, D. King-Hele; HEREDITY AND YOUR LIFE, A. M. Winchester; INSECTS AND INSECT LIFE, S. W. Frost; PRINCIPLES OF STRATIGRAPHY, A. W. Grabau; TEACH YOURSELF SERIES.**

HISTORY OF SCIENCE AND MATHEMATICS

DIALOGUES CONCERNING TWO NEW SCIENCES, Galileo Galilei. This classic of experimental science, mechanics, engineering, is as enjoyable as it is important. A great historical document giving insights into one of the world's most original thinkers, it is based on 30 years' experimentation. It offers a lively exposition of dynamics, elasticity, sound, ballistics, strength of materials, the scientific method. "Superior to everything else of mine," Galileo. Trans. by H. Crew, A. Salvio. 126 diagrams. Index. xxi + 288pp. 5⅜ x 8. S99 Paperbound **$1.65**

A DIDEROT PICTORIAL ENCYCLOPEDIA OF TRADES AND INDUSTRY, Manufacturing and the Technical Arts in Plates Selected from "L'Encyclopédie ou Dictionnaire Raisonne des Sciences, des Arts, et des Métiers" of Denis Diderot. Edited with text by C. Gillispie. This first modern selection of plates from the high point of 18th century French engraving is a storehouse of valuable technological information to the historian of arts and science. Over 2000 illustrations on 485 full page plates, most of them original size, show the trades and industries of a fascinating era in such great detail that the processes and shops might very well be reconstructed from them. The plates teem with life, with men, women, and children performing all of the thousands of operations necessary to the trades before and during the early stages of the industrial revolution. Plates are in sequence, and show general operations, closeups of difficult operations, and details of complex machinery. Such important and interesting trades and industries are illustrated as sowing, harvesting, beekeeping, cheesemaking, operating windmills, milling flour, charcoal burning, tobacco processing, indigo, fishing, arts of war, salt extraction, mining, smelting, casting iron, steel, extracting mercury, zinc, sulphur, copper, etc., slating, tinning, silverplating, gilding, making gunpowder, cannons, bells, shoeing horses, tanning, papermaking, printing, dyeing, and more than 40 other categories. Professor Gillispie, of Princeton, supplies a full commentary on all the plates, identifying operations, tools, processes, etc. This material, presented in a lively and lucid fashion, is of great interest to the reader interested in history of science and technology. Heavy library cloth. 920pp. 9 x 12. T421 Two volume set **$18.50**

DE MAGNETE, William Gilbert. This classic work on magnetism founded a new science. Gilbert was the first to use the word "electricity", to recognize mass as distinct from weight, to discover the effect of heat on magnetic bodies; invent an electroscope, differentiate between static electricity and magnetism, conceive of the earth as a magnet. Written by the first great experimental scientist, this lively work is valuable not only as an historical landmark, but as the delightfully easy to follow record of a perpetually searching, ingenious mind. Translated by P. F. Mottelay. 25 page biographical memoir. 90 figures. lix + 368pp. 5⅜ x 8. S470 Paperbound **$2.00**

A CONCISE HISTORY OF MATHEMATICS, D. Struik. Lucid study of development of mathematical ideas, techniques from Ancient Near East, Greece, Islamic science, Middle Ages, Renaissance, modern times. Important mathematicians are described in detail. Treatment is not anecdotal, but analytical development of ideas. "Rich in content, thoughtful in interpretation," U.S. QUARTERLY BOOKLIST. Non-technical; no mathematical training needed. Index. 60 illustrations, including Egyptian papyri, Greek mss., portraits of 31 eminent mathematicians. Bibliography. 2nd edition. xix + 299pp. 5⅜ x 8. T255 Paperbound **$1.75**

See also: **NON-EUCLIDEAN GEOMETRY, R. Bonola; THEORY OF DETERMINANTS IN HISTORICAL ORDER OF DEVELOPMENT, T. Muir; HISTORY OF THE THEORY OF ELASTICITY AND STRENGTH OF MATERIALS, I. Todhunter and K. Pearson; A SHORT HISTORY OF ASTRONOMY, A. Berry; CLASSICS OF SCIENCE.**

PHILOSOPHY OF SCIENCE AND MATHEMATICS

FOUNDATIONS OF SCIENCE: THE PHILOSOPHY OF THEORY AND EXPERIMENT, N. R. Campbell. A critique of the most fundamental concepts of science in general and physics in particular. Examines why certain propositions are accepted without question, demarcates science from philosophy, clarifies the understanding of the tools of science. Part One analyzes the presuppositions of scientific thought: existence of the material world, nature of scientific laws, multiplication of probabilities, etc.: Part Two covers the nature of experiment and the application of mathematics: conditions for measurement, relations between numerical laws and theories, laws of error, etc. An appendix covers problems arising from relativity, force, motion, space, and time. A classic in its field. Index. xiii + 565pp. 5⅝ x 8⅜. S372 Paperbound **$2.95**

WHAT IS SCIENCE?, Norman Campbell. This excellent introduction explains scientific method, role of mathematics, types of scientific laws. Contents: 2 aspects of science, science & nature, laws of science, discovery of laws, explanation of laws, measurement & numerical laws, applications of science. 192pp. 5⅜ x 8. S43 Paperbound **$1.25**

THE VALUE OF SCIENCE, Henri Poincaré. Many of the most mature ideas of the "last scientific universalist" covered with charm and vigor for both the beginning student and the advanced worker. Discusses the nature of scientific truth, whether order is innate in the universe or imposed upon it by man, logical thought versus intuition (relating to math, through the works of Weierstrass, Lie, Klein, Riemann), time and space (relativity, psychological time, simultaneity), Hertz's concept of force, interrelationship of mathematical physics to pure math, values within disciplines of Maxwell, Carnot, Mayer, Newton, Lorentz, etc. Index. iii + 147pp. 5⅜ x 8. S469 Paperbound **$1.35**

SCIENCE AND METHOD, Henri Poincaré. Procedure of scientific discovery, methodology, experiment, idea-germination—the intellectual processes by which discoveries come into being. Most significant and most interesting aspects of development, application of ideas. Chapters cover selection of facts, chance, mathematical reasoning, mathematics, and logic; Whitehead, Russell, Cantor; the new mechanics, etc. 288pp. 5⅜ x 8. S222 Paperbound **$1.35**

SCIENCE AND HYPOTHESIS, Henri Poincaré. Creative psychology in science. How such concepts as number, magnitude, space, force, classical mechanics were developed, and how the modern scientist uses them in his thought. Hypothesis in physics, theories of modern physics. Introduction by Sir James Larmor. "Few mathematicians have had the breadth of vision of Poincaré, and none is his superior in the gift of clear exposition," E. T. Bell. Index. 272pp. 5⅜ x 8. S221 Paperbound **$1.35**

PHILOSOPHY AND THE PHYSICISTS, L. S. Stebbing. The philosophical aspects of modern science examined in terms of a lively critical attack on the ideas of Jeans and Eddington. Discusses the task of science, causality, determinism, probability, consciousness, the relation of the world of physics to that of everyday experience. Probes the philosophical significance of the Planck-Bohr concept of discontinuous energy levels, the inferences to be drawn from Heisenberg's Uncertainty Principle, the implications of "becoming" involved in the 2nd law of thermodynamics, and other problems posed by the discarding of Laplacean determinism. 285pp. 5⅜ x 8. T480 Paperbound **$1.65**

EXPERIMENT AND THEORY IN PHYSICS, Max Born. A Nobel laureate examines the nature and value of the counterclaims of experiment and theory in physics. Synthetic versus analytical scientific advances are analyzed in the work of Einstein, Bohr, Heisenberg, Planck, Eddington, Milne, and others by a fellow participant. 44pp. 5⅜ x 8. S308 Paperbound **60¢**

THE NATURE OF PHYSICAL THEORY, P. W. Bridgman. Here is how modern physics looks to a highly unorthodox physicist—a Nobel laureate. Pointing out many absurdities of science, and demonstrating the inadequacies of various physical theories, Dr. Bridgman weighs and analyzes the contributions of Einstein, Bohr, Newton, Heisenberg, and many others. This is a non-technical consideration of the correlation of science and reality. Index. xi + 138pp. 5⅜ x 8.
S33 Paperbound **$1.25**

THE PHILOSOPHY OF SPACE AND TIME, H. Reichenbach. An important landmark in the development of the empiricist conception of geometry, covering the problem of the foundations of geometry, the theory of time, the consequences of Einstein's relativity, including: relations between theory and observations; coordinate and metrical properties of space; the psychological problem of visual intuition of non-Euclidean structures; and many other important topics in modern science and philosophy. The majority of ideas require only a knowledge of intermediate math. Introduction by R. Carnap. 49 figures. Index. xviii + 296pp. 5⅜ x 8.
S443 Paperbound **$2.00**

MATTER & MOTION, James Clerk Maxwell, This excellent exposition begins with simple particles and proceeds gradually to physical systems beyond complete analysis: motion, force, properties of centre of mass of material system, work, energy, gravitation, etc. Written with all Maxwell's original insights and clarity. Notes by E. Larmor. 17 diagrams. 178pp. 5⅜ x 8.
S188 Paperbound **$1.35**

THE ANALYSIS OF MATTER, Bertrand Russell. How do our senses concord with the new physics? This volume covers such topics as logical analysis of physics, prerelativity physics, causality, scientific inference, physics and perception, special and general relativity, Weyl's theory, tensors, invariants and their physical interpretation, periodicity and qualitative series. "The most thorough treatment of the subject that has yet been published," THE NATION. Introduction by L. E. Denonn. 422pp. 5⅜ x 8.
T231 Paperbound **$1.95**

SUBSTANCE AND FUNCTION, & EINSTEIN'S THEORY OF RELATIVITY, Ernst Cassirer. Two books bound as one. Cassirer establishes a philosophy of the exact sciences that takes into consideration newer developments in mathematics, and also shows historical connections. Partial contents: Aristotelian logic, Mill's analysis, Helmholtz & Kronecker, Russell & cardinal numbers, Euclidean vs. non-Euclidean geometry, Einstein's relativity. Bibliography. Index. xxi + 465pp. 5⅜ x 8.
T50 Paperbound **$2.00**

PRINCIPLES OF MECHANICS, Heinrich Hertz. This last work by the great 19th century physicist is not only a classic, but of great interest in the logic of science. Creating a new system of mechanics based upon space, time, and mass, it returns to axiomatic analysis, to understanding of the formal or structural aspects of science, taking into account logic, observation, and a priori elements. Of great historical importance to Poincaré, Carnap, Einstein, Milne. A 20-page introduction by R. S. Cohen, Wesleyan University, analyzes the implications of Hertz's thought and the logic of science. Bibliography. 13-page introduction by Helmholtz. xlii + 274pp. 5⅜ x 8.
S316 Clothbound **$3.50**
S317 Paperbound **$1.85**

THE PHILOSOPHICAL WRITINGS OF PEIRCE, edited by Justus Buchler. (Formerly published as THE PHILOSOPHY OF PEIRCE.) This is a carefully balanced exposition of Peirce's complete system, written by Peirce himself. It covers such matters as scientific method, pure chance vs. law, symbolic logic, theory of signs, pragmatism, experiment, and other topics. Introduction by Justus Buchler, Columbia University. xvi + 368pp. 5⅜ x 8.
T217 Paperbound **$1.95**

ESSAYS IN EXPERIMENTAL LOGIC, John Dewey. This stimulating series of essays touches upon the relationship between inquiry and experience, dependence of knowledge upon thought, character of logic; judgments of practice, data and meanings, stimuli of thought, etc. Index. viii + 444pp. 5⅜ x 8.
T73 Paperbound **$1.95**

LANGUAGE, TRUTH AND LOGIC, A. Ayer. A clear introduction to the Vienna and Cambridge schools of Logical Positivism. It sets up specific tests by which you can evaluate validity of ideas, etc. Contents: Function of philosophy, elimination of metaphysics, nature of analysis, a priori, truth and probability, etc. 10th printing. "I should like to have written it myself," Bertrand Russell. Index. 160pp. 5⅜ x 8.
T10 Paperbound **$1.25**

THE PSYCHOLOGY OF INVENTION IN THE MATHEMATICAL FIELD, J. Hadamard. Where do ideas come from? What role does the unconscious play? Are ideas best developed by mathematical reasoning, word reasoning, visualization? What are the methods used by Einstein, Poincaré, Galton, Riemann? How can these techniques be applied by others? Hadamard, one of the world's leading mathematicians, discusses these and other questions. xiii + 145pp. 5⅜ x 8.
T107 Paperbound **$1.25**

FOUNDATIONS OF GEOMETRY, Bertrand Russell. Analyzing basic problems in the overlap area between mathematics and philosophy, Nobel laureate Russell examines the nature of geometrical knowledge, the nature of geometry, and the application of geometry to space. It covers the history of non-Euclidean geometry, philosophic interpretations of geometry—especially Kant—projective and metrical geometry. This is most interesting as the solution offered in 1897 by a great mind to a problem still current. New introduction by Prof. Morris Kline of N. Y. University. xii + 201pp. 5⅜ x 8.
S232 Clothbound **$3.25**
S233 Paperbound **$1.60**